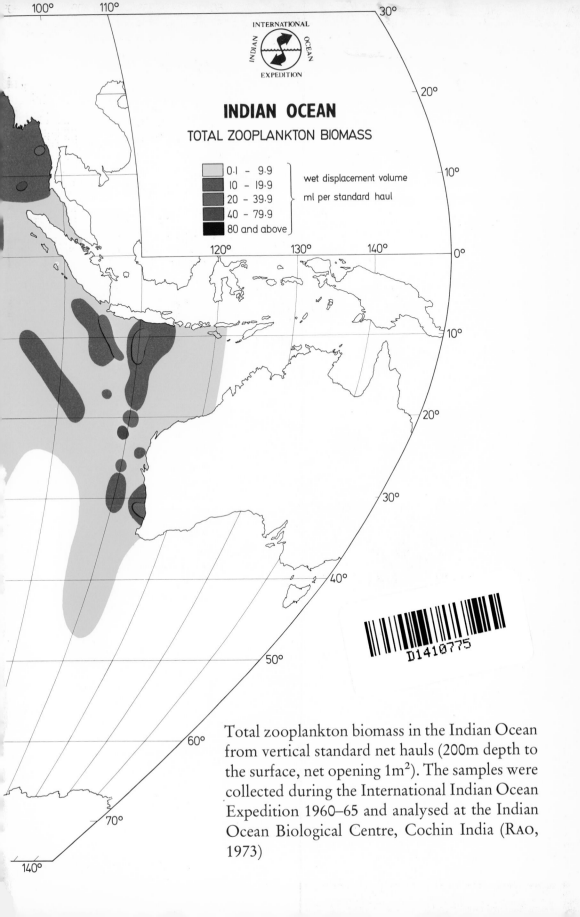

INDIAN OCEAN

TOTAL ZOOPLANKTON BIOMASS

0·1 – 9·9	
10 – 19·9	wet displacement volume
20 – 39·9	ml per standard haul
40 – 79·9	
80 and above	

Total zooplankton biomass in the Indian Ocean from vertical standard net hauls (200m depth to the surface, net opening 1m²). The samples were collected during the International Indian Ocean Expedition 1960–65 and analysed at the Indian Ocean Biological Centre, Cochin India (RAO, 1973)

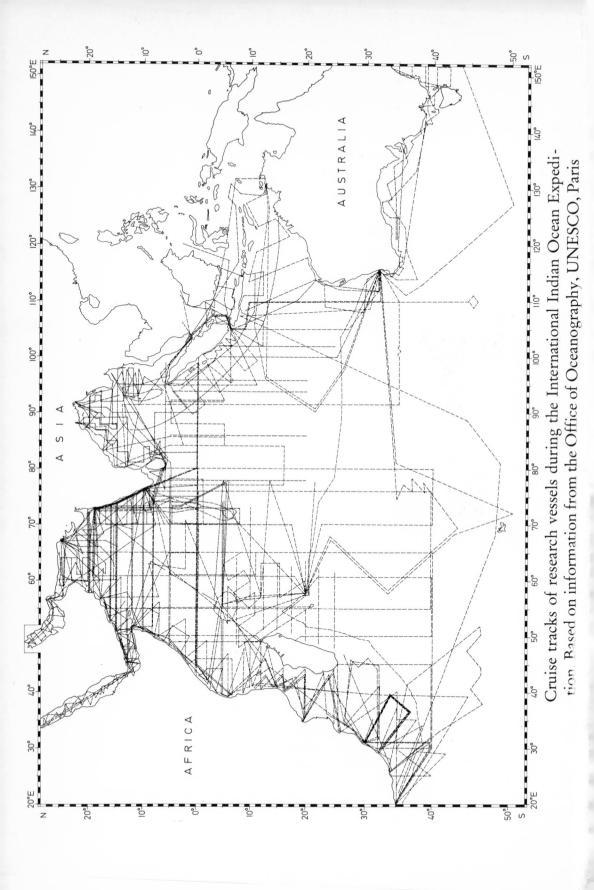

Cruise tracks of research vessels during the International Indian Ocean Expedition. Based on information from the Office of Oceanography, UNESCO, Paris

Ecological Studies

Analysis and Synthesis

Edited by

J. Jacobs, München · O. L. Lange, Würzburg
J. S. Olson, Oak Ridge · W. Wieser, Innsbruck

Volume 3

The Biology of the Indian Ocean

Edited by
Bernt Zeitzschel

In Cooperation with
Sebastian A. Gerlach

With 286 Figures

Springer-Verlag New York · Heidelberg · Berlin 1973

Dr. Bernt Zeitzschel
Institut für Meereskunde an der Universität Kiel
D–2300 Kiel
Düsternbrooker Weg 20

Prof. Dr. Sebastian A. Gerlach
Institut für Meeresforschung
D-2850 Bremerhaven
Am Handelshafen 12

Library
I.U.P.
Indiana, Pa.

574.927   B521i
C. 1

ISBN 0-387-06004-9 Springer-Verlag New York · Heidelberg · Berlin
ISBN 3-540-06004-9 Springer-Verlag Berlin · Heidelberg · New York
ISBN 0-412-12070-4 Chapman & Hall Limited London

This work is subject to copyright. All rights are reserved, whether the whole or part of the material is concerned, specifically those of translation, reprinting, re-use of illustrations, broadcasting, reproduction by photocopying machine or similar means, and storage in data banks.

The use of registered names, trademarks, etc. in this publication does not imply, even in the absence of a specific statement, that such names are exempt from the relevant protective laws and regulations and therefore free for general use.

Under § 54 of the German Copyright Law where copies are made for other than private use, a fee is payable to the publisher, the amount of the fee to be determined by agreement with the publisher.

© by Springer-Verlag Berlin · Heidelberg 1973. Library of Congress Catalog Card Number 72-90196.
Printed in Germany. Typesetting: Union Druckerei GmbH Stuttgart. Printing and bookbinding: Druckerei Georg Appl, 8853 Wemding.

Preface

This volume contains the proceedings of a Symposium held at the University of Kiel, Germany, from 31 March to 6 April, 1971. The Symposium was organized by the Scientific Committee on Oceanic Research (SCOR) and the Marine Productivity section of the International Biological Programme (IBP/PM) with the assistance of the United Nations Educational, Scientific and Cultural Organization (UNESCO), the Food and Agriculture Organization (FAO), and the International Association of Biological Oceanography (IABO). The aim of the Symposium was to summarize present knowledge of the biology of the Indian Ocean.

Twenty-two presentations by invited speakers reviewed the research work carried out during the International Indian Ocean Expedition (IIOE) 1959−1965, the first cooperative project coordinated by the Intergovernmental Oceanographic Commission (IOC). In addition, reports were presented of postexpedition examination of material and of more recent investigations relevant to the aims of the IIOE.

In keeping with the aims of "Ecological Studies", the present volume contains much new information and some synthesis, all directed towards obtaining an understanding of the functioning and organization of the ecosystem of the Indian Ocean. The plan of the Symposium was to present the relevant meteorological, physical, chemical and geological background and to follow this with the various aspects of biological oceanography.

Because of the uneven stage of development of the different disciplines, the papers included in this volume vary in their analytical level.

The papers are included more or less as written for the Symposium. However, in order to obtain uniformity the manuscripts have been edited, overlapping review material has been removed, references have been grouped together and most figures have been redrawn. I would like to thank all contributors for their cooperation.

The scientific work received substantial support from various organizations, such as:
Deutsche Forschungsgemeinschaft (BOJE et al., KREY, LENZ)
Oceanographic Institute of the University of S. Paulo Brazil (VANNUCCI and NAVAS)
Pakistan Navy (HAQ et al.)
University of Kerala, Trivandrum, India (SHAH)
U.S. National Science Foundation (EL-SAYED and JITTS)
U.S. National Science Foundation (GB 12412) and Marine Life Research Program of the Scripps Institution of Oceanography (FLEMINGER and HULSEMANN)
U.S. National Data Center, U.S. National Science Foundation (GP-821) and U.S. Coast Guard Academy (MCGILL)
and others.

The journals in the reference list are in most cases abbreviated according to the new "World List of Periodicals for Aquatic Sciences and Fisheries" in preparation by the FAO Fisheries Division. I would like to thank Mr. AKYÜZ for his kind assistance.

The organization of the Symposium and the subsequent preparation of the volume were immense tasks, made possible by the generous and substantial help of the Auswärtiges Amt, Bonn, the University of Kiel, and the Institut für Meereskunde, Kiel. Special thanks are due to Mrs. G. KREDEL, for her extraordinarily helpful assistance throughout the organization of the Symposium and the editing of this volume. Prof. S. A. GERLACH, Bremerhaven, read all manuscripts. I acknowledge his valuable comments. With pleasure we acknowledge the stimulating discussion and encouragement provided by Dr. G. HUMPHREY, CSIRO, Marine Biochemistry Unit, Sydney University.

Kiel, February 1973   BERNT ZEITZSCHEL

Contents

1. The Environment

2. Primary Production and Standing Stock of Phytoplankton and Bacteria

3. Standing Stock and Distribution of Phytoplankton, Zooplankton and Particulate Matter in Selected Areas

4. Standing Stock and Distribution of Zooplankton

Contributors

ALI KHAN, J., Institut für Meereskunde, Universität Kiel, Kiel, W. Germany

ARAVINDAKSHAN, P. N., Indian Ocean Biological Centre, National Institute of Oceanography, Cochin, India

ARUGA, Y., Dr., Tokyo University of Fisheries, Tokyo, Japan

BABENERD, B., Institut für Meereskunde, Universität Kiel, Kiel, W. Germany

BALACHANDRAN, T., Indian Ocean Biological Centre, National Institute of Oceanography, Cochin, India

BOJE, R., Dr., Institut für Meereskunde, Universität Kiel, Kiel, W. Germany

BRINTON, E., Dr., Scripps Institution of Oceanography, University of California, La Jolla, CA, USA

CHUGTAI, S., Department of Marine Biology, University of Karachi, Karachi, Pakistan

COHEN, D. M., Dr., National Marine Fisheries Service, U.S. National Museum Washington, DC, USA

CURRIE, R. I., Dunstaffnage Marine Research Laboratory, Oban, Scotland

CUSHING, D. H., Dr., Ministry of Agriculture, Fisheries and Food, Fisheries Laboratory, Lowestoft, Suffolk, England

DE DECKER, A., Dr., Division of Sea Fisheries, Cape Town, South Africa

DIETRICH, G. †, Prof., Institut für Meereskunde, Universität Kiel, Kiel, W. Germany

EL-SAYED, S. Z., Prof., Department of Oceanography, Texas A & M University, College Station, TX, USA

FENAUX, R., Dr., Station Zoologique Villefranche sur Mer, Université de Paris, France

FISHER, A. E., National Institute of Oceanography, Wormley, England

FLEMINGER, A., Dr., Scripps Institution of Oceanography, University of California, La Jolla, CA, USA

GOPALAKRISHNAN, K., Scripps Institution of Oceanography, University of California, La Jolla, CA, USA

GOPALAKRISHNAN, T. C., Indian Ocean Biological Centre, National Institute of Oceanography, Cochin, India

HAQ, S. M., Prof., Department of Marine Biology, University of Karachi, Karachi, Pakistan

HARGREAVES, P. M., National Institute of Oceanography, Wormley, England

HULSEMANN, K., Dr., Scripps Institution of Oceanography, University of California, La Jolla, CA, USA

JACOB, P. G., Indian Ocean Biological Centre, National Institute of Oceanography, Cochin, India

JITTS, H. R., Dr., Commonwealth Scientific and Industrial Research Organization, Marine Laboratory, Cronulla, Australia

JOHNSON, D. H., Meteorological Office College, Reading, England

KASTURIRANGAN, L. R., Indian Ocean Biological Centre, National Institute of Oceanography, Cochin, India

KIMOR, B., Prof., Sea Fisheries Research Station, Haifa, Israel

KREY, J., Prof., Institut für Meereskunde, Universität Kiel, Kiel, W. Germany

KUMARAN, S., Indian Ocean Biological Centre, National Institute of Oceanography, Cochin, India

KURIAN, C. V., Prof., Department of Marine Sciences, University of Cochin, India

LENZ, J., Dr., Institut für Meereskunde, Universität Kiel, Kiel, W. Germany

McGILL, D. A., Prof., US Coast Guard Academy, New London, USA

MENON, N. R., Dr., College of Fisheries, University of Agricultural Sciences, Mangalore, India

MONTECINO, V., Department of Biology, Faculty of Philosophy and Education, University of Chile, Santiago, Chile

NAIR, K. K. C., Indian Ocean Biological Centre, National Institute of Oceanography, Cochin, India

NAIR, V. R., Indian Ocean Biological Centre, National Institute of Oceanography, Cochin, India

NAVAS, D., FAPESP Fellow (proc. Biol. 69/599) – S. Paulo, Brazil

NELLEN, W., Dr., Institut für Meereskunde, Universität Kiel, Kiel, W. Germany

NEYMAN, A. A., Dr., P. P. Shirshov Institute of Oceanology, USSR Academy of Sciences, Moscow, USSR

PASTERNAK, F. A., Dr., P. P. Shirshov Institute of Oceanology, USSR Academy of Sciences, Moscow, USSR

QASIM, S. Z., Dr., Central Marine Fisheries Research Institute, Cochin, India

RAO, T. S. S., Prof., Indian Ocean Biological Centre, National Institute of Oceanography, Cochin, India

RHEINHEIMER, G., Prof., Institut für Meereskunde, Universität Kiel, Kiel, W. Germany

SAIJO, Y., Dr., Water Research Laboratory, Faculty of Science, Nagoya University, Nagoya, Japan

SAKTHIVEL, M., Indian Ocean Biological Centre, National Institute of Oceanography, Cochin, India

SARASWATHY, M., Dr., Indian Ocean Biological Centre, National Institute of Oceanography, Cochin, India

SCHMIDT, H.-E., Zoologisches Institut, Universität Gießen, Gießen, W. Germany

SEIBOLD, E., Prof., Geologisch-Paläontologisches Institut und Museum, Universität Kiel, Kiel, W. Germany

SHAH, N. M., Dr., Oceanographic Laboratory, University of Kerala, Cochin, India

SOKOLOVA, M. N., Dr., P. P. Shirshov Institute of Oceanology, USSR Academy of Sciences, Moscow, USSR

STEINITZ, H. †, Prof., Department of Zoology, Hebrew University, Jerusalem, Israel

SUDA, A., Dr., Far Seas Fisheries Research Laboratory, Shimizu, Japan

TAYLOR, F. J. R., Dr., Institute of Oceanography, University of British Columbia, Vancouver, Canada

TRANTER, D. J., Dr., Commonwealth Scientific and Industrial Research Organization, Marine Laboratory, Cronulla, Australia

VANNUCCI, M., Dr., UNESCO Curators, Indian Ocean Biological Centre, National Institute of Oceanography, Cochin, India

VINOGRADOVA, N. G., Dr., P. P. Shirshov Institute of Oceanography, USSR Academy of Sciences, Moscow, USSR

WYRTKI, K., Prof., Department of Oceanography, University of Hawaii, Honolulu, HI, USA

1. The Environment

1.1

The Unique Situation in the Environment of the Indian Ocean

G. DIETRICH

There were two reasons why the Indian Ocean was chosen for the largest international oceanographic investigation ever made. First, the Indian Ocean is the least-known ocean. To make real progress in the knowledge of this ocean an investigation was needed, not by one ship, not even by one nation with several ships, but by numerous research vessels acting in concert. Before 1957 nobody knew if an international cooperation involving dozens of ships would work. But in 1957, which is really a remarkable date in the history of marine sciences, the first multinational program took place during the International Geophysical Year (IGY). The various oceanographic surveys made in the North Pacific and North Atlantic oceans proved that several nations had a great willingness and capability for scientific cooperation. The IGY meeting in Gothenburg (Sweden) 1957, the meeting of the so-called CSAGI (Conseil Scientifique Année Géophysique Internationale), was the beginning of the IIOE. In the same year the international body, SCOR (Scientific Committee on Oceanic Research), was founded and its first great task became the International Indian Ocean Expedition (IIOE).

Little was known of the oceanographic conditions in the Indian Ocean, which was the main reason why the IIOE was planned. But there was also a second reason: the Indian Ocean has a unique position among the oceans because the surface circulation in the northern part reverses every half year. In winter we have the NE, and in summer the SW monsoon circulation. There is no better place on earth to study the reaction of an ocean with the atmosphere than the northern Indian Ocean.

Both the general survey of the Indian Ocean and the investigation of the monsoon circulation were to be carried out in the same program. Now, 6 years after the expedition, in which 20 nations with 40 research vessels participated, we can say it was successful. It is true that not all expectations were fulfilled, mainly because the observations in large areas were not very extensive. Perhaps there would be no criticisms if the expedition had followed the plan made by WÜST (1959), which is based on a schematic grid system of sections with repeated observations in different seasons. Such a plan is ideal but unrealistic. The IIOE had to be worked out by scientists from many countries who took part voluntarily and were interested in a variety of scientific programs. Some regions are extremely rich in problems, e.g. the monsoon effect which can be studied only in certain areas of the Indian Ocean, and some regions lack specific problems, like the southern Westerlies in the Circumpolar Current. The ocean was not investigated in a manner resembling a military manoeuvre, but according to the demands of scientific problems in selected regions (see map oposite title page). As a result the observations are unevenly distributed. Therefore we congratulate RAMAGE on the great cooperative work in meteorology (RAMAGE et al., 1972) and WYRTKI on his Oceanographic Atlas of the Indian Ocean

(WYRTKI, 1971); both had to contend with the inhomogeneity of the observations. Even with this material many problems could be solved, but numerous other questions await future work.

The following remarks are restricted to the main facts which make the environmental conditions of the Indian Ocean different from the other oceans. The new contour map (DIETRICH and ULRICH, 1968) confirmed many well-known features in the bottom topography: the system of ridges and basins as well as the relative paucity of shallow water areas. It also shows some of the features discovered during the IIOE, namely the Eastern Indian Ridge with a length of 4800 km, and the fracture zones and seamounts. Many

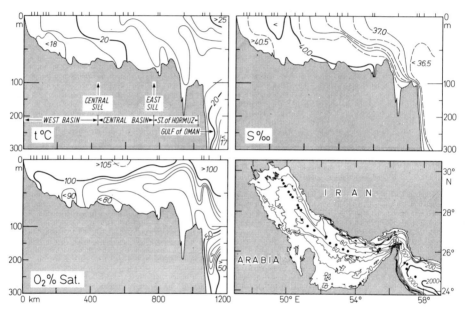

Fig. 1. Longitudinal section of temperature (in ° C), salinity (in S⁰/₀₀) and oxygen (in % saturation) in the Persian Gulf. (After KOSKE, 1972 and RABSCH, 1972). The map shows the contour lines (in m) and the positions of the stations used in the sections. Note the change of depth scale below 100 m

special features are not included in the atlas, e.g. canyons, fans, oil and gas reservoirs on the Indian shelf. The geophysical measurements concentrating especially on the magnetic field showed the spreading of the ocean floor and even gave data for the rate of spreading. This amounts to 2 cm year^{-1} and implies that the Indian Ocean is about 10^8 years old.

The contour maps demonstrate a very simple fact, if we look at the situation of the ocean, relative to the Equator. This is the asymmetric shape imposed by the existence of the Asian continent. It has two main consequences: first, the ocean is separated from deep-reaching vertical convection areas in the northern hemisphere; second, the Asian continent is large enough to develop its own far-reaching atmospheric circulation which influences the ocean down to 10° S and is known as the monsoon circulation.

The first condition means that it is only in the higher southern latitudes, in the subpolar and polar seas, that water of low temperature reaches high density on the sea surface and initiates a deep circulation. Therefore, the meridional circulation of the Indian Ocean is similar to that occurring in an estuary: heavy water on the bottom spreads to the head of the bay, light water in the upper layer to the mouth. Although only a part of the Indian Ocean lies in the northern hemisphere, its own rudimentary meridional

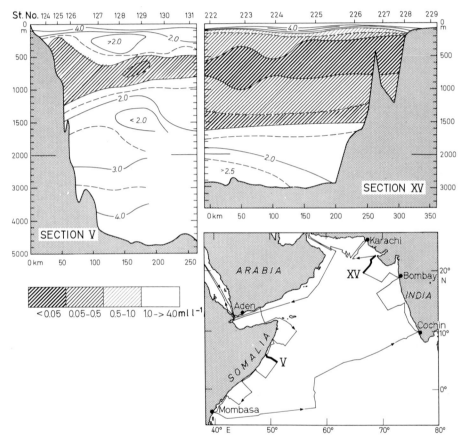

Fig. 2. Distribution of oxygen (in ml l⁻¹) on 2 sections of RV "Meteor" in the Arabian Sea off Somalia (section V, December 1964) and off India (section XV, March 1965) during the IIOE. The map shows the position of the sections. Note the change of exaggeration in 2000 m depth: Hundred-fold 0−2000 m, twohundredfold 2000−5000 m. (After GRASSHOFF, in DIETRICH et al., 1966)

circulation is initiated by the water masses of the Red Sea and the Persian Gulf. Both seas are relatively small, yet they both have a very effective deep-reaching convection, especially in winter in the northern parts, in the Gulf of Suez and off the mouth of Shatt-el-Arab. Fig. 1 shows the Persian Gulf, observed by "Meteor" in March 1965 and evaluated by KOSKE (1972) and RABSCH (1972). Cold water with high salinity is formed by the considerable evaporation in the inner Gulf and it spreads on the bottom. This deep water leaves the Gulf through the exit on the bottom, sinks further down and forms a layer in parts of the Arabian Sea. Some renewal takes place thanks to this process, but is relatively small, yet the water is not as poor in O_2 as it would be without this renewal with water

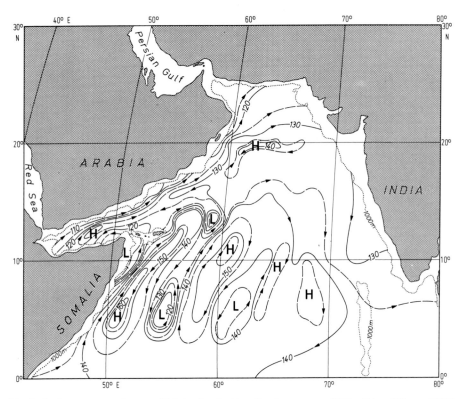

Fig. 3. Surface currents (geostrophic) in the Arabian Sea in summer 1963. (After DÜING, 1970) Represented by the dynamic topography of the sea surface (in dynamic cm), referred to the 800 decibar surface. H: Height of the sea level, center of anticyclonic gyres. L: Lows of the sea level, center of cyclonic gyres. Dotted line: 1000 m

rich in O_2. This can be shown by comparing the O_2 distribution of the western and the eastern parts of the Arabian Sea.

The outflow of Persian Gulf water and of Red Sea water influenced by the Coriolis forces prefers the western boundary, the eastern boundary being low in renewal. Two examples of the O_2 sections worked by "Meteor", one off Somalia, the other off the Indian coast, are shown in Fig. 2. In both cases the O_2 content is low, sometimes lower than 0.5 ml l^{-1}, but much lower off India than off Somalia. The layer with values below 0.5 ml l^{-1} reaches from 100 to 1500 m, and the values in a layer of 500 m thickness are even below 0.05 ml l^{-1}, which means less than 1% saturation. This is the lowest O_2 content in such a large region in the entire open world ocean. Additional measurements by

GRASSHOFF (in DIETRICH et al., 1966) showed that the $NO_3^- - N$ is reduced to $NO_2^- - N$, but there was no H_2S in the open water.

These extreme O_2 conditions are of special biological interest. Two facts are worth noting: first, the poor O_2 layer extends onto the shelf of India, as shown in Fig. 2. This situation was found during the NE monsoon. In the SE monsoon season conditions are different because the semi-annual reversal of the surface circulation has a great influence on the O_2 distribution and this affects the bottom fauna as well as the commercial fishes. The second surprising fact concerns the deep echo-scattering layer. We followed the daily ups and downs of the scattering layers entering the layer of extreme O_2 depletion and concluded that organisms, causing these deep scattering layers of sound, can exist for at least 12 hours without O_2.

The first result of the asymmetric configuration of this ocean is this O_2-poor layer due to the weak deep circulation of the northern Indian Ocean. The other one is the reversal of the surface circulation with the monsoon, which is significant for the Indian Ocean. RAMAGE (1969) has already published his results relating to the atmospheric circulation. The ocean north of $10°S$ is a classical example of monsoons, and there is no area more suitable for studying the response of the ocean circulation to a changing wind system. The total reversal of winds and currents was well known, but the mechanism of this reversal was unknown before the IIOE. Theoretical considerations of some scientists and the evaluation by DÜING (1970) of the quasi-synoptic observations made in summer 1963 prove the breakdown of the circulation in a series of large gyres in the Arabian Sea (Fig. 3). Theoretical, mathematical calculations of models of the Arabian Sea indicated that one monsoon period of approximately 5 months is not long enough to establish a stationary current system. The surveys had therefore to be intensified to analyze the changes over time. This can be done by the concentration of several research vessels during a monsoon period and by recording the infrared radiation of the sea surface by satellites. Fig. 4 shows a map of the surface temperature with values obtained by the weather satellite "Nimbus 2" in summer 1966 and evaluated by SZEKIELDA (1970a, b). The absolute temperature shown in this figure may not be exact, but the relative temperature is, hence the gradients in the cloudless regions are correct. The upwelling along the Somali coast is obvious from the low surface temperature, but this upwelling is not constant along the whole coast, as shown by the patches of low temperature. The upwelling is a process which varies with time and place in the region of the shelf edge in form of large eddies. These cold eddies drift with the Somalia Current and turn with this current to the east south of Socotra.

The reversing wind system also influences the equatorial current system. The Equatorial Undercurrent (first observed in 1954) is a strong ocean current in the Pacific and in the Atlantic Ocean. Measurements indicate that in the Indian Ocean the Equatorial Undercurrent is only occasionally present. The rules are not known, but various observations independent of each other showed that even in winter during the NE monsoon, i. e. when the atmospheric circulation resembles the trade wind circulation in the other oceans, the undercurrent does not exist. This is what "Meteor" found early in 1965.

To summarize the characteristics of the Indian Ocean as compared with other oceans, four special facts make it different from the others:

a) Semi-annual reversal of the surface circulation north of $10°S$
b) Break-up of this circulation into large eddies

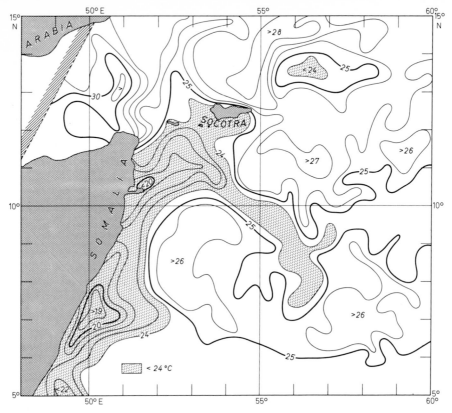

Fig. 4. Radiation temperature (in ° C) of the sea surface in the western Arabian Sea on July 3, 1966 (After Szekielda, 1970 a). The evaluation is based on radiation measurements of the weather satellite Nimbus 2. Hatched area has a surface temperature below 24° C

c) Time-dependent Equatorial Undercurrent

d) Extremely poor renewal of the deep water, especially in the northern parts

We know that special conditions exist, but we do not know the details and exact causes of the mechanism. Thus there is an important field for future work in physical oceanography in the Indian Ocean.

1.2

Recent Satellite Studies

D. H. JOHNSON

During the past decade the global networks of meteorological observations have been richly supplemented by a growing wealth of satellite data. Amongst the quantities of interest to meteorologists or oceanographers, measured or derived from satellite observations over the oceans are: cloud amount and type; reflected short wave radiation and albedo; total outgoing long-wave radiation; long-wave radiation in selected wave bands; the radiation balance of the earth-atmosphere system; temperature and height of cloud tops; sea surface temperature; atmospheric vertical temperature profile; atmospheric water vapour content; low-level wind speeds; winds at cloud levels; the fields of divergence and vorticity of the air flow; the sea state; and the extent of sea ice. In addition there are proposals for the future measurement of chlorophyll and plankton population by spectrometry .

For some of these quantities the work so far undertaken and described has been concerned mainly to establish the feasibility of the instrumental technique or method of analysis. For others the global climatology has been studied and in these the Indian Ocean area is naturally included. As yet, very few investigations have dealt specifically with Indian Ocean problems. A useful review of basic techniques and of the data which are available or will soon be available for study from United States sources has been provided by LEESE, BOOTH and GODSHALL (1970). One omission in the last paper is reference to the recent work on the deduction of sea states and surface wind conditions from sun-glint patterns (STRONG and RUFF, 1970).

I. Radiation Measurements

Studies of the earth's radiation budget, using global observations made with low resolution radiometers carried by the TIROS and ESSA satellites have confirmed, not surprisingly, that the earth-atmosphere system is in near radiative equilibrium. The outgoing long-wave radiation measured from satellites has a latitudinal variation which follows closely that obtained from presatellite computations with magnitudes, as reported by VONDER HAAR and SUOMI (1969) generally higher than, but within 5% of those computed in the earlier studies. The mean annual planetary albedo has been computed by the latter authors from the satellite data to be 29%, but they point out that the values measured for the tropics are much lower than was earlier assumed. It appears that the observations of clouds made from the surface by tropical observers probably overestimate the opaque cloud cover, and it must be concluded that about 30% more energy is absorbed by the earth-atmosphere system in the tropics than was previously supposed. As a result, previous estimates of poleward heat transport must also be increased. The question remaining is whether the increased transports take place primarily in the air or the sea.

In the latter case, as VONDER HAAR and SUOMI (1969) point out, the importance of air-sea interaction would receive fresh emphasis. Figs. 1 and 2 show the mean annual geographic distributions of planetary albedo and outgoing infrared radiation. In both cases there are pronounced east-west variations within the tropics.

The high-resolution infrared radiometers (HRIR) carried by the NIMBUS satellites have measured radiation in the 3.4 to 4.2 μ atmospheric window. They scan horizon to horizon in a direction perpendicular to the orbital track and give a resolution at the

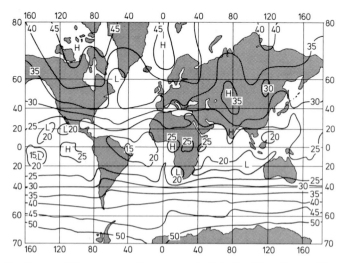

Fig. 1. The distribution of the mean annual planetary albedo in %. (After VONDER HAAR and SUOMI, 1969)

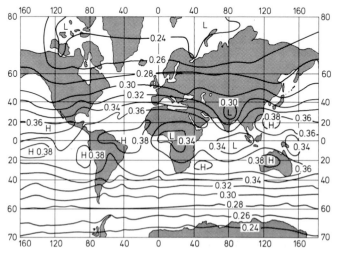

Fig. 2. The distribution of the mean annual outgoing longwave radiation in cal cm^{-2} min^{-1}. (After VONDER HAAR and SUOMI, 1969)

sea surface of about 4 nautical miles. These data allow the temperature of the radiating surfaces beneath the satellite to be calculated. Over the oceans for clear skies the temperatures derived are those of the sea surface. The main problem arising in the mapping of sea surface temperatures from these data lies in the separation of the clear sky values from those contaminated by cloud. Most areas of cloud can be identified by their appreciably lower temperatures in comparison with those of the cloud-free ocean surface nearby and in analyses given for individual days by WARNECKE, MCMILLIN and ALLISON (1969) such cloudy areas are simply excluded. In other studies several days measurements for individual 1° latitude or larger squares have been examined and the highest value selected as representative for the sea surface, the argument again being that cloud-

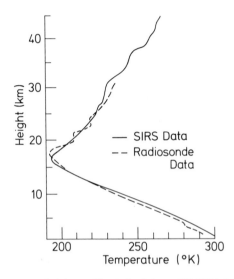

Fig. 3. Atmospheric temperature-height profile derived from NIMBUS 3 SIRS data (solid curve) near Jamaica and the corresponding radio sonde profile (dotted curve) observed at Kingston at 1112 E.S.T. on 14 April 1969. (After WARK and HILLEARY, 1969)

contaminated measurements will always be colder than those taken under clear skies. This procedure is likely to over-estimate the sea-surface temperature, however, due to the incidence of the random instrumental errors. A neat statistical method which objectively discriminates between cloud-free and cloud-contaminated observations has been developed by SMITH et al. (1970). It takes due account of atmospheric attenuation and instrumental random error or noise. For a 1° square over 200 NIMBUS HRIR measurements are generally available on one day, and for a 2.5° square the number is more than 1000. The method involves inferring the Gaussian distribution of surface radiances for the clear atmospheric case from observed histograms of generally cloud-contaminated radiances. Comparisons with conventional ship observations indicate that the random errors of the sea temperatures inferred are less than 1°K. There is also a bias of about 1°K which might be due to a real difference between the temperature of the surface microlayer seen by the satellite sensor and the subsurface temperatures sampled by ships, or to instrumental calibration. The technique of data reduction given by

Smith et al. (1970) is objective and suited to bulk processing by computer, permitting global analyses of sea temperature to be made available for daily operational use.

Studies of the sea temperatures measured by satellite over the Indian Ocean are in progress at the Goddard Space Flight Center, and first results have been made available by Szekielda (1970a) (see Fig. 4, Dietrich, 1973, this volume) and Szekielda, Salomonson and Allison (1970).

Three different experiments designed to provide vertical temperature profiles using spectrometer measurements have been tested in NIMBUS flights. They show very great potential. An early result obtained by Wark and Hilleary (1969) from the Satellite Infrared Spectrometer (SIRS) data is shown in Fig. 3. The comparison with the vertical profile obtained from a conventional radio sonde ascent made nearby is impressive. The accuracy and resolution of the satellite values do not yet match those of the radio sonde but these are early days and it is expected that with further research and development it will be possible to map the global pressure fields with an accuracy at least as high as is now possible in more limited areas with conventional data.

II. Cloud Distributions

Two main classes of satellites are equipped to provide pictures of the visible radiation reflected during the day from the underlying surfaces by television photography. They are the polar-orbiting satellites as in, e.g., the ESSA and NIMBUS series, and the geo-stationary craft in equatorial orbit known as the Applications Technology Satellites (ATS). The former are sun-synchronous, providing a global survey of the cloud cover once per day from heights of order $1000-1500$ km. Each picture covers an area of diameter $30°$ latitude. ATS satellites are located at about 36 000 km over the central equatorial Pacific and western equatorial Atlantic. They provide pictures at a frequency of $20-30$ minutes covering a region of diameter $100°$ latitude.

Meteorologists the world over have become accustomed to using the ESSA and NIMBUS pictures in their daily operational work. At a number of places in the Indian Ocean area, including for example, Singapore, Gan Island ($00°41'$S; $73°09'$E) and Mauritius, there are ground stations equipped to receive the daily automatic picture transmissions. Fig. 4 is an example of one such picture. It shows a chain of clusters of cumulonimbus clouds lying along the Straits of Malacca. The clouds were generated in a line squall of a type known locally as a Sumatra.

Clusters of cumulonimbus clouds of dimension 0.5 to $2°$ are a common constituent of tropical weather systems. They represent an important scale of organization. According to the GARP Study Group (1969) cumulonimbus clusters of scale 50 km contain up to ten cumulonimbus cells; what is visible is the canopy of cirrus cloud to which they give rise. Fig. 5 is an ESSA 3 picture covering the northwestern part of South America on 12 April 1967. The cumulonimbus clusters are scattered over the area without any obvious degree of organization. Cloud distributions similar to that of Fig. 5 can be found at times over the tropical parts of each of the continents and over sizeable islands such as Borneo. They usually exhibit a distinct diurnal variation with maximum size in the after-noon. Isolated cumulonimbus clusters and small groups are also to be found over the Indian Ocean, but normally there is a higher degree of organization. Fig. 6 is the ESSA 3 computerized mosaic (composite cloud picture) for the Indian Ocean sector on 23 January

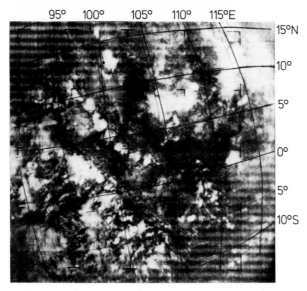

Fig. 4. A chain of cumulonimbus clusters along the Straits of Malacca at 0256 Z on 31 May 1967. The chain extends northwestwards from the centre of the picture. Each cluster is of diameter about 1° of latitude. The picture was received at an APT ground station in Singapore from ESSA 4

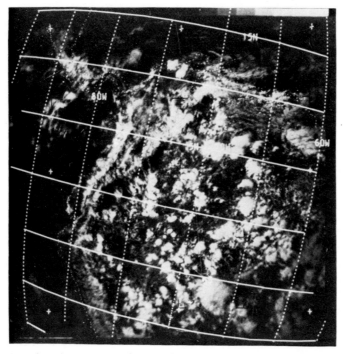

Fig. 5. Cumulonimbus clusters scattered over northern parts of South America on 12 April 1967. ESSA 3 picture. Parallels and meridians are superimposed at 5° intervals

1967. The Intertropical Convergence Zone (ITCZ) was present as a broken band of cloud centred upon the Equator. The cloud bands associated with the oceanic convergence zones have been found typically to be composed of series of cloud systems of dimensions 5 to 15° with relatively clear areas in between. Following the suggestion of the GARP Study Group (1969), cloud systems of this scale have become known as "cloud clusters". There is some risk of confusion in the use of the terms cumulonimbus cluster and cloud cluster: it should be noted that the latter are of a scale an order higher than that of the former.

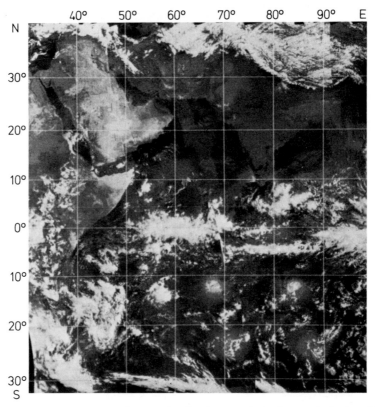

Fig. 6. Composite cloud picture showing the distribution of cloud over the Indian Ocean on 23 January 1967. ESSA 3 computerized mosaic

Except in the dissipation stage, active cloud clusters appear to have a cellular structure and to be composed of agglomerations of cumulonimbus clusters. The cirrus canopies of the cells unite in time, however, to form a large shield covering the whole cloud cluster. Many cloud clusters are amorphous or broadly oval-shaped, but they also take the form of spiral vortices, waves and lines. The Sumatra is a special case. Another is the tropical cyclone. Fig. 7 is an ESSA 3 picture of a tropical cyclone located over the SE Indian Ocean. The eye and spiral bands are visible. NE of the cyclone lies another very active cloud cluster which also developed into a cyclone, although there were few signs of cyclonic organization at the time of the picture. The detection and tracking of tropical cyclones is, of course, one of the most important functions of the operational satellites. DAVY

(1971) illustrates an occasion when 4 major cyclones were present simultaneously in the southern Indian Ocean.

The role of the tropical cloud cluster in vertically transporting heat, mass and momentum and its significance for the atmospheric global circulation is to be studied as a matter of priority in the Global Atmospheric Research Project (GARP), which is being organized jointly by the World Meteorological Organisation and the International Union of Geodesy and Geophysics.

Fig. 7. A tropical cyclone over the Indian Ocean, west of Australia on 19 January 1967. ESSA 3 picture. Parallels and meridians are superimposed at 5° intervals

The ITCZ of the Indian Ocean has been found to behave differently from that of the Atlantic and Pacific Oceans. Fig. 8 contains maps of average total cloud prepared by SADLER (1968) from analyses of satellite cloud pictures. They are for two-year periods and can be expected to represent the longer term only as far as the gross features are concerned. Neglecting the areas west of the American and African continents where sheets of low cloud overlie the cold ocean currents throughout the year, SADLER's maps, which are available for each month, can be taken to reflect the relative frequencies and intensities of the showers and storms taking place throughout the tropics. As indicated in Fig. 8, over the central and eastern Pacific and over the Atlantic, cloudiness maxima persist throughout the year to the north of the Equator. They are embedded in mean surface easterlies except over the eastern Pacific in the northern summer, when they lie in westerly flow to the south of surface troughs of low pressure. Daily satellite pictures show that zones of cloudiness exist on most individual days over the Atlantic and Pacific in the locations indicated by the mean maps. Throughout the year in the Atlantic and

JANUARY (1966-67)

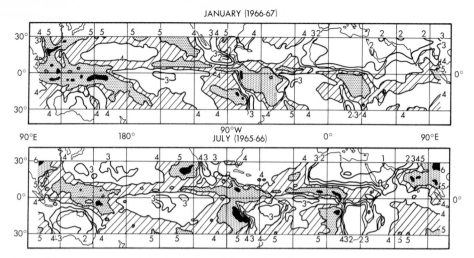

JULY (1965-66)

Fig. 8. Two-year averages of cloudiness derived from polar orbiting satellite data by SADLER (1968). Isopleths represent the total cloud amount approximately in oktas (eighths of sky covered)

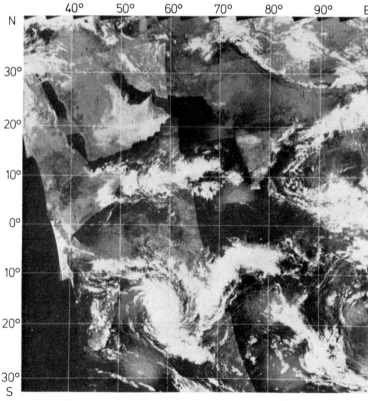

Fig. 9. Composite cloud picture showing the presence of 2 convergence zones over the Indian Ocean on 12 January 1967. The southern zone was in course of disruption by a tropical cyclone. ESSA 3 computerized mosaic

eastern Pacific the low cloudiness of the southern subtropical anticyclones tends to extend northwards to the Equator; in some months the minimum is found at the Equator itself. Over the eastern Pacific a secondary zone of maximum cloudiness is sometimes found several degrees south of the Equator but this forms *in situ* and does not arise through the southward translation of the North Pacific ITCZ. Over the Indian Ocean in January a cloudy zone extends northeastwards from Malagasy to Sumatra. In this case the average is often unrepresentative of the distribution on individual days and in individual years. There are occasions when the Indian Ocean cloud systems take up broadly the orientation shown in Fig. 8 but the Indian Ocean zones are more variable in their character and location than are those of the East Pacific. The zone established at the Equator on 23 January 1967 (Fig. 6) was earlier to be found further to the north as shown in Fig. 9, which is an ESSA 3 mosaic for 12 January 1967. An older zone, seen south of the Equator in Fig. 9, was in process of disruption by the tropical cyclone and it did not subsequently reform; instead, the newer zone to the north moved southwards to take its place. In Fig. 10 is plotted the daily latitude at longitude 60° E of the convergence zones which

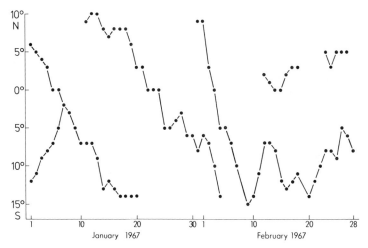

Fig. 10. The movement over the Indian Ocean of the centre of the Intertropical Convergence Zone at 60° E during January and February 1967. (JOHNSON, 1970)

moved over the Indian Ocean during January and February 1967. Zones repeatedly formed over the north of the ocean and shifted southwards irregularly over periods of weeks to replace or merge with older, more southerly systems.

Whatever their form, wave, vortex or amorphous, the cloud clusters of the trades are typically westward-moving with a speed of translation of order 5° of longitude per day. They are long-lived and can usually be tracked over periods of 10 days or more. Over the Indian Ocean, the disturbances are not predominantly westward-moving but such systems do occur in due season over those regions subject to tropical cyclones. The cloud clusters which form in the monsoon Westerlies, however, are quasi-stationary and short-lived, persisting for only a day or two. They are also longer than those of the trades, often being of diameter 10 to 20° latitude. Although the individual monsoon cloud clusters do not move in a well ordered fashion there are, nevertheless, changes in the broad patterns of the cloud clusters which reflect shifts in the location of the major weather activity within the monsoon zone. Shifts of this kind were partly responsible for the fluctuations of the quantities graphed in Fig. 11, which illustrates the marked variations

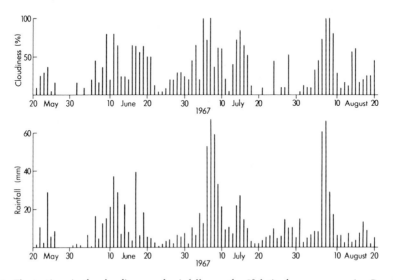

Fig. 11. Fluctuations in the cloudiness and rainfall over the 5° latitude square covering Bangladesh during the SW monsoon. Between 15 and 22 stations were available of computing the mean daily rainfall over the area. Cloudiness was derived from ESSA 3 and ESSA 5 satellite pictures. (JOHNSON, 1970)

taking place over periods of from 10 to 20 days in monsoon weather activity over Bangladesh. The satellite data reveal variations in cloudiness and rainfall on a similar scale over the equatorial Indian Ocean.

III. Sea Ice and Plankton

Snow and ice fields appear in satellite pictures as bright white areas. In a single picture it is often difficult to discriminate between snow and cloud. However, a skilled analyst, making use of continuity and taking into account the texture of the white areas, shadows, landmarks and other indications, can successfully deduce the extent of the sea ice if the solar illumination is sufficiently strong. McCLAIN and BAKER (1969) have described a method known as minimum brightness compositing which objectively filters the clouds from scenes containing snow or ice fields. This depends upon the computer storage of brightness values taken from the daily pictures at a global array of closely-spaced grid points. For each grid point the minimum brightness recorded over a period of 5 days is selected and a picture composed of the minimum values is printed. Cloud-free land or ocean is much less reflective than ice, snow and clouds, so this process retains as bright areas only those which represent slowly-changing fields of ice and snow or those few areas of bright cloud which may persist throughout the period. Minimum brightness composites are prepared and issued as routine from the National Environmental Satellite Service, Suitland, U.S.A.

Chlorophyll has been measured at sea from low-flying aircraft equipped with spectrometers (CLARKE, EWING and LORENZEN, 1970). The planned installation of a spectrometer for measurement of chlorophyll in an Earth Resources Technology Satellite will make it possible to investigate the dynamics of plankton populations in upwelling areas.

IV. Concluding Remarks

There are 3 ways in which satellites can be of use to marine biologists: 1. by the direct observation of quantities of immediate interest such as sea temperature and chlorophyll distribution; 2. by permitting important advances to be made in physical sciences, meteorology and physical oceanography, with which the marine biologist inevitably becomes involved; and 3. as a communications agent. An indication of the possibilities for the use of satellite sensors has been given in the above account. The third use of satellites as a communications aid should also be mentioned. They can be used to receive, record and retransmit signals broadcast from automatic sensing apparatus at the ocean surface or in the atmosphere. The apparatus may be mounted on anchored or drifting observing platforms or on submersible vehicles. Transmitters attached to marine organisms which visit the ocean surface might be used as tracers.

Observations made by United States satellites are made available, usually at the cost of reproduction, from two agencies: National Weather Records Center, NOAA, Asheville, N.C., U.S.A.; and National Space Science Data Center, Goddard Space Flight Center, Code 601, Greenbelt, Maryland 20771, U.S.A. A useful first guide to what is available is given in the ESSA Technical Report NESC 53 which can be obtained from the Clearinghouse for Federal Scientific and Technical Information, U.S. Dept. of Commerce, Sills Building, 5285 Port Royal Road, Springfield, Va. 22151.

1.3

Physical Oceanography of the Indian Ocean

K. WYRTKI

During the preparation of the Atlas on the physical oceanography of the Indian Ocean (WYRTKI, 1971) a comprehensive analysis of its oceanographic conditions had to be undertaken to construct meaningful maps, sections and diagrams, and to interpret the structure and circulation of this ocean, which is in so many ways different from the other oceans. On a large scale 3 distinct circulation systems can be delineated. These are:

I. the seasonally changing monsoon gyre
II. the south hemispheric subtropical anticyclonic gyre
III. the Antarctic waters with the Circumpolar Current

While the last 2 systems are essentially similar to the corresponding systems in the other oceans, a reversing monsoon gyre is not found anywhere else in the oceans. This gyre is separated from the southern subtropical gyre by a very pronounced front in the hydro-chemical structure at about 10°S, a unique feature of the Indian Ocean. But also the nutrient-poor southern subtropical gyre differs in many respects from those in other oceans. It lacks a well developed eastern boundary current along Australia. The Agulhas Current, its western boundary current, is the strongest in the southern hemisphere.

The division into these 3 circulation systems is not too obvious from an inspection of maps of the surface circulation alone, Fig. 1. However, when structural features of the ocean are included in the analysis, this division becomes quite apparent. In the northern portions of the South Equatorial Current a tongue of low salinity water originating off Sumatra stretches west near 10°S extending all the way to Africa. This boundary is even more marked by a subsurface front in the chemical characteristics, which separates the waters of low oxygen content and high nutrients in the northern Indian Ocean from those of high oxygen content and low nutrient content in the subtropical gyre. The monsoon gyre consists during the NE monsoon of the North Equatorial Current, a southward flow off the coast of Somalia, and the countercurrent, which runs east between the Equator and about 8°S, across the entire width of the ocean. During the SW monsoon, the gyre consists of the northern portions of the South Equatorial Current, which now extends almost to the Equator, the strong Somali Current flowing north as a western boundary current and the monsoon current, into which the countercurrent has merged.

The anticyclonic subtropical gyre consists of the South Equatorial Current, the Agulhas Current system and the eastward flow situated to the north of the subtropical convergence and driven by the prevailing westerly winds south of the atmospheric high pressure ridge. The circulation is closed by slow equatorward movements over most of the subtropical gyre, but a pronounced eastern boundary current is lacking. To the south of the sub-

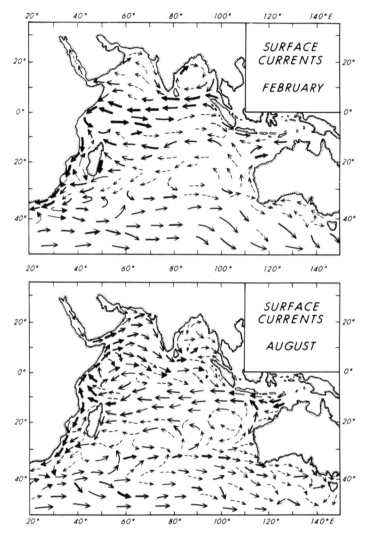

Fig. 1. Surface circulation of the Indian Ocean in February and August according to Monatskarten
für den Indischen Ozean, Deutsches Hydrographisches Institut (1960)

tropical convergence, the oceanographic conditions associated with the west wind drift, the Antarctic Circumpolar Current and the Antarctic waters are essentially the same as elsewhere around Antarctica.

The division of the Indian Ocean into these 3 circulation systems is very well reflected by the distribution of chemical properties, especially the phosphate content, which is shown in Fig. 2 for the depth of 100 m. The monsoon gyre in the northern Indian Ocean is marked by high $PO_4^{3-} - P$ contents, the front near 10°S by a drop from concentrations above 1.0 to less than 0.4 μg-at l^{-1} and the subtropical gyre by very low values. Only in the range of the Somali Current is the phosphate concentration at 100 m depth reduced, most likely due to the strong advection of water from the South Equatorial Current during the SW monsoon. In Antarctic waters the phosphate content rises again from the sub-

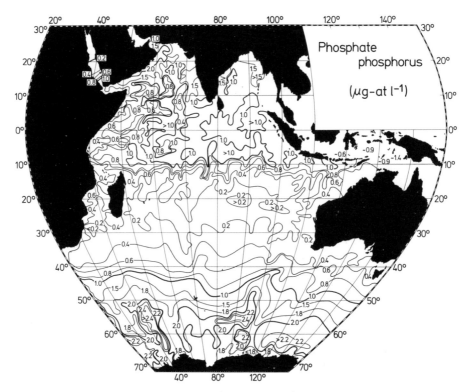

Fig. 2. Distribution of $PO_4^{3-} - P$ in μg-at l^{-1} at 100 m depth

tropical convergence to maximal values near the Antarctic divergence. This distribution characterizes the monsoon area and the Antarctic waters as potentially rich and the subtropical region as poor with regard to biological activity.

I. The Monsoon Gyre

During the NE monsoon water movements to the north of the Equator are from east to west, forming the NE monsoon current. This flow starts developing in November, reaches its greatest strength in February and subsides in April. Current velocities are usually strongest to the south of Ceylon and in the southern Arabian Sea, where they exceed 1 knot. From November to January a strong branch of this current turns north and flows along the west coast of India, carrying low salinity water from the Bay of Bengal into the eastern Arabian Sea. The NE monsoon drift appears to be rather shallow and seems to exert little influence on the waters below the thermocline. Off the coast of

Somalia most of its water turns south, crosses the Equator and forms the Equatorial Countercurrent. The southward flow off Somalia is strongest in December, but lasts until March. In November and December the countercurrent flows along both sides of the Equator, extending from about 3°N to 5°S. Later, from January through April, the countercurrent is entirely south of the Equator and its southern boundary is near 10°S. It should be noted that some of the water of the countercurrent at its western origin is drawn from the South Equatorial Current. At its eastern end only some of the water returns north into the monsoon drift, while a large part continues to the SE as the Java Coastal Current or turns directly into the South Equatorial Current. The proximity of this current to the Equator makes geostrophic computations rather uncertain and therefore does not allow a numerical evaluation of the transports of the various branches. During the NE monsoon season an Equatorial Undercurrrent is also developed in the Indian Ocean, as measured by TAFT and KNAUSS (1967). This undercurrent is, however, rather weak and appears variable and sometimes connected with the surface counter-current.

In general it can be said that during the NE monsoon, which is a rather gentle phenomenon, the oceanic circulation is also only moderately strong developed. The surface flow does not appear to penetrate much beyond the thermocline and no striking upwelling areas develop. Some shoaling of the thermocline, which under favorable wind conditions may occasionally result in weak upwelling, seems to occur only along the eastern shore of the Andaman Sea and in the northern part of the Arabian Sea off Karachi.

With the onset of the SW monsoon the circulation changes drastically. In April the NE monsoon current collapses, water starts to flow north along Somalia, and by May almost everywhere north of the Equator water starts flowing east. In July the Somali Current has reached its greatest strength, the monsoon current flowing east everywhere to the north of the Equator has formed and the countercurrent has shifted north and joined the monsoon current. The South Equatorial Current does not appear to shift much to the north, but it becomes stronger, and most of its water turns north into the Somali Current. Off Sumatra the monsoon current crosses the Equator and turns into the South Equatorial Current. These 3 currents, monsoon current, South Equatorial Current and Somali Current, form a very strong wind driven gyre in the equatorial Indian Ocean. The associated current speeds are stronger than those during the NE monsoon period. This circulation is maintained throughout September, and only in October does it start to break down and is slowly replaced by the NE monsoon circulation.

The more vigorous atmospheric and oceanic circulation during the SW monsoon causes not only the development of a strong western boundary current, the Somali Current, but also intense upwelling in several places. The circulation appears to penetrate deeper, affecting the movements of water masses below the thermocline. The formation of the Somali Current as a strong western boundary current of the monsoon gyre causes a strong baroclinic adjustment of the structure along the coast of Somalia. This baroclinic structure is noticeable as deep as 1000 m, but is especially pronounced in the upper 400 m. The strong winds parallel to the coast intensify the baroclinicity in the upper layer and cause, in addition, strong upwelling along the coast. Large parts of the Somali Current are recirculated in an intense eddy, the center of which is about 300 km offshore. This elongated eliptical eddy stretches for about 1000 km parallel to the coast, and is explained by DÜING (1970) as the westernmost of a system of eddies in the Arabian Sea which is intimately connected with the dynamics of the monsoon gyre. On the basis of direct current measurements, SWALLOW and BRUCE (1966) have shown that during the SW monsoon transports in the Somali Current in the upper 200 m increase from 30 megatons sec^{-1} at 3° S to more than 50 megatons sec^{-1} at 8° S. The total geostrophic transport is about 65 megatons sec^{-1}, demonstrating that most of the high speed flow is concentrated in the surface layer.

The upwelling along the coast is most intense between 5° N and 11° N, where the entire warm surface layer is removed and subsurface water with temperatures well below 20° C reaches the sea surface (WARREN, STOMMEL and SWALLOW, 1966). $PO_4^{3-} - P$ concentrations reach more than 10 μg-at l^{-1} and $NO_3^- - N$ concentrations more than 10 μg-at l^{-1} in contrast to values of 0.2 and 0.5, respectively, in the off-shore areas. Water with such high nutrient concentrations is otherwise found at 150 m depth. When the Somali Current leaves the coast near 11° N and turns east, the cool upwelled water continues to follow for some hundred kilometers. In the north, the upwelling region is terminated by a flow of warm surface water out of the Gulf of Aden, forming a strong temperature front. This warm surface water coming from the Gulf of Aden and flowing east into the central Arabian Sea also separates the Somali upwelling from the upwelling along the coast of Arabia.

Strong winds also blow parallel to the coast of Arabia east of 55° E during the SE monsoon, and cause upwelling. This upwelling is different from the Somali upwelling, as no strong current develops parallel to the coast. In volume it may even be stronger than the Somali upwelling, and also the nutrient enrichment is more intense with maximum values in excess of 1.5 μg-at l^{-1} for $PO_4^{3-} - P$ and a larger area affected by higher concentrations of both $PO_4^{3-} - P$ and $NO_3^- - N$.

During the SW monsoon weak upwelling may also develop under favorable conditions along some parts of the east coast of India, but does not seem to have very noticeable effects. Along the west coast of India subsurface water comes very close to the surface, and the 20° C isotherm rises to less than 50 m depth in July and August as a result of the baroclinic adjustment of the water structure in the Arabian Sea to the anticyclonic monsoon circulation. When this circulation becomes very strong, cool water may locally appear at the sea surface and be taken as upwelling. Although this water is rich in nutrients, it is also extremely depleted in O_2 and may cause adverse biological effects, as discussed by BANSE (1968).

Two different surface water masses are formed in the northern Indian Ocean, the high-salinity water of the Arabian Sea and the low-salinity water of the Bay of Bengal; these are caused by the excess of either evaporation or precipitation, which is intensified by the large runoff into the Bay of Bengal. The low-salinity water of the Bay of Bengal flows during the NE monsoon south of Ceylon to the west, with one branch continuing west-ward along 5° N, and the other northwestward along the coast of India. During the SW monsoon it flows to the SE along the coast of Sumatra where its salinity is further reduced by the high rainfall in this region. This low-salinity tropical surface water then flows west-ward in the northern portions of the South Equatorial Current, and can be followed near 10° S as a surface-salinity minimum extending all the way to Africa. The salinity of this water is kept low by the strong rainfall in the Intertropical Convergence Zone during the NE monsoon season.

High-salinity surface water is formed by the strong excess of evaporation in the central and northern Arabian Sea. This water spreads SW into the area off Somalia during the NE monsoon and is drawn from there into the Equatorial Countercurrent, where it can be followed as a distinct tongue of comparatively high salinity to 90° E. During the SW monsoon it first spreads south and then turns east and penetrates with the monsoon current into the region south of Ceylon. Some portions of this high-salinity water sink in the Arabian Sea and form a subsurface-salinity maximum in the upper portions of the thermocline at temperatures between 26° and 22° C, Fig. 7. This salinity maximum is spread at the different seasons with the various branches of the surface circulation throughout the entire monsoon gyre north of 10° S. It does not penetrate into the Bay of Bengal. Two other sources of high-salinity water, the outflow from the Persian Gulf and from the Red Sea, are affecting the intermediate layers of the Arabian Sea. Persian Gulf water appears as a strong salinity maximum at 300 m depth only in the Gulf of Oman, and Red Sea water in the Gulf of Aden at 800 m depth. In the central Arabian Sea the subsurface high-salinity water masses, the Arabian Sea water, the Persian Gulf water and the Red Sea water, form a thick layer which is vertically of almost uniform salinity, although the individual layers may still be recognizable at most stations as weak salinity maxima. This whole layer may be called the North Indian high-salinity intermediate water and occupies a depth range from about 150 to 900 m in the Arabian Sea. A comprehensive study of the vertical and horizontal fluxes of heat and salt which lead to this structure and of the effect of contraction during mixing on the exchange processes has been made by BENNETT (1970). From this high-salinity layer water proceeds at various depths with the different branches of the circulation throughout most of the monsoon gyre. Near 300 m depth high-salinity water spreads east with the SW monsoon current and at that depth fills the region to the west of Sumatra and also the entire Bay of Bengal. A weak salinity maximum of Red Sea water can be recognized between 600 and 900 m depth in the entire equatorial region. This Red Sea water is most pronounced in the western part of the ocean, where it penetrates near 1 100 m through the Madagascar Channel to 25° S.

The Hydro-Chemical Front at 10° S

The monsoon gyre is separated from the subtropical gyre of the southern Indian Ocean by a strong front in the hydrographic and chemical structure. This front is more pronounced in subsurface layers than at the surface and also more in the structure than in the circulation. This is because during the NE monsoon the South Equatorial Current does not belong to the monsoon gyre, while during the SW monsoon, its northern parts form part of the monsoon gyre. At the surface the boundary zone between the 2 gyres is marked by a horizontal salinity minimum stretching from Sumatra to Africa. This band of low salinity is rather wide in a north-south direction and its center is difficult to define. However, in maps of salinity at all horizons between 100 and 500 m depth, there is a distinct horizontal salinity minimum stretching along 10° S all the way from Timor to the north of Madagascar. This minimum separates the high-salinity water masses of the northern Indian Ocean from the subtropical high-salinity water of the subtropical gyre. It is caused by advection of low-salinity water by the South Equatorial Current from the Timor Sea and the waters between Australia and Indonesia.

The front is even more pronounced in the distribution of chemical properties (Fig. 3). It separates the low-nutrient, high$-O_2$ content waters of the subtropical gyre from the high-nutrient, low$-O_2$ content waters of the monsoon gyre. The front is inclined, and slopes from about 100 m depth at $10°$ to $12°$ S to 800 m depth at $16°$ to $18°$ S. It is steepest in oxygen, phosphate and nitrate content and somewhat less steep in silicate content. Near Australia and NW of Madagascar the front is somewhat less pronounced because of meridional circulation. The front is maintained by the continuous formation of essentially different water masses in the 2 big gyres.

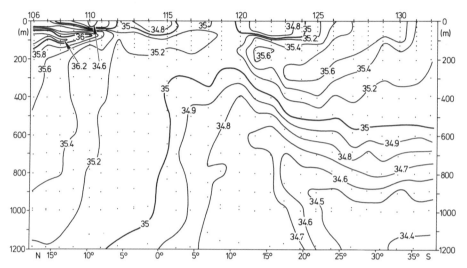

Fig. 3 a – d. Distribution of salinity ($^0/_{00}$ S), O_2 content, $PO_4^{3-} - P$, and $SiO_4^{4-} - Si$ along $70°$ E during cruise 2 of the "Anton Bruun" in May and June 1963

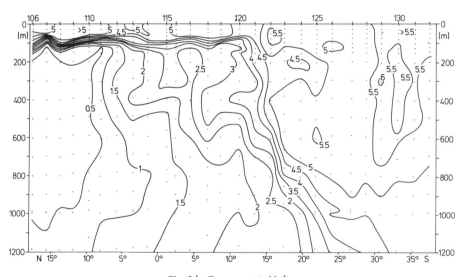

Fig. 3 b. O_2 content (ml l^{-1})

Library
I.U.P.
Indiana, Pa.

574.927   B521i

c.1   25

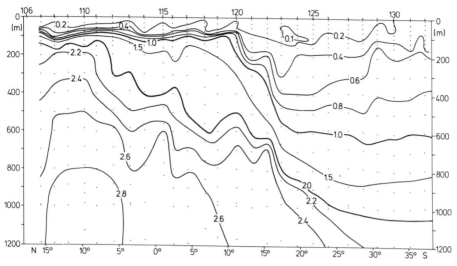

Fig. 3 c. $PO_4^{3-} - P$ concentration (μg-at l^{-1})

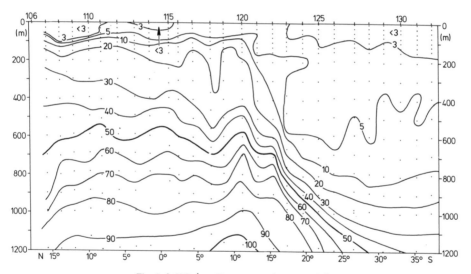

Fig. 3 d. $SiO_4^{4-} - Si$ concentration (μg-at l^{-1})

II. The Subtropical Anticyclonic Gyre

The subtropical gyre consists of the South Equatorial Current, the Agulhas Current system and those portions of the west wind drift, which lie north of the subtropical convergence, situated near 40° S. There is little evidence of an eastern boundary current along Australia. The warm water in the gyre extends rather deep, the 12° C isothermal surface is depressed to more than 600 m depth in the southwestern Indian Ocean, while it is at about 300 m depth along the northern boundary of the gyre. The anticyclonic flow in the gyre penetrates even deeper, certainly to the level of the intermediate water near 1000 m depth and much deeper in the huge Agulhas eddy off South Africa.

The subtropical gyre of the southern Indian Ocean is developed somewhat differently from the corresponding gyres in the other oceans as an inspection of the dynamic topography (Figs. 4 and 5) demonstrates. A long high-pressure ridge extends from the Agulhas

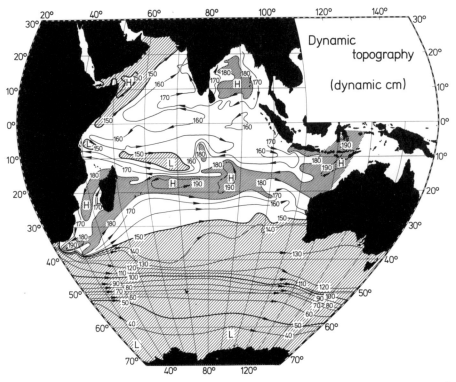

Fig. 4. Dynamic topography of the sea surface relative to 1000 decibars during January and February

Current system clear across the entire ocean into the Timor Sea, dividing the westward flow to the north of the ridge from the eastward flow south of it. The familiar equatorward turn of the isobars in mid-latitudes is lacking, as is an eastern boundary current off Australia. In fact, water movements along the west coast of Australia are weak and variable. Near the shore, water movements to the south prevail from January to July. The bulk of the northward flow occurs farther offshore between 95° and 105° E. It seems, however, that equatorward movements prevail farther offshore and extend over most of the ocean. The reason for this anomaly seems to be the lack of a continuously north-south running coastline and the existing, although restricted connection with the Pacific Ocean at low latitudes.

The South Equatorial Current, situated north of this high-pressure ridge is formed to the south of Java. It draws some water from the Timor Sea, and southwest of the Sunda Strait it is strengthened by water from the countercurrent or the monsoon current, turning south and west. In the western parts of the ocean the current transports between 40 and 55 megatons sec^{-1}, with highest transports occurring during the SW monsoon. When approaching the northern tip of Madagascar, the current splits with about two-

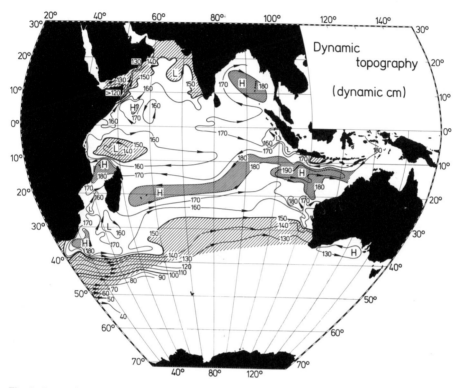

Fig. 5. Dynamic topography of the sea surface relative to 1000 decibars during July and August

thirds of the water passing north of Madagascar and one-third turning south along its east coast.

An upwelling area is developed south of Java during the SW monsoon season, when winds are blowing strongly from the SE between Australia and Indonesia. During this season the South Equatorial Current flows right along the coast of Java and the baroclinic adjustment in the current together with offshore Ekman transports cause a substantial uplift of subsurface water, but little depression of the surface temperature. Nutrient concentrations in the layer above 100 m depth increase substantially, although not as much as in the region off Arabia. On the other hand, the enriched area is much larger, which is probably due to the advection of water from the upwelling areas in the Banda and

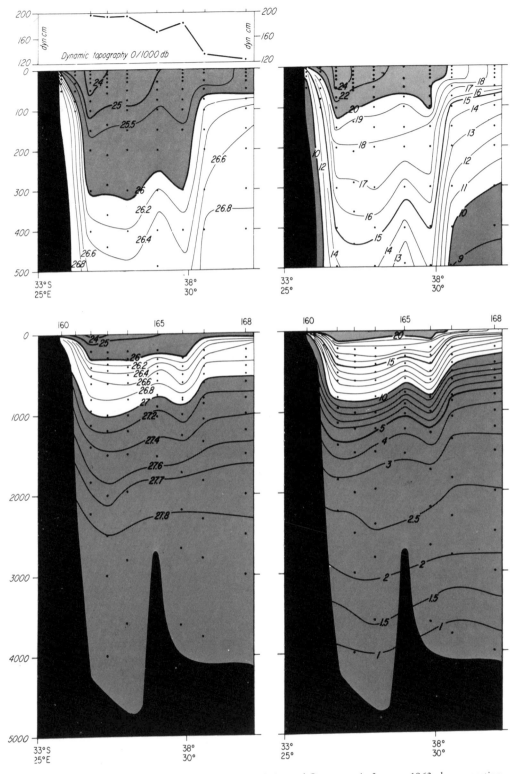

Fig. 6. Distribution of density, temperature, salinity and O$_2$ content in January 1963 along a section
shown above

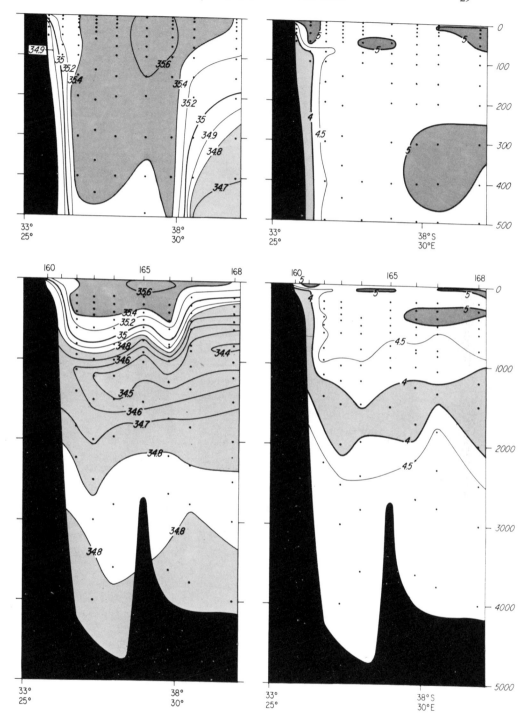

from East London, South Africa to the SE. The dynamic topography relative to 1000 decibars is
the density section

Arafura Seas through the Timor Sea. With the onset of the NE monsoon, when the inter-tropical convergence lies south of Java, the South Equatorial Current deviates southward from Java, and a coastal current to the east develops along the south coast of Java. It is an extension of the Equatorial Countercurrent and carries low salinity and warm water into the area.

The Agulhas Current is the western boundary current of the Indian Ocean and the strongest part of the Agulhas Current system, which is rather complex and somewhat different from other western boundary currents. This current system draws its water essentially from the South Equatorial Current through the Madagascar Channel and to the south of Madagascar from a rather narrow and swift current flowing south along its east coast. In the Madagascar Channel a strong, apparently permanent anticyclonic geostrophic eddy is developed, intensifying flow to the south along the coast of Africa and causing northward flow along Madagascar.

The Agulhas Current itself is a narrow high-speed flow along the SE coast of South Africa. Between Durban and Port Elizabeth it flows close to the shore, has average veloci-ties of 1 m sec^{-1} and often exceeds 2 m sec^{-1} at its core. The current is strongly barocline, but since parts of it are over the continental shelf and the high-speed core is often over the continental slope, geostrophic computations of its transports are difficult to make. Computations and estimates by DUNCAN (1970) give transports as high as 80 megatons sec^{-1}, making the Agulhas Current the strongest western boundary current of the southern hemisphere, although average transports are more like 50 megatons sec^{-1}. The current reaches great depths and its baroclinic structure is apparent in hydrographic sections deeper than 2000 m, Fig. 6. When reaching the Agulhas Bank and the longitude of Cape Agulhas the current turns south and east in a sharp anticyclonic eddy and forms the Agulhas Return Current. The Agulhas Current and Agulhas Return Current form the large elongated Agulhas eddy, which is a permanent feature of the circulation and stretches along the coast approximately 300 km offshore. The center of this eddy is filled with warm, high-salinity subtropical surface water, which with salinities of 35.4‰ extends down to 500 m depth (Fig. 6). From this analysis it appears that the Agulhas Current and the Agulhas Return Current are the geostrophic flow around a thick tongue of light sub-tropical water, which presses southwestward from the subtropical gyre into the wedge between the African continent and the Circumpolar Current. This situation may also explain the strong variability of the Agulhas Current and the frequent shedding of eddies from the main anticyclonic flow. These eddies drift west into the Atlantic Ocean. There is no direct and continuous flow of subtropical water from the Indian to the Atlantic Ocean.

At the confluence of the Agulhas Return Current and the west wind drift the subtropical convergence forms a rather pronounced front near 41° S. However, the Agulhas Return Current soon broadens, one branch turns north and recycles water into the Agulhas Current, the other branch continues east, but widens into a wind drift. Over the central part of the ocean, where surface flow usually has a northward component, the subtropical convergence is not well marked, especially not during summer, when a shallow summer thermocline develops. Convergent movements near 40° S may temporarily occur, when strong west winds drive cooler water from the more temperate regions to the north and force it to sink below the warmer subtropical water. During the winter, when strong cooling leads to vertical convection, a deep uniform mixed layer develops, which can exceed 400 m in depth. Under favorable wind conditions, considerable sinking must occur at these locations. In any case, over most of the central Indian Ocean and the Great Australian Bight, the subtropical convergence is a zonal strip of water along the boundary between warm subtropical water of high salinity and cooler, temperate water of lower salinity, along which under favorable wind conditions sinking may occur. The mean position of this strip is 40° to 41° S, and before reaching Tasmania the feature has practically vanished.

Subtropical surface water of high salinity forms in the subtropical anticyclonic gyre under the influence of an excess of evaporation over precipitation. The highest surface salinities are found in a belt between 25° and 35° S, where water movements are generally to the east. The absolute maximum of surface salinity occurs rather close to Australia and coincides with the maximum of excess evaporation. Winter convection and downward fluxes of salt and heat cause the subtropical water to extend with salinities above 35‰ to more than 500 m depth. From the high salinity core a subsurface salinity maximum extends throughout the entire subtropical anticyclonic gyre. This maximum spreads chiefly equatorwards within the thermocline and is carried west by the South Equatorial Current, where it lies between 250 and 150 m depth beneath fresher surface water (Fig. 7). Its southward penetration is rather limited and its structure is often destroyed by sinking along the subtropical convergence. A weak oxygen minimum is found near a depth of 180 m in the central and northern parts of the subtropical gyre. The subtropical gyre is of very low nutrient content down to a considerable depth. At 500 m depth most of the gyre shows $PO_4^{3-} - P$ of less than 1.0 μg-at l^{-1}, $NO_3^- - N$ less than 15 μg-at l^{-1}, and $SiO_4^{4-} - Si$ less than 10 μg-at l^{-1} (Fig. 3). At 100 m depth only the coastal regions off Australia, South Africa, and Madagascar Channel show somewhat higher nutrient concentrations (Fig. 2).

Below the subtropical water a layer of high oxygen content is found at temperatures between 10° and 12° C in depths of 400 to 500 m. This layer originates in the transition area south of the subtropical convergence by vertical convection and spreads north as an oxygen maximum. It participates in the general anticyclonic circulation of the subtropical gyre. Also the Antarctic intermediate water characterized by a salinity minimum between 800 and 1200 m depth follows an anticyclonic path. The movements of these 2 water masses clearly demonstrate the great vertical penetration of the subtropical anticyclonic gyre, which is considerably deeper than that of the monsoon gyre.

III. The Antarctic Waters

The hydrographic structure in Antarctic waters in the Indian Ocean is very similar to that in the other 2 oceans. It is governed by the surfacing of the main oceanic thermocline and by the strong, deep-reaching Circumpolar Current. Between about 40° S and 50° S the temperature and salinity decrease rapidly from more than 15° C and 35.0‰ to less than 5° C and 34.0‰, indicating the surfacing of the main oceanic thermocline, which divides the warm-water sphere form the cold-water sphere. The strong inclination of this boundary, rising from almost 1000 m depth to the sea surface, causes a powerful geostrophic current, the Antarctic Circumpolar Current, to flow east. Strong west winds over the whole area keep the front in position by preventing the light water of the warm-water sphere from flowing over the heavier water of the cold-water sphere.

The Antarctic surface water is cold and of low salinity because of excessive precipitation and melting ice. Salinites are generally below 34.0‰ and temperatures near freezing in winter. During the summer months, a shallow, slightly warmer layer forms at the surface, leaving a temperature minimum near 100 m depth, a remnant of the last winter water. This cold low-salinity water is pressed north by the prevailing west winds, where it meets the warmer waters of higher salinity in the Antarctic polar front. Along this front, which stretches all the way around Antarctica, and where strong currents flow to the east, the 2 water masses mix intensively. The mixing products sink down under the lighter water to the north, and this process is aided by the winds. This sinking water forms the layer of the Antarctic intermediate water, which spreads north as the uppermost water mass in the cold water sphere. Simultaneously the continuous removal of the mixing products by sinking keeps the front strong and well marked. In the western Indian Ocean the polar front is near 48° S, but shifts progressively farther south, and to the south of Australia it lies near 53° S. This position appears to be rather stable, and seasonal and irregular fluctuations do not seem to move it more than 2 degrees of latitude in either direction from its mean position, demonstrating the great stability of the large-scale baroclinic structure of the oceans.

The water forming the main oceanic thermocline under the subtropical gyre is generated between the polar front and the subtropical convergence in the transition area by sinking, deep convection and downward sliding along surfaces of constant density. These processes may at various seasons and wind conditions affect water of different properties and lead to the renewal of different strata. Since all this water derives from the sea surface and is of high oxygen content, an oxygen maximum forms within the main oceanic thermocline at temperatures between 10° and 12° C.

The Antarctic Circumpolar Current ist the strong geostrophic current associated with the baroclinic structure resulting from the surfacing of the main oceanic thermocline. Although this structure is most intense in the upper 1000 m, the slope of lines of equal density continues down to the bottom. Geostrophic transports calculated relative to 3000 decibars are about 120 megatons sec^{-1}, making the Circumpolar Current by far the most powerful current in the oceans. The fact is that the path of this current is influenced by the bottom topography, and recent measurements of flow near the bottom make it likely that transports may be even higher (REID and NOWLIN, 1971). The strongest surface flow lies to the north of the polar front where the meridional slope of the sea surface is strongest.

Beside the polar front, 2 other frontal systems are associated with the Circumpolar Current, the subtropical convergence and the Antarctic divergence. The subtropical convergence, discussed earlier, is the northern boundary of the transition water. It coincides approximately with the northern limit of strong westerly winds, and can be taken as the northern boundary of the Circumpolar Current. The Antarctic divergence, found in the Indian Ocean near 65° S, is near the southern boundary of the prevailing west winds or along the ice edge. There, west winds cause a divergence and ascending movements by which nutrient-rich subsurface water (Fig. 2) is brought into the surface layer. The upwelling water is also of higher salinity than the Antarctic surface water. The relations of these frontal systems to the Circumpolar Current and to the wind conditions in summer and winter have been explained by WYRTKI (1960), who showed a strong dependence of the development of convergences and divergences on the changing wind system.

The circumpolar water is situated below the Antarctic surface water of low salinity.

Its upper strata have temperatures between 1° and 2° C, and salinities slightly above 34.70‰ at depths between 500 and 1500 m. This water is of very high nutrient content and enriches the surface layer by upwelling and upward nutrient fluxes. Below this intermediate temperature and salinity maximum, the transition to the Antarctic bottom water takes place, which has temperatures less than 0° C and slightly lower salinities near 34.68‰ in the Indian Ocean sector.

IV. The Deep Circulation

The deep circulation can only be inferred from the spreading of characteristic water masses (Fig. 7), since no direct measurements of the flow are available, and the precision of dynamic calculations in the very deep layers is poor and affected by the arbitrary choice

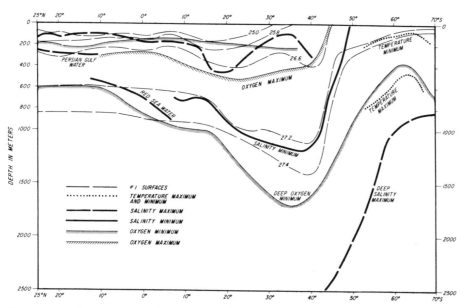

Fig. 7. Depth of the major core layers along 65° E in the western Indian Ocean together with the depth of some sigma-t surfaces

of a reference level. In general, it may be concluded that the deep circulation of the Indian Ocean is weaker than that of the Atlantic Ocean. Both the bottom water and the deep water are derived from the Atlantic Ocean, and there is no real evidence for the formation of bottom water along the Antarctic Continent in the Indian Ocean.

The Antarctic bottom water is formed in the Weddell Sea, sinks to the bottom, and parts of it spread east into the Indian Ocean along the Antarctic continent. Water of less than 0° C potential temperature penetrates north into the Cape Basin, the East Crozet Basin and east into the Indian Antarctic Basin, and reaches upwards to 2000 m near Antarctica. During its spreading it warms slowly, but on its way northward fills all the deep sea basins of the Indian Ocean with water of potential temperatures as cold as 1.2° C in the Arabian Basin, 1.0° C in the Central Indian Basin and 0.7° C in the NW Australian Basin. The spreading of the bottom water will be affected by some active flow, at least when it crosses the sills in the various ridges dividing the basins.

The deep water of the Indian Ocean, characterized by a weak salinity maximum, originates from the North Atlantic deep water. It enters the Indian Ocean to the south of Africa at a depth between 2500 and 3200 m with salinities of about 34.84‰, a potential temperature of 2.2° C and a rather high O_2 content of 5 ml l^{-1}. It spreads east with the Circumpolar Current and its core layer can be followed into the Pacific Ocean. Below the polar front, the core layer rises sharply and reaches to less than 800 m depth below the Antarctic divergence (Fig. 7). Together with the bottom water it forms a rather uniform water mass of great volume, the circumpolar water, which flows east in the lower parts of the Circumpolar Current. The deep water also spreads north into the central Indian Ocean, where its core layer can be followed as a salinity maximum to the north of Madagascar and into the NW Australian Basin. Its northward spreading seems to be diffusive rather than caused by a real flow. The O_2 content in both the bottom water and the deep water is high, but decreases in the direction of spreading. Nutrient concentrations, which are also high, generally increase to the north.

The Arabian Sea is filled with high-salinity water. It is formed at the sea surface and intensified by the outflow of high salinity water from the Persian Gulf near 300 m depth and from the Red Sea near 800 m depth. Vertical mixing in this rather isolated sea forms a thick layer of high salinity which may be called the North Indian intermediate water and downward fluxes of salt extend it to great depth. At 2000 m depth salinity in the Arabian Sea is still as high a 34.8‰. Horizontal mixing and probably some advection spread this layer throughout the northern Indian Ocean, even into the Bay of Bengal, and salinity at 1500 m depth exceeds 34.8‰ everywhere to the north of 5° S. The isolation and stagnation of the North Indian intermediate water and the lack of substantial horizontal advection together with the high productivity of the northern Indian Ocean cause the development of a large layer of extremely low oxygen concentration. This layer extends from above 200 m to more than 1200 m depth in the Arabian Sea, and has O_2 content of less than 1.0 ml l^{-1} everywhere to the north of 3° N.

Directly connected with this huge layer of very low oxygen content is the deep oxygen minimum, which is present over the entire Indian Ocean (Fig. 8). Near the Equator it lies at about 800 m depth, deepens to more than 1700 m near 40° S, and rises again to about 400 m depth below the Antarctic divergence. In the South Indian Ocean it lies above the deep water and below the Antarctic intermediate water. The O_2 content within the oxygen minimum increases slowly southward and reaches 4 ml l^{-1} at 40° S. Without being able to substantiate the conclusion, it appears that most of the water ascending from the bottom and the deep water returns south in the layer near the oxygen minimum, especially along the western side of the ocean.

The lowest oxygen concentrations in the oxygen minimum of the Indian Ocean are in an entirely different location compared to the other 2 oceans. There the strongest oxygen minimum is found at the eastern side of the ocean on both sides of the Equator. In the Indian Ocean it is found in the 2 northern bays, the Arabian Sea and the Bay of Bengal. This difference may be due not only to the fact that the Indian Ocean is landlocked in the north, but more so to the advection of water of moderate oxygen concentration from the Pacific Ocean through the Indonesian waters.

The Antarctic intermediate water originates from the Antarctic surface water by intense mixing and sinking along the polar front. It sinks rapidly to more than 1000 m depth along the inclined density surface of 27.25 forming a salinity minimum between the subtropical water above and the deep salinity maximum below (Fig. 7). This low salinity layer is 500 and more meters thick. Below the subtropical gyre it rises slowly to 700 m depth near 10° S. Salinity and temperature in the core layer increase slowly to the

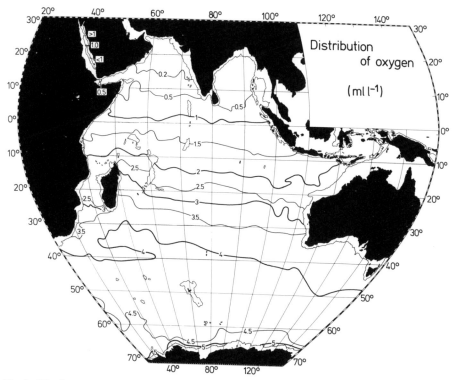

Fig. 8. Distribution of O_2 content in the deep oxygen minimum in ml l^{-1}. The 1000 m depth contour is shown

north, but the density stays rather constant. At the same density surface the salinity minimum is opposed by the North Indian intermediate water of high salinity, which at that depth is chiefly of Red Sea origin. This leads to a split of the salinity minimum into an upper and lower branch near 15° S. The upper branch terminates at about 10° S near 700 m depth with temperatures of about 7° C and salinities near 34.7‰. The lower branch, which is enhanced by an inflow of low salinity water from the Banda Sea, is found at about 1000 m depth with a temperature of about 5° C and a density near 27.45. In the range of the subtropical gyre the intermediate water participates in a slow anticyclonic circulation, which is somewhat intensified along the western side of the ocean. This circulation is an indication that the anticyclonic movements in the gyre extend to a depth of at least 1000 m.

Above the intermediate water the main oceanic thermocline is found, in which the temperature increases from about $8°$ C to $15°$ C. The water of this layer is formed in the transition region between the polar front and the subtropical convergence, as discussed earlier, and is identical with the central water, as defined by SVERDRUP, JOHNSON and FLEMING (1942). The most pronounced feature in this main thermocline is the oxygen maximum, which clearly points to the origin of this entire water mass at the sea surface. The oxygen maximum is found in the entire subtropical gyre at depths between 400 and 500 m and at temperatures between $10°$ and $12°$ C, and the O_2 content decreases only very slightly to the north. Between $15°$ S and $10°$ S, where the strong hydrochemical front of the Indian Ocean is situated, the O_2 suddenly decreases from 5 ml l^{-1} to less than 3 ml l^{-1}, but the oxygen maximum can be followed much farther to about $8°$ N. In the western part of the ocean, the oxygen distribution deviates from this general pattern, and water of relatively high oxygen content spreads north, especially under the influence of the Somali Current. The oxygen maximum layer is situated between the shallow oxygen minimum near 200 m depth and the deep oxygen minimum (Fig. 7). North of about $8°$ N these 2 layers melt into one huge layer of extremely low oxygen content, and an organized oxygen maximum is no longer present, although at some station a weak maximum can still be found.

Comparison with the Other Oceans

After this gross discussion of the physical oceanography of the Indian Ocean it seems worthwhile to compare it with the other 2 oceans and to emphasize those features, which are unique to the Indian Ocean. Morphologically, the Indian Ocean is landlocked in the north, and does not extend into the cold climatic regions of the northern hemisphere. This causes an asymmetrical development of its structure and circulation, which is most obvious in the development of the huge layers of extremely low oxygen content in the Arabian Sea and the Bay of Bengal. The land mass of Asia also affects the ocean climatologically by causing the seasonally changing monsoons, which in turn reverse the oceanic circulation over its northern part. Connected with this seasonally changing circulation are various upwelling areas, which operate only during one season, in contrast to all the other major upwelling areas in the world. Another outgrowth of the geographical and climatological situation is the formation of high salinity waters in the Arabian Sea, and even more extreme in the Red Sea and the Persian Gulf. These water masses form a huge high-salinity layer in the Arabian Sea and affect the circulation in intermediate depth rather drastically by preventing water of the southern hemisphere from penetrating efficiently into the northern Indian Ocean.

Arabian Sea Upwelling

R. I. Currie, A. E. Fisher and P. M. Hargreaves

When the IIOE was planned, it was considered a valuable objective to examine the upwelling regions which had been reported in the Arabian Sea (Bobzin, 1922) but had never before been the object of scientific observation.

The only subsurface observations available from these areas were those made by

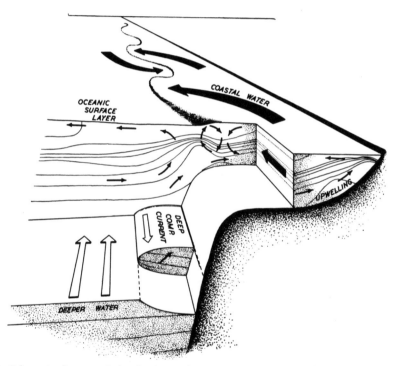

Fig. 1. Schematic diagram of the circulation during upwelling in Benguela Current. The features shown seem to be common to all major coastal upwelling regions – the mirror image would hold good in the northern hemisphere. (From Hart and Currie, 1960)

the John Murray Expedition during the NE monsoon period of 1933–34, and no information was available from the summer months during which the upwelling took place.

The results of observations made on the following voyages have been used in the present paper to describe the characteristics of the upwelling on the Somali and SE Arabian coast areas:

a) "Vladimir Vorob'ev" (USSR): winter 1960−61.

b) "Atlantis II" (USA): summer 1963.

c) "Discovery" (UK): summer 1963.

d) "Anton Bruun" (USA): autumn, 1963.

e) "Discovery" (UK): spring and summer, 1964.

f) "Argo" (USA): summer 1964.

Fig. 1 gives an idealized picture of the general pattern which seems to hold good in all the major upwelling regions. Smith (1968) gives a review of the subject.

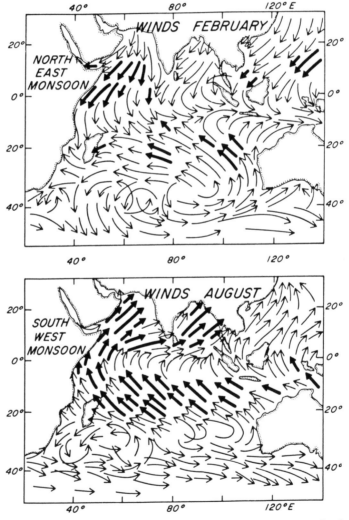

Fig. 2. Idealized wind distribution in the Indian Ocean according to Monatskarten für den Indischen Ozean, Deutsches Hydrographisches Institut (1960)

I. The Monsoon Regime

DÜING (1970) has summarized the regime of surface winds (Fig. 2) and currents (see Fig. 1, WYRTKI 1973, this volume) prevailing in the Arabian Sea. The SW monsoon commences in May—June, and develops as a strong wind from the SW, blowing more or less parallel to the Somali and Arabian coasts. It reaches its peak in July—August and fades away in September—October. The winter months show a reversal of wind as the weaker NE monsoon sets in.

During the SW monsoon a strong western boundary current develops flowing northwards on the Somali coast (SWALLOW and BRUCE, 1966) and likewise a pronounced flow to the north-east is evident off the Arabian coast (Royal Society, 1963).

1. Southeast Arabian Coast

a) Hydrographic Observations

SERYI and KHIMITSA (1963) show from their Masira section that in December 1961 there was a south-westerly flow of highly saline surface water along the Arabian coast from the Gulf of Oman, which would be consistent with the sinking of water rather

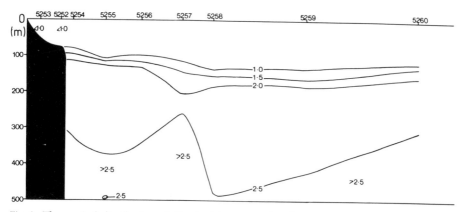

Fig. 3. The vertical distribution of dissolved inorganic phosphate on a section normal to the SE Arabian coast, from observations by RRS "Discovery" a in March, 1964, b in May, 1964 and c in July, 1963, showing stages in the development of upwelling. Concentrations are expressed in μg-at l^{-1} or mg-at m^{-3}

than upwelling in the proximity of the coast. They also noted the comparatively low PO_4^{3-}-P concentrations in this water, a feature which is also evident in the "Discovery" section of March, 1964 off the Kuria Muria Islands (Fig. 3 a). Both these sets of observations bear out the absence of upwelling in these months.

In May, 1964, however, the "Discovery" repeated the same section off the Kuria Muria Islands and the results show a marked weakening and seawards displacement of the south-westerly surface flow, while along the coast the isotherms of the upper layers show a lift upwards to the coast. Likewise there was a markedly higher dissolved inorganic PO_4^{3-}-P concentration in the upper layers near the coast (Fig. 3b). The level of the 1.0 mg-at m^{-3} isoline for PO_4^{3-}-P which lay at a depth of 100 m in March, reached the surface in May.

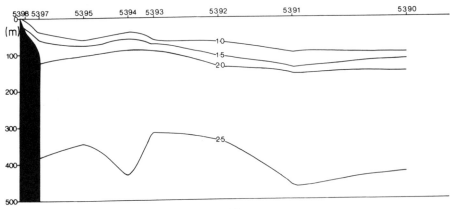

Fig. 3 b

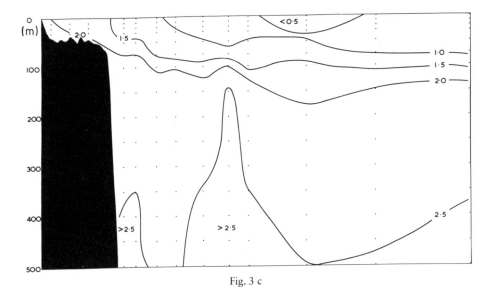

Fig. 3 c

The "Discovery" observations in the summer of 1963 provide the most complete picture of the circulation at the peak of the SW monsoon (Royal Society, 1963). Five lines of stations, roughly normal to the Arabian coast, were worked at the end of June and beginning of July, and on 4 of these sections there is evidence of very active upwelling in the coastal belt. The extent of this can be seen from the depression of sea surface temperature (Fig. 4). PO_4^{3-}-P values in the upper layer at the coast ranged between 1.5 – 2.0 mg-at m^{-3} during this survey (Fig. 3 c).

The observations made by the "Anton Bruun" on Cruise 4A in October, 1963 (U.S. Program in Biology IIOE, 1965), complete the picture of the cycle of events. Stations 175 – 180 virtually repeat the "Discovery" section off the Kuria Muria Islands; they show no indication of upwelling, and the warm surface layer is present at the station closest to the coast. The 1.0 mg-at P m^{-3} isoline at this time lay deeper than 50 m.

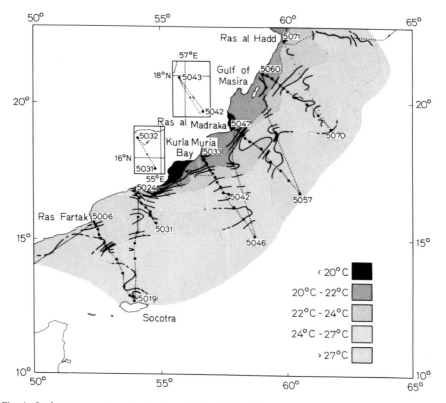

Fig. 4. Surface temperature distribution off the SE Arabian coast during the SW monsoon of 1963 from observations made by RRS "Discovery"

b) The Southeast Arabian Upwelling

The "Discovery" stations of July and August, 1963 were positioned at 10 mile intervals close to the coast opening to a 30-mile separation further offshore. The distance between transects varied, as did their length, but lay around 100 miles between the sections while the sections extended up to 200 miles or more from the coast. Throughout the survey strong SW winds prevailed and there was a considerable degree of hydrographic complexity, emphasizing the extremely dynamic state of the circulation (Fig. 5).

The lack of continuity identifiable between the individual transects also suggests that much of the temporal and spatial scale of the circulation was of smaller magnitude than could be resolved by the observations. BOTTERO (1969) from a numerical analysis of the physical data confirms that upwelling extends at least 400 km offshore and parallels the Arabian coast for a distance of over 1000 km. It is most intense in a narrow band adjacent to the coast.

The most significant feature of the South Arabian upwelling is the breadth of the

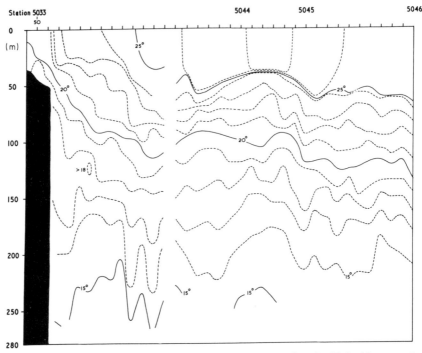

Fig. 5. The vertical distribution of temperature on a section normal to the SE Arabian coast in the vicinity of the Kuria Muria Islands from BT observations made by RRS "Discovery" in July, 1963

upwelling zone and, because of this, water appears to be supplied from much greater depths than is usual in other coastal upwelling regions.

BOTTERO (1969) has computed the vertical and horizontal fields of motion and where possible compared the computed currents with those observed. His derived mass transport for the surface layer (Fig. 6) shows that the main flow in the upper 100 m is north-eastwards with an offshore component. The vertical motion is most pronounced in the coastal belt but is present over the whole area of survey. In the computations for deeper levels there is an appreciable upward movement in the 300−700 m layer (Fig. 7).

The vertical speeds computed are of the order of 10^{-2} cm sec^{-1} in the more active cells and this comparatively high velocity is attributed to the considerable strength and

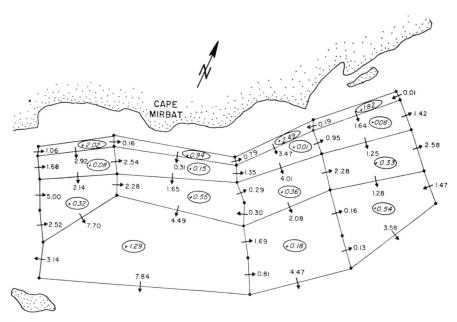

Fig. 6. Horizontal mass transports on the SE Arabian coast between the ocean surface and 100 m. The circled numbers are vertical mass transports at 100 m. Units are 10^6 tons sec^{-1} from "Discovery" data, 1963. (From BOTTERO, 1969)

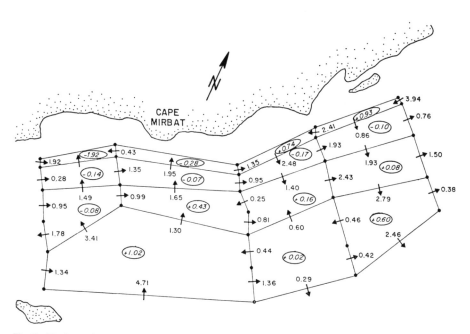

Fig. 7. Horizontal mass transports between 300 m and 700 m. The circled numbers are vertical mass transports at 700 m. Units are 10^6 tons sec^{-1}. (From BOTTERO, 1969)

constancy of the monsoon wind. It will be shown later that the biological phenomena observed are also affected by this high degree of activity.

The upward movement varies considerably on different parts of the coastline and, indeed, as can be seen from the surface temperature distribution, "centres" of particularly intense upwelling appear to occur at the Kuria Muria Islands and Ras Madraka (Figs. 4 and 8).

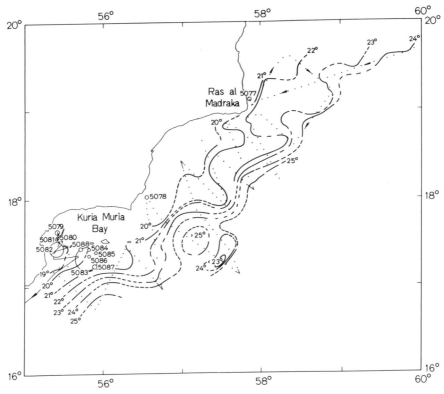

Fig. 8. Surface temperature in the vicinity of the Kuria Muria Islands, July 1963

c) Biological Events

The effects of the SE Arabian upwelling on the biology of the region can be seen in Fig. 9 which shows the average concentration of dissolved inorganic PO_4^{3-}-P, chlorophyll a in the particulate matter, and zooplankton biomass in the upper 100 m of the water column. On the left of the figure the observations shown are from the 5 lines of stations of the "Discovery" survey of July—August, 1963. These are arranged in sequence from the bottom of the figure upwards, in progression north-eastwards along the Arabian coast. On the right-hand side of the figure, the third section is shown again with the repeated observations on the same section in March and May, 1964.

During the summer of 1963, the very high PO_4^{3-}-P values resulting from the upwelling

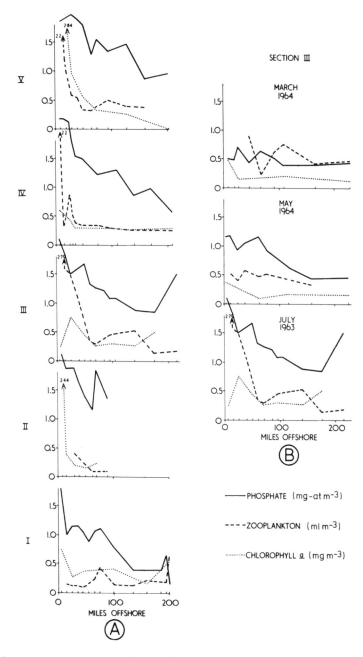

Fig. 9. The average concentration of dissolved inorganic phosphate, chlorophyll *a* in the particulate matter and zooplankton in the upper 100 m at stations off the SE Arabian coast, from observations made by RRS "Discovery". On the left of the diagram (A) the observations from the summer of 1963 are plotted on sections normal to the coast, section I at Ras Fartak and II, III, IV and V progressively further east along the coast. Section III is off the Kuria Muria Islands. On the right-hand side (B) the observations on section III are reproduced together with repeat observations of the same stations made in March and May, 1964

are clearly shown on all except the first section which lay somewhat west of the main part of the upwelling region and was probably partly under the influence of events within the Gulf of Aden. The highest values occurred consistently close to the coast, falling to levels of about 1.0 mg-at m^{-3} offshore.

Chlorophyll *a* values also tended to be high close to the coast and fall rather more rapidly seawards than the PO$_4$$^{3-}$-P did; the zooplankton biomass follows a similar pattern. Neither chlorophyll *a* nor zooplankton show an exceptional abundance. Only in one solitary bloom of *Gonyaulax polyhedra* were cell numbers of the order of 10^7 per l encountered. More generally counts ranged from 10^5 per l inshore to 10^3 per l offshore. *Streptotheca* sp. was one of the most abundant diatoms of the coastal belt, along with other chain-forming species of *Chaetoceros* and *Fragillaria*.

These facts again seem to point to the very active state of the circulation, but how far they represent "steady state" levels during the upwelling period remains to be seen.

In so far as they can be compared, the repetitions of section 3 may be considered to present the progression of the development of upwelling in the region of the Kuria Muria Islands. Rather than a continuous progression, however, they must be looked upon as representative phases of this development.

The contrast is most marked in the levels of dissolved inorganic PO$_4$$^{3-}$-P, but in the algal stock and zooplankton biomass, also, a significantly greater amount was found at the time of upwelling than in the premonsoon period. The "Anton Bruun" observations in October 1963 include measurements of PO$_4$$^{3-}$-P and chlorophyll *a*. These have not been plotted, since only three stations were sited within 200 miles of the coast, but the values for these stations are shown in Table I and will be seen to differ little from the March 1964 values of "Discovery".

Table 1. Average values of dissolved inorganic phosphate (mg-at m^{-3}) and chlorophyll *a* (mg m^{-3}) for the 0–100 m layer from "Anton Bruun" stations in October, 1963

Station	175	176	177
Distance offshore in miles	36	104	171
PO$_4$$^{3-}$-P	0.68	0.75	0.51
Chlorophyll *a*	0.41	0.30	0.69

2. Somali Coast

a) Hydrographic Observations

The RRS "Discovery" and RV "Argo" conducted a survey of the Somali Current in August–September, 1964 and the pattern of stations (Royal Society, 1965) was set out in such a way as to make it possible to examine the upwelling area in the vicinity of Ras Hafun, reported by Puff (1890). Warren, Stommel and Swallow (1966) and Swallow and Bruce (1966) have described the water masses observed and the currents measured on these surveys.

Fig. 10 shows the distribution of surface temperature in the area where upwelling water was present and it is clear that the latter corresponds closely in distribution with that described by Puff (1890) in the Ras Hafun area; Puff, however, also describes the upwelling as extending in a belt close to the coast southward to Cape Warscheik (02° 30′ N). Certainly, within the Somali Current the tilting of the isotherms up towards the coast inevitably leads to a general lowering of temperature as the coast is approached, but the "Discovery" and "Argo" observations suggest that it was not until north of about 08° 30′ N that the true upwelling region began in 1964.

In the more southerly part of the Somali Current the thermocline lay at depths of about 90 m close to the coast, deepening steadily offshore. Assuming the 20° C isotherm to be a fair index of its depth, it can be seen, as SWALLOW and BRUCE (1966) showed,

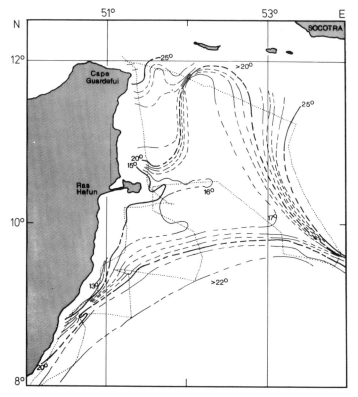

Fig. 10. Surface temperature (° C) off the Somali coast in the summer of 1964. ("Discovery" and "Argo" observations)

that proceeding northwards along the East African coast from 1° N to 8° 30 ′N, the thermocline shoaled gradually by 50 m under the fastest part of the Somali Current. At the same time the upward slope of the isotherms towards the coast increased so that a point was reached in about 08° 30′N where the thermocline appeared at the surface on the landward edge of the current.

If upwelling is taken to imply the appearance of sub-thermocline water at the surface, then this point can also be taken to mark the southern limit of the upwelling region. This is also the point at which the main stream of the Somali Current sweeps away from the coast, and on its northern boundary there is a rapid seaward extension of the area of cool water at the surface (Fig. 10) as it follows the eastward sweep of the current.

Along the coast, the cool water extended northwards beyond Ras Hafun but in about 11° N appears to come up against a tongue of warmer water pressing southwards along the coast from Cape Guardafui and originating from the Gulf of Aden. At some distance from the coast, however, the cool water achieved a greater northward extension, and temperatures below 17° C were found at least 100 km farther north in 52° E longitude. The eastward margin was again bounded by warm water reaching more than 25° C.

The pattern of distribution of the cold surface water is thus seen to form a belt paralleling the northward boundary of the Somali Current and developing, at its northward extremity, into a cyclonic eddy with the warmer water penetrating southward from

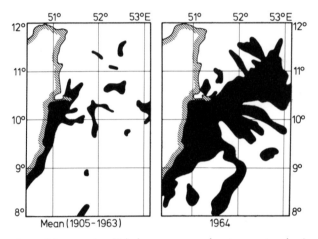

Fig. 11. A comparison of the areas in which the mean sea surface temperature for August was below 20° C, between the mean for the years 1905 – 1963, and 1964. (From G. P. BRITTON, unpublished)

the Gulf of Aden. The direct current measurements described by SWALLOW and BRUCE substantiate this pattern.

It is interesting to compare the extent of the cold surface water observed in 1964 with the mean distribution shown by surface temperature records over the years 1905 – 1963 (Fig. 11, BRITTON, unpublished). This shows that 1964 appears to have been a rather exceptional year in which the cold waters was considerably more extensive than is usual. This may account for the extent of the fish mortality recorded by FOXTON (1965) during "Discovery" survey.

SWALLOW and BRUCE have described direct current measurements made on these surveys, but there is considerable difficulty in deriving any reliable estimate of the input of cold water into the upwelling area. They do, however, make an estimate of vertical velocity based on the upward displacement of the 20° C isotherm, in the Somali Current and this amounts to 7×10^{-3} cm sec^{-1}.

b) Biological Events

The distributions of dissolved inorganic PO_4^{3-}-P, chlorophyll *a* and zooplankton biomass on the Somali coast are shown in Fig. 12 in a manner similar to the data from the SE Arabian coast. The lower diagramm (section III) (Stns. 5533 – 42) lay in the more

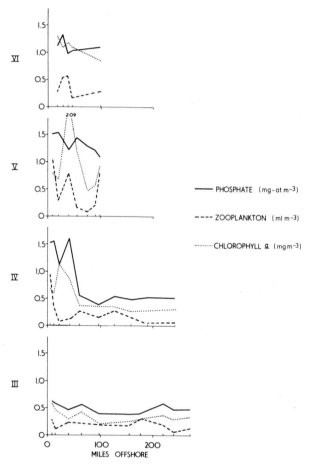

Fig. 12. Data on the average concentration of dissolved inorganic phosphate, chlorophyll *a* and zooplankton off the Somali coast in 1964. The observations are plotted in a manner similar to Fig. 9. Positions of the sections are described in the text

southerly part of the Somali Current, section IV (Stns. 5542 – 53) lay at the point where the current leaves the coast (in about 08° 30′ N, with the section more or less normal to the current) and sections V (Stns. 5554−60) and VI (Stns. 5565−61) progressively farther north across the cold water region and the area where it meets the warmer Gulf of Aden water. In the southerly part of the Somali Current all values were consistently low, but at the point of its departure from the coast (the inshore end of section IV) a marked increase in the levels of PO_4^{3-}-P and chlorophyll *a* was recorded. Section V (entirely within the cold surface water area) showed the highest values of PO_4^{3-}-P and chlorophyll *a* accompanied by an increase in the amount of zooplankton. On section VI all stations appeared to lie within the warmer "Gulf of Aden" surface water and yet the values of PO_4^{3-}-P and chlorophyll were still comparatively high.

The "Discovery" returned to the area after an interval of about 8 days and found that very active convection was taking place between the upwelling water and the warmer "Gulf of Aden" surface water. A cyclonic displacement of the surface isotherms had taken place in the interval and the boundary between the two water masses had sharpened considerably. At one station (5557) 2 sets of observations were made while the ship drifted between the warm and the cold water. The warmer water had a well-mixed layer at the surface, some 50 m thick, whereas the cold water showed pronounced stability in this layer. The line of demarcation between the two was clearly visible because of a tenfold difference in chlorophyll *a* between the 2 water masses. A considerable degree of mixing must have been taking place between the upwelled water and the adjacent flow of "Gulf of Aden" surface water.

II. The Significance of the Upwelling to Fisheries

It is not practicable for an oceanographical expedition to obtain any proper evaluation of the abundance of fish in a region, and statistical data from the Arabian Sea area under consideration are so sparse that little guidance can be derived from that source.

During these cruises of RRS "Discovery", however, continuous echo-soundings were taken with a 10 kc sec⁻¹ echo-sounder. These showed the presence of diffuse midwater acoustic scattering, single mid-water targets and discrete fish shoals. The fish shoals which almost invariably occurred in the $110-310$ m layer could be counted and it was felt that the occurrence of these shoals might give some indication of the effect of the upwelling off the Arabian and Somali coasts on the abundance of fish.

1. Characteristics of Shoals and Assessment of their Abundance

The beam of the precision echo-sounder used can be likened to a cone some 28° wide, and the fish shoals show up on the records as typically crescent−shaped marks (Fig. 13). While these vary in size by a factor of 2 or 3, and in the denser regions may even coalesce, simple enumeration at least provides a crude measure of fish abundance. While the records were being taken, the ship's speed varied from zero to a maximum of $11-12$ knots. Therefore, in the first place the counts which are a function of depth and time on the echo-sounder records had to be converted into a sensible measure of their spatial abundance. This was done by dividing the records into 5-minute periods and counting all the identifiable shoals. Knowing the speed of the ship over the ground, the counts could then be expressed in terms of their geographical abundance, by dividing the average rate of incidence of fish shoals per hour by the ship's speed over the ground determined from the appropriate part of the ship's track chart. The resultant figures represent the concentration of fish shoals per mile of the ship's track.

Frequently, the echo-sounder transmission was gated, generally when weather conditions or the nature of the sea bed were such that bottom soundings became difficult to record. This leads to a record on which it is impossible to identify fish shoals and so the corresponding parts of the ship's track when the sounder was gated had to be distinguished by showing them as a broken line on the charts. Likewise, a broken line was used to indicate occasions when unsuitable gain settings were used and records were doubtful, and all parts of the track covered during the hours of darkness when the fish shoals migrated to the surface and became unidentifiable from the dense scattering and reverberation in the surface layers. These distribution charts have been deposited in the FAO Fisheries Data Center.

Fig. 13. Precision echo-sounder trace showing the nature of the fish shoals. The scale width of the record is 200 fathoms (366 m) and the vertical broken lines are 5-min time marks

2. Southeast Arabian Coast

Most of the higher concentrations of fish seemed to be encountered a short distance seaward of the edge of the continental shelf in the region of the 1000 to 2000 m depth contours but, of course, the number of observing miles steamed over much of the region and in particular the deeper waters was not very great: the coverage of negative observations is consequently very poor. Nevertheless, where observations were made farther offshore they show little evidence of abundance.

The depth distribution of the shoals exhibited pronounced diurnal movement, rising into the surface layers at night; the day-time depths were remarkably constant. The complete range of daytime depth extended from 110−310 m but the standard deviation from the mean depth (220 m) was only ± 45 m.

3. The Somali Coast

The survey off the Somali coast in August 1964 showed an extreme patchiness in the occurrence of fish shoals, probably largely owing to the patchiness of observing periods, but the only area of any consistently high abundance was on the continental shelf between about 8° 30′ N and 9° 30′ N. There the shoals occurred at an average depth of 73 ± 36 m. The region north of this where upwelling was taking place proved to be surprisingly barren. Further south between about 4° and 6° 30′ N, a section well offshore showed echoes to be present some 100 − 300 miles out from the coast and, although at a lower level of abundance, they did occur over a fairly wide area. The depth of occurrence of these latter shoals was similar to that off the Arabian coast − an average of 220 ± 33 m.

4. Distribution of Fish in Relation to Upwelling

Nothing, of course, can be said on the species of fish responsible for these echoes but it seems well established that the South-east Arabian coast shows substantial quantities of a resource which would warrant further investigation. Off Somalia, however, so far as the evidence goes, it would appear that fish of the type responsible for the echoes are comparatively less abundant. Sea birds, which were also abundant on the Arabian coast, were notably absent in the Somalia upwelling area.

It seems probable that the time scale of the biological events in the Ras Hafun area is such that the higher levels of the food web may be reached only in the area north of that surveyed and possibly in the vicinity of Socotra. The distribution of birds is, of course, so closely linked to the availability of nesting sites that its significance may be somewhat irrelevant.

III. Discussion

The obersvations of these cruises demonstrate the existence of extensive areas of upwelling on the western margin of the Arabian Sea during the SW monsoon. BANSE (1968) showed that upwelling also occurs at the same time of year along the eastern margin of the Arabian Sea. Thus it appears that during the SW monsoon the Arabian Sea is potentially an exceptionally fertile area.

The upwelling on the Arabian coast seems to conform in general principle and shows no great deviation from the classical pattern of wind-induced upwelling characteristic of the western continental coasts. Nevertheless, there are significant differences. The area of divergence appears to be very much wider than usual and the depth of upward vertical motion much greater. The wind stress in contrast to the other major upwelling regions is poleward rather than equatorward.

By contrast, the upwelling on the Somali coast in the Ras Hafun area appears to result from the density structure of the Somali Current rather than from the direct effect of the local wind stress on the sea surface. SWALLOW and BRUCE (1966) point out that, if the flow of the Somali Current is in fact geostrophic, then the more water is carried in the current, the further South would be the point at which the thermocline comes to the surface at the coast. The extent of the Ras Hafun upwelling may thus be closely associated with the volume transport of the Somali Current and subject to fluctuations in the latter, and this could account for the absence of some features characteristic of possibly more stable upwelling areas − the abundance of fish and seabirds, and for events such as the fish mortality reported by FOXTON (1965). Further observations may in time clarify the reality of this dependence.

1.5

Light and Nutrients in the Indian Ocean

D. A. McGill

I. Light Measurements

Light in the marine environment presents many difficulties. There is a lack of agreement about the kind of light parameter to measure in the sea and about the means to employ to obtain measurements of the greatest value. Early workers have emphasized transparency, as determined by simple instruments such as the Secchi disk, but other aspects of the spectral distribution are now studied with a variety of specialized instrumentation.

1. Transparency

While the Secchi disk specifically measures the depth of visibility of the instrument, variations in boundary conditions of the sea surface may act to reduce the precision of measurements in comparison with photoelectric determinations of transparency (MURPHY, 1959). Although individual observations of the depth of visibility with the Secchi disk have only limited value, the average of a series of measurements has been accepted as valid (TYLER, 1968). While the size and reflectance of the disc are significant factors, there is marked variation in the diameter of the disk used for obtaining much of the data currently available.

a) Observations of Transparency in the Indian Ocean

The records of the U.S. National Oceanographic Data Center (World Data Center A) for the IIOE list 738 observations of transparency for the Indian Ocean made from 1 September 1959 through 31 December 1965. Spatial distribution of these observations is shown in Fig. 1. Over half of the total observations, 409 stations or 55.43% of the total, were obtained in the "post-monsoon months" (QASIM, BHATTATHIRI and ABIDI, 1968) of November, December and January. The remainder of the observations are about equally spaced throughout the other quarters of the year. For example, a further 126 stations or 17.17% of the total, were taken in May, June and July, corresponding to the onset of the SW monsoon. In all instances the concentration of observations is notably massed in the eastern Indian Ocean and shows some preference for inshore locations.

VOYTOV and DEMENT'YEVA (1970) have compiled a chart of relative transparency for the Indian Ocean and the related sector of Antarctica, based on a total of 824 observations with the Secchi disk and having the greatest frequency of sampling (704 observations) in the winter period from November to March. Their resulting distribution for average transparency in winter is redrawn as Fig. 2. A relatively uniform transparency of 30 to 35 m is found over the entire open part of the ocean. This agrees with the earlier observations of Jerlov (1964).

"An extensive region in which relative transparencies above 35 m and even 40 m predominate corresponds to the central anticyclonic gyre that occupies almost the entire latitude belt south of 20° S. This region is also plankton poor." (Voytov and Dement-yeva, 1970 English transl. pp. 35). The boundary zone between the Equatorial Current and the Equatorial Counter Current appears as areas of low (less than 30 m) relative

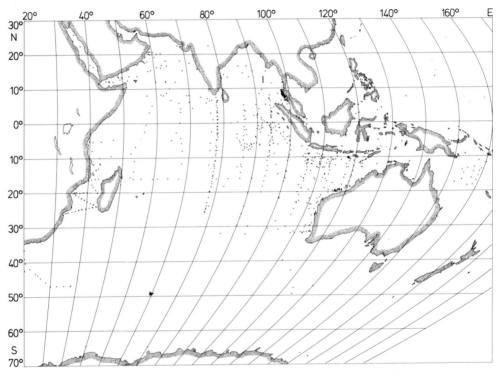

Fig. 1. Distribution of 738 observations on transparency on file at the U.S. National Oceanographic Data Center. IIOE 1 Sept. 1959 to 31 Dec. 1965

transparency, running from SW to NE in the Equatorial region of the central Indian Ocean.

Previous to the IIOE very few transparency observations for the Indian Ocean are available. Prasad (1952) conducted visibility tests in the Bay of Bengal and observed a general depth range from 10 to 24 m, off the east coast of India. At a station located close to the mouths of the Ganges, Prasad found the transparency to be reduced to about 4 m, due to the influx of mud-laden water from the river.

The second factor in transparency of the area, according to T. S. S. Rao, (1957) is the influence of the monsoon circulation on the movement of surface waters of the Bay of Bengal during the various months of the year. In November—December, the west drift of the NE monsoon picks up turbid river discharge and transports it all along the east coast. This results in the waters all along the east coast of India showing uniform transparency under the influence of the prevailing southerly current. In February—April there is a reversal of the direction of water movement and the waters are of a higher transparency because the new southerly source is more barren and oceanic in nature. In addition, the average of the Secchi disk readings taken off Visakhapatnam shows a marked rise from the months of August through November—December and again a rise to a peak in

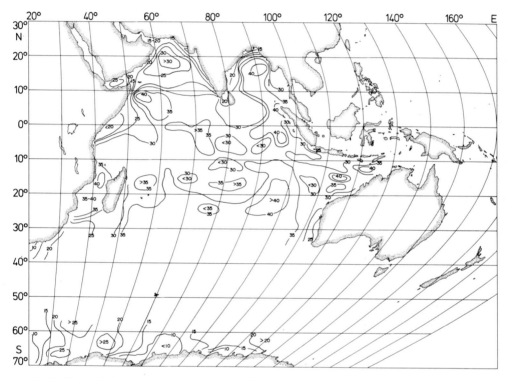

Fig. 2. Chart of the relative transparency (m) of Indian Ocean waters and the related sector of Antarctica in winter. Based on VOYTOV and DEMENT'YEVA, 1970

February—April. There is an increase in transparency and a fall in turbidity in January and February. RAO (1957) has correlated these changes in transparency with variations in the concentration of copepod and chaetognath populations.

Numerous inshore transparency studies were conducted during the IIOE. SARMA and GANAPATI (1968) in Kakinada Bay confirm the observations of RAO on seasonal variation in the extinction coefficients. QASIM, BHATTATHIRI and ABIDI (1968) examined the Cochin backwater and found the light penetration to be at a low level throughout the year but at a minimum during the monsoon months when the estuary becomes highly turbid as a result of the inflow of considerable amounts of fresh water (see QASIM, 1973, this volume).

WICKSTEAD (1962) correlates plankton populations from the East African area of the Indian Ocean with Secchi disk readings, showing a related decline in plankton (dry weight m^{-3}) in the topmost 200 m with increase in transparency. "The bulk of the plankton reacts according to the degree to which the transparency of the water permits penetration of light. This reaction modifies vertical behavior movements due to negative geotropism, inherent vertical migration patterns, etc. Variations of the plankton are not indicative of richer or poorer areas but of the relative transparency at the time of sampling." (WICKSTEAD, 1962, pp. 1225).

b) Color

VOYTOV and DEMENT'YEVA (1970) list a total of 638 observations of color, with over 90% of these from the winter period corresponding to the main concentration of transparency observations. However, "color scale values of I to II predominate over the entire northern equatorial part of the Indian Ocean, except for the littoral regions". Such values correspond to a maximum irradiance transmittance in the blue wavelengths, according to JERLOV (1965). This blue color of the open ocean is due to selective absorption by the water itself, while multiple scattering by the water molecules also favors short wave length. In turbid waters, selective absorption by particles and yellow substance leads to a shift of color towards longer wave lengths (JERLOV, 1965). Thus, WICKSTEAD (1961 b) has noted the bottle-green color of the sea over the North Kenya banks and compared this with temperate waters such as the North Sea. Such an area is markedly different from the usual clear blue of the offshore East African waters and also the "dirtier blue or pale green of the inshore waters". Increasing organic production is commonly associated with a change toward longer wave lengths.

2. Extinction (= Attenuation) Measurements

The light extinction is a measure of the reduction of light intensity in a vertical distance in the sea and may be defined by a coefficient, k:

$$k = 2.30 \, (\mathrm{Log_{10}} \, I_{\lambda z} - \mathrm{Log_{10}} \, I_{\lambda z+1})$$

where $I_{\lambda z}$ and $I_{\lambda z+1}$ are the illuminations of a wave length (λ) at depths z and z+1. The use of the terms attenuation and attenuation coefficient has replaced the concept of extinction in recent accounts of optical studies (JERLOV, 1963; 1968), but most Indian Ocean data in the literature has been expressed as extinction.

The early studies of T. S. S. RAO (1957) related the extinction coefficient for the visible light rays to the Secchi disk values by use of the formula:

$$k = 1.7/D \text{ (in m)}$$

where D is the maximum depth of visibility in m, as determined from Secchi disk readings. This numerical conversion was originally derived by POOLE and ATKINS (1929) in the English Channel for blue light and is believed to be suitable for moderately clear oceanic water. MURPHY (1959) has suggested, however, that there may be considerable differences among the spectral transmittance of various waters. Although GRAHAM (1966) found a statistically significant correlation between Secchi disk observations and extinction coefficients, he warns that caution should be used when extrapolating a relationship from one oceanic environment to another. Thus, QASIM , BHATTATHIRI and ABIDI (1968)

have preferred a value of $k = 1.5/D$ in the turbid estuarine waters near Cochin, while
STRICKLAND (1958) cites an expression, $k = 1.9/D$, for very clear oceanic waters. Such
evaluations result in an expression of extinction (or attenuation) for any water layer of
1 m thickness as a percent of the incident daylight radiation.

a) Applications of Extinction Values

WYRTKI (1962) correlates the transparency of East Australian waters with the seasonal
upwelling, noting that subtropical water has an extinction below $0.12 \, m^{-1}$, which is
close to the extinction of pure water (thus indicating the absence of suspended matter).
"Upwelling areas south of Java have a much higher extinction coefficient, indicating an
abundance of particles, probably plankton. The highest values are found off the coast
of Australia, where strong tidal currents are responsible for an enrichment of the water
with particulate matter from the shelf bottom. In general, the distribution of the extinction
coefficients very closely resembles that of the plankton biomass." (WYRTKI, 1962,
pp. 223 – 224.) Similar observations in other areas of Indian Ocean upwelling would be
valuable but are not available in the literature.

Results such as those above may, however, be compared with findings of GRAHAM
(1966) in the NW Pacific, where cells of high extinction coefficient (greater than 0.16)
were associated with areas of summer upwelling or river discharge. "In offshore locations
where seasonal warming produced sharp thermoclines and shallow surface layers during
the summer, extinction coefficients were high and sometimes exceeded the highest values
obtained (in costal waters)." (GRAHAM, 1966, p. 184).

b) Irradiance Measurements

A transparency meter was used on INS "Kistna" by RAMAM and MURTHY (1968)
to determine percent transparency as the difference of overall readings and ambient
readings. For depths from 0 to 20 m, transparencies increased toward 100% from a low
of 40% in inshore waters and near the bottom. Waters off Madras (Coromandel coast)
were somewhat more transparent than near Cochin (Malabar coast).

CLARKE and KELLY (1964) have determined transparency in the western Indian
Ocean at midday for radiation at wavelengths centered at 480 nm, using a deep sea photo-
multiplier photometer. Attenuation coefficients were found as follows:

$$0- \; 30 \, m: k = 0.70 \text{ to } 0.192$$
$$30-100 \, m: k = 0.023 \text{ to } 0.066$$
$$100-900 \, m: k = \text{Low values, to a minimum of } 0.021$$

The variations of attenuation are related to the complexity of water movements in the
equatorial regions. Thus, extremely optically clear water corresponded roughly with
the tongue of Indian Ocean central water in the section at $60°\,E$ longitude. There is a
tendency throughout for rates of attenuation of visible light to become less with increasing
depth. In most cases, the authors found no further change in transparency below 300 m.
One value at 900 m ($k = 0.0021$; "Anton Bruun" station 154, 22° 58′ S, 59° 45′ E)
represents an irradiance of $6 \times 10^{-9}\%$ of the surface value, a range 10 times greater than
that for comparable observations in other areas (JERLOV, 1951). It thus represents the
most transparent water ever recorded below 100 m. It is estimated that a deep sea fish
could probably detect the presence of daylight at 1300 m at noon in this part of the Indian

Ocean. The least transparent water found (at Station 145 A: 10° 39′ N, 60° 07′ E) was estimated to allow daylight perception to about 700 m in deep sea fish. "These values indicate the ranges of depths down to which daylight would be sufficient for vision and for the control of vertical diurnal migration." (CLARKE and KELLY, 1964, p. 150).

c) Relation to Biological Studies

The primary significance of irradiance measurements today lies in their usefulness to the interpretation of productivity. A standard procedure that can provide adequate data on depths of relative extinction is still not available to many of those interested in such information. It has remained easier for many people to sample the productivity throughout the euphotic zone at standard depth intervals which only approximate the preferred depths of relative light extinction.

It is common practice for primary productivity workers to estimate the depth of the euphotic zone — the depth reached by 1% of the ambient radiant energy — by multiplying the Secchi disk depth by 3. HOLMES (1970) suggests that a factor of 3.5 is more appropriate for turbid waters where the depth reading is under 5 m, and that a factor of 2.0 would apply for depths between 5 and 12 m in his data. Thus, the relationship between Secchi disk depth and the 1% optical depth merits additional study.

The behavioral aspects of light penetration are currently under intensive investigation. DUNTLEY (1962) noted that there is no simple conversion between Secchi disk data and the sighting ranges of other objects. MURPHY (1959) felt that Secchi disk data had only limited value in the evaluation of the vision of tuna or their ability to sense fishing gear. "The evidence shows that trolling, which depends on a positive visual response, is most efficient in clear water, whereas gill netting, which is dependent on non-response, is most efficient in turbid water ... Water clarity may be an important ecological factor in the ocean in that the efficiency of sight feeders will be reduced as turbidity increases." (MURPHY, 1959, p. 86).

In an analysis of the distribution of primary production and chlorophyll a by RYTHER et al. (1966), it is suggested that much of the observed light extinction, especially in areas of patchy phytoplankton distribution, may be due to non-living organisms. MENZEL (1967) and NEWELL and KERR (1968) agree, however, that the surface standing stock of organic particles has no influence on the concentration of particles found at depth. In fact, a pronounced minimum around 200 m is found just at those depths where minimum stability might be expected to result in maximum accumulation of surface materials. It is accordingly suggested that the amount of organic particles present at any depth is a function of advection rather than sedimentation (NEWELL and KERR, 1968).

JERLOV (1953) has reported a high particle content in the divergence between the South Equatorial Current of the Indian Ocean and the countercurrent and in the region of the equatorial divergence. GORDEYEV (1964) reported the concentration of suspended matter in surface layers from stations of R V "Vityaz" to show a range from $0.3-1.0$ g m^{-3}, while the remaining areas — Red Sea, Andaman Sea, Bay of Bengal, northern part of the Arabian Sea, equatorial region and the region south of 38° 30′ S contained more than 0.5 g m^{-3}. Below the surface, the waters of the Indian Ocean have been shown to contain from $1-2$ g m^{-3} of suspension; toward the continental slopes the concentration reached $2-4$ g m^{-3} and sometimes 10 g m^{-3} (LISITZIN, 1960b). Furthermore, SEROVA

(1969) finds terrigenous materials at distances over 2000 km from the shore in the Bay of Bengal and the Arabian Sea, as well as off Antarctica. Thus, PAVLOV (1961) has been able to distinguish the optical characteristics of major water masses in part by the silt zones between them.

II. Studies on Nutrient Distribution

The sampling of the Indian Ocean for nutrients was conducted on a widespread basis during IIOE. Their statistics are summarized in Table 1 for the period from 1 September 1959 to 31 December 1965:

Inorganic phosphate-phosphorus	3844 stations (Fig. 3)
Inorganic nitrate-nitrogen	1803 stations (Fig. 4)
Inorganic silicate-silicon	2233 stations (Fig. 5)

The geographic distribution of these stations is shown by the respective figures. There is no readily discernible bias to any particular part of the year, nor any distinct preference to inshore over deep water observations. The available information clearly shows the recognition of the importance of data on nutrient distribution in the area; the data should be suitable for a considerable advance of our knowledge about the region. Assuming

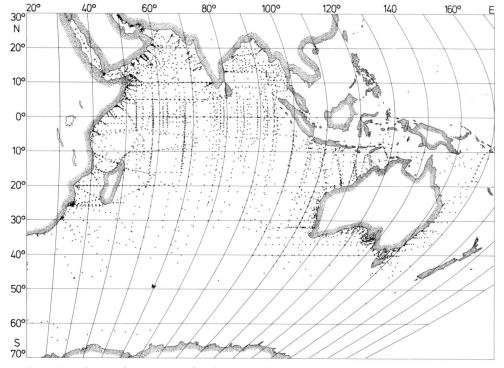

Fig. 3. Distribution of 3844 stations for observation of inorganic phosphate concentration on file at the U.S. National Oceanographic Data Center. IIOE 1 Sept. 1959 to 31 Dec. 1965

Table 1. Indian Ocean data in the archives of the U.S. National Oceanographic Data Center, World
Data Center A. (NODC, 1969)

I. Distribution of station data by months or seasons, terminology for seasonal cycle adapted from
QASIM, BHATTATHIRI and ABIDI (1968).
   1. Jan. — Feb. — Mar.   ("premonsoon"): 2709 stations
   2. Apr. — May — June   ("onset, SW monsoon"): 2270 stations
   3. July — Aug. — Sept.   ("end, SW monsoon"): 2166 stations
   4. Oct. — Nov. — Dec.   ("post-monsoon"): 2391 stations
                  Total, all months: 9536 stations.

II. Distribution of station data by depth range
                              depth range to bottom
      1. Total of all stations: 9536
                                    surface to 450 m: 3509 stns
      2. Total exceeding   450 m: 6027
                                    bottom at 450 — 950 m: 1052 stns
      3. Total exceeding   950 m: 4975
                                    bottom at 950 — 1950 m: 1993 stns
      4. Total exceeding 1950 m: 2982
                                    bottom more than 1950 m: 2982 stns
                        Total stations, all depths: 9536

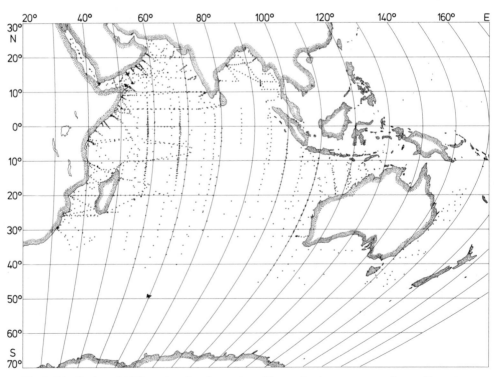

Fig. 4. Distribution of 1803 stations for observation of inorganic nitrate concentration on file at the
U.S. National Oceanographic Data Center. IIOE 1 Sept. 1959 to 31 Dec. 1965

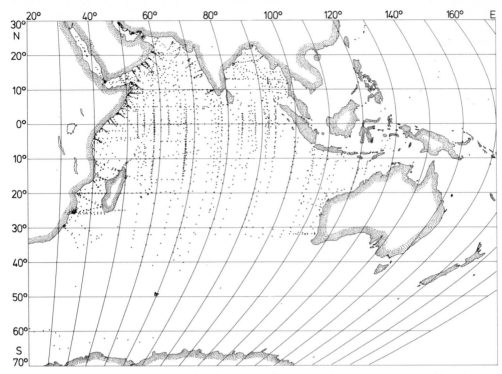

Fig. 5. Distribution of 2233 stations for observation of inorganic silicate concentration on file at the U.S. National Oceanographic Data Center. IIOE 1 Sept. 1959 to 31 Dec. 1965

multiple depths at any station, the magnitude of the data bank quickly becomes even more impressive, if not overwhelming. Selected biogeochemical aspects of the data are reviewed below, but the presentation is in all cases imcomplete, particularly with respect to contributions from Russian research which must be dealt with largely in translation.

1. Geographic Variation in the Concentration of Nutrients

a) Western Indian Ocean and Arabian Sea

α) Oxygen and Inorganic Phosphate

The relationships between the nutrient properties of various water masses are further complicated in the Indian Ocean by the control over circulation exerted in the northern Indian Ocean by the monsoon winds. This is well seen in the western Indian Ocean at the time of the SW monsoon in 1963 when RV "Atlantis II" surveyed the area (MCGILL, 1966). During the SW monsoon, the strong and persistent winds which blow offshore from Africa may directly transport surface waters away, with a resulting replacement by deep nutrient-rich waters (as also encountered by RRS "Discovery" along the coast of Arabia during the Spring of 1963).

αα) Surface Observations (Fig. 6)

Observations near Cape Guardafui and Socotra correspond with the peak of the upwelling induced by the monsoon, as indicated by surface temperatures less than 18° C found along the African coast. Profiles from offshore into the coast of Arabia taken only a month or two earlier by RRS "Discovery" showed a marked shoreward uptilting of isotherms and phosphate isopleths in that area, with the 18° C isotherm in one case rising from 200 m at the offshore end of the section to the surface at the shoreward end (Royal Society, 1963). $PO_4^{3-} - P$ in the region of the Socotra upwelling reaches values at the surface greater than 1 μg-at l^{-1}. For the SW Indian Ocean, ORREN (1963) has reported values of 0.25 to 0.54 μg-at l^{-1}, with the higher values being found southward. Surface phosphate was high near the South African coast but then steadily decreased seaward.

The highest O_2 concentration in Fig. 6 is found in the Gulf of Aden, but other values in excess of 5 ml l^{-1} are also seen in the western equatorial region and south of Madagascar. The water masses of the northern Arabian Sea have been analysed by RAMAM, KURUP and MURTHY (1968). Low salinities associated with Indus water are not apparent in Fig. 6 but could be expected to be more prominent in the post-monsoon interval.

ββ) Observations at 200 m (Fig. 7)

Most indications of the surface upwelling have been lost by the 200 m depth (Fig. 7), but the circulation along the African coast clearly indicates the pattern given to the Equatorial Undercurrents as they are drawn into the complex Somali Current system. An excessive O_2 depletion (to the level of 0.25 ml l^{-1} and a minimum concentration of 0.05 ml l^{-1}) is seen in the Arabian Sea, but no H_2S concentrations were observed by "Atlantis II", contrary to reports of some Russian surveys (IVANENKOV and ROZSNOV, 1961). The very low O_2 concentrations distinguish this Arabian Sea subsurface water mass of MOKIEVSKAYA (1961) from the Central Indian Ocean subsurface water mass to the south.

REDDY and SANKARANARAYANA (1968 a) have noted considerable variation in the concentration and thickness of the layers of phosphate and silicate in the upper 200 m of the central western North Indian Ocean. They distinguish three regions of convergence—from latitudes 15° 30′ N to 16° 30′ N along 68° E longitude, around 8° N and 71° 30′ E and around 5° N and 75° E in the Maldive Islands. These areas distinguish the North Equatorial Indian Ocean from the geographically similar regions of the Pacific and Atlantic Ocean. RAO and JAYARAMAN (1968 a) have considered the same area during the NE monsoon period.

RYTHER and MENZEL (1965) conclude that the general levels of nutrients in the western Arabian Sea are appreciably higher than those of the North Atlantic. "Phosphate concentrations within the upper 200 m of the Arabian Sea exceed those found at any depth in the Sargasso Sea. Phosphate is used here merely as an index of nutrients in general. Nitrate and silicate, which were measured, and undoubtedly other non-conservative nutrient elements, are distributed much the same as is inorganic phosphate ... Roughly speaking, it could be said that nutrient concentrations in the Arabian Sea are about twice those in the North Atlantic." (RYTHER and MENZEL, 1965, p. 202).

γγ) Observations at 600 m (Fig. 8)

The depth of 600 m (Fig. 8) represents the beginning of the zone of the phosphate maximum. Values are found in the Arabian Sea as high as 2.70 μg-at l^{-1}. This phosphate maximum zone is found to occur beneath the level of the O_2 minimum, as recognized by MOKIEVSKAYA (1961).

δδ) Observations at 1200 m (Fig. 9)

The maximum phosphate values of 3.00 μg-at l^{-1} or more are found in the Arabian Sea at 1200 m (Fig. 9). These readings are slightly higher than the maximum concentrations noted by ROZANOV (1964). Values for the central and equatorial regions are from 2.50 μg-at l^{-1} to about 2.80 μg-at l^{-1}. The $PO_4^{3-}-P$ concentration in the Antarctic Intermediate water south of the Equator is similar to the level found in the Atlantic Ocean (2.50−2.70 μg-at l^{-1}), and these values agree with those reported by ROZANOV (1964).

The O_2 minimum has now been traversed, and values at 1200 m in the North Indian Ocean range from 0.3 to 1.25 ml l^{-1}. Oxygen values decrease northward in the Antarctic Intermediate water about 1.50 ml l^{-1} in the area east of the Mascarene Ridge between the Seychelles and Mauritius.

εε) Observations at 2000 m (Fig. 10)

The zone of the phosphate concentration remains high in the northern areas (more than 2.60 μg-at l^{-1}) and it is only slightly lower to the south. MOSTERT (1966) has found the area near South Africa to have a maximum concentration of phosphate at 1000 to 1500 m followed by "a thick bottom layer with relatively little change with depth". He reports that pockets of high $PO_4^{3-}-P$ (up to 2.6 μg-at l^{-1}) appear throughout the area and may perhaps be attributed to the regeneration of phosphate from decaying matter sinking to the bottom. ORREN (1963) found a region of maximum phosphate concentration at about 2000 m for the SW Indian Ocean.

O_2 concentrations in the deeper waters are increasing, but a north-south gradient from 2.00 ml l^{-1} to 4.00 m l^{-1} is still seen near Madagascar in the data of Fig. 10.

ζζ) Observations at 3000 m (Fig. 11)

At 3000 m, as shown in Fig. 11, the schematic bottom topography delineates the top of the mid-ocean ridge system, including the Mascarene Ridge. The Arabian Sea basin shows O_2 levels of 3.00 to 3.50 ml l^{-1} at this depth and $PO_4^{3-}-P$ values greater than 2.50 μg-at l^{-1}. The phosphate level decreases to less than 2.00 μg-at l^{-1} near South Africa. In this same southern location the O_2 content is greater than 5.00 ml^{-1}.

ηη) Observations at 4000 m (Fig. 12)

The bottom depths of the western Indian Ocean are represented by Fig. 12 at 4000 m, which is designated by IVANENKOV and GUBIN (1960) as the top of the distinct bottom water masses. The Arabian Sea area shows O_2 concentrations of 3.75 to 3.80 ml l^{-1} and phosphate from 2.40 to 2.50 μg-at l^{-1}. The South Indian Ocean bottom water (temperature 1.1−1.5° C, salinity 34.72−34.73‰) has an O_2 content of more than 4.00 ml l^{-1}, increasing southward, while the $PO_4^{3-}-P$ concentration is close to 4.00 μg-at l^{-1}. South of the Mozambique Channel is a water mass closely corresponding to Antarctic Bottom Water (temperature less than 1°C, salinity 34.73‰) with an O_2 content of more than 5.00 ml^{-1}. The phosphate concentration of this water is 2.10 μg-at l^{-1}, which is lower than in the other regions at this depth.

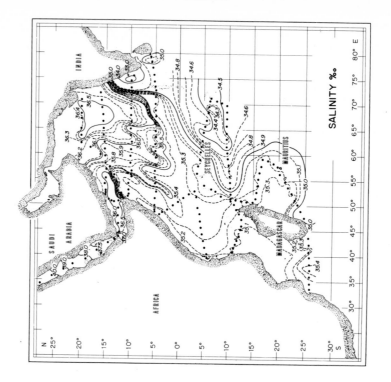

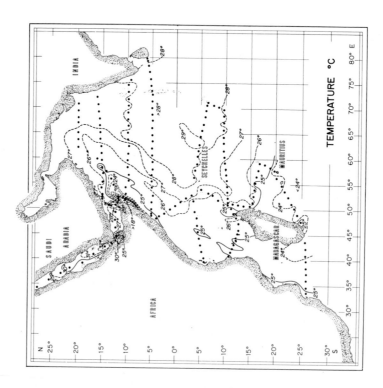

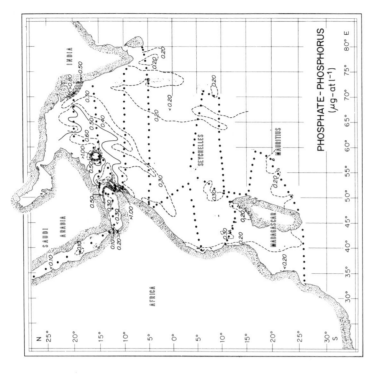

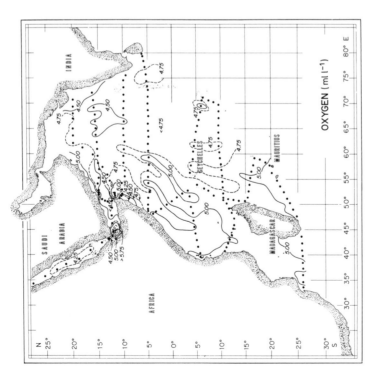

Fig. 6. Distribution of oceanographic parameters at the surface in the western Indian Ocean during the SW monsoon period, as sampled during the "Atlantis II" expedition in 1963

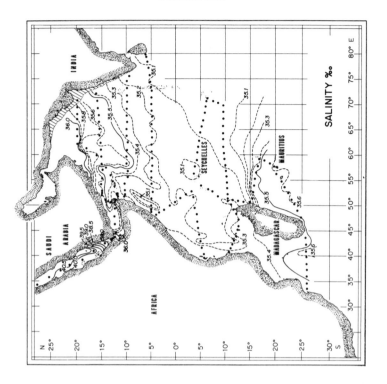

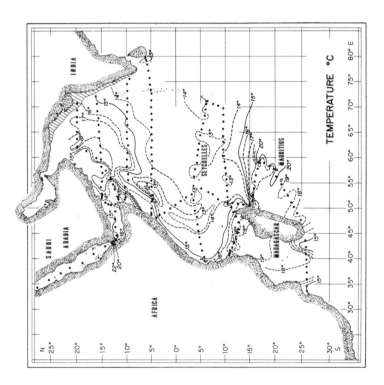

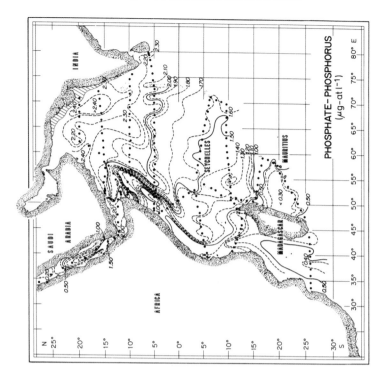

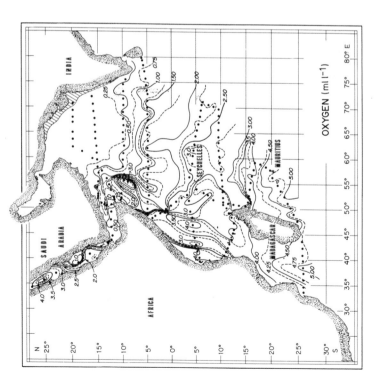

Fig. 7. Distribution of oceanographic parameters at 200 m in the western Indian Ocean during the SW monsoon period, as sampled during the "Atlantis II" expedition in 1963

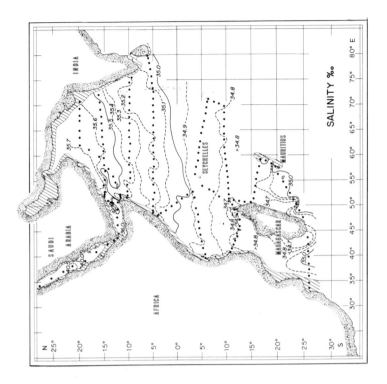

SALINITY ‰

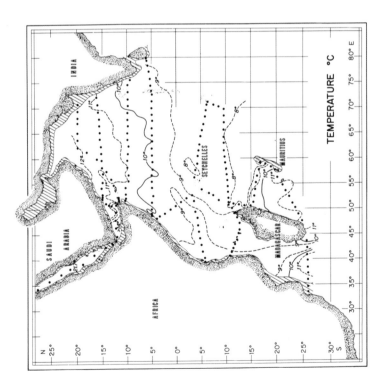

TEMPERATURE °C

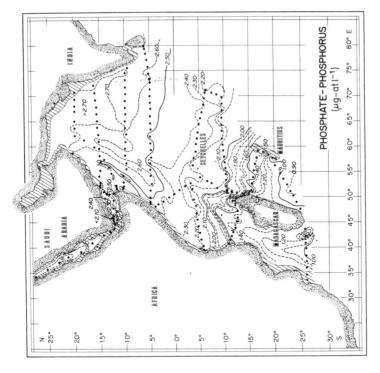

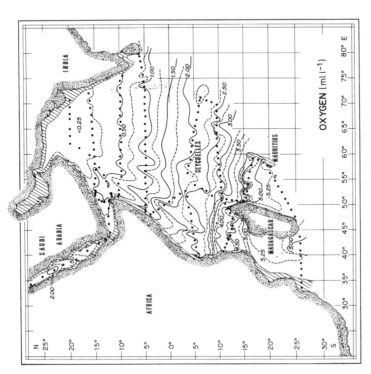

Fig. 8. Distribution of oceanographic parameters at 600 m in the western Indian Ocean during the SW monsoon period, as sampled during the "Atlantis II" expedition in 1963

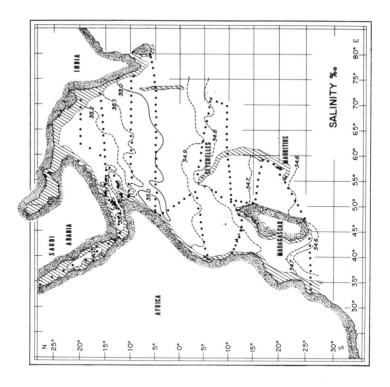

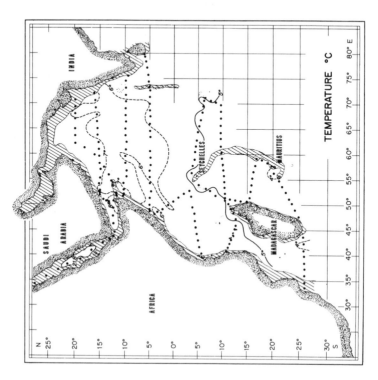

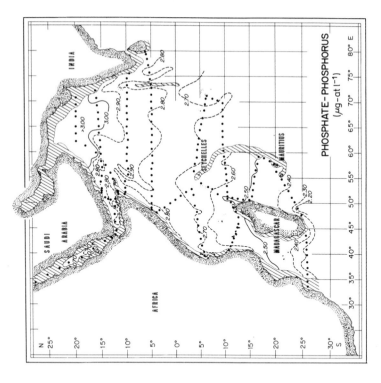

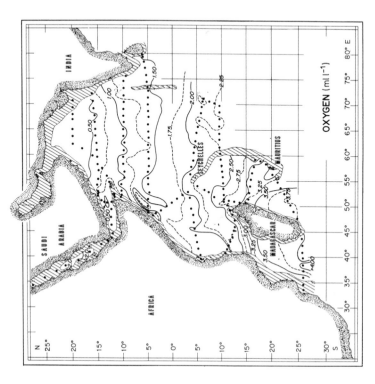

Fig. 9. Distribution of oceanographic parameters at 1200 m in the western Indian Ocean during the SW monsoon period, as sampled during the "Atlantis II" Expedition in 1963

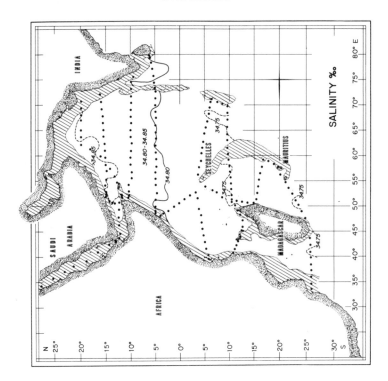

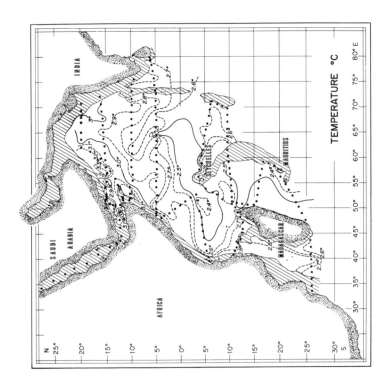

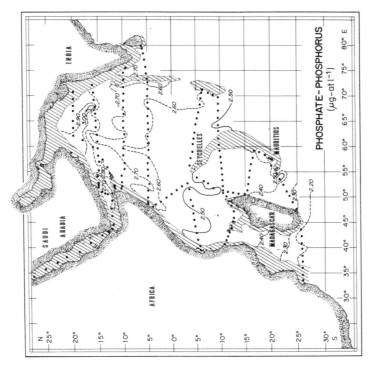

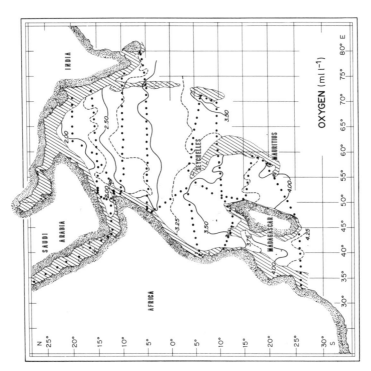

Fig. 10. Distribution of oceanographic parameters at 2000 m in the western Indian Ocean during the SW monsoon period, as sampled during the "Atlantis II" expedition in 1963

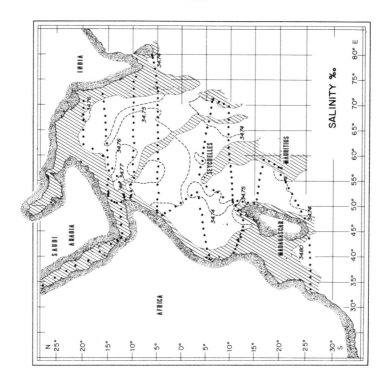

SALINITY ‰

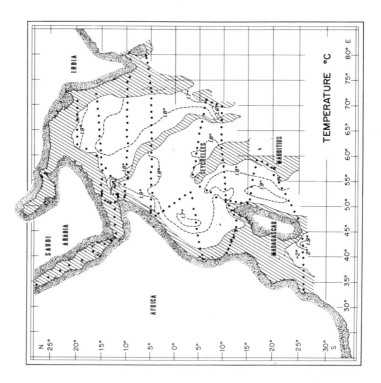

TEMPERATURE °C

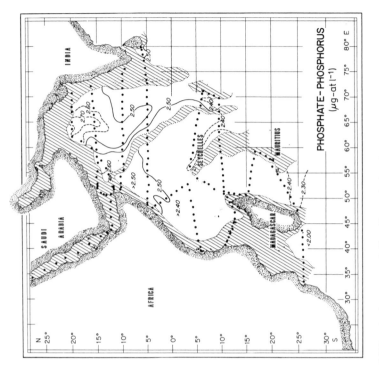

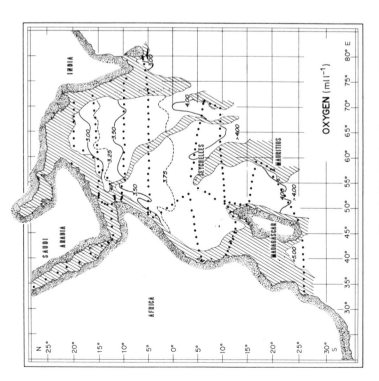

Fig. 11. Distribution of oceanographic parameters at 3000 m in the western Indian Ocean during the SW monsoon period, as sampled during the "Atlantis II" expedition in 1963

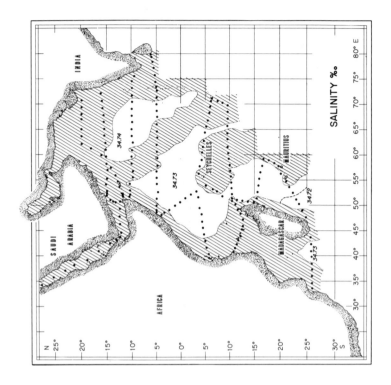

SALINITY ‰

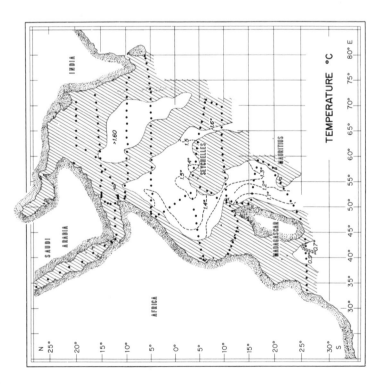

TEMPERATURE °C

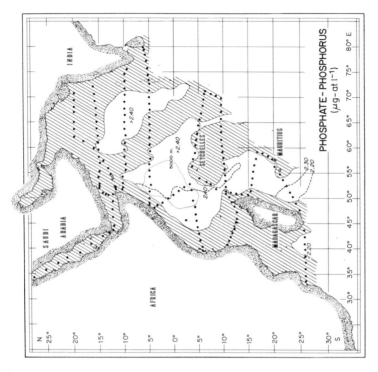

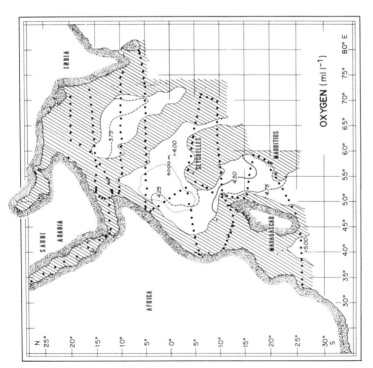

Fig. 12. Distribution of oceanographic parameters at 4000 m in the western Indian Ocean during the SW monsoon period, as sampled during the "Atlantis II" expedition in 1963

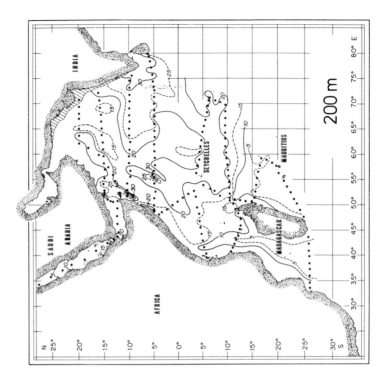

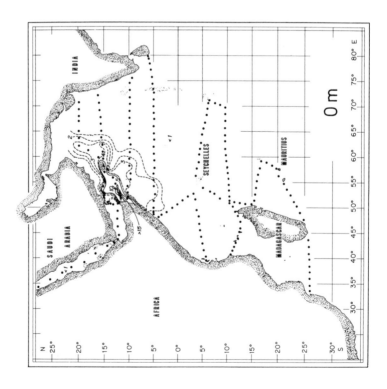

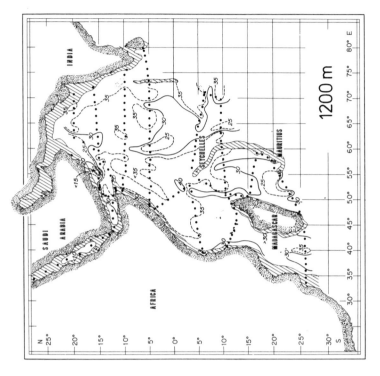

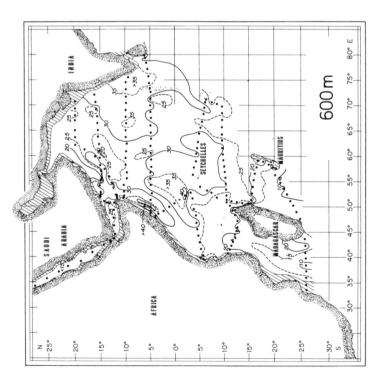

Fig. 13. Distribution of inorganic nitrate-nitrogen in the western Indian Ocean during the SW monsoon, at depths from the surface to 1200 m, as sampled during the "Atlantis II" expedition in 1963

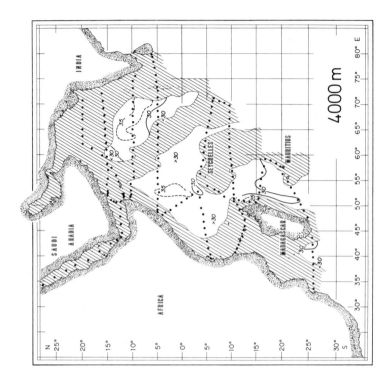

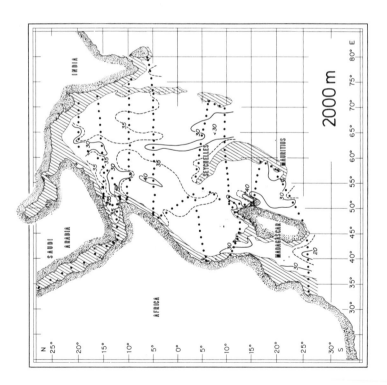

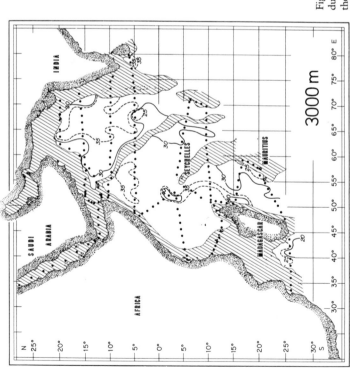

Fig. 14. Distribution of inorganic nitrate-nitrogen in the western Indian Ocean during the SW monsoon, at depths of 2000, 3000, and 4000 m, as sampled during the "Atlantis II" expedition in 1963

β) Nitrogen Distribution Patterns

αα) Distribution of Inorganic Nitrate-Nitrogen

The distribution of nitrate in the western Indian Ocean was determined for the same "Atlantis II" survey. The shallower levels of this distribution are represented in Fig. 13. The only significant nitrate concentration at the surface occurs near Socotra in the upwelling of the SW monsoon. Values from 5 to more than 15 μg-at l^{-1} are seen in this area, while negligible amounts are detected elsewhere at the surface. KABANOVA (1964) found the surface waters in the Gulf of Aden and Somali Current region were still enriched by nitrite- and nitrate-nitrogen to some extent in the post-monsoon season (October to April). Some increases of the primary production to the west of the Maldive Island and in the eastern portion of the Arabian Sea could also be correlated by KABANOVA with a level of nitrate concentration from 0.5 to 1.5 μg-at l^{-1} at that period. In the central part of the Arabian Sea she found only a negligible surface nitrate concentration, however.

The western Arabian Sea shows the highest nitrate levels at 200 m (over 25 μg-at l^{-1}); but there is not so wide a separation from the concentrations of other regions. A maximum of over 30 μg-at l^{-1} is found near South India and Ceylon, which may be an indication of coastal conditions there. The equatorial area is distinguished by values less than 20 μg-at l^{-1}. The concentration of nitrate at 200 m decreases to less than 5 μg-at l^{-1} in the waters to either side of Madagascar.

At 600 m there is a small nitrate maximum on the East African coastal waters and also near the Seychelles Bank. A large area of high concentration is found near the South Indian coast. At 1200 m the whole Arabian Sea shows nitrate levels of about 35 μg-at l^{-1}; lower concentrations are seen in the intrusive Antarctic Intermediate water east of the Mascarene Ridge

The concentrations of NO_3^--N in the deeper water layers are shown in Fig. 14. At 2000 m, there is a general concentration of 30 to 35 μg-at l^{-1}. Nitrate values near 30 μg-at l^{-1} persist at 3000 m and at 4000 m, such values cover nearly the entire region of the western Indian Ocean basin.

ββ) Evaluation of Organic Nitrogen Fractions

FRAGA (1966) detected a high concentration of dissolved organic nitrogenous matter in the surface layers of the equatorial region from 0 to 8° N and found this extending down to the deep layers. At latitudes 20° N and 20° S, he showed two zones of lower nitrogen content, extending from the bottom up to a depth of 500 to 300 m. Values for both dissolved and particulate organic nitrogen indicated a convergence in the equatorial region but this was not constant since there was no continual decrease in the organic nitrogen content with depth. FRAGA suggested that pockets may be formed at about 1000 m which could be due to seasonal variations in the organic matter produced at the surface with the change of the monsoon or transported horizontally from other richer areas.

"The vertical distribution of particulate nitrogen had a maximum at 10 m and a very clear diurnal variation extending down to 340 m. During the night the nitrogen increased from 0 to 60 m and decreased from 60 to 340 m. It is supposed that this was due to zooplankton migration. The vertical distribution of dissolved organic nitrogen had a peak at 20 m and another very large one between 100 and 170 m." (FRAGA, 1966, p. 413).

The latter peak is presumed to be produced by phytoplankton which had died and sunk below the compensation depth, excreting soluble parts of the protoplasm. "Also augmenting the soluble nitrogen in this layer are the metabolites excreted by the zooplankton during the day. Thus, there is a daily transport of soluble nitrogen from the superficial layer where the zooplankton feeds to the deeper waters where it retreats to spend the day. Hence, an accumulation of soluble organic substances produced both by chemical and by bacterial decomposition occurs at the deeper level." (FRAGA, 1966, p. 417).

ROZANOV and BYKOVA (1964) found a thin layer of NO_2^--N (up to a concentration of 2 μg-at l^{-1}) in the thermocline and a second nitrite maximum that reached a concentration of 5 μg-at l^{-1} in depths from 150 to 1500 m. They related this to the reducing conditions of the Arabian Sea waters in their area of observation.

KABANOVA (1961, 1964) has correlated the replenishment of nitrogen compounds with the productivity of Indian Ocean areas. DUGDALE, GOERING and RYTHER (1964) report high rates of nitrogen fixation in the northern Arabian sea, which they related to the abundance of *Trichodesmium*. DUGDALE and GOERING (1967) have also estimated the concentration of the regenerated fractions of available nitrogen, as measured by the ammonia uptake. They obtain a ratio of carbon to nitrogen of 7.1 : 1; there is some suggestion from their data that the ratio of light-to-dark uptake of ammonia and nitrate is lower in tropical than in temperature waters.

b) Eastern Indian Ocean and Bay of Bengal

Numerous investigators have concerned themselves with the eastern region of the Indian Ocean. Results of the various surveys may best be summarized on a regional basis.

α) Offshore Nutrient Concentrations in the Northern and Equatorial Waters of the Eastern Indian Ocean

ROZANOV (1964) has found low surface PO_4^{3-}-P values of 0.1 μg-at l^{-1} in the Bay of Bengal and the Andaman Sea, increasing to a maximum of 2.90 μg-at l^{-1} at depth. KABANOVA (1964) cites an extremely low surface value for phosphate in the Bay of Bengal, while in the Andaman Sea the increase of primary production causes the exhaustion of the phosphate to analytical zero. The dissolved nitrate and nitrite values in the Bay of Bengal are likewise low in the surface waters, but then increase sharply to 15 to 20 μg-at l^{-1} in the thermocline and to 22 of 26 μg-at l^{-1} with depth. After achieving these concentrations, the content of NO_3^--N changes little in the deep waters, according to ROZANOV and BYKOVA (1964). Greater concentrations of nitrate (1.5—2.0 μg-at l^{-1}) are reported in the euphotic zone in the central part of the Andaman Sea than in the other regions investigated by KABANOVA (1964).

The distribution of dissolved silicate is characterized by a constant increase from the thermocline layer to the bottom. While the maximum content of silicate is 150 to 160 μg-at l^{-1} in the Arabian Sea, it is 140 μg-at l^{-1} in the Bay of Bengal and 130 to 140 μg-at l^{-1} in the northern equatorial part of the Indian Ocean (ROZANOV, 1964). RAKESTRAW (1964) reported a range of silicate in stations south of the Equator from 60° E to 100° E that went from 4 to 148 μg-at l^{-1} between the surface and depth. The silicate maximum is very much greater in the Indian Ocean than in the Atlantic, but somewhat less than that found in the Pacific. No intermediate maximum of silicate was observed, and the concentration below about 2000 m is nearly constant.

β) Concentrations of Nutrients in the SE Indian Ocean

The numerous papers of ROCHFORD should be consulted for the details of nutrient conditions in the waters of the SE Indian Ocean and around Australia. Two areas of upwelling were identified by ROCHFORD (1962): 1. Along the shelf and slope region of NW Australia, south of Timor, as distinguished by high surface phosphate levels of 0.2 to 0.3 μg-at l^{-1}, with the maximum upwelling occurring before September, and 2. along the shelf and slope region of the eastern Arafura Sea, from the Aroe Islands to the Gulf of Carpentaria, where the highest surface phosphate values in the oceanic waters of Autralia were found (0.66 μg-at l^{-1}) and the maximum upwelling probably occurred before August, "During the period of the SE trade winds, enough uplift of deeper water occurs along the NW coast of Australia to increase the surface phosphate content of these coastal waters to about three times that of the surrounding areas. During the same period, the phosphate values of the surface waters in the eastern Arafura Sea increased to about 6 times that of the surrounding area." (ROCHFORD, 1962, p. 250). In contrast, phosphate values in the Great Australian Bight were only about one-quarter to one-half those in subtropical waters elsewhere. This has been attributed by ROCHFORD to the continual isolation from the waters of higher phosphate content to the south, since he finds a residence time, based upon salinity, of at least $1-2$ years.

WYRTKI (1962), on the other hand, locates the main upwelling of the SE monsoon season along the coast of Java and Sumbawa in a region characterized by very high concentrations of inorganic phosphate (over 0.7 μg-at l^{-1}) at the bottom of the euphotic zone. It was believed that the NW monsoon season would not show similar enrichment by upwelling, however. BRUJEWICZ et al. (1966) have reported seasonal changes of the concentration of nutrients in the low latitudes, especially in the eastern part of the equatorial and southern tropical zone of the Indian Ocean. A marked change of dynamic conditions due to monsoon changes affects the layers from the surface down to 1500 m in this region.

γ) Inshore Areas of the Bay of Bengal and South Indian Peninsula

The development of upwelling areas during the monsoon has special significance for the coastal areas near the large population centers of Asia, since the nutrient enrichment may have important relations to the fisheries. A number of authorities have examined various locations around the Bay of Bengal for upwelling conditions, but the seasonal and yearly variation in the conditions of this circulation introduce much confusion. Many authors cite the particular significance of the estuarine character of Bay of Bengal waters (T. S. S. RAO, 1957). Thus, SANKARANARAYANAN and REDDY (1968) believe that the highly estuarine nature of the Bay narrows the biological influence of the nutrients and emphasizes the contribution of suspended organic and inorganic particulate matter. They conclude that the conditions in the Bay necessitate the use of extensive small regional and temporal observations to obtain an integrated picture of the property distributions.

αα) Andaman Sea and Burmese Coast

REDDY, MURTY and SANKARANARAYANAN (1968) report very high PO_4^{3-}-P concentrations (>12 μg-at l^{-1}) in the waters around the Andaman Islands and suggest an association between the occurrence of coral banks and the abnormal phosphate levels. It is noteworthy that the Andaman Sea is a region of the highest productivity by phytoplankton, according to ZERNOVA and IVANOV (1964). GARG, MURTY and JAYARAMAN (1968) analysed the vertical distribution of O_2 in February—March and found greater thickness of an O_2-rich layer in the Bay of Bengal than in the Andaman Sea. Below this, an O_2-poor layer showed greater thickness in the Andaman Sea and decreased toward the north in the Bay of Bengal, suggesting a northerly flow at these depths. Upwelling along the Burmese coast during the NE Monsoon is reported by LAFOND and LAFOND (1968), based on observations during the period of shift from NE to SW monsoon winds (March). RAO and JAYARAMAN (1968 b) find the spreading of river discharge from the Irrawaddy in the upper 75 m a major influence in the SE area in the premonsoon months.

ββ) Northern Latitudes, Bay of Bengal-Calcutta, Waltair

SANKARANARAYANAN and REDDY (1968) studied the distribution of phosphate, nitrate and silicate in relation to hydrographical features of the NW region of the Bay between 16°N and 19°N latitude during the month of January. Although there was marked regional variation, the distribution was found to be related to the prevailing currents. The chief feature observed was the commencement of coastal upwelling along the east Indian coast which develops as the SW monsoon winds become established (April). RAO and RAO (1968) report variation in the surface values for total phosphorus from a low of 0.99 μg-at l^{-1} in April to a high of 3.4 μg-at l^{-1} in July.

The high values of total phosphorus in the summer coincide with low values of inorganic phosphate, following the variations in the standing stock. The total phosphorus is generally low in surface waters and increases with depth up to 500 m, after which the values decrease. SANKARANARAYANAN and REDDY likewise find vertical movement of the water down to 500 m. The inorganic phosphate maximum occurs between 600 and 800 m, the nitrate maximum at 300 to 800 m. Silicate concentrations, on the other hand, continue to increase with depth.

No enrichment of the surface waters by inorganic phosphate in the SW monsoon was found by RAO and RAO (1968). Rather, they attribute the high total phosphorus value to the large quantities of dissolved organic phosphorus present, which can contribute 80 to 90% of the total phosphorus.

γγ) Coromandel Coast-Madras, Porto Novo, Kalinda

BANSE (1968) finds no marked seasonal upwelling off Madras. He further claims the river discharge during the SW monsoon does not contribute important amounts of phosphate-phosphorus to the sea. MURTY and VARADACHARI (1968) review the physical characteristics of surface waters off Madras and Karaikal and find only weak upwelling in the premonsoon season. Water from shallow depths reaches the surface nearshore but there is no marked lowering of the surface temperature. This is in distinct opposition to the prominent upwelling seen off Waltair during both premonsoon and monsoon as the water from deeper layers off the shelf appears to reach the surface causing considerable fall of surface temperatures near the coast. MURTY and REDDY (1968) also find little evidence for pronounced upwelling near Madras, based on total phosphorus distribution in the sediments.

δδ) Southwest Coast of India-Malabar Coast

PANNIKAR and JAYARAMAN (1966) reviewed the evidence for upwelling conditions on the SW coast of India and concluded that upwelling was prevalent along the coast between 7° N and 18° N latitudes, from August to early October. SHARMA (1968) finds the upwelling extending progressively from south to north throughout the period from February to July/August. This agrees with REDDY and SANKARANARAYANAN (1968, a and b), for data on the distribution of phosphates and silicates in the upper 200 m. The regional differences in the concentration of nutrients along the coast in the closing phase of the SW monsoon are attributed to the varying intensities of this upwelling. The post monsoon is characterized by more vertical stability of the waters and by uniform distribution of the nutrient properties.

S. V. S. RAO (1957) reported high values of total phosphorus for the inshore waters of the Malabar coast off Calicut for January to March and July to October. These high values of total P coincide with high inorganic phosphate in the SW monsoon period; but as noted above the relationship on the east coast is inverse. JAYARAMAN and SESHAPPA (1957) reported higher values of total phosphorus on the west coast of India when compared with the east coast for both SW and NE monsoon periods. The total phosphorus in the sediments also reflects the prevalence of upwelling conditions (MURTY, REDDY and VARADACHARI, 1968; SIDDIQUE and CHAUDHURY, 1968; CHATERJI, KARUNAKARAN and SIDDIQUE, 1968).

An offshore region of upwelling is reported by RAO and JAYARAMAN (1966) in the Minicoy area of the Arabian Sea. However, this seems to be more related to postmonsoon conditions. It is suggested that such enrichment may have a considerable impact on the peak tuna catches in this region. Likewise, PANIKKAR and JAYARAMAN (1966) correlate the upwelling on the SW coast with the main region of the sardine-mackerel fishery. A full understanding of the factors responsible for the enrichment conditions is not yet available since it falls into no single cause-and-effect category but is a result of complex interactions. As BANSE (1966) states, the continuing scarcity of studies during the biologically most important season in a region which produces much of India's marine fish makes interpretation tenuous.

2. Evaluation of Organic Phosphorus Concentrations

Measurements of the concentrations for various components of the complete cycle for phosphorus were also made during IIOE. Determinations for total phosphorus, when carried out along with evaluations of the inorganic phosphate concentration, provide an estimate of the total organic phosphorus by difference. In addition, when separate determinations of organic phosphorus in the particulate matter from a filtered water sample are made, the distinction of the particulate and dissolved organic fractions is possible by difference. Such data provide for the evaluation of the relationships in the phosphorus cycle.

a) Western Indian Ocean and Arabian Sea

Determinations of the various organic components of the phosphorus cycle were carried out by the author on the "Atlantis II" expeditions. Equivalent areas were sampled at periods almost exactly at 6 months opposite to each other in the yearly cycle, and each cruise covered the Arabian Sea at the peak of monsoon conditions. Nutrient observations from the 1963 SW monsoon have already been presented in this paper and elsewhere (McGILL, 1966). The available data on the organic phosphorus concentrations have been grouped as a frequency distribution, using 0.00, 0.05, 0.10 μg-at l^{-1} as the class mid-points, for various depth intervals throughout the water column. The mean ($\bar{x}$), variance (s^2), standard deviation (s) and standard error of estimate (s/$\sqrt{n}$, where n is the number of observations) are given in Table 2 through 5, for each area and depth level selected.

a) Observations during the SW Monsoon Period, 1963

Data for the Arabian Sea sections at 20°N, 15°N and 9°N were obtained in August and early September. This also includes the stations in the region of the Gulf of Aden and around Socotra and Cape Guardafui. Equatorial sections were sampled in September, and most of the southern areas were visited in October. It may be assumed that this distribution represents monsoon and post-monsoon conditions and particularly reflects the seasonal upwelling near Cape Guardafui, as already discussed in a preceding section.

aa) Total Organic Phosphorus

Results of the statistical treatment of the frequency distribution for the data on total organic phosphorus are given in Table 2. The total water column was sampled and the data divided into 1000 m increments. Since the first 1000 m segment includes so many more sampling depths than the others, it is more nearly equivalent to all the depth levels below 1000 m, which is the right-hand column given for each set of data in Table 2. Accessory regions are those locations in which enough data were grouped together in a close geographical area that it justified separate statistical treatment from that of the latitudinal sections. Also, south of the Equator the western end of some sections was separated from the easterly, mid-ocean part of the section. The pattern of distribution for the calculated mean concentrations in μg-at l^{-1} at each depth interval has been plotted in Fig. 15.

High mean values of total organic phosphorus (from 0.12 to 0.185 μg-at l^{-1}) are found in the surface to 1000 m depth segment. Almost all other depths of all sections show little significant concentrations of organic phosphorus. Most values in the deeper parts of the water column are 0.03 μg-at l^{-1} or less. The effects of upwelling along the Arabian coast and near Socotra can be seen in the high surface levels north of the Equator. Slight enrichment in organic phosphorus at the deeper depths of the Arabian Sea presumably results from the surface productivity associated with upwelling conditions (YENTSCH, 1965, redrawn in McGILL and LAWSON, 1966). There is a slight enrichment noted at 25°S in the section across the Mozambique Channel. With that exception, however, all distributions for mean organic phosphorus concentration show a trend to higher values north of the Equator than south. There is no equatorial peak in organic phosphorus, as was seen in an similar data treatment for the Atlantic Ocean, based in IGY data (McGILL, 1963). This difference presumably is due to the special effects of the monsoon circulation.

ββ) Particulate and Dissolved Organic Phosphorus

For the surface to 200-m depth level, particulate phosphorus was determined by filtration for all water samples. The statistical data on particulate, dissolved and total organic phosphorus at these surface levels is presented in Table 3. Mean concentrations are plotted in Fig. 16. A separation of total organic phosphorus in the photic zone (0−200 m)

Table 2. Statistical parameters for total organic phosphorus in the western Indian Ocean during the SW monsoon (1963), based on a frequency distribution analysis. The principal crossings are arranged by mean latitude, with accessory regions having sufficient data concentrated in a specific geographocal region separately grouped at the left. South of the Equator the data are divided into a western border region between Madagascar and the coast of Africa and the central basin east of Seychelles and Madagascar. Data are grouped in 1000 m increments of the water column, plus a total of all depths below 1000 m. The mean ($\bar{x}$), variance (s^2), standard deviation (s) and standard error of estimate ($s/\sqrt{n}$, where n is the number of observations) are indicated for each grouping

Principal latitude crossings:

Area	Statistic	0–999 m	1000–1999 m	2000–2999 m	3000–3999 m	Over 4000 m	Total below 1000 m
20° N	n	122	24	20	6	–	50
	$\bar{x}$	0.1852	0.0375	0.0050	0.0417		0.0230
	s^2	0.0542	0.0041	0.0017	0.0037		0.0034
	s	0.2328	0.0642	0.0412	0.0605		0.0582
	$s/\sqrt{n}$	0.0211	0.0131	0.0092	0.0246		0.0082
15° N	n	221	48	25	26	–	99
	$\bar{x}$	0.1312	0.0406	0.0580	0.0462		0.0434
	s^2	0.0406	0.0062	0.0057	0.0075		0.0066
	s	0.2015	0.0790	0.0758	0.0866		0.0815
	$s/\sqrt{n}$	0.0136	0.0114	0.0132	0.0170		0.0082
10° N	n	293	59	40	30	14	143
	$\bar{x}$	0.1606	0.0314	0.0263	0.0100	0.0179	0.0241
	s^2	0.0358	0.0023	0.0027	0.0064	0.0034	0.0025
	s	0.1891	0.0483	0.0523	0.0799	0.0580	0.0503
	$s/\sqrt{n}$	0.0110	0.0063	0.0083	0.0146	0.0155	0.0042
5° N	n	376	72	53	31	12	168
	$\bar{x}$	0.1299	0.0125	0.0019	–0.0033	–0.0042	0.0051
	s^2	0.0224	0.0013	0.0014	0.0069	0.0006	0.0012
	s	0.1498	0.0366	0.0369	0.0833	0.0243	0.0344
	$s/\sqrt{n}$	0.0077	0.0043	0.0051	0.0150	0.0070	0.0027

Accessory regions (grouped at left):

Area	Statistic	0–999 m	1000–1999 m	2000–2999 m	3000–3999 m	Over 4000 m	Total below 1000 m
Red Sea	n	111	10	–	–	–	10
	$\bar{x}$	0.1779	0.1800				0.1800
	s^2	0.0411	0.0299				0.0299
	s	0.2028	0.1730				0.1730
	$s/\sqrt{n}$	0.0192	0.0547				0.0547
Gulf of Aden	n	120	21	7	–	–	28
	$\bar{x}$	0.1433	–0.0075	0.0000			–0.0054
	s^2	0.0316	0.0019	0.0010			0.0015
	s	0.1779	0.0433	0.0309			0.0392
	$s/\sqrt{n}$	0.0162	0.0206	0.0117			0.0074
Socotra	n	88	6	8	5	–	19
	$\bar{x}$	0.1511	0.0167	0.0187	–0.0200		0.0079
	s^2	0.0358	0.0007	0.0033	0.0025		0.0028
	s	0.1892	0.0258	0.0574	0.0500		0.0531
	$s/\sqrt{n}$	0.0202	0.0105	0.0203	0.0224		0.0122

The statistic rows for each region are n, $\bar{x}$, s^2, s, $s/\sqrt{n}$.

Left block

Region	stat						
Western perimeter 5° S	n	162	30	15	10	9	64
	$\bar{x}$	0.1123	0.0083	−0.0033	−0.0050	0.0111	0.0039
	s^2	0.0187	0.0010	0.0010	0.0012	0.0015	0.0011
	s	0.1368	0.0313	0.0308	0.0353	0.0387	0.0333
	$s/\sqrt{n}$	0.0107	0.0057	0.0080	0.0112	0.0129	0.0042
Mozambique Channel 10° S	n	176	33	20	5		58
	$\bar{x}$	0.1077	0.0167	0.0175	0.0300	—	0.0181
	s^2	0.0153	0.0009	0.0020	0.0045		0.0016
	s	0.1237	0.0303	0.0444	0.0671		0.0402
	$s/\sqrt{n}$	0.0093	0.0053	0.0099	0.0300		0.0053
Seychelles Banks	n	62	11	7	7	2	27
	$\bar{x}$	0.1395	0.0500	0.0429	0.0214	0.0000	0.0370
	s^2	0.0361	0.0657	0.0022	0.0024	0.0000	0.0034
	s	0.1901	0.0431	0.0464	0.0488	0.0000	0.0583
	$s/\sqrt{n}$	0.0241	0.0198	0.0175	0.0184	0.0000	0.0112
Chagos Shoals	n	61	14	6			20
	$\bar{x}$	0.1360	0.0357	0.0250	—	—	0.0325
	s^2	0.0248	0.0014	0.0007			0.0015
	s	0.1576	0.0371	0.0272			0.0391
	$s/\sqrt{n}$	0.0202	0.0099	0.0111			0.0087
Mozambique Channel 25° C	n	118	22	13	14	3	52
	$\bar{x}$	0.0979	0.0500	0.0308	0.0536	−0.0167	0.0423
	s^2	0.0109	0.0043	0.0037	0.0041	0.0008	0.0038
	s	0.1042	0.0654	0.0607	0.0638	0.0291	0.0619
	$s/\sqrt{n}$	0.0096	0.0139	0.0168	0.0171	0.0168	0.0086

Right block

Lat.	stat						
0°	n	114	20	17	14	16	67
	$\bar{x}$	0.1215	0.0425	0.0029	0.0179	0.0219	0.0224
	s^2	0.0207	0.0027	0.0012	0.0023	0.0023	0.0022
	s	0.1438	0.0523	0.0340	0.0482	0.0482	0.0467
	$s/\sqrt{n}$	0.0135	0.0117	0.0082	0.0129	0.0120	0.0057
5° S	n	189	39	23	28	4	94
	$\bar{x}$	0.1492	0.0244	0.0283	0.0196	0.0000	0.0229
	s^2	0.0297	0.0022	0.0019	0.0014	0.0000	0.0019
	s	0.1723	0.0470	0.0434	0.0378	0.0000	0.0431
	$s/\sqrt{n}$	0.0125	0.0075	0.0090	0.0071	0.0000	0.0044
10° S	n	238	44	28	22	6	100
	$\bar{x}$	0.1500	0.0205	0.0250	0.0182	0.0167	0.0210
	s^2	0.0299	0.0010	0.0010	0.0006	0.0007	0.0009
	s	0.1729	0.0309	0.0315	0.0246	0.0257	0.0292
	$s/\sqrt{n}$	0.0112	0.0047	0.0060	0.0052	0.0105	0.0029
15° S	n	155	32	20	23	11	86
	$\bar{x}$	0.1445	0.0219	0.0225	0.0152	0.0136	0.0192
	s^2	0.0225	0.0007	0.0011	0.0006	0.0011	0.0008
	s	0.1500	0.0268	0.0332	0.0236	0.0330	0.0291
	$s/\sqrt{n}$	0.0120	0.0047	0.0074	0.0049	0.0099	0.0031
20° S	n	166	31	20	15	10	76
	$\bar{x}$	0.1527	0.0242	0.0100	0.0100	0.0350	0.0197
	s^2	0.0281	0.0026	0.0018	0.0014	0.0070	0.0027
	s	0.1679	0.0511	0.0423	0.0375	0.0839	0.0520
	$s/\sqrt{n}$	0.0130	0.0092	0.0095	0.0097	0.0265	0.0060

Table 3. Statistical parameters for particulate, dissolved and total organic phosphorus in surface waters (0–200 m) and total organic phosphorus in subsurface (200–1000 m) in the western Indian Ocean during the SW monsoon (1963), based on a frequency distribution analysis. Aside from the difference in depht range of the data, the analytical groupings follow the description in Table 2

Area	Particulate Organic Phosphorus (0–200 m)	Dissolved Organic Phosphorus (0–200 m)	Total Organic Phosphorus (0–200 m)	Total Organic Phosphorus (200–1000 m)	Statistic	Area	Particulate Organic Phosphorus (0–200 m)	Dissolved Organic Phosphorus (0–200 m)	Total Organic Phosphorus (0–200 m)	Total Organic Phosphorus (200–1000 m)
Red Sea	71	77	73	38	n	20° N	72	77	78	44
	0.0570	0.1760	0.2267	0.0842	$\bar{x}$		0.0681	0.2045	0.2538	0.0636
	0.0097	0.0308	0.0496	0.0103	s^2		0.0049	0.0553	0.0791	0.0095
	0.0986	0.1755	0.2227	0.1015	$s/\sqrt{n}$		0.0702	0.2353	0.2811	0.0976
	0.0117	0.0200	0.0261	0.0165			0.0083	0.0268	0.0318	0.0147
Gulf of Aden	73	80	80	40	n	15° N	77	76	138	83
	0.0527	0.1656	0.2663	0.0400	$\bar{x}$		0.0792	0.1757	0.1978	0.0223
	0.0076	0.0426	0.0640	0.0059	s^2		0.0086	0.0458	0.0604	0.0049
	0.0869	0.2063	0.2530	0.0770	$s/\sqrt{n}$		0.0925	0.2141	0.2458	0.0705
	0.0102	0.0231	0.0283	0.0122			0.0105	0.0246	0.0209	0.0077
					n	10° N	178	179	179	114
					$\bar{x}$		0.0506	0.1760	0.2260	0.0579
					s^2		0.0035	0.0300	0.0606	0.0063
					$s/\sqrt{n}$		0.0588	0.1732	0.2462	0.0795
							0.0044	0.0129	0.0184	0.0074
Socotra	52	54	54	34	n	5° N	242	230	230	146
	0.0750	0.1546	0.2269	0.0324	$\bar{x}$		0.0465	0.1533	0.1972	0.0240
	0.0075	0.0247	0.0506	0.0018	s^2		0.0023	0.0251	0.0416	0.0033
	0.0863	0.1572	0.2249	0.0423	$s/\sqrt{n}$		0.0477	0.1583	0.2040	0.0570
	0.0102	0.0214	0.0306	0.0073			0.0031	0.0104	0.0135	0.0047

Location	Latitude	Stat								
Western Perimeter 5° S	0°	n	90	88	96	66	—	—	70	44
		x̄	0.0400	0.1210	0.1667	0.0333			0.1807	0.0273
		s²	0.0018	0.0137	0.0267	0.0034			0.0287	0.0032
		s	0.0428	0.1171	0.1634	0.0584			0.1694	0.0566
		s/√n	0.0045	0.0125	0.0167	0.0072			0.0202	0.0085
Mozambique Channel 10° S	5° S	n	106	107	106	70	117	115	115	74
		x̄	0.0325	0.1252	0.1557	0.0364	0.0278	0.1826	0.2100	0.0615
		s²	0.0008	0.0135	0.0214	0.0025	0.0014	0.0312	0.0423	0.0051
		s	0.0280	0.1163	0.1462	0.0497	0.0372	0.1768	0.2058	0.0715
		s/√n	0.0027	0.0112	0.0142	0.0059	0.0034	0.0165	0.0192	0.0083
Seychelles Bank 9°	10° S	n	35	36	36	18	144	144	144	94
		x̄	0.0271	0.1542	0.1847	0.0750	0.0333	0.1736	0.2101	0.0580
		s²	0.0006	0.0221	0.0320	0.0085	0.0029	0.0286	0.0363	0.0035
		s	0.0253	0.1485	0.1788	0.0924	0.0537	0.1691	0.1905	0.0592
		s/√n	0.0043	0.0248	0.0300	0.0218	0.0045	0.0141	0.0159	0.0061
Chagos Shoals	15° S	n	36	36	36	25	94	91	96	59
		x̄	0.0278	0.1722	0.1986	0.0480	0.0149	0.1720	0.1932	0.0653
		s²	0.0014	0.0212	0.0360	0.0026	0.0007	0.0233	0.0025	0.0038
		s	0.0374	0.1457	0.1897	0.0505	0.0270	0.1527	0.1568	0.0613
		s/√n	0.0062	0.0243	0.0316	0.0101	0.0028	0.0160	0.0160	0.0080
Mozambique Channel 25° S	20° S	n	77	71	72	46	108	103	103	63
		x̄	0.0130	0.1049	0.1361	0.0413	0.0134	0.1738	0.1937	0.0857
		s²	0.0010	0.0102	0.0183	0.0035	0.0056	0.0305	0.0372	0.0101
		s	0.0311	0.1008	0.1353	0.0594	0.0748	0.1748	0.1929	0.1007
		s/√n	0.0035	0.0120	0.0159	0.0088	0.0072	0.0172	0.0190	0.0127

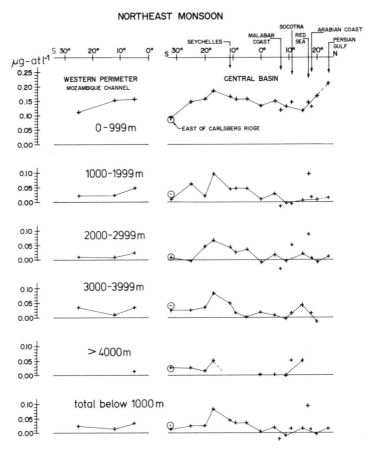

Fig. 15. Distribution of total organic phosphorus in the western Indian Ocean, showing a comparison of the conditions during the SW monsoon period and during the NE monsoon period, both sampled by "Atlantis II" expeditions

from the concentrations in the 200–1000 m depth interval is also given. It is clear that high concentrations of organic phosphorus are directly associated with the photic zone.

In the photic zone, the dissolved organic phosphorus concentration represents $^2/_3$ to $^3/_4$ or more of the total organic phosphorus present. Only in the Arabian Sea north of the Equator does particulate phosphorus approach a significant level, but it remains at a concentration which is only about $^1/_4$ to $^1/_3$ of the total organic phosphorus. The highest particulate phosphorus concentration is found at 15° N and in the stations near Socotra, corresponding with the areas of high productivity.

β) Observations during the NE Monsoon Period, 1965

Data for the Arabian Sea sections at 9° N and 20° N were obtained in March, while the section at 15° N was sampled in early April. The Red Sea and Socotra areas were traversed in February, the Persian Gulf and Arabian coast stations in March. Equatorial

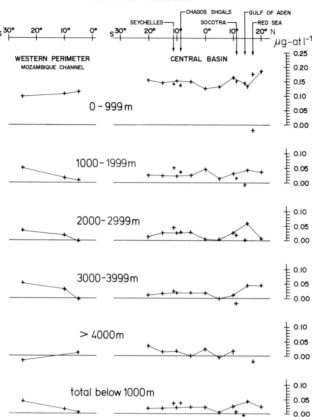

SOUTHWEST MONSOON

areas from the Malabar coast to about 10° S were covered in April and early May. Remaining areas were sampled in June. Included in these observations is a series of stations taken east of the Carlsberg Ridge at 32° S in the eastern Indian Ocean in July.

αα) Total Organic Phosphorus

The statistical results of the frequency distribution for total organic phosphorus, as grouped by 1000 m depth increments, are given in Table 4. Data are shown graphically in Fig. 15, where comparison with the data at the opposing season is also presented. High levels of organic phosphorus occur in the 0−999 m segment of the water column for all areas. The maximum organic phosphorus is found in the Persian Gulf. At 20° S the concentration is higher than at 20° N. Otherwise, mean values in the surface segment of the water column have much the same range in both seasonal distributions. Areas throughout the lower depths of the water column in the southern Indian Ocean, however, are consistently higher than those in the Arabian Sea at this season. This distinction is particularly pronounced for the mid-ocean areas east of Madagascar, where each latitudinal section reaches higher concentrations than are found in the Mozambique Channel. This

SOUTHWEST MONSOON

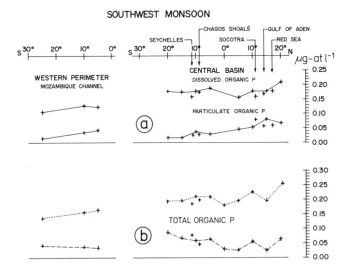

NORTHEAST MONSOON

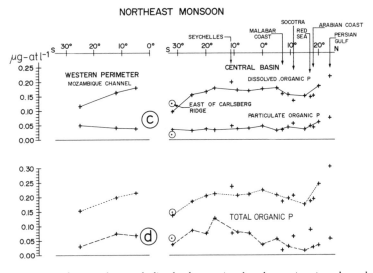

Fig. 16. Distribution of particulate and dissolved organic phosphorus (a, c) and total organic phosphorus (b, d) in the western Indian Ocean, during the SW monsoon period (a, b) and during the NE monsoon period (c, d), both sampled by "Atlantis II" expeditions. (Dotted line: 0−200 m; broken line: 200−1000 m)

is in marked contrast with the pattern seen in deep water levels for the SW monsoon data. The maximum concentrations near 20° S correspond with the area of maximum productivity at this season, as assessed by chlorophyll distribution data (McGILL and LAWSON, 1966).

$\beta\beta$) Particulate and Dissolved Organic Phosphorus

When particulate and dissolved organic phosphorus values for the photic zone (0 – 200 m) are analysed, the particulate values appear to be nearly constant at 0.03 to 0.04 μg-at l^{-1} for the whole western Indian Ocean, as seen in Table 5. This represents about one fifth of the total organic phosphorus, while the remaining four fifth occurs as dissolved organic phosphorus (0.15 to 0.18 μg-at l^{-1}). The values of dissolved organic phosphorus are not widely divergent, although a decline toward lower concentrations from 20°S to 32°S may be noted. When the total organic phosphorus levels from 0 – 200 m and 200 – 1000 m are compared, it can be seen that the productivity near 20°S has a consistent and pronounced effect on the data at this season for the year.

There is no pronounced accumulation of organic phosphorus at the Equator at any depth, as was found for the Atlantic Ocean. The decline in the southerly latitudes is in marked contrast to the increasing organic phosphorus levels as one moves southward in the Atlantic Ocean (McGILL, 1963). Presumably, such differences reflect the variable influence of Antarctic water masses in the two areas.

b) Eastern Indian Ocean and Bay of Bengal

Details on the distribution of organic phosphorus in the eastern Indian Ocean are somewhat more limited. RAO and RAO (1968) present some data on particulate and dissolved organic phosphorus fractions for areas of the Bay of Bengal along with the distribution of total phosphorus and inorganic phosphate. Particulate organic P values are shown to be very low in all depth levels throughout the area, much as in the western Indian Ocean regions. However, the high total phosphorus values found are due in part to large quantities of dissolved organic phosphorus which makes up 80 to 90% of the total organic phosphorus throughout the region so that the particulate organic portion becomes almost negligible.

The data of RAO and RAO are presented in a slight rearrangement in Table 6. The mean values given are not derived from a frequency distribution analysis as with the western Indian Ocean areas. Spacing of the data was selected to give an indication of the variation for depth of each phosphorus fraction. It is clear from the Table that the Andaman Sea has lower organic phosphorus values than the area near the Burmese coast, while the northern Bay of Bengal region shows high levels of organic phosphorus in the surface waters. Values obtained for depths below 1000 m in the Bay of Bengal area, however, do not show any significant concentrations of organic phosphorus in any form.

KUMARI (1968) has examined phosphorus fractions in Porto Novo waters and has reported on conditions in the mouth of the Vellar estuary as compared with the 10 fathom depth offshore. His data are summarized in Table 7. In the estuary, all phosphorus fractions at the surface are minimal in September and maximum in January. At the 10 fathom line, total phosphorus and dissolved organic phosphorus are at a maximum in March and at a minimum in May. KUMARI suggests that his data show rapid recycling rates for phosphorus, as well as the effects of discharge from the Vellar estuary. "The high concentration of organic phosphorus may mostly be due to the rapid oxidation of plankton, detritus and decomposing matter. But as the waters are nearshore, and mixed with the discharge of the estuarine waters of the Vellar river, it may be expected to contribute to the high concentration of organic phosphorus ... The high phosphorus content

Table 4. Statistical parameters for total organic phosphorus in the western Indian Ocean during the NE monsoon (1965), based on a frequency distribution analysis. See Table 2 for details of information included

Area	0–999 m	1000–1999 m	2000–2999 m	3000–3999 m	Over 4000 m	Total below 1000 m	Statistic	Area	0–999 m	1000–1999 m	2000–2999 m	3000–3999 m	Over 4000 m	Total below 1000 m
Persian Gulf	44	8	5	—	—	13	n		114	20	11	3	—	34
	0.2080	0.0125	0.0100			0.0115	$\bar{x}$	20° N	0.1671	0.0075	−0.0091	−0.0167		−0.0015
	0.0240	0.0010	0.0005			0.0008	s^2		0.0365	0.0013	0.0011	0.0008		0.0011
	0.1548	0.0314	0.0224			0.0277			0.1910	0.0355	0.0330	0.0283		0.0331
	0.0233	0.0111	0.0100			0.0077	$s/\sqrt{n}$		0.0159	0.0079	0.0099	0.0163		0.0057
Arabian Coast	43	12	4	3	—	19	n		260	41	18	12	2	73
	0.1291	0.0167	0.0000	0.0167		0.0132	$\bar{x}$	15° N	0.1163	0.0061	0.0194	0.0417	0.0500	0.0164
	0.0007	0.0006	0.0013	0.0009		0.0007	s^2		0.0189	0.0019	0.0034	0.0020	0.0000	0.0027
	0.0258	0.0247	0.0356	0.0292		0.0265			0.1375	0.0440	0.0578	0.0448	0.0000	0.0516
	0.0065	0.0071	0.0178	0.0169		0.0061	$s/\sqrt{n}$		0.0085	0.0069	0.0136	0.0129	0.0000	0.0060
Red Sea	73	26	8	—	—	34	n		383	57	31	34	19	141
	0.1432	0.0923	0.0875			0.0912	$\bar{x}$	9° N	0.1294	−0.0053	−0.0048	−0.0029	−0.0026	−0.0096
	0.0214	0.0091	0.0112			0.0097	s^2		0.0239	0.0027	0.0018	0.0015	0.0013	0.0018
	0.1463	0.0956	0.1060			0.0983			0.1546	0.0519	0.0424	0.0389	0.0363	0.0428
	0.0171	0.0187	0.0375			0.0169	$s/\sqrt{n}$		0.0079	0.0069	0.0076	0.0067	0.0083	0.0036
Socotra	119	14	6	4	2	26	n		364	61	24	19	5	109
	0.1450	−0.0071	0.0500	0.0125	0.0500	0.0135	$\bar{x}$	5° N	0.1477	0.0279	0.0146	0.0079	0.0000	0.0202
	0.0271	0.0031	0.0045	0.0015	0.0050	0.0033	s^2		0.0263	0.0043	0.0014	0.0013	0.0040	0.0030
	0.1647	0.0560	0.0670	0.0383	0.0707	0.0578			0.1622	0.0658	0.0378	0.0363	0.0633	0.0549
	0.0151	0.0150	0.0274	0.0192	0.0500	0.0113	$s/\sqrt{n}$		0.0085	0.0084	0.0077	0.0083	0.0283	0.0053
Malabar Coast	90	27	14	—	—	41	n		114	21	11	9	6	47
	0.1183	−0.0148	−0.0321			−0.0207	$\bar{x}$	0°	0.1316	0.0119	−0.0091	0.0167	0.0000	0.0064
	0.0206	0.0050	0.0079			0.0059	s^2		0.0299	0.0012	0.0011	0.0010	0.0008	0.0011
	0.1437	0.0708	0.0890			0.0769			0.1730	0.0109	0.0324	0.0312	0.0290	0.0326
	0.0151	0.0136	0.0238			0.0120	$s/\sqrt{n}$		0.0162	0.0024	0.0098	0.0104	0.0118	0.0048

The table is printed rotated on the page. Each data block lists the statistics n, $\bar{x}$, s^2, s, $s/\sqrt{n}$ across six measurement columns. Two halves (left-hand and right-hand data) are reproduced below.

Left-hand data

Location	Stat	1	2	3	4	5	6
Western Perimeter 5°S	n	157	22	9	6	4	41
	$\bar{x}$	0.1564	0.0477	0.0222	0.0333	0.0125	0.0366
	s^2	0.0324	0.0057	0.0025	0.0042	0.0031	0.0044
	s	0.1800	0.0754	0.0500	0.0645	0.0560	0.0666
	$s/\sqrt{n}$	0.0144	0.0161	0.0167	0.0263	0.0280	0.0104
Mozambique Channel 12°S	n	101	19	13	6	—	38
	$\bar{x}$	0.1505	0.0237	0.0077	0.0083		0.0158
	s^2	0.0306	0.0087	0.0061	0.0071		0.0070
	s	0.1749	0.0930	0.0778	0.0841		0.0836
	$s/\sqrt{n}$	0.0174	0.0213	0.0216	0.0343		0.0136
Seychelles Bank	n	59	14	12	7	—	33
	$\bar{x}$	0.1754	0.0429	0.0417	0.0500		0.0439
	s^2	0.0353	0.0030	0.0027	0.0032		0.0028
	s	0.1879	0.0547	0.0515	0.0567		0.0529
	$s/\sqrt{n}$	0.0245	0.0146	0.0149	0.0214		0.0092
Western Perimeter 25°S	n	125	18	5	7	—	30
	$\bar{x}$	0.1092	0.0222	0.0100	0.0357		0.0233
	s^2	0.0172	0.0019	0.0012	0.0022		0.0018
	s	0.1310	0.0435	0.0350	0.0464		0.0420
	$s/\sqrt{n}$	0.0117	0.0103	0.0157	0.0175		0.0077
35°S East of Carlsberg Ridge	n	61	25	6	5	2	38
	$\bar{x}$	0.0893	0.0280	0.0083	0.0400	0.0250	0.0263
	s^2	0.0077	0.0059	0.0021	0.0030	0.0012	0.0048
	s	0.0878	0.0771	0.0456	0.0548	0.0354	0.0693
	$s/\sqrt{n}$	0.0112	0.0154	0.0186	0.0245	0.0250	0.0112

Right-hand data

Latitude	Stat	1	2	3	4	5	6
5°S	n	103	18	9	6	—	33
	$\bar{x}$	0.1558	0.0472	0.0389	0.0000		0.0364
	s^2	0.0294	0.0092	0.0033	0.0000		0.0059
	s	0.1715	0.0957	0.0571	0.0000		0.0768
	$s/\sqrt{n}$	0.0169	0.0226	0.0190	0.0000		0.0134
9°S	n	268	50	32	15	—	97
	$\bar{x}$	0.1554	0.0480	0.0266	0.0167		0.0361
	s^2	0.0265	0.0060	0.0036	0.0024		0.0045
	s	0.1629	0.0772	0.0604	0.0495		0.0672
	$s/\sqrt{n}$	0.0100	0.0109	0.0107	0.0128		0.0068
17°S	n	98	17	8	8	2	35
	$\bar{x}$	0.1811	0.0971	0.0688	0.0812	0.0500	0.0843
	s^2	0.0296	0.0106	0.0067	0.0078	0.0000	0.0087
	s	0.1720	0.1027	0.0821	0.0884	0.0000	0.0931
	$s/\sqrt{n}$	0.0174	0.0249	0.0290	0.0313	0.0000	0.0157
20°S	n	115	21	10	11	7	49
	$\bar{x}$	0.1543	0.0214	0.0450	0.0318	0.0143	0.0276
	s^2	0.0270	0.0032	0.0114	0.0053	0.0099	0.0054
	s	0.1642	0.0569	0.1066	0.0729	0.0994	0.0732
	$s/\sqrt{n}$	0.0153	0.0124	0.0337	0.0220	0.0376	0.0105
25°S	n	73	9	11	4	4	49
	$\bar{x}$	0.1459	0.0611	−0.0045	0.0250	0.0250	0.0250
	s^2	0.0198	0.0061	0.0002	0.0025	0.0008	0.0027
	s	0.1408	0.0789	0.0152	0.0500	0.0288	0.0520
	$s/\sqrt{n}$	0.0165	0.0261	0.0046	0.0250	0.1440	0.0098
32°S West of Carlsberg Ridge	n	98	39	14	13	6	72
	$\bar{x}$	0.0908	0.0090	0.0071	0.0231	0.0250	0.0125
	s^2	0.0112	0.0022	0.0013	0.0018	0.0025	0.0020
	s	0.1059	0.0469	0.0358	0.0423	0.0504	0.0444
	$s/\sqrt{n}$	0.0107	0.0075	0.0096	0.0117	0.0206	0.0052

Table 5. Statistical parameters for particulate, dissolved and total organic phosphorus in surface waters (0 – 200 m) and total organic phosphorus in subsurface waters (200 – 1000 m) in the western Indian Ocean during the NE monsoon (1965), based on a frequency distribution analysis. Aside from the difference in depth range of the data, the analytical groupings follow the description in Table 2

Area	0 – 200 m Particulate Organic Phosphorus	0 – 200 m Dissolved Organic Phosphorus	0 – 200 m Total Organic Phosphorus	200 – 1000 m Total Organic Phosphorus	Statistic	Area	0 – 200 m Particulate Organic Phosphorus	0 – 200 m Dissolved Organic Phosphorus	0 – 200 m Total Organic Phosphorus	200 – 1000 m Total Organic Phosphorus
Persian Gulf	26	27	27	17	n	20° N	72	72	72	42
	0.0731	0.2185	0.3037	0.0559	$\bar{x}$		0.0597	0.1847	0.2465	0.0310
	0.0078	0.0619	0.1082	0.0031	s^2		0.0069	0.0320	0.0672	0.0030
	0.0884	0.2488	0.3289	0.0559	s		0.0830	0.1789	0.2592	0.0548
	0.0173	0.0479	0.0633	0.0136	$s/\sqrt{n}$		0.0098	0.0211	0.0305	0.0065
Arabian Coast	27	27	27	16	n	15° N	163	161	162	98
	0.0407	0.1500	0.1907	0.0250	$\bar{x}$		0.0344	0.1494	0.1778	0.0148
	0.0009	0.0150	0.0407	0.0007	s^2		0.0009	0.0171	0.0259	0.0014
	0.0295	0.1226	0.2018	0.0258	s		0.0304	0.1308	0.1609	0.0374
	0.0057	0.0236	0.0388	0.0065	$s/\sqrt{n}$		0.0024	0.0103	0.0126	0.0038
Red Sea	41	41	41	32	n	9° N	234	234	234	149
	0.0451	0.1476	0.1854	0.0890	$\bar{x}$		0.0406	0.1549	0.1932	0.0292
	0.0019	0.0206	0.0383	0.0124	s^2		0.0018	0.0197	0.0339	0.0036
	0.0440	0.1436	0.1957	0.1113	s		0.0427	0.1403	0.1842	0.0602
	0.0069	0.0224	0.0306	0.0197	$s/\sqrt{n}$		0.0028	0.0092	0.0120	0.0049
Socotra	74	69	69	50	n	5° N	230	222	222	142
	0.0527	0.1334	0.2036	0.0640	$\bar{x}$		0.0300	0.1768	0.2077	0.0539
	0.0094	0.0192	0.0387	0.0068	s^2		0.0009	0.0284	0.0346	0.0057
	0.0307	0.1385	0.1967	0.0822	s		0.0297	0.1687	0.1859	0.0757
	0.0036	0.0167	0.0237	0.0116	$s/\sqrt{n}$		0.0021	0.0113	0.0125	0.0064
Malabar Coast	54	54	54	36	n	0°	70	69	70	44
	0.0306	0.1565	0.1861	0.0167	$\bar{x}$		0.0479	0.1717	0.2207	0.0352
	0.0125	0.0186	0.0277	0.0037	s^2		0.0042	0.0214	0.0434	0.0021
	0.1118	0.1363	0.1664	0.0612	s		0.0651	0.1464	0.2084	0.0436
	0.0152	0.0185	0.0226	0.0102	$s/\sqrt{n}$		0.0078	0.0176	0.0249	0.0070

Region	Statistic				
Western Perimeter 5° S	n	98	98	97	60
	$\bar{x}$	0.0342	0.1765	0.2124	0.0658
	s^2	0.0011	0.0313	0.0447	0.0091
	s	0.0332	0.1770	0.2114	0.0955
	$s/\sqrt{n}$	0.0034	0.0179	0.0215	0.0123
Mozambique Channel 12° S	n	63	63	63	38
	$\bar{x}$	0.0397	0.1619	0.1984	0.0711
	s^2	0.0015	0.0199	0.0324	0.0053
	s	0.0393	0.1411	0.1801	0.0726
	$s/\sqrt{n}$	0.0050	0.0178	0.0227	0.0118
Seychelles Bank	n	36	36	36	23
	$\bar{x}$	0.0431	0.1986	0.2375	0.0782
	s^2	0.0010	0.0324	0.0489	0.0059
	s	0.0320	0.1800	0.2211	0.0771
	$s/\sqrt{n}$	0.0053	0.0300	0.0368	0.0161
Mozambique Channel 25° S	n	89	82	81	44
	$\bar{x}$	0.0455	0.1122	0.1525	0.0295
	s^2	0.0024	0.0111	0.0226	0.0027
	s	0.0487	0.1053	0.1502	0.0516
	$s/\sqrt{n}$	0.0052	0.0116	0.0167	0.0078
32° S East of Carlsberg Ridge	n	30	24	24	37
	$\bar{x}$	0.0183	0.1229	0.1438	0.0541
	s^2	0.0006	0.0097	0.0158	0.0066
	s	0.0245	0.0985	0.1256	0.0812
	$s/\sqrt{n}$	0.0045	0.0201	0.0256	0.0133
5° S	n	81	62	62	41
	$\bar{x}$	0.0387	0.1685	0.2097	0.0744
	s^2	0.0018	0.0236	0.0369	0.0107
	s	0.0419	0.1537	0.1922	0.1037
	$s/\sqrt{n}$	0.0046	0.0195	0.0244	0.0162
9° S	n	168	165	165	103
	$\bar{x}$	0.0348	0.1700	0.2039	0.0777
	s^2	0.0010	0.0225	0.0339	0.0077
	s	0.0319	0.1500	0.1841	0.0879
	$s/\sqrt{n}$	0.0025	0.0117	0.0143	0.0087
17° S	n	63	63	63	35
	$\bar{x}$	0.0325	0.1762	0.2103	0.1286
	s^2	0.0014	0.0189	0.0386	0.0180
	s	0.0374	0.1375	0.1966	0.1342
	$s/\sqrt{n}$	0.0047	0.0173	0.0248	0.0227
20° S	n	90	71	71	44
	$\bar{x}$	0.0372	0.1648	0.2042	0.0739
	s^2	0.0027	0.0176	0.0344	0.0803
	s	0.0524	0.1326	0.1855	0.2833
	$s/\sqrt{n}$	0.0055	0.0157	0.0220	0.0427
25° S	n	43	44	44	29
	$\bar{x}$	0.0314	0.1557	0.1852	0.0862
	s^2	0.0006	0.0143	0.0196	0.0077
	s	0.0244	0.1197	0.1403	0.0875
	$s/\sqrt{n}$	0.0037	0.0180	0.0212	0.0162
32° S West of Carlsberg Ridge	n	76	55	55	43
	$\bar{x}$	0.0329	0.0964	0.1345	0.0349
	s^2	0.0021	0.0065	0.0166	0.0023
	s	0.0455	0.0809	0.1289	0.0475
	$s/\sqrt{n}$	0.0052	0.0109	0.0174	0.0072

Table 6. Distribution of phosphorus fractions (μg-at l^{-1}) in the eastern Indian Ocean (Adapted from data of RAO and RAO, 1968)

		Nicobar Sea	Andaman Sea	Cost of Burma	Northern Bay of Bengal
Total phosphorus					
Surface to 50 m	n	12	10	13	21
	Range	0.35 – 1.38	0.43 – 0.80	0.68 – 2.10	0.90 – 1.52
	Mean	0.985	0.59	1.12	1.23
50 to 200 m	n	9	2	3	11
	Range	1.61 – 3.33	–	0.61 – 2.76	1.52 – 2.64
	Mean	2.14	1.945	1.74	2.06
200 to 500 m	n	7	2	2	13
	Range	2.48 – 2.91	–	3.90 – 5.40	2.64 – 4.60
	Mean	2.62	2.72	4.65	3.09
500 to 1000 m	n	4	1	2	11
	Range	2.59 – 2.71	–	–	2.86 – 3.20
	Mean	2.67	2.70	3.01	2.97
1000 to 2000 m	n				7
	Range	–	–	–	2.62 – 3.15
	Mean				2.90
Over 2000 m	n				7
	Range	–	–	–	2.41 – 3.15
	Mean				2.79
Inorganic phosphate					
Surface to 50 m	n	11	10	13	19
	Range	0 – 0.30	0 – 0.08	0 – 0.90	0.02 – 0.44
	Mean	0.06	0.03	0.25	0.105
50 to 200 m	n	9	2	3	11
	Range	0.09 – 2.19	–	0.55 – 1.81	0.21 – 1.72
	Mean	1.06	1.59	1.10	1.15
200 to 500 m	n	7	2	2	13
	Range	2.23 – 2.55	–	–	2.51 – 2.91
	Mean	2.41	2.525	2.62	2.73
500 to 1000 m	n	4	1	2	11
	Range	2.65 – 2.73	–	–	2.76 – 3.22
	Mean	2.69	2.69	2.91	2.93
1000 to 2000 m	n				7
	Range	–	–	–	2.61 – 3.19
	Mean				2.92
Over 2000 m	n				7
	Range	–	–	–	2.40 – 3.08
	Mean				2.68
Dissolved organic P					
Surface to 50 m	n	11	10	13	19
	Range	0.22 – 1.23	0.36 – 0.75	0.50 – 1.11	0.64 – 1.63
	Mean	0.86	0.51	0.81	1.06
50 to 200 m	n	9	2	3	11
	Range	0.28 – 2.85	0.09 – 0.49	0.86 – 0.96	0.39 – 1.87
	Mean	0.93	0.29	0.90	0.98

Table 6 (continued)

200 to 500 m	n	7	2	2	13
	Range	0.09−0.32	−	1.15−2.89	0.07−1.84
	Mean	0.21	0.165	2.02	0.36
500 to 1000 m	n	4	1	2	11
	Range	0−0.06	−	−	0−0.16
	Mean	0.015	0.01	0.095	0.025
1000 to 2000 m	n				7
	Range	−	−	−	−
	Mean				0.00
Over 2000 m	n	−	−	−	7
	Range	−	−	−	0−0.31
	Mean				0.09
Particulate organic P					
Surface to 50 m	n	10	10	13	20
	Range	0.03−0.08	0.02−0.08	0.03−0.09	0.03−0.15
	Mean	0.05	0.05	0.06	0.055
50 to 200 m	n	7	2	3	10
	Range	0.02−0.06	−	−	0−0.12
	Mean	0.04	0.065	0.07	0.03
200 to 500 m	n	5	2	2	13
	Range	0−0.06	−	−	0−0.04
	Mean	0.02	0.03	0.015	0.01
500 to 1000 m	n	2	1	2	10
	Range	−	−	−	0−0.05
	Mean	0	0	0	0.005
1000 to 2000 m	n				7
	Range	−	−	−	0−0.03
	Mean				0.005
Over 2000 m	n				7
	Range	−	−	−	0−0.06
	Mean				0.03

Table 7. Observations on the distribution of phosphorus (μg-at l^{-1}) in nearshore areas near Porto Novo (KUMARI, 1968)

	Mouth of the Vellar estuary		Offshore at the ten-fathom line	
	Surface water	Bottom	Surface water	Bottom
Total phosphorus	1.1 −4.55	1.2 −5.12	1.1−11.5	1.2−11.8
Inorganic phosphate	0.22−1.10	0.22−1.10	Traces−1.0	Traces−1.1
Dissolved organic phosphorus	0.60−3.45	0.70−4.70	0.70−11.5	0.70−11.8

observed in the present study in January and March might be due to non-utilization of inorganic phosphate and its conversion to organic form." (KUMARI, 1968, p. 90).

MURTY and REDDY (1968) examined the distribution of total phosphorus in the marine sediments of the east coast of India. Shelf sediments in the northern area between Chilka Lake and "Swatch of No Ground" are uniformly rich in their phosphorus content, while the sediments near Madras are uniformly poor. The distribution is believed to reflect the presence of a dominant upwelling followed by a slow rate of deposition of detrital materials. Here also, however, the influence of the rivers must be cited. It is suggested that they bring in a sediment load, with resulting absorption of dissolved phosphate in the water by silts and clays, followed by settling to the bottom. This is particularly true in the northern region where the Ganges and Brahmaputra carry large amounts of suspended terrigenous material to the Bay. In more southerly regions, between Visakhapatnam and Karaikal, differences have been attributed to the variation in upwelling and the corresponding differences in the level of biological productivity.

ROCHFORD (1963) has reported that the organic phosphorus in the upper 200 m in the SE Indian Ocean has its maximum values (0.20 − 0.38 μg-at l^{-1} for mean concentrations) along the southern boundary of the South Equatorial Current, along the Equatorial divergence, and within the boundary of the Counter Current and North Equatorial Current. In general, there was great variation in the surface concentration with latitude throughout the region surveyed. Pronounced maxima were also observed in the vertical profiles of organic phosphorus. Subsurface organic phosphorus maxima at 500 − 700 m and again at 1000 − 1500 m tended to coincide with the O_2 minimum zones. A maximum in bottom waters near 4320 m at one station consisted of about 40% particulate and 60% dissolved organic phosphorus. In stations between Java and NW Australia, the organic phosphorus maximum consisted of between 40% and 100% particulate organic phosphorus. It appears that the ROCHFORD values are the only ones available for particulate phosphorus concentrations in the deeper parts of the water column. More detailed data on such fractions in deep water for all ocean areas are needed to help understand the regeneration of nutrients.

It is possible that particulate maxima represent the occurrence of "refractory compounds" (McGILL, 1963) which are extremely resistant to recycling. REDDY and SANKARANARAYANAN (1968 b) find evidence in shallow waters of a more rapid release of some nutrients relative to others. "Nitrates in general show an inverse relationship with the other nutrients, particularly in the surface ... These differences in maxima of respective nutrients might be due to more rapid release of certain nutrients earlier than others and it provides a mechanism by which nitrogen and phosphorus may be fractionated and this may explain the variation in the ratio of these elements in the sea water. ... The ratio between elements Si, N and P ... is highly variable, unlike that of the temperate region. This variation may presumably be due to the differential and rapid rates of regeneration and consumption of the nutrients accompanied by extensive mixing of water masses which seems a characteristic features of tropical waters." (REDDY and SANKARANARAYANAN, 1968 b, p. 219). Others have evaluated the problem in a different light, attempting to derive ratios between biological decomposition and uptake (MIYAKE, 1966), or expressing the phosphorus variability as related to O_2 variation (VISWANATHAN and GANGULY, 1968).

1.6

Biogenic Sedimentation of the Persian Gulf

E. SEIBOLD

The remains of skeletal hard parts in marine sediments are of particular interest to the geologist. If he is able to relate these remains in recent sediments to the environment of deposition (water movement, water chemistry, water depth, distance from land, distance from the open ocean, bottom type, etc.) he is then able to deduce the environment of deposition of ancient sediments.

With this goal in mind a team of geologists from the Geological-Paleontological Institute of Kiel University took part in the International Indian Ocean Expedition and visited the NE part of the Persian Gulf from March 3 to April 24, 1965 (DIETRICH et al., 1966). Detailed descriptions of the results thus far completed are to be found in the "Meteor-Forschungsergebnisse" (see references).

I. Environmental Framework

Morphology (SEIBOLD and VOLLBRECHT, 1969): The Persian Gulf (Fig.1) is divided by the central and eastern swells into the Western Basin (depths to 73 m), the Central Basin (depths to 105 m), and the Hormuz Region (depth south of Tunb 192 m, within

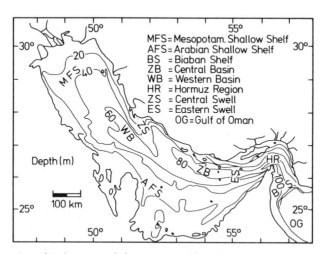

Fig. 1. Bathymetric and index map of the Persian Gulf. (After SEIBOLD and VOLLBRECHT, 1969)

the Masandam Channel 302 m). The mean depth of the Gulf is 35 m. The Biaban Shelf with its slope break at $110-120$ m forms the transition to the continental slope.

Hydrology (HARTMANN et al., 1971; SEIBOLD, 1970): The Persian Gulf lies within an arid climate region. The high loss of water through evaporation (annual mean 144 cm) is not compensated for by precipitation and river inflow. As a result, surface water from the Indian Ocean enters the Gulf along the Iranian coast. During the summer, surface waters reach temperatures of up to 36° C in the Central Gulf. Even higher readings have been recorded in near-shore areas. Temperatures in winter, however, may fall below 20° C (Fig. 2). Salinity increases at the surface from approx. 36.6‰ near the entrance to about 40.6‰ in the NE-Gulf (Fig. 3). There, due to cooling and evaporation, the highly

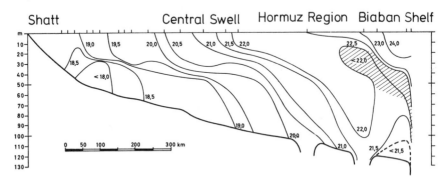

Fig. 2. Distribution of temperature (° C) in the Persian Gulf in spring 1965 (Hartmann et al., 1971)

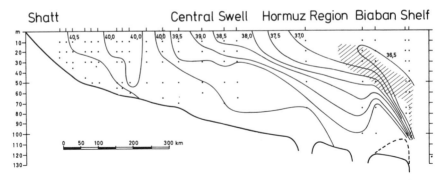

Fig. 3. Distribution of salinity (‰) in the Persian Gulf in spring 1965 (Hartmann et al., 1971)

saline water sinks to the bottom raising the salinity and lowering the temperature of the bottom water in comparison with the surface. Water flowing out of the Persian Gulf follows the deeps near the Arabian coast (Fig. 2 and 3). The predominantly northwesterly Shemal winds, often of prolonged duration, tend to homogenize the surface waters to a depth of about 30 m. Because of the previously mentioned circulation pattern, the waters of the Persian Gulf contain oxygen all the way down to the bottom. The content of nutrients, however, is low with the exception of mixing zones that extend from the shelf margin to the Hormus Region. (Hatched in Figs. 2 and 3).

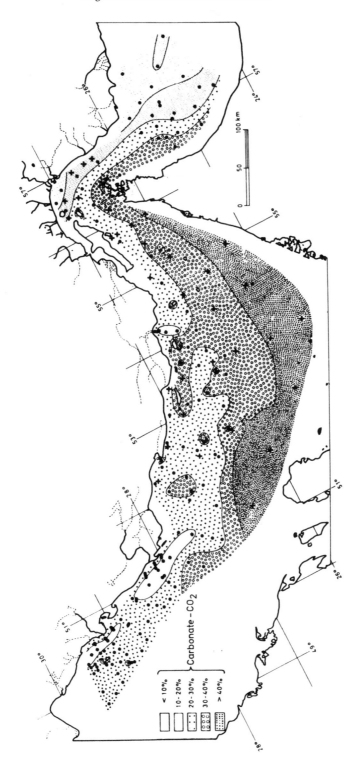

Fig. 4. Distribution of carbonate-CO_2 in surface sediments. Large dots indicate RV "Meteor" stations (HARTMANN et al., 1971), crosses indicate USS "Requisite" stations (PEERY, 1965)

II. Carbonate Content

Except for near-shore areas along the Iranian coast, the sediments of the Persian Gulf nearly always contain more than 50% carbonate minerals (Fig. 4, see also Hart-mann et al., 1971). These values reach 80% towards Arabia and on shallows within the Gulf. Fig. 5 shows that an increase in carbonate content generally parallels an increase in mean grain diameter and vice versa. This fact alone suggests that near the Iranian coast organisms are the primary contributors of carbonate to the sediments; the contribution of carbonate through river inflow and the bioturbate mixing of relict sediments will be discussed below.

Emery (1956) pointed out that for the entire Gulf area the mean biogenic carbonate content of the sediments lies between 60% and 87%, of which 54—69% are shell fragments. Typical samples from the main sedimentary environments are given in Table 1.

The silt fraction of the sediment (0.02—0.06 mm) is currently under investigation. It is difficult, even with the use of a scanning electron microscope, to differentiate between recent, subfossil, and fossil remains. Biogenic carbonate generally forms between $^1/_2$ and $^1/_3$ of the silt fraction (Fütterer, unpublished).

III. Benthic Organisms

Benthic organisms are the most important contributors of carbonate to the sediment of the Persian Gulf. In the Gulf of Oman, however, benthic organisms take second place to the planktonic organisms as carbonate contributors. Current results indicate that coarse biogenic carbonate sediment particles are rarely subject to more than very local transport (exceptions: near-shore currents in shallow water, outflow channel on the Biaban Shelf). This is suggested by the coincidence of living and dead benthic foraminifera fauna (Haake, Lutze, unpublished). Therefore, these biogenic remains may generally be regarded as autochthonous and are direct indicators of the above mentioned environmental conditions. The areas influenced by the inflow from Iranian rivers are recognizable by an abundance of ostracods (Fig. 6) and benthic fora-minifera in the sediment. These areas are further characterized by land-plant fragments which are transported on the bottom like sand particles and which have been found up to 30 km off-shore (Sarnthein, 1971). Benthic foraminifera are indicators of water depth. For example *Quinqueloculina crassicarinata* Collins occurs predominantly at a depth of 30 m (Fig. 7). Some of the depth zones characterized by a particular fauna become somewhat deeper as the mouth of the Gulf is approached. This may indicate dependency of certain fauna on water properties (Figs. 2 and 3; Haake, 1970; Lutze, unpublished). On the continental slope at water depths greater than 200 m, benthic foraminifera decrease in numbers; this decrease is even more pronounced in the benthic mollusks (Sarnthein, 1971).

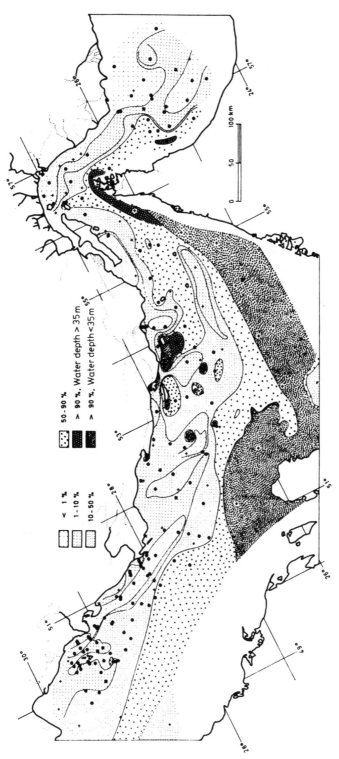

Fig. 5. Distribution of grain sizes > 63 μ. Station symboles as in Fig. 4. Qatar region after HOUBOLT (1957)

E. Seibold:

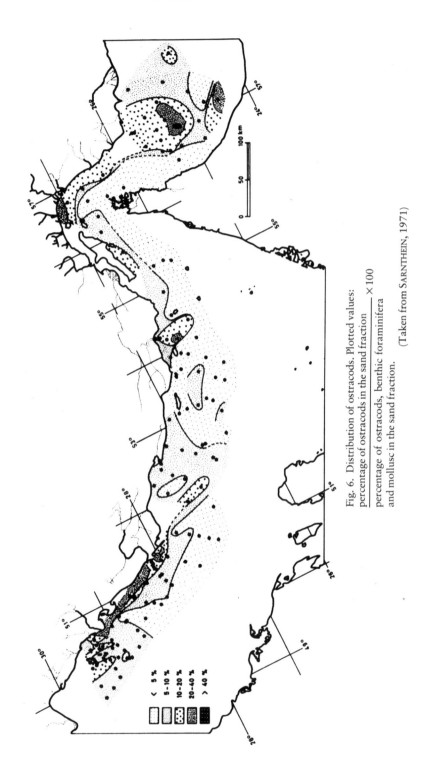

Fig. 6. Distribution of ostracods. Plotted values:

$$\frac{\text{percentage of ostracods in the sand fraction}}{\text{percentage of ostracods, benthic foraminifera and mollusc in the sand fraction.}} \times 100$$

(Taken from Sarnthein, 1971)

Table 1. Composition of typical sediment samples from the Perisan Gulf (based on SARNTHEIN, 1971)

Sample type	1) Clayey Marl (with few coarse grains)		2) Calcareous Marl (rich in coarse material)		3) Calcareous Marl (with fine sands)		4) Calcarenite (coarse)		5) Clay (for comparison)	
Distribution	Near shore (River mouths)		Near shore with limited terrigenous-inflow and offshore in basins		Off river mouths (in shallow water)		Shallows and Island Slopes		Continental Slope Gulf of Oman	
Carbonate-CO$_2$%	18.15%		32.3%		23.4%		41.7%		10.6%	
Fraction: mm	0.06–2	>2	0.06–2	>2	0.06–2	>2	0.06–2	>2	0.06–2	>2
%	0.16	–	57.4	1.92	37.12	0.05	89.65	7.33	14.74	–
Subdivision:	%	%	%	%	%	%	%	%	%	%
Foraminifera:										
Calcareous	41.3	–	11.25	–	1.45	–	6.9	0.35	1.06	–
Arenaceous	0.5	–	4.65	–	1.75	–	0.9	–	–	–
Planktonic	–	–	0.06	–	–	–	–	–	28.8	–
Sponges:	Tr.	–	–	–	–	–	–	–	–	–
Corals	–	–	Tr.	–	–	–	–	0.14	–	–
Bryozoa	–	–	0.16	–	Tr.	–	1.2	0.25	–	–
Molluscs:										
Benthic	22.3	–	40.9	49.0	1.1	92.2	7.5	7.9	Tr.	–
Planktonic	5.4	–	3.05	0.12	Tr.	–	0.25	–	Tr.	–
Crustacea:										
Balanus	0.1	–	Tr.	1.5	Tr.	–	0.1	0.12	–	–
Decapods	0.9	–	3.95	0.6	0.2	7.8	0.9	0.2	Tr.	–
Ostracods	5.45	–	1.1	–	0.5	–	Tr.	–	0.1	–
Echinoids	14.9	–	1.05	0.3	.45	–	0.3	Tr.	Tr.	–
Ophiurids	0.05	–	0.85	–	0.3	–	0.3	–	–	–
Fish remains	1.65	–	0.1	–	Tr.	–	0.12	Tr.	0.55	–
Plant remains	1.15	–	Tr.	–	0.3	–	–	0.1	0.1	–
Calc. Algae	–	–	–	–	–	–	Tr.	2.2	–	–
Biogenic relict components	–	–	10.7	16.3	–	–	68.6	38.8	–	–
Miscellaneous carbonate and noncarbonate grains	6.3	–	22.0	32.2	93.8	–	12.7	50.0	69.2	–

The wave base, the lower limit of frequently and strongly agitated waters, seems to be reflected in a maximum concentration of echinoderm fragments within the sediment (15−50 m depending on fetch; SARNTHEIN, 1970). As yet unexplained is the fact that of the echinoderms, the echinoids dominate in the Western Basin and on the central swell while the ophiuroids dominate in the Central Basin. This difference appears unrelated to sediment character (SARTNHEIN, 1971).

The relationships between fauna and bottom type are numerous (SARTNHEIN, 1971). Even the rocky bottoms of the shallows and island slopes (sediment type 4 of Table 1)

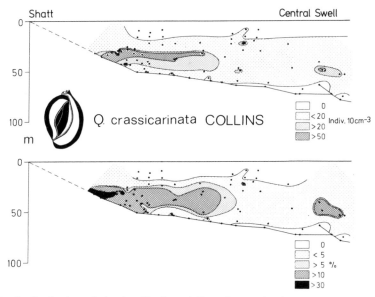

Fig. 7. Depth distribution of the benthic foraminifera *Quinqueloculina crassicarinata* COLLINS (HAAKE, 1970)

today remain free of coral reef formation on the Iranian side of the Persian Gulf, except for a weak indication of reef building west of Kais (−16 m). The larger foraminifera, such as *Heterostegina* sp. populate such rocky bottoms. Field observations and laboratory experiments have demonstrated that this group of foraminifera alone may contribute 150 g of $CaCO_3$ m^{-2} year^{-1}; this corresponds to 10 cm 1000 year^{-1} (LUTZE, GRABERT and SEIBOLD, 1971). Hard bottom sediments (sediment type 2) which dominate the basins, especially the Central Basin (including the near-shore zone when terrigenous influx is absent) are characterized by an abundance of epibenthic organisms such as solitary corals, bryozoans, molluscs, especially gastropods and barnacles. Hard parts of worm tubes are also present. Fig. 8 shows that several foraminiferal species prefer this type of bottom sediment. Soft bottom sediments have to be subdivided into two groups according to their respective population. In areas with high sedimentation rates (up to several m 1000 year^{-1}) epi-benthic organisms and molluscs are generally less important (sediment type 1). It is difficult to determine whether this reflects the high content of suspended matter and the resultant reduction in light, the lack of plant life, the frequent predatory ophiuroids or the different soil-mechanical properties. In areas where low sedimentation rates prevail, molluscs increase in frequency in comparison to high sedimentation areas. Molluscs generate a type of hard bottom with their own shell remains. Fine sand bottoms where sediment is being moved, as in near-shore, shallow-water areas, have only been investigated at one locality by the RV "Meteor". No epi-benthic organisms were encountered (sediment type 3).

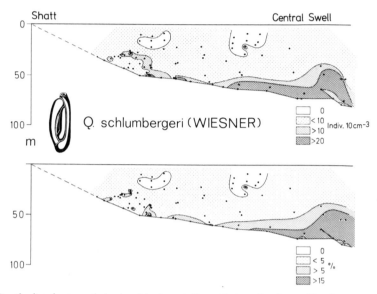

Fig. 8. Depth distribution of the benthic foraminifera *Quinqueloculina schlumbergeri* (WIESNER) (HAAKE, 1970)

IV. Planktonic and Nektonic Organisms

Planktonic foraminifera are the main constituents of the sand-sized fraction and are thus responsible for the carbonate content of the continental slope sediments (sediment type 5, Table 1). They gradually decrease in frequency as compared to benthic forms with increasing distance from the Indian Ocean. The ratio of planktonic to benthic foraminifera is 50 : 50 near the shelf margin; this is the typical world-wide shelf margin figure. The ratio decreases rapidly further off-shore and drops to 5% in the Central Basin (LUTZE, unpublished; SARNTHEIN, 1971), (Fig. 9). The maximum values are clearly displaced towards the Iranian coast, a direct indication of surface water inflow.

Fish remains (bones, scales, teeth, otoliths) accumulate on the continental slope near the Gulf of Oman and at river mouths along the Iranian coast (SARNTHEIN, 1971). These concentrations are the result of increased nutrient content and its related increase in plankton content. These findings furthermore demonstrate that careful sediment analysis may show up areas which have had high fish concentrations over a prolonged period of time.

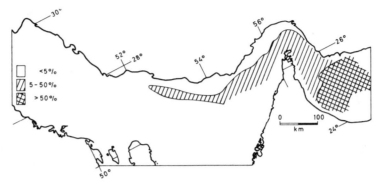

Fig. 9. Regional distribution of the plankton-benthos ratio of foraminifera. Plotted values:

$$\frac{\text{percentage of planktinic foraminifera in the sand fraction}}{\text{percentage of total foraminifera in the sand fraction}} \times 100$$

(Based on Sarnthein, 1971)

V. Bioturbation

Core analysis and radiography have shown that the sediments of the Persian Gulf are in general poorly stratified. The primary stratification is in most cases completely obliterated by bioturbation. Horizontal and vertical burrows, several cm in diameter and tens of cm in length have been found. Some were filled with the neighboring sediment, but others contained significant enrichments of biogenic particles (Melguen, Werner, unpublished). Sand-sized particles may be moved upwards in the sediment column a maximum distance of somewhat over 2 m. The youngest sediments of the Persian Gulf overlie Holocene and Late-Pleistocene relict sediments formed at a lower sea-level stand. Oolitic sands, lithified as well as unlithified carbonate-mud pebbles, mollusc shell fragments, corals and bryozoa are the main components of these shallow-water fossil sediments. In about 66% of our samples which contained relict sediment the recent sediment thickness was less than 0.5 m. As a result the content of fossil sediment grains may be as high as 60% – 80% and thus affects the carbonate content. Within the central parts of the basins with their reduced sedimentation rates, such phenomena are of regional importance (Sarnthein, 1971).

VI. Organic Carbon Content

Fig. 10 shows the organic carbon content of the sediments. In the Persian Gulf the content lies below 2% and in the Gulf of Oman above 2%. These values reflect first of all the primary production. Nutrient deficiency in the western basin is responsible for holding the organically bound carbon values below 1%. Secondly, dilution by terrigenous material is important in areas such as the northern part of the Bay of Hormuz and near the Iranian coast. On the other hand, terrigenous dilution is of lesser importance in the Gulf of Oman region. Thirdly, the generally well known relationship between organic carbon content and sediment grain size plays a role: The coarser the sediment, the lower the organic carbon content. Examples can be seen from the shallows of the Central Basin.

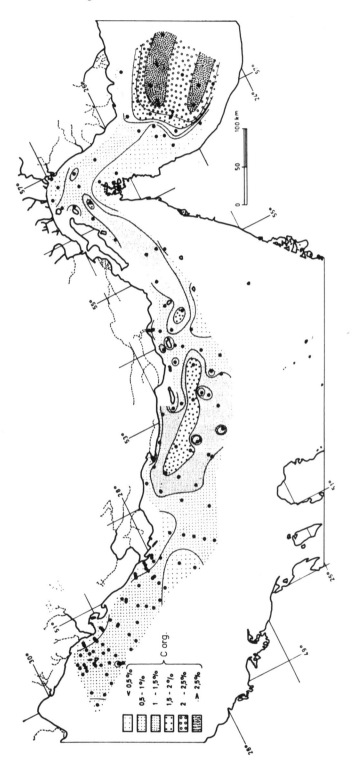

Fig. 10. Distribution of organic carbon content (HARTMANN et al., 1971)

Finally, the high O_2 content of the water near the bottom of the Gulf and the oxygen deficiency on the continental slope towards the Gulf of Oman may also play an important role in explaining the organic carbon distribution (HARTMANN et al., 1971).

It is surprising that the recent sediments of the Persian Gulf contain so little organically bound carbon as the recent Persian Gulf is in many respects very similar to the Mesozoic and Cenozoic seas which had all the prerequisites for rich petroleum formation.

2. Primary Production and Standing Stock of Phytoplankton and Bacteria

2.1

Primary Production in the Indian Ocean I

J. Krey

One of the basic aims of the International Indian Ocean Expedition (IIOE) was to accumulate data on the rate of primary production in the region and the environmental phenomena that regulate it. These data could then be used to prepare distribution charts which would show, among other things, areas of seasonal extremes in high and low productivity, and their spatial and temporal variations. A good understanding of these processes in the Indian Ocean is of great importance in the construction of models of seasonal energy transfer and the food pyramid and for their theoretical interpretation. Such models must take into consideration the influences of the Indian Ocean monsoons, intensity of upwelling, circulation pattern, etc., and the effects of these on rate of sedimentation, secondary production and spatial transfer. From the models, we could then estimate the level of fish production that each area could theoretically support and indicate regions of potentially exploitable fisheries.

Under the expedition program, a large number of research ships belonging to several countries carried out intensive investigations in the region during the period 1959–1965. It is extremely unfortunate that, except for restricted areas of individual interest, the cruise itineraries were not coordinated with regard to times and points of observation and methods so as to ensure a somewhat more uniform series of investigations over the whole region. The consequent heterogeneity in distribution, both spatial and temporal, means that observation points cluster around certain areas while there are large gaps in some other regions. The 110°E longitudinal section under the Australian program and the Arabian Sea were well studied, the latter clearly because of the number of unique oceanographic phenomena observed there; in contrast, the central southern Indian Ocean region was not adequately covered. To obtain a more complete picture for the whole Indian Ocean, observations carried out before and after the IIOE are also taken into consideration in the following discussions.

I. Phytoplankton Distribution

During the "Meteor" expedition, Hentschel (1936) made a detailed study of both the latitudinal and vertical distribution of phytoplankton in the southern Atlantic Ocean on the basis of a large number of comparable samples concentrated by centrifugation.

One of his most outstanding results was to show the distinct relationship between regions of high phosphate concentration and areas of large phytoplankton accumulations, irrespective of the size of the organisms contributing to the maxima; in general, these were the regions of upwelling and river discharge. Hentschel also found a close correlation with the different ecological entities which were constructed on the basis of spatial current charts. In principle, it should be possible to extrapolate such a pattern of plankton distribution for the Indian Ocean region, provided the other relevant environmental factors remain constant.

On the basis of these observations, HENTSCHEL evolved certain principles as a theoretical basis for understanding the patterns of phytoplankton distribution in general and tried to project this distribution pattern on to a broadly based theoretical model of an ocean (Fig. 1). This model could perhaps guide us in understanding the latitudinal and vertical distribution of plankton in the Indian Ocean in a generalized way, although its

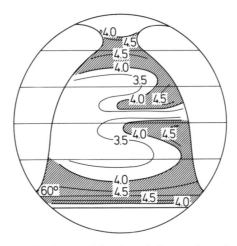

Fig. 1. Scheme of the general distribution of the phytoplankton in the surface layer of a model of an ocean (log of numbers of cells per l). After HENTSCHEL (1936)

application is necessarily limited by the morphological and topographical dissimilarity between the model and the Indian Ocean, which is landlocked on the north by the continent of Asia. The whole picture is further complicated by the way in which the Indian Ocean monsoons control and regulate the basic biological phenomena in the region. MOISEEV (1969) recently published some detailed charts showing the concentrations of organically bound particulate C in the world ocean (see map on the inside of the back cover). If we compare the broad distribution patterns for each ocean, particularly the patterns of particulate C concentrations in this instance, we find that HENTSCHEL'S theoretical model is applicable to 3 oceans with only minor discrepancies.

HENTSCHEL also mapped the qualitative distribution of the various systematic groups as well as of the most important species which make a bulk contribution to production. Since the environmental requirements conducive to the growth of each species remain more or less constant in all areas where these species appear, it is possible to predict with reasonable accuracy the type of flora which could be expected in ecological provinces having similar environmental conditions. In other words, similar oceanic ecological provinces always yield more or less similar floral associations. Considerations based on this fundamental principle will enable us to prepare provisional distribution charts for the various phytoplankton groups in the Indian Ocean, once the various ecological provinces in the area have been identified and properly characterized.

Plankton-geographical Regions of the Indian Ocean

Meteorological and hydrographical parameters play a very important part in determining the growth conditions of plankton organisms in any water mass and hence in characterizing the various ecological provinces. On the basis of these characteristics, the

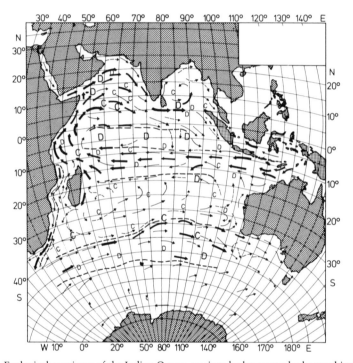

Fig. 2. Ecological provinces of the Indian Ocean, as given by long-term hydrographical observations, for the main period of the SW monsoon (D: divergence, C: convergence)

Indian Ocean area is divided into 8 plankton-geographical regions which can be considered as a basis for discussing the various ecological realms in the regions. The 8 regions are given in the first column of Table 1.

This classification cannot be considered a detailed or complete list, as such biologically important provinces as the shelf areas, river mouths (e.g. Indus and Ganges) etc. are not taken into consideration. The backwater and estuarine areas also deserve special mention.

The two accompanying ecological charts (Figs. 2 and 3) show the comparative limits of the different water masses throughout the year. It will be seen that in addition to the basic division into the different plankton-geographical regions, the seasonal variations of their boundaries and biological characteristics must also be given due consideration. The

northern Indian Ocean region is a very good example and can be divided into 4 biologically distinct seasons:

1. SW monsoon season: June – August.
2. NE monsoon season: December – February.
3. Intermonsoon period: October – November.
4. Intermonsoon period: March – May.

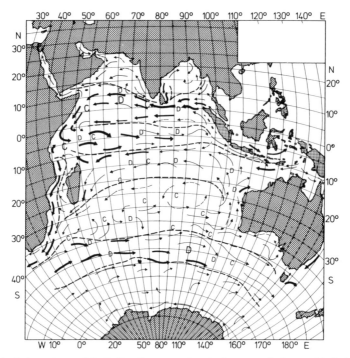

Fig. 3. Ecological provinces of the Indian Ocean, as given by long-term hydrographical observations,
for the main period of the NE monsoon (D: divergence, C: convergence)

Special mention should also be made of the oceanic regions of convergences and
divergences.

The 8 plankton-geographical regions are not to be considered as homogeneous but
merely as a basis for understanding the general pattern; nor do they precisely coincide
with each other in their periods of occurrence. Thus the intermonsoon period is clearly
experienced in the Arabian Sea only in March and in the Bay of Bengal only in September – October. South of 5° S, only the winter (May to October) and the summer (November to April) seasons are outstanding. The role played by currents and other water
movements is also not inconsiderable, particularly if the organisms normally have a longer
life period; they transport the plankton organisms, from the area of production to areas
of pure survival or destruction, as in the regions of convergence and divergence.

Using HENTSCHEL'S conclusions for the southern Atlantic Ocean regarding the nature
of plankton associations in each type of oceanic ecological province and relating their

distribution to the existing pattern of oceanic circulation in the area, we built up the following composite picture of qualitative plankton associations or predominance in the various plankton-geographical regions in the Indian Ocean (Table 1).

Table 1. Phytoplankton predominance in 8 plankton-geographical regions of the Indian Ocean

Area	Predominance	Secondary Dominance
1. Coastal upwelling areas a. Southern Arabia, b. Western Australia, c. Indonesia	Diatoms	Dinoflagellates, partly Blue-green algae
2. Central Arabian Sea and Bay of Bengal	Dinoflagellates, Blue-green algae	Diatoms, Coccolithophores
3. Somali Current region a. NE section b. SW section	Diatoms	Dinoflagellates, partly Blue-green algae
4. Mozambique Current region	Diatoms	Dinoflagellates, Coccolithophores
5. Equatorial Current region	Dinoflagellates, Coccolithophores	Diatoms, Blue-green algae
6. Southern subtropical gyre between southern subtropical convergence and the southern tropical front	Dinoflagellates	Coccolithophores, Diatoms
7. West-wind drift region	Diatoms	Dinoflagellates, Coccolithophores
8. Antarctic gyre up to the subantarctic convergence	Diatoms	Dinoflagellates, Coccolithophores

Where this distribution pattern differs most from that of the Atlantic Ocean is in the frequency of blue-green algae. This is due exclusively to the surface blooms of *Trichodesmium erythraeum,* a blue-green alga which is endemic to the Indian Ocean.

It is interesting to consider the most important species from the viewpoint of their bulk contribution to primary production in the area. SUBRAHMANYAN and SARMA (1960), on the basis of prolonged studies in Indian waters, compiled a list of 37 phytoplankton organisms (of which 29 were diatoms, 7 dinoflagellates and 1 blue-green algae) which they called the mass forms. These contribute 70–80% to the total biological processes in the area (Table 2), in accordance with the hypothesis put forth by ZENKEWICH (1960).

Although this list includes mostly neritic forms, it could apply to the entire Indian Ocean area with very slight alterations, mainly the addition of the predominant oceanic forms.

So far we have discussed qualitative distribution. If we now make a detailed analysis of HENTSCHEL'S charts of latitudinal quantitative distribution of phytoplankton organisms in the Atlantic Ocean and enter the degrees of abundance in the corresponding ecological provinces of the Indian Ocean, we get roughly the following picture of their quantitative distribution. The antarctic gyre and part of the west-wind drift region are regions of high plankton concentration with a range of abundance between 10 000 and 100 000 cells l^{-1}. The pattern of plankton abundance and distribution in the Antarctic sections of all

3 oceans is rather constant. Concentrations of over 100 000 cells l^{-1} would also be expected in the upwelling regions along the Arabian coast and the SW coast of India. The Equatorial Current region and the Arabian Sea would have an abundance of some 10 000 cells l^{-1}, and the southern subtropical gyre and central Bay of Bengal region low to very low plankton concentrations, usually less than 5 000 cells l^{-1}.

Table 2. List of mass forms of the phytoplankton in the Indian Ocean

Bacillariophyceae:	
Asterionella japonica	*Nitzschia seriata*
Bacteriastrum hyalinum var. *princeps*	*N. sigma* var. *indica*
Biddulphia heteroceros	*Rhizosolenia alata*
B. mobiliensis	*R. robusta*
Chaetoceros affinis	*R. stolterfothii*
C. brevis	*Sceletonema costatum*
C. compressus	*Schröderella delicatula*
C. contortum	*Thalassiothrix frauenfeldii*
C. curvisetus	*T. longissima*
C. lasciniosus	
C. lauderii	*Dinophyceae:*
C. lorenzianus	*Ceratium fusus*
C. pelagicus	*C. macroceros*
C. socialis	*C. tripos*
Coscinodiscus asteromphalus	*Dinophysis caudata*
C. oculus-iridis	*Glenodinium lenticula* f. *asymmetrica*
Fragilaria oceanica	*Noctiluca miliaris*
Guinardia flaccida	*Peridinium depressum*
Lauderia annulata	
Leptocylindrus danicus	*Myxophyceae:*
	Trichodesmium erythraeum

II. Distribution of Chlorophyll

Fig. 4 shows the annual average distribution and the variations in concentration of chlorophyll in the upper 50 m layer of the Indian Ocean; the range in variation is of the order of 1:100. This would give only a rough estimate of the total photosynthetic capacity of the water mass since we cannot differentiate between living and dead chlorophyll. Hentschel calculated on the basis of his observations that no living chlorophyll is present below a depth of 200 m. The chlorophyll distribution charts are of limited use in estimating standing stock accumulations or primary production rates; for a better correlation, we have to allow for the fluctuations in per-cell chlorophyll concentration from species to species, the physiological state of the population, particularly the light adaptation level, vertical transportation and grazing rates, and the amount of detritus in the standing stock, etc. Figs. 4 and 5 show the horizontal distribution of chlorophyll concentration during the periods June—September and December—March, which gives us some idea of the extent and locations of the fertile areas during the various biological seasons. If, for the June—September period, we define areas with a chlorophyll concentration above 0.5 mg m^{-3} as fertile and those below it as infertile from the point of view of primary productivity, there are clearly two areas of high fertility, one on the east coast of South Africa and another more extensive one in the NW Arabian Sea. Conversely, the areas to the north and south of the Equator, except in the immediate vicinity of the equatorial current, stand out as regions of infertility; similar areas are known to exist in the Atlantic and Pacific oceans.

The chlorophyll distribution chart for the June—September period (Fig. 4) presents a very similar pattern to that of the preceding season. Extensive regions of very high fertility with a chlorophyll concentration of over 0.5 mg m^{-3} are seen along the west

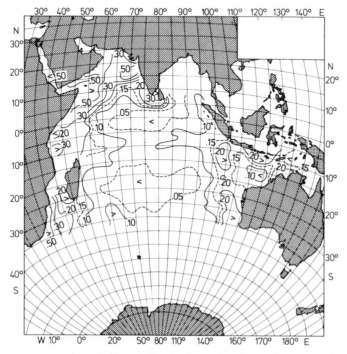

Fig. 4. Average concentration of chlorophyll a in the surface layer of 0—50 m during June to September

coast of India, the Somali coast (the Somali Current region) and the SE coast of the Arabian Peninsula. The dynamic spiral motion of the monsoon currents of the Arabian Sea brings up nutrient-rich water from about 300 m depth and enriches the surface layers off the Somali coast. The SE coast of the Arabian Peninsula is also an area of intensive upwelling of nutrient-rich bottom water. The upwelling along the west coast of India is caused by wind-driven water movements during the monsoon seasons. Other fertile areas of secondary importance are the west and north coasts of Australia and the Banda Sea (south of Java to Timor).

From the limited amount of data on chlorophyll distribution available for the December—March period (no averages could be calculated for its distribution), it is clear that the most fertile areas are the SE coast of the Arabian peninsula and the west coast of India (chlorophyll concentration >0.50 mg m^{-3}) and a minor one off Mombasa (chlorophyll concentration >0.30 mg m^{-3}). It is noteworthy that the vast and highly fertile regions seen in the Arabian Sea (off the Arabian and Indian coasts) during the SW monsoon, although still existent, have shrunk considerably both spatially and quantitatively. The moderately fertile regions of the Banda Sea, also persisting from the preceding season, could only be recognized as remnants. High chlorophyll values of 0.50 mg m^{-3} are also obtained from the regions of the west-wind drift and Antarctic gyre. Food fertility is to be expected in the vicinity of this circumpolar drift because of the dynamic mixing conditions existing there. As already mentioned, the Antarctic sectors of all 3 oceans belong to the same ecological realm which has already been explored for both the other

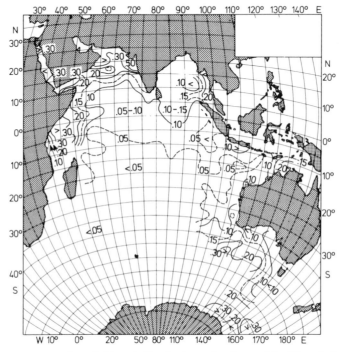

Fig. 5. Average concentration of chlorophyll *a* in the surface layer of 0–50 m during December to March

oceans. The central Indian Ocean yields very low figures of 0.05 mg m^{-3}, quite clearly as a result of the strong thermal stratification there.

The role of chlorophyll *c* in the photosynthetic assimilation of phytoplankton organisms is still not properly understood. Thus the contour profiles of the chlorophyll *c* distribution are necessarily the same as those for chlorophyll *a*, except that the degree of concentration is different; in other words, areas poor in chlorophyll *a* are also poor in chlorophyll *c*, and vice versa. During the October–March period, the latitudes south of 35° S are found to be rich in absolute concentrations of chlorophyll *c*.

A study of the distribution of chlorophyll as an indicator of the level of primary productivity potential should simultaneously consider the amount of error introduced by the unknown quantity of inactive or "dead" chlorophyll present in the standing stock. A methodological step towards differentiating this proportion has been taken by DEREN-

BACH (1969), who tried to distinguish between chlorphylls of different ages by measuring their red fluorescence. However, chlorophyll values could at most indicate only the degree or level of primary production in an area.

III. Distribution of Potential Assimilation

Several investigators have attempted to convert the incubator ^{14}C assimilation values into real *in situ* primary production rates by means of conversion factors. Such attempts

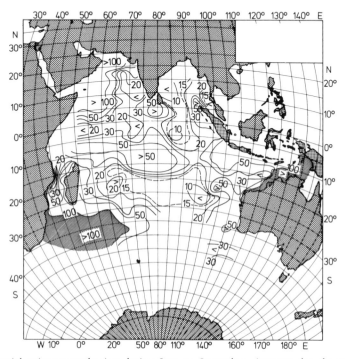

Fig. 6. Potential primary production during June to September. Averages for the surface layer $(0-50 \text{ m})$ in mg C m^{-3} h^{-1}

should be accepted with reservations because of the numerous uncertainties involved, particularly at the methodological level. The ideal would be direct *in situ* measurements, but the daily routine of most research ships, particularly the bigger ones, does not allow for this. Simulated *in situ* experiments are also only of limited use as long as the temperature of the individual samples is not standardized to the original *in situ* level, especially in those cases where stenotherm phytoplankton organisms constitute more than 50% of the total phytoplankton biomass. Both these *in situ* methods have the further disadvantage that the results are directly influenced by the duration of sunshine and the amount of cloud cover during the experiment. In comparison, incubator experiments have the clear advantage of being performed under known and constant conditions (light, temperature etc.). The results could be interpreted as the primary productivity potential under standard conditions for each area.

During the June – September period, the general pattern of the distribution of potential primary production (Fig. 6) agrees quite well with that of chlorophyll concentrations (Fig. 4), so the integrated average for chlorophyll in the upper 50 m water column is considered here. Three main areas of high potential production are outstanding in the SW Indian Ocean, northern Arabian Sea and the shelf regions off Australia. The Equatorial Current region yields medium values, while the "desert regions" north and south

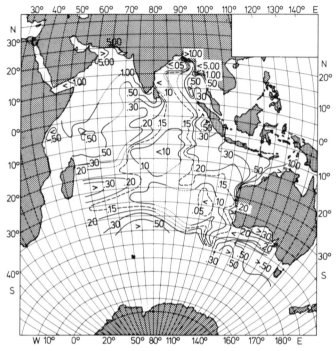

Fig. 7. Potential primary production during December to March. Averages for the surface layer (0 – 50 m) in mg C m^{-3} h^{-1}

of this area have the lowest values (0.1 – 0.2 mg C m^{-3} h^{-1}). Very few observations are available from the southerly latitudes, but by interpolation one could assume a production potential of 0.50 – 1.50 mg C m^{-3} h^{-1} for this area.

During the southern summer period, December to March, the entire Arabian Sea possesses a high potential productivity of >0.50 mg C m^{-3} h^{-1}; regionally the values even reach over 1 mg C m^{-3} h^{-1} (Fig. 7). Owing to the decrease in fertility in the Equatorial Current region, the infertile regions (of the preceding season) north and south of the Equator more or less combine to form a vast expanse with poor production rates. South of 40° S, a high rate of production potential is usually recorded. The nature of production in the SW Indian Ocean is not clear owing to lack of data.

If we now consider only the potential assimilation rates for the surface layer, its basic distribution pattern alters far less than one would expect (Figs. 6 and 7). A zone of extremely high productivity is distinguished between the mouth of Indus River and the

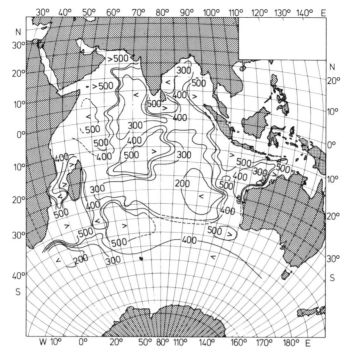

Fig. 8. *In situ* primary production during the SW monsoon season in mg C m⁻² day⁻¹

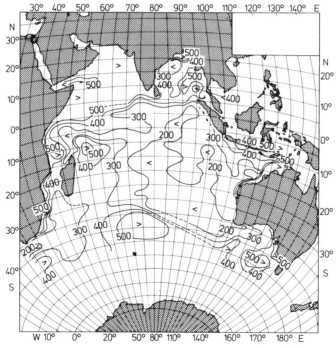

Fig. 9. *In situ* primary production during the NE monsoon season in mg C m⁻² day⁻¹

Gulf of Oman with potential production values of 5 mg C m^{-3} h^{-1}. This is due to the combined effect of river drainage and upwelling water.

Charts have been prepared showing the distribution of *in situ* primary production during both the above-discussed seasons. These were drawn on the basis of the very few direct observations available and calculations based on daily production rates for the surface layers, derived from the potential assimilation rates (Figs. 8 and 9). The basic trends in the distribution of fertile and infertile areas, as evidenced by the chlorophyll distribution charts, are clearly maintained here, too. The "desert regions" on both sides of the Equator are still the least productive while the most productive regions are the northern Arabian Sea, coastal waters of Ceylon, west coast of Indonesia, west-wind drift region and to some extent the Equatorial Current region.

The general correlation between productive regions and areas of mixing and upwelling is evident. The water movements transport nutrient-rich deep water to the surface; these water masses may be designated young water as against old water from the point of view of fertility potential. Such old water masses are seen in the central Indian Ocean region to the south and north of the Equator where currents are weak and the thermocline is very well developed. In the polar zones, light also plays an important role, acting as a limiting factor.

In conclusion, the following table (Table 3) is quoted from MOISEEV (1969) as it gives a comparative idea of the level and range of primary production in the different ecological zones discussed above.

Table 3. Primary production of different water bodies in the Indian Ocean (after MOISEEV, 1969)

Type of water	Average production in mg C m^{-2} day^{-1}	limits mg C m^{-2} day^{-1}	total area in 10^3 km^2	% of the Indian Ocean	Total annual production in 10^9 t C
Oligotrophic waters (central and subtropical)	70	100	19 599	27	0.5
Transition areas between subtropical and subpolar region; peripheral regions of equatorial divergences	140	100−150	23 750	33	1.2
equatorial divergences subpolar regions	200	150−250	18 886	27	1.4
coastal waters upwelling	340	250−500	7 944	12	1.0
neritic waters	1 000	500	5 289	1	1.9

Primary Production in the Indian Ocean II

Y. ARUGA

The first measurements by the ^{14}C technique were made during the Danish "Galathea" Expedition (STEEMANN NIELSEN, 1952; STEEMANN NIELSEN and AABYE JENSEN, 1957). Fairly intensive studies carried out during the International Geophysical Year and the IIOE covered a considerable part of the Indian Ocean (KABANOVA, 1968).

The ^{14}C technique measures the photosynthetic incorporation of carbon into organic matter and is a value between net photosynthesis and gross photosynthesis (STEEMANN NIELSEN and HANSEN, 1959). The respiratory rate is important when we consider primary net production and gross production, especially in evaluating results of *in situ* measurements of long duration and tank experiments of short duration. This difficulty should be taken into consideration when we analyze the result of ^{14}C uptake measurements in relation to environmental factors.

In the present paper, the relation of primary production in the Indian Ocean to chlorophyll, light, nutrients, and other factors will be reviewed and discussed.

I. Standing Stock and Primary Production

RYTHER et al. (1966) and YENTSCH (1965) reported the primary production of the western Indian Ocean in relation to its chemistry and hydrography. The areas of high primary production seem to be closely related to the high level of chlorophyll. Vertical distribution of chlorophyll and phaeophytin generally showed subsurface maximum, which can be related to the light penetrating the water column and to vertical mixing. The depth where maximum concentrations of total pigment, chlorophyll, and phaeophytin occur is greater in stable waters than in less stable waters. In the upper layer of the euphotic zone, the fraction of chlorophyll in the total pigment is usually greater, and it decreases with depth in the lower layer. The relation of the chlorophyll-phaeophytin ratio to light penetration in water is not linear; vertical changes in the ratio are closely related to the depth of mixed layer or to the extent of vertical mixing of water.

In the eastern part of the Indian Ocean, Japanese scientists carried out measurements of the photosynthetic rate of phytoplankton and the chlorophyll content of water during the period from December to January (SAIJO, 1965). Photosynthetic rates measured by the tank method were generally low except for the region of upwelling south of Java. West of 100°E, the photosynthetic rate of phytoplankton in water sampled near the surface was 0.2–0.4 mgC m^{-3}h^{-1} to the north of 5°S and 0.1 mgC m^{-3}h^{-1} to the south of 5°S. To the east of 100°E, it was over 0.4 mgC m^{-3}h^{-1} to the north of 10°S and 0.1–0.3 mgC m^{-3}h^{-1} to the south of 10°S.

The depth of maximum photosynthetic activity obtained in tank experiments was 25 m in the north on the 78°E line, while it was at 50 m or 75 m in the south. The depth of maximum photosynthetic activity was always deeper than the depth of maximum production in the *in situ* experiments.

Chlorophyll *a* in the eastern part of the Indian Ocean was generally low from December to January, being about 0.1 mg m^{-3} in the north and less than 0.05 mg m^{-3} in the south at the surface to the west of 100° E, and about 0.05 mg m^{-3} at the surface to the east of 100° E. Maximum chlorophyll concentration was often observed in the lower part of the euphotic zone, 50–125 m eg. 50–75 m in the equatorial region and 100–125 m in the south, corresponding to the upper limit of the thermocline. The depth of maximum chlorophyll concentration did not coincide with the depth of maximum photosynthetic acitivity obtained by the tank experiments. The results of the tank experiments suggested that the chlorophyll at the depth of the chlorophyll maximum had almost lost its photosynthetic ability (Saijo, 1965).

Daily primary production estimated by the *in situ* experiments from December to January was generally 0.1–0.2 gC m^{-2} d^{-1} in the eastern Indian Ocean. Comparatively high values, 0.3–0.7 gC m^{-2} d^{-1}, were obtained in the region to the south of Java, corresponding to the region of upwelling with high photosynthetic rate of phytoplankton, though the chlorophyll content of water was rather low. Wyrtki (1962) reported that during the SE monsoon the region is characterized by very high concentrations of inorganic phosphate at the bottom of the euphotic layer and by a high plankton biomass; the transparency of the water is low, indicating a high concentration of suspended matter. Ryther and Menzel (1965) obtained a linear regression of the C m^{-2} assimilation under natural illumination on living C m^{-2}, both values integrated over the euphotic zone.

The depth of the euphotic zone is, in general, inversely related to the amount of chlorophyll and other suspended and dissolved materials in water which characteristically absorb light (Aruga and Ichimura, 1968). The light attenuation in water, together with the weather conditions, determines the lower limit of photosynthetic activity of phytoplankton near the bottom of the euphotic zone. This consequently influences the integrated daily primary production over the euphotic zone (Steemann Nielsen and Aabye Jensen, 1957). The depth of the euphotic zone in the Indian Ocean varies with region as well as with season according to the variations of solar radiation on the sea surface and the attenuation coefficient. Panikkar (1969) summarized the amount of chlorophyll in the water column under unit area of sea surface in various regions of the Indian Ocean in relation to upwelling and monsoons. In the SW part of the Indian Ocean to the Antarctic Ocean Ichimura and Fukushima (1963) made measurements of chlorophyll in the surface water and found that the amount of chlorophyll increased from the Indian Ocean to the Antarctic Ocean.

II. Seasonal Variations of Primary Production

Very few areas have been studied. Fairly intensive studies have been made in the southeast Indian Ocean, especially along 110° E by Australian scientists (Humphrey, 1966; Humphrey and Kerr, 1969; Jitts, 1969). Mean primary productivity (cumulative light-saturated photosynthesis obtained by tank experiments) of the column from 0 to 150 m increased from 50 mgC m^{-2}h^{-1} in August to a maximum (62 mgC m^{-2}h^{-1}) in October, then decreased to a minimum (4 mgC m^{-2}h^{-1}) in January, after which it increased slowly to 25 mgC $m^{-2}h^{-1}$ in April—May, then sharply to 45 mgC $m^{-2}h^{-1}$ in late May, and remained at that level until August. Mean productivity for the year was 37 mgC $m^{-2}h^{-1}$. The depth of the layer in which a significant amount of photosynthesis (more than 0.10 mgC $m^{-3}h^{-1}$) was measured in samples exposed to constant saturating light varied between 130 m in October and 60 m in January. In January—February there was low productivity (approximately 4 mgC $m^{-2}h^{-1}$). In April—May the productivity remained uniform along the meridian but increased to 24 mgC $m^{-2}h^{-1}$. At other times there were 4 latitudinal intervals with distinctive seasonal variations. From 9 to 15° S, waters with high productivity and sharp stratification, caused by equatorial upwelling, were found during the period from May to October.

On the other hand, the mean daily rate of primary production estimated by the simulated *in situ* method in the region along 110° E varied from 0.13 gC $m^{-2}d^{-1}$ in August to 0.08 gC $m^{-2}d^{-1}$ in October to early May, rising sharply in late May to 0.18 gC $m^{-2}d^{-1}$ and again in early August to 0.27 gC $m^{-2}d^{-1}$. High values (more than 0.3 gC $m^{-2}d^{-1}$) were obtained in waters from 9 to 15° S in June—August. The depth of the euphotic zone varied between 76 m in October and 63 m in July—August, with a mean of 68 m. Months and latitudes with high daily rates of primary production, as mentioned above, agree with those of high chlorophyll concentration but the depth of the chlorophyll maximum does not necessarily coincide with that of maximum productivity.

KABANOVA (1968), summarizing the results of primary production measurements in the Indian Ocean by the expeditions of various countries, indicated that the period of summer SW monsoon was more productive than the period of the winter NE monsoon.

III. Nutrients and Primary Production

STEEMANN NIELSEN and AABYE JENSEN (1957) discussed the relation of the photosynthetic activity of phytoplankton to the concentrations of phosphate and nitrate in the Indian Ocean. PANIKKAR (1969) illustrated the regions of high phosphate concentration in the Indian Ocean in relation to productivity. In some regions the concentration of phosphate seems to be limiting the primary production. KABANOVA (1961) concluded that the level of primary production was controlled by the content of biogenous elements especially by the content of N; on the other hand, phosphate and nitrate would rapidly be exhausted with increasing primary production (KABANOVA, 1964).

MAXIMOVA (1971) summarized the distribution of nutrients in relation to primary productivity. The distribution of primary production in the areas north of 40° S followed the same general pattern as that of nutrients. There was positive correlation between the average values in 5° latitudinal zones of the primary production and of the nutrients in the surface 100 m layer. In the 100—200 m layer the correlation of primary production and nutrients was less distinct. In the regions where the intensity of phytoplankton photosynthesis was not restricted by light, high levels of primary production were observed in the areas with phosphate content in the 100 m surface layer above 60 μg-at m^{-2}, and primary production was characteristically low where phosphate was below 40 μg-at m^{-2}.

IV. Distribution of Primary Production

RYTHER et al. (1966) reported the distribution of the daily rate of primary production in the western Indian Ocean. KABANOVA (1968) summarized the distribution of the mean daily rate of primary production in the whole Indian Ocean together with the distribution in summer and winter. PRASAD, BANERJI and NAIR (1970) described the production in the Indian Ocean with a figure showing the distribution of the daily rate of primary production in the Ocean. KOBLENTZ-MISHKE, VOLKOVINSKY and KABANOVA (1970) presented the distribution of the daily rate of primary production in the world oceans obtained by direct ^{14}C measurements and partially supplemented by the indirect estimate from the data of phytoplankton biomass (see map on the inside of the back cover). The distribution of daily primary production seems to agree generally with that of chlorophyll a in the euphotic zone. High values of daily production have usually been observed in areas of upwelling, which at least in part are closely associated with monsoons, and consequently with high nutrient concentrations. However, except for a few areas where fairly intensive studies have been made, the seasonal variation of production has not been studied fully enough for an estimate of the level of annual primary production in different areas of the Indian Ocean.

For a comparison of patterns of production with other oceans of the world, see the map inside the back cover. (Note that this map already provides more detail on geographic patterns than the front map in Vol. 1 of Ecological Studies.) The absolute rates of production given in both maps will require further adjustment in the future. The two chapters just completed, the localized reports which follow them, chapters 6.1 and 6.2, and the recent references cited are constructive steps toward a better view of world oceanic productivity.

2.3

Phytoplankton Production
in the Southeastern Indian Ocean

S. Z. EL-SAYED and H. R. JITTS

The main interest in this paper is to present the data on primary production and the standing stock of phytoplankton collected during "Eltanin" cruise 46, 20 Nov. 1970 – 20 Jan. 1971 (EL-SAYED, 1971). Efforts will be made to correlate the productivity data

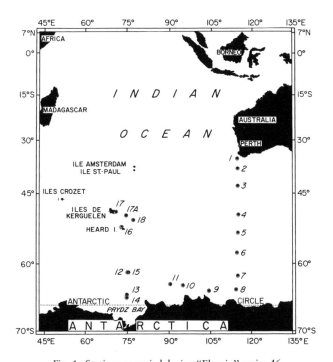

Fig. 1. Stations occupied during "Eltanin" cruise 46

with the physical and chemical parameters studied. Attention should be drawn to the preliminary nature of the results presented here which will assume more meaning as a more detailed analysis of the data is completed and as additional findings are published from this multi-discipline cruise, which was a part of the U.S. Antarctic Research Program in the Southern Ocean. A total of 19 stations were occupied. Stations 8, 9, 10, 11, 13 and 14, were occupied in pack ice (Fig. 1).

I. Methods

1. Primary Production

Primary organic production was determined by the ^{14}C uptake method of Steemann Nielsen (1952) as modified by Strickland and Parsons (1968). Both *in situ* and simulated *in situ* ^{14}C uptake experiments were carried out. Measurements of submarine light penetrations were made about an hour before Local Apparent Noon (LAN), using a wide-band photometer with a quantum-corrected response in the visible spectrum. Water samples were collected by Niskin samplers at various depths in the euphotic zone. These depths corresponded to 100, 50, 25, 12, 6 and 3% of the quantum energy falling at the sea surface. Pyrex glass bottles (65 ml) were filled with sea-water and each bottle inoculated with 1 ml of 10 μc of NaH^{14}CO$_3$ and lowered to the depth from which the sample was taken. The incubation period lasted between LAN and sunset. Concurrently with the *in situ* ^{14}C uptake experiments, simulated *in situ* experiments (using a deck incubator and a set of blue glass filters) were carried out using identical technique to that of *in situ* experiments.

2. Pigment Analysis

Water samples for pigment analysis were taken from the same water collected for primary productivity studies. Chlorophyll *a* was estimated by 2 methods: a) spectro-photometrically (Richards and Thompson, 1952; Creitz and Richards, 1955), and b) fluorometrically, using a modification of the procedure described by Holm-Hansen et al. (1965). The latter method was also used for the estimation of the phaeopigments, phaeophytin and phaeophorbin.

3. Nutrients

Water samples were taken from the regular hydrocasts for the determination of silicates, phosphates and nitrates according to Strickland and Parsons (1968).

II. Results

1. Distribution of Temperature between Australia and Antarctica

The temperature profiles taken between 35° and 65° S latitude along a 115° E transect (Fig. 2) show that the areas between Australia and Antarctica can be divided into 4 fairly well-defined water masses, namely, the Subtropical, the Subantarctic, the Polar Front (Antarctic Convergence) and the Antarctic surface water. The main transport of water between 40° S and 60° S is from west to east in what is known as the Circumpolar Current. Superimposed upon the eastward circumpolar movement are north-south components. Its northern limit, the Antarctic surface water, sinks beneath the less dense, south-flowing Subantarctic water to form the Antarctic intermediate water. Close to the Antarctic continent, bottom water is formed. Immediately above this water mass there is an exceptionally thick, warm, water mass, the deep water, which is characterized by high salinity and high nutrient salts. The Polar Front was crossed between stations 4 and 5 during the south-bound leg of the cruise. During the north-bound leg, stations 17 and 17A were located in the Polar Front. Station 18 seemed to be situated on the Antarctic side of the Convergence.

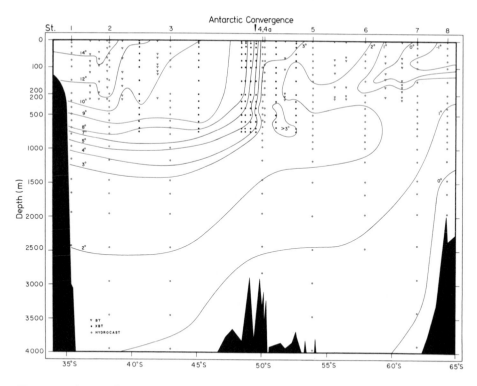

Fig. 2. Distribution of temperature (° C) in a transect between South Australia and Antarctica along 115° E

Table 1. Minimum, maximum, average, standard deviation and number of observations of surface and integrated values of primary production, chlorophyll *a*, phaeopigment, phosphate, silicate and nitrate taken during "Eltanin" cruise 46

	Min.	Max.	Aver.	Std. dev.	No. of observ.
[14]C uptake (mgC m^{-3} day^{-1})	0.09	8.65	2.38	2.82	14
[a]Integrated ^{14}C uptake (gC m^{-2} day^{-1})	0.06	0.20	0.13	0.05	13
Chlorophyll *a* (mg m^{-3})	0.04	0.73	0.28	0.21	21
[a]Integrated chlorophyll *a* (mg m^{-2})	10.0	46.0	19.5	10.2	15
[b]Integrated chlorophyll *a* (mg m^{-2})	9.7	78.5	34.8	23.1	21
Phaeopigment (mg m^{-3})	0.04	0.91	0.25	0.25	20
[a]Integrated phaeopigment (mg m^{-2})	7.1	46.9	17.3	9.5	15
[b]Integrated phaeopigment (mg m^{-2})	10.9	81.0	34.2	22.4	21
PO_4^{3-}-P (μg-at l^{-1})	0.13	1.50	0.86	0.33	19
[b]Integrated PO_4^{3-}-P (g-at m^{-2})	0.07	0.30	0.18	0.05	20
SiO_4^{4-}-Si (μg-at l^{-1})	0.1	54.7	21.4	18.3	18
[b]Integrated SiO_4^{4-}-Si (g-at m^{-2})	0.48	9.32	4.54	3.11	20
NO_3^--N (μg-at l^{-1})	0.3	27.3	15.01	7.27	20
[b]Integrated NO_3^--N (g-at m^{-2})	0.44	5.12	3.31	1.32	20

[a]Integrated values from 0 m to depth of euphotic zone.
[b]Integrated values from 0 m to 200 m.

2. Distribution of Plant Pigments

The data for surface and integrated (i.e. within the euphotic zone, and/or to 200 m) chlorophyll *a*, phaeopigments, primary productivity, and nutrient salts are included in Table 1. Surface chlorophyll *a* values at most of the stations occupied during "Eltanin" cruise 46 were moderate; the average value was 0.28 mg m^{-3}. High chlorophyll *a* values were found at station 4, located just to the north of the Polar Front, and in the region between Heard and Kerguelen Islands. The highest surface chlorophyll *a* values during this cruise (0.73 mg m^{-3}) were recorded at station 16, off Heard Island, and at station

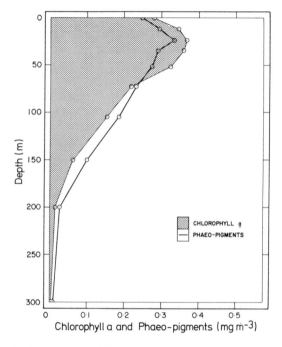

Fig. 4. Vertical distribution of chlorophyll *a* and phaeopigments based on average values of all stations combined during "Eltanin" cruise 46 (20 Nov. 1970 – 20 Jan. 1971)

17A, situated to the SE of the Kerguelen Islands. The chlorophyll *a* values at these stations are as high, or even higher, than those reported from the highly productive regions in the northern and western Arabian Sea. (Krey, 1973; McGill and Lawson, 1966.)

The vertical distribution of chlorophyll *a* (Fig. 3) shows that at the majority of the stations, maximum chlorophyll *a* concentrations were found at subsurface depths; these depth maxima varied between 10 m at station 17A and 120 m at station 7. Maximum chlorophyll *a* values, in general, occurred at depths corresponding to 25 – 12% of surface

Fig. 3. Vertical distribution of chlorophyll *a* and phaeopigments (mg m^{-3}) at stations occupied during "Eltanin" cruise 46. Position of arrows indicate depth of euphotic zone

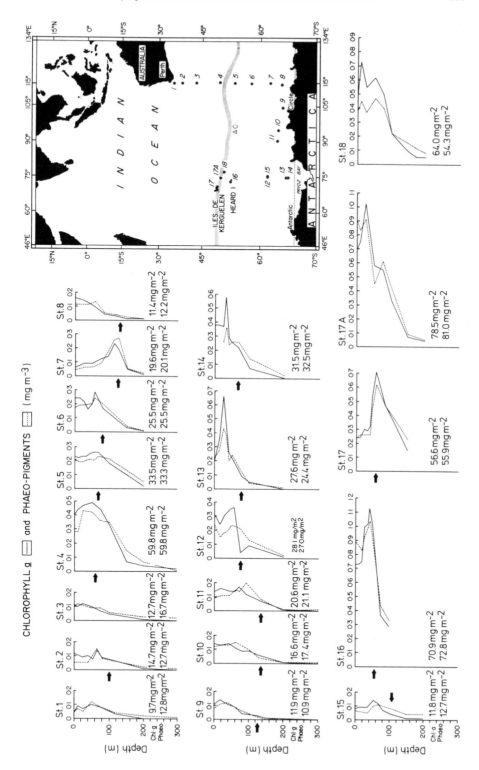

light intensity. Following the chlorophyll *a* maxima, there is a general decline in the concentration of the plant pigment to the depth of 200 m; below this depth the quantity is very much reduced. At several of the stations, substantial quantities of chlorophyll *a* are found below the euphotic zones (arrows in Fig. 3). This is clearly shown at stations 4 and 17 which are located in the vicinity of the Polar Front. The integrated chlorophyll *a* gave an average value of 19.5 mg m^{-2} for the present cruise compared to 12.62 mg m^{-2} and 15.94 mg m^{-2} for the Pacific and Atlantic sectors, respectively (El-Sayed, 1970).

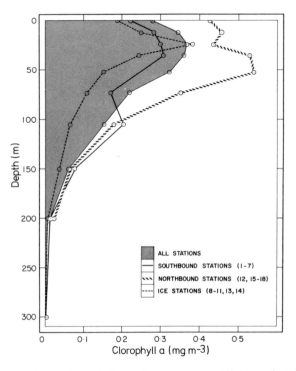

Fig. 5. Vertical distribution of chlorophyll *a* at the stations occupied during the 3 legs of "Eltanin" cruise 46

The vertical distribution of the phaeopigments (Fig. 3) showed a similar distribution to that of chlorophyll *a*. Maximum concentrations of phaeopigments either coincided with that of chlorophyll *a*, or were located about 10 m deeper as in Lorenzen's study (1967) off Baja California. Fig. 4 demonstrates that, whereas chlorophyll *a* concentrations were higher than phaeopigments in the upper 50 m, the latter pigments were consistently higher than the former at the depths sampled below 70 m. There were distinct geographical variations in the concentration of the standing stock of phytoplankton in the SE Indian Ocean as based on pigment data (Fig. 5).

The northbound stations were by far the richest; they were followed by the stations occupied in the southbound leg of the cruise. The least productive stations were those occupied in pack-ice.

3. Distribution of Primary Production

The vertical distribution of primary production (Fig. 6) bears a close resemblance to that of the distribution of chlorophyll *a*. In general, higher photosynthetic rates characterize those stations occupied in the northbound leg of the cruise compared to those of the southbound stations. The lowest carbon assimilation appears to be typical of the pack-ice stations. At the northbound stations, maximum photosynthetic activity occurred

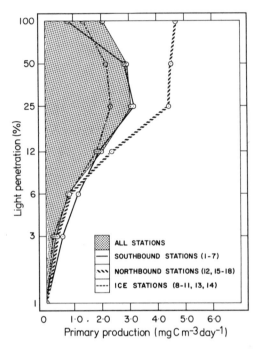

Fig. 6. Vertical distribution of primary production versus percent light penetration during "Eltanin" cruise 46

at the surface; at the rest of the stations, maximum ^{14}C assimilation took place at depths corresponding to 25% of surface light intensity.

The data collected during this cruise were plotted together with those obtained by RYTHER et al. (1966) (Fig. 7). The primary productivity values in the SE Indian Ocean are far lower than those collected by RYTHER et al. in the NW Indian Ocean. Even the high productivity values encountered at the "Eltanin" stations 16, 17A and 18 do not remotely approximate the very high figures reported by RYTHER et al., or RYTHER and MENZEL (1965) in the NW Indian Ocean (e.g. 6.4 gC m^{-2} day^{-1}, off the SE tip of Arabia). If one overlooks the highly productive stations off the coasts of Saudi Arabia, off Pakistan and the east coast of South Africa, however, the general levels of primary production in the oceanic waters in the NW and SE regions are surprisingly close. The similarity becomes more plausible when the variations in the sampling seasons and the differences in the techniques used in measuring primary production aboard the 2 research

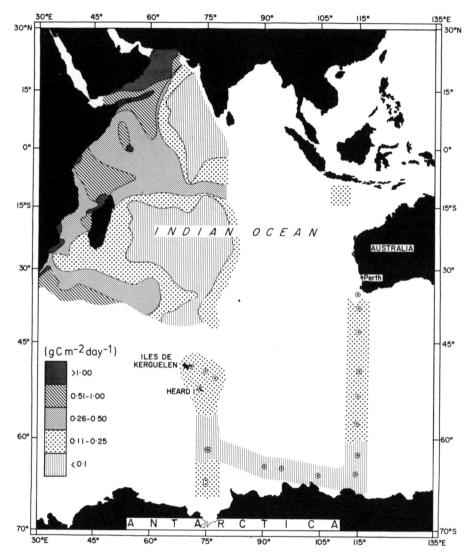

Fig. 7. Distribution of primary production (gC m^{-2} day^{-1}) in the Indian Ocean based mainly on "Eltanin" cruise 46 and "Anton Bruun" cruises 2, 3, 4A, 5, 6, 7, and 8 (RYTHER et al., 1966)

vessels are taken into consideration. For instance, the "Eltanin" primary productivity data are based on the *in situ* experiments, while those of the "Anton Bruun" are the results from incubation on board ship. The simulated *in situ* ^{14}C uptake measurements carried out during the "Eltanin" cruise gave consistently higher figures than those of the *in situ* ^{14}C uptake assimilation. Despite the significant differences between the productivity data in both regions, it is surprising that our average primary production value (0.13 gC m^{-2} day^{-1}) is only slightly less than half the mean rate of production for the western Indian Ocean (0.35 gC m^{-2} day^{-1}) reported by RYTHER et al. (1966).

Despite the seasonal variations, the data obtained at the southbound stations of the "Eltanin" cruise were quite similar to those reported by JITTS (1969) who reported a rate of production of 0.13 gC m^{-2} day^{-1} at 9° 30′S in September. STEEMANN NIELSEN and AABYE JENSEN (1957) reported a slightly higher value (0.17 gC m^{-2} day^{-1}) at 10°S in September, and SAIJO (1965) found a value of 0.18 gC m^{-2} day^{-1} at 12°S in December – January.

4. Distribution of the Nutrients in Relation to Phytoplankton Standing Stock

The phosphate data (Fig. 8) compare favorably with those recorded in the highly productive areas in the western regions of the Indian Ocean during the upwelling season

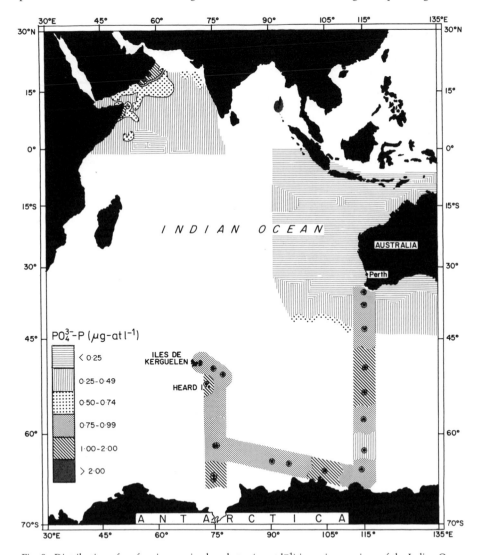

Fig. 8. Distribution of surface inorganic phosphates (μg-at l^{-1}) in various regions of the Indian Ocean

(WOOSTER, SCHAEFER and ROBINSON, 1967). Fig. 9 shows the "Eltanin" surface silicate data to be much higher than those collected in the NW region.

There appears to be an inverse relationship between silicate and phytoplankton. Very

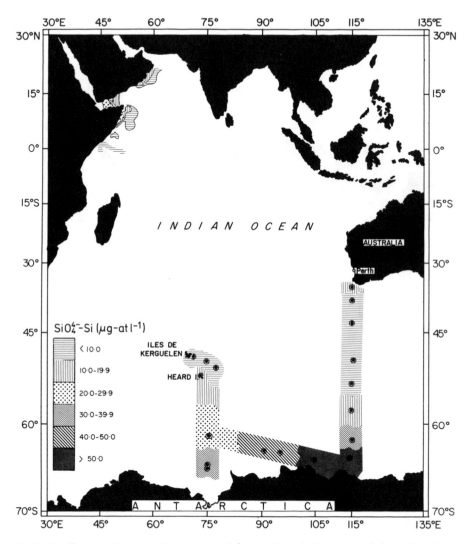

Fig. 9. Distribution of surface silicates (μg-at l^{-1}) in NW and SE regions of the Indian Ocean

low values of surface silicates occurred at stations 4, 16, 17A and 18, which had a high phytoplankton standing stock (Fig. 10), while conspicuously low chlorophyll a values were found at those stations with the highest surface silicates values (e.g., stations 7, 8, 9, 10, 11). This indicates that, although the surface silicates were severely depleted, they did not limit the growth of the algal populations at these highly productive stations. The distribution of surface phosphate and nitrate (not included in Fig. 10) did not show a discernible trend with the chlorophyll *a* concentration at the stations occupied. The data suggest that a high standing stock of phytoplankton is associated with high surface phosphate.

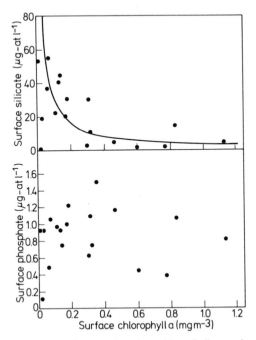

Fig. 10. Relationship between distribution of surface chlorophyll *a* and surface phosphate and silicate obtained at the stations occupied during "Eltanin" cruise 46

III. Discussion

The values of primary production found are far lower than those reported from the NW Indian Ocean. However, disregarding the highly productive stations in the regions of upwelling off the coast of Saudi Arabia and Pakistan, the general level of primary production in the oceanic waters is surprisingly close in the NW, E and SE regions of the Indian Ocean. Several investigators have attributed their high productivity values from the Arabian Sea to the high nutrient concentrations during the upwelling season, yet the phytoplankton production in the area studied during "Eltanin" cruise 46, was much lower than in the regions of upwelling, even though the nutrient concentrations were much higher. It is possible that the limiting factor is the rate of diffusion of these salts (FOGG, 1970).

The low levels of production characteristic of the southern stations were in marked contrast to the high productivity of the stations occupied off the Heard and Kerguelen Islands, where the land-mass effect seemed to be operative. High standing stock of phytoplankton was not restricted to the stations occupied near land masses or in proximity to islands, e.g. station 12, located in the deep oceanic waters away from a land mass effect, was noted for its rich phytoplankton populations. High phytoplankton standing stock and primary production were also noted at stations 4 and 18, located just to the north and to the south of the Polar Front, respectively. Whether the high biological productivity of the latter stations is related to their proximity to the Antarctic Convergence with its concomitant hydrographic effects, is not clear.

The effect of the Polar Front on the distribution of the nutrient salts is quite noticeable from the data collected during this cruise, e.g. NO_3^--N values at stations 2 and 4, north of the Polar Front, were 0.3 and 10.8 μg-at l^{-1}, compared to 21.1 and 24.7 μg-at l^{-1}, at stations 5 and 8 located south of the Front. In general, higher concentrations of nutrients were found south of the Polar Front than north of it, with conspicuous increases from north to south as the Convergence was crossed.

The effect of the Polar Front was also noticeable with regard to the species composition of the phytoplankton at the stations occupied. Analysis of the phytoplankton samples collected has shown that the dinoflagellates constituted an important component of the phytoplankton at the stations occupied north of the Polar Front (mainly species of *Ceratium* and *Peridinium*). South of the Polar Front, the diatoms were the dominant element in the phytoplankton. Of the 88 species of diatoms identified, the 10 most frequently encountered species were: *Asteromphalus hookeri, Chaetoceros atlanticum, C. dichaeta, Corethron criophilum, Dactyliosolen antarcticus, Eucampia balaustium, Fragilariopsis kerguelensis, Rhizosolenia alata* f. *inerme, R. hebetata* f. *semispina,* and *Thalassiothrix antarctica.* A more detailed account will be published of the effect of the Polar Front on the distribution and abundance of the phytoplankton.

2.4

Productivity of Backwaters and Estuaries

S. Z. QASIM

The main reason why the backwaters and estuaries have been included in the Symposium on "The Biology of the Indian Ocean" is that, in certain regions of the Indian Ocean, the backwaters with their associated river system form a fairly large part of the inshore waters and influence the hydrography of the coastal water considerably. The term

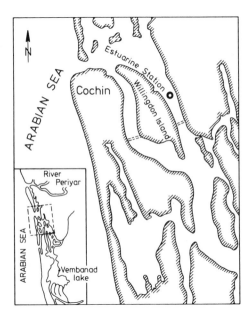

Fig. 1. Map showing a portion of the backwaters around Cochin. The estuarine site to which the data refer has been indicated by open circle. Inset shows the backwater system with its marine and freshwater connections

"backwater" or "backwaters" is of local origin and refers to a system of shallow, brackish-water lagoons and swamps found in Kerala State along the SW coast of India. They occupy an area of hundreds of square kilometers. Although the backwaters have their own physiography and geomorphology, most of them behave like estuaries. The areas which are close to the permanent connection with the sea are influenced by the regular tidal rhythm and have been referred to as tropical estuaries (QASIM et al., 1969; SANKARANARAYANAN and QASIM, 1969).

Fig. 1 shows the backwaters around Cochin, the main area under investigation for several years. The connection between the Arabian Sea and this backwater is maintained by a channel, about 450 m wide, which forms an entrance to Cochin harbour. Several rivers, irrigation channels and sewers open into this backwater which terminates in a large lake called Vembanad Lake. The area is accessible to all types of craft, including ocean-going vessels (to the harbour). The backwater is intensely polluted and most of the area is less than 3 m deep, except for the shipping channels which are dredged to a depth of 10 to 12 m.

I. Environmental Features

The hydrography of the backwater is largely influenced by two main factors: the short-term changes induced by the tides and the seasonal changes brought about by the monsoon system. The magnitude of variation within the backwater largely depends upon the place of observation (nearness to the sea or freshwater source). In this communication, therefore, descriptions are provided of the environmental features at a site where conditions remain typically estuarine (Fig. 1). The changes in the different parameters can be summarized as follows:

1. Tides

The tides at Cochin are of a mixed, semidiurnal nature. Two high and two low watermarks occur each day and differ in height (Fig. 2). The influence of tides on some of the environmental features has been described by QASIM and GOPINATHAN (1969).

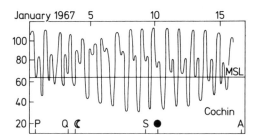

Fig. 2. Tidal cycle at Cochin during the first fortnight of Jan. 1967. The phases of the moon have also been indicated, MSL: mean sea level

Temperature, salinity, dissolved O_2, pH, seston, nutrients, alkalinity and chlorophyll are all influenced by the tides. The magnitude of variations is dependent upon the seasons when the observations are made.

2. Light Penetration

The backwater receives maximum solar radiation ($500 - 580$ g cal cm^{-2} day^{-1}) from January to April and minimum ($250 - 300$ g cal cm^{-2} day^{-1}) in July and August (Fig. 3). The decrease in solar radiation is largely dependent upon cloudiness (QASIM, BHATTATHIRI and ABIDI, 1968).

The high turbidity prevailing in the estuary greatly reduces light penetration. Fig. 4 gives the pooled data of percentage transmission at various depths in 3 different seasons:

February—May (premonsoon), June—September (monsoon) and October—January (postmonsoon). For convenience, the 2 monsoons (SW and NE) have been referred to as monsoon and postmonsoon seasons. During the monsoon season, as a result of considerable inflow of freshwater, the turbidity in the backwater increases and the light penetration falls to about 20% of the incident illumination at 1 m and 1% at 3 m (mean $k = 1.37$). During the postmonsoon season light penetration increases somewhat (32% at 1 m and 1% at 4 m (mean $k = 1.18$), but in the premonsoon season it again falls

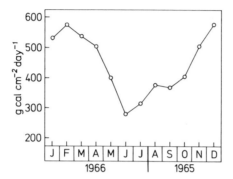

Fig. 3. Average values of solar radiation at Cochin in different months of the year 1965—66

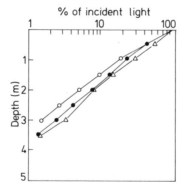

Fig. 4. Light penetration in Cochin Backwater. The values of percentage transmission at different depths have been pooled into 3 seasons. Open circles: monsoon season (June—September); open triangles postmonsoon season (October—January); closed circles: premonsoon season (February—May)

(24% at 1 m and < 1% at 4 m; mean $k = 1.36$). The compensation depth, which is taken as 1% of the surface illumination, ranges between 2 and 6 m during the year.

The seasonal variability of other environmental factors is also chiefly controlled by the monsoon cycle. The backwater remains seawater-dominated for about 6 months, and then, with the commencement of rains, it becomes freshwater-dominated and continues to remain so with varying degrees for the next 6 months. The changes in other environmental features are also divisible into premonsoon, monsoon and postmonsoon seasons (SANKARANARAYANAN and QASIM, 1969).

3. Temperature

During the premonsoon season of maximum solar radiation and warm weather, the temperature throughout the water column remains uniform and records its maximum. With the onset of rains in May, the water temperature decreases and a clear thermal

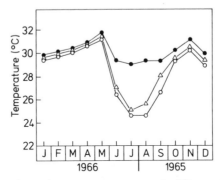

Fig. 5. Average monthly values of water temperature at 3 different depths of the backwater. Surface: closed circles; mid depth: triangles; bottom: open circles

gradient develops in the water column (Fig. 5). The difference in temperature from the surface to the bottom may be more than 5° C. The thermal gradient persists until about September.

4. Salinity

The salinity remains homogeneous throughout the water column during the pre-monsoon season, indicating that the water is well mixed (Fig. 6). During the monsoon months large quantities of freshwater enter the estuary, resulting in low salinity water

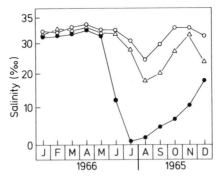

Fig. 6. Average monthly values of salinity at 3 different depths of the backwater. Symbols as in Fig. 5

at the surface and denser water at the bottom. Because of a clear stratification which exists during the monsoon months, the surface and bottom waters remain quite distinct. The stratification is broken up during the postmonsoon months when homogeneous conditions are gradually restored.

5. Oxygen

The dissolved O_2 shows little change at different depths during the premonsoon season. With the start of the monsoon rains, the O_2 values at the surface increase, but at deeper layers a decrease in the dissolved O_2 is noticed (Fig. 7). The vertical gradient normally continues until marine conditions in the backwater are restored.

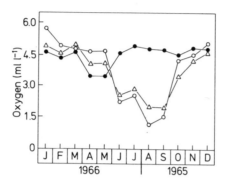

Fig. 7. Average monthly values of dissolved oxygen at 3 different depths of the backwater. Symbols as in Fig. 5

6. Hydrogen Ion Concentration

The pH showed seasonal fluctuation at all depths. The values remain high when conditions are marine and fall progressively as the system becomes freshwater-dominated (Fig. 8).

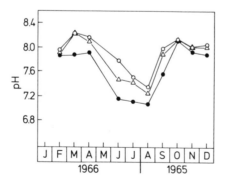

Fig. 8. Average monthly values of pH at 3 different depths of the backwater. Symbols as in Fig. 5

7. Alkalinity

Fig. 9 shows the variation in alkalinity. Like salinity, the alkalinity of the water showed small changes during the premonsoon period and large changes during the monsoon months.

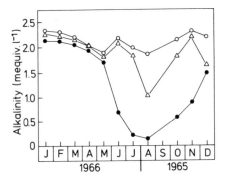

Fig. 9. Average monthly values of alkalinity at 3 different depths of the backwater. Symbols as in Fig. 5

8. Inorganic Phosphorus

During the premonsoon season the inorganic PO_4^{3-}-P at all depths ranges between $0.5 - 1.0$ μg-at l^{-1}. From May onwards when the monsoon rains start, the values of the water column are subject to pronounced changes (Fig. 10). The PO_4^{3-}-P concentrations at mid-depth and at the bottom become much higher than those at the surface.

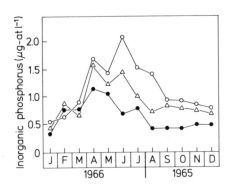

Fig. 10. Average monthly values of inorganic phosphorus at different depths of the backwater. Symbols as in Fig. 5

9. Organic Phosphorus

The amount of organic phosphorus was generally greater at the bottom than at the surface (Fig. 11). Larger fluctuations in the values were noticed at the bottom than at the surface.

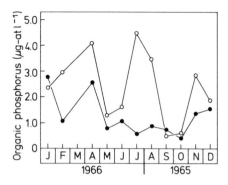

Fig. 11. Average monthly values of organic phosphorus at 2 different depths of the backwater. Surface: closed circles; bottom: open circles

10. Nitrate-Nitrogen

When the backwater remains marine-dominated the values of NO_3^--N are low, but during the monsoon months the values become suddenly high. The distribution of NO_3^--N remains homogeneous throughout the water column in all the seasons (Fig. 12).

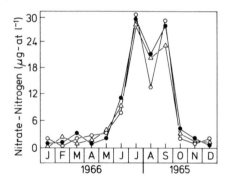

Fig. 12. Average monthly values of nitrate-nitrogen at 3 different depths of the backwater. Symbols as in Fig. 5

11. Nitrite-Nitrogen

Pronounced changes in the NO_2^--N were noticed during the monsoon months (Fig. 13) but these were mostly in deeper layers. The water at the surface showed maximum value in May whereas three peaks of NO_2^--N were recorded at mid-depth and at the bottom (Fig. 13).

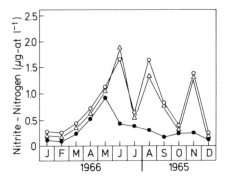

Fig. 13. Average monthly values of nitrite-nitrogen at 3 different depths of the backwater. Symbols as in Fig. 5

12. Silicate-Silicon

The silicon values in the backwater were closely related to the silt-loaded freshwater discharge, thus making the values very high during the monsoon months (Fig. 14).

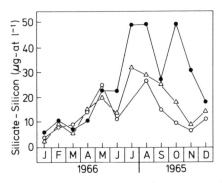

Fig. 14. Average monthly values of silicate-silicon at 3 different depths of the backwater. Symbols as in Fig. 5

II. Rate of Primary Production

The rate of photosynthesis was measured by the light and dark bottle O_2 technique and the ^{14}C method of STEEMANN NIELSEN (1952). The former method gave a measure of gross production and the latter of net production. The factor for converting the O_2 changes to C assimilation was 0.375/PQ, where the value of PQ was taken as 1.2 (STRICKLAND, 1960). Experiments with light and dark bottle and ^{14}C were conducted *in situ*, using a float throughout the year, at the site shown in Fig. 1.

The primary production in relation to depths is given in Fig. 15. The data for different months have been pooled according to the 3 seasons. It is clear from the figure that about 90% of the total production is confined to the topmost layer. Maximum production occurs either at the surface or slightly below. This is because highly turbid conditions prevail in the backwater, more particularly during the monsoon season. Monthly values of gross and net production for the euphotic zone are given in Fig. 16. The average values of respiration for the euphotic zone in different months, calculated from the O_2 decrease in the dark bottle during the light and dark bottle experiments, have also been included in the figure. This was done on the assumption that the rate of respiration in the

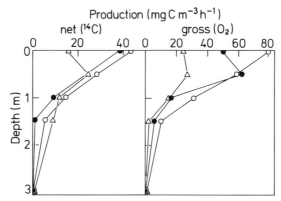

Fig. 15. Primary production (gross and net) in the backwater in relation to depths. The data have been pooled into 3 seasons. Monsoon season: closed circles; postmonsoon season: triangles; premonsoon months: open circles

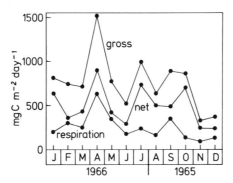

Fig. 16. Seasonal changes in gross and net primary production in the backwater. Community respiration has also been included in the figure. The values of production and respiration refer to the euphotic zone

dark is the same as that during the corresponding period of light in conjunction with photosynthesis.

The column production showed 3 peaks: one in April, the second in July and the third in October. These peaks were of a short duration and amounted to a 3−4 fold increase. Therefore, the backwater behaves like other tropical areas where primary production is reported to go on at a uniform rate throughout the year, with little seasonal increase (MENZEL and RYTHER, 1961). (In temperate regions the seasonal increase in production during the summer months may be 50 times greater than in winter.)

III. Chlorophyll *a* Cycle

Seasonal changes in the chlorophyll *a* concentration are given in Fig. 17. A comparison of the chlorophyll cycle with that of primary production (Fig. 15) reveals that the two are not synchronous. This may be due to the presence of dead and inactive chlorophyll from detrital material and stirred-up sediment (Qasim and Reddy, 1967). The quantity of

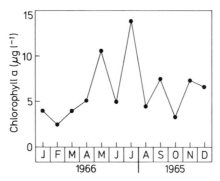

Fig. 17. Average monthly values of chlorophyll *a* in the surface water of the backwater

chlorophyll, which was later found to be predominantly phaeophytin, was much greater during the monsoon months when light penetration in the backwater was greatly reduced (unpublished data).

IV. Assimilation Ratio

The ratio between ^{14}C assimilation and chlorophyll *a* ranged from 0.6 in November to 14.8 in April (Fig. 18). Such a large variation in the ratio further indicates that the entire observed chlorophyll may not be photosynthetically active. The presence of inactive chlorophyll would make the monthly variations in the ratio somewhat different from the seasonal rises and falls of the primary production.

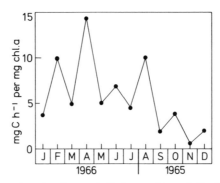

Fig. 18. Average monthly ratios of carbon assimilation to chlorophyll *a* in the surface water of the backwater

V. Primary Production and Environmental Factors

A comparison between the annual cycle of primary productivity and the seasonal variation in the environmental features described above reveals that the peaks in production are independent of the high and low values of solar radiation falling on the surface of water. Monthly variations in total solar radiation are never a limiting factor, although light penetration in the water column is considerably reduced by high turbidity and thus becomes a serious limiting factor for maximum photosynthesis in the backwater. The water temperature seems to have no direct effect on primary production, but changes in salinity are important in favouring phytoplankton productivity. The peaks in primary production occur during the monsoon months when salinity in the backwater is low. The predominant phytoplankton during the monsoon months consists of diatoms and green algae. To test whether low salinity would influence the growth of phytoplankton, the following experiments were conducted:

Several organisms isolated from the inshore areas were cultured in enriched seawater. When the cultures became sufficiently dense, known volumes of these were added to bottles containing seawater of different salinities, 5–35 ‰. These were exposed to constant illumination and their rates of photosynthesis were measured by ^{14}C assimilation (QASIM, BHATTATHIRI and DEVASSY, 1972a). Table 1 shows the range in salinity at which maximum photosynthesis was obtained. It is clear from the table that maximum photo-

Table 1. Range in salinity at which maximum photosynthesis occurred in different unialgal cultures of diatoms and flagellates

Organisms	Salinity range ‰
Bacillariophyceae:	
Nitzschia closterium	10–15
Planktoniella sol	15–20
Triceratium favus	10–20
Asterionella japonica	10–20
Chaetoceros lorenzianus	10–20
Coscinodiscus radiatus	10–20
Biddulphia sinensis	10–20
Rhizosolenia styliformis	15–20
Thalassiosira subtilis	14–24
Dinophyceae:	
Ceratium furca	6–10
Dinophysis miles	10–15
Dichtyocha sp.	20–25

synthesis occurred at low salinities. These experiments confirmed the field observations that organisms are more abundant in areas of low salinity or in seasons when the salinity is rapidly decreasing.

Seasonal variations in the concentration of different nutrients have been shown in Figs. 10–14. During the monsoon period the backwater contains very high concentrations of nutrients. These are largely associated with freshwater discharge and land run-off. The annual cycle of primary productivity (Fig. 16) showed only brief pulses of bloom.

There was no substantial increase in the rate of production when the water was rich in nutrients. This indicates that the nutrient requirement of different phytoplankton species is highly variable and that the high concentration of nutrients alone is not conducive to a substantial increase in phytoplankton productivity. This was experimentally verified by taking cultures of the dinoflagellate *Ceratium* and the diatom *Biddulphia* and exposing them to different concentrations of phosphate and nitrate. Their rates of photosynthesis were measured by the ^{14}C uptake as a function of time (QASIM, BHATTATHIRI and DEVASSY, 1972b). The concentrations of PO_4^{3-}-P and NO_3^--N used were 0.5, 1.0, 2.0, 5.0 and 10.0 μg-at l^{-1}. In *Ceratium* the rate of photosynthesis increased with higher PO_4^{3-}-P concentrations and reached its maximum at a concentration of 10 μg-at l^{-1} in about 10 days. A similar situation was found with *Biddulphia* where maximum photosynthesis was attained within 10 days with increasing concentrations of phosphate. However, when different concentrations of nitrate were used in *Ceratium,* maximum photosynthesis was obtained at 0.5 μg-at l^{-1} and any further increase in the concentration of nitrogen inhibited photosynthesis. In *Biddulphia* an increase in the concentration of nitrate led to a progressive increase in photosynthesis. Similar results were obtained when phosphorus and nitrogen were used in a combined state. In *Ceratium* maximum photosynthesis occurred when the concentration of each was 0.5 μg-at l^{-1}, whereas in *Biddulphia* peak photosynthesis was obtained when the concentration of each was 5.0 − 10.0 μg-at l^{-1}. These experiments indicate that the nutrient requirement of the two species is very different. From these results it can also be postulated that the changing concentrations of nutrients may lead to a succession in the growth of phytoplankton organisms. Such a succession is of common occurrence in the backwater.

VI. Food Chain

The average gross production in the estuary is 280 gC m^{-2} year^{-1} and the net production for days is approximately 195 gC m^{-2} year^{-1} and for days and nights (24 hrs) about 124 gC m^{-2} year^{-1}. The estimated annual rate of consumption of the daily net production by the zooplankton herbivores is 30 gC m^{-2} year^{-1} (QASIM, 1970). The rate of consumption is greater during the premonsoon season (46%) than in other seasons (QASIM et al., 1969). This gives rise to a large surplus of primary production which falls to the bottom as detritus. The shallow euphotic zone increases the fallout of basic food material which forms an important link in the food chain (QASIM, 1970). The detritus is consumed by a variety of benthic animal communities and thus leads to several alternate pathways in the food chain (QASIM, 1971).

Continuous collections of detritus falling on the bottom were made throughout the year (QASIM and SANKARANARAYANAN, 1972). The quantity of detritus in the backwater was much greater than that previously reported from the Southampton waters (TREVALLION, 1967) or from the North Sea and Kiel Bay (KREY, 1961). The values in the backwater ranged from 67 g m^{-2} day^{-1} in March to 1013 g m^{-2} day^{-1} in May and amounted to 90 − 99% of the total phytoplankton productivity. The biochemical composition of detritus and its calorific value were determined (QASIM and SANKARANARAYANAN, 1972). Dried pellets of detritus offered as food to a penaeid prawn *(Metapenaeus dobsoni)* in the laboratory were readily eaten. The prawns lived exclusively on detritus for a long time and moulted several times in aquarium tanks.

2.5

General Features of Dinoflagellate Material Collected by the "Anton Bruun" during the International Indian Ocean Expedition

F. J. R. TAYLOR

I. Biology of Dinoflagellates and their Role in the Food Web

Dinoflagellates are a nutritionally diverse group and cannot be totally included with the diatoms, coccolithophorids and blue-green algae as primary producers. Many are photosynthetic autotrophs, although typically these have strong requirements for organic micro-nutrients such as vitamin B_{12} (auxotrophs), a characteristic they share with many planktonic diatoms. Secondly, some of the autotrophs are also capable of ingesting other cells (BIECHELER, 1936), presumably as a supplement to their photosynthetic nutrition (myxotrophs). This phenomenon appears to be relatively rare although the large ventral opening in the thecae of the marine ceratia may be an adaptation for this phenomenon (NORRIS, 1969) in addition to rarely observed sexual conjugation (VON STOSCH, 1964). Whether or not this phenomenon is ecologically significant on a large scale has not been accurately evaluated. Thirdly, a large number of dinoflagellates lack any photo-synthetic ability and it is assumed that these are phagotrophic grazers. Although the largest of these colourless dinoflagellates may regularly be observed to contain ingested cells (e.g. *Noctiluca scintillans*), many of the dinoflagellates below 40 or 50 μ in size, such as many neritic species of *Peridinium,* cannot be seen to contain ingested cells. Two large, specialized vacuoles termed "pusules" are usually present in these smaller non-pigmented forms (and also in some pigmented species), typically one being much larger than the other and sometimes occupying a great part of the epicone. The content of these pusules is a fluid which is sometimes distinctly pinkish or violet in colour. The function of the pusules is unknown at present but it is tempting to assign a nutritional role to them. It seems possible that many of these small, colourless dinoflagellates are feeders on very small particulate organic material, perhaps including bacteria, or even large organic molecules. Whether or not the pusule participates, this type of nutrition would explain the absence of observed food vacuoles containing recognizable ingested cells.

There is a further type of nutritional mechanism which, although usually considered rare, may be less so among tropical dinoflagellates and may be significant in assessing the food-web roles of these species. This is the formation of symbiotic consortia between photosynthetic and non-photosynthetic organisms. It is now well known that dinoflagellate autotrophs are among the commonest endosymbionts of marine invertebrates, and particularly the coelenterates. Consequently their role in the ecosystems of coral reefs is evident although not quantitatively assessed as yet. Much less well known is a reverse situation found in the tropical plankton involving nonphoto-synthetic dinoflagellates and blue-green algae. This seems to be particularly common among the morphologically elaborate dinophysoid genera, *Ornithocercus* (Fig. 5 c),

Parahistioneis, Histioneis (Fig. 4e) and *Citharistes* (Fig. 4g) in which the blue-green algal cells were termed "phaeosomes" by early authors. According to NORRIS (1967), who has cultured 2 of the blue-green partners (the isolation having been achieved on cruises I and II of the "Anton Bruun"), some or all of the bodies formerly considered to be chloroplasts (chromatophores) within some genera such as *Amphisolenia* may also be endosymbiotic blue-greens. From the point of view of the ecologist, it is the total effect of the consortium on the food web which is important. Consequently it becomes an academic question as to the precise nature of the carbon fixer in cases like this, just as in the case of nitrogen fixation associated with patches of *Trichodesmium*. A most interesting possibility is that the blue-green partners of dinophysoid dinoflagellates are nitrogen fixers as well as carbon fixers. Such an attribute would presumably be of great value in the Indian Ocean where nitrogen-depleted conditions seem to be much more frequent than phosphorus depletion in terms of photosynthetic requirements.

In view of the apparently widespread nature of endocyanosis (endocellular blue-green symbionts) in tropical dinoflagellates, it is important that this be studied in much greater detail to determine if such consortia are "functional autotrophs" and significant as primary producers. In this connection KHMELEVA (1967) believes that radiolaria/zooxanthella consortia are more highly productive in the Red Sea than the phytoplankton.

In summary, many dinoflagellates can participate in primary production as auxotrophic (vitamin-requiring) autotrophs. An undetermined fraction of these may also ingest other cells, thus acting as primary consumers as well as primary producers (myxotrophs). Nonphotosynthetic dinoflagellates, also numerous, may function as grazers or feeders on particulate or even dissolved organic matter. Finally, those forming consortia with blue-green algal cells may be shown in the future to be "functional autotrophs" and thus primary producers.

Many of the photosynthetic dinoflagellates are apparently able to tolerate remarkably low inorganic nutrient levels, a factor which might explain their relative success in oligotrophic tropical oceanic waters. While this may be theroretically attributed to a greater efficiency in nutrient uptake, perhaps related to their motility (such as a more efficient "flushing" of their uptake surfaces), the observation of QASIM (1973) that the photosynthetic rate of a species of *Ceratium* was depressed by an increase of nitrate in culture relative to diatoms, suggests that a difference in metabolism may also be involved in some tropical species.

II. The "Anton Bruun" Material

1. Species Composition

This contribution is based on the floristic analysis of the dinoflagellates from 213 samples of microplankton. They were collected routinely during the International Indian Ocean Expedition (IIOE) by the RV "Anton Bruun" on 9 cruises (designated A, I–VIII) in the northern and western regions of the Indian Ocean during 1963 and 1964 (Figs. 1, 2). All samples were collected by vertical net tows from 200 m to the surface and preserved with formalin.

Over 300 species, including many varieties and forms, from more than 40 genera, were identified and illustrated. It was for this reason that a fully illustrated report is being prepared in the hope that the range of material covered will make it useful in identifying tropical and subtropical dinoflagellates. The scanning electron microscope has proved a valuable adjunct to conventional observational methods (Figs. 5a—c, 6a—e) and has increased the precision of the identifications. The value of the instrument in this study has been discussed elsewhere (TAYLOR, 1972a).

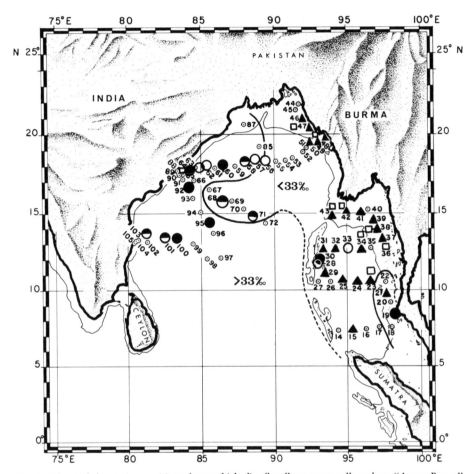

Fig. 1. Chart of the station positions from which dinoflagellates were collected on "Anton Bruun" cruise I, March—April, 1963. The position of the 33‰ surface isohaline is plotted. Symbols indicate the presence of the following organisms: Open circles: *Histioneis* spp; blackcircles: members of the subgenus *Archaeceratium* excluding *Ceratium praelongum*; open squares: *Dinophysis miles* var. *indica*; black triangles: *D. miles* var. *schroeteri*

The obvious deficiency of the "Anton Bruun" material was that the 5% formalin preservation was not adequate for the fixation of many non-thecate species. Ideally these should be studied alive. In fact NORRIS (1966) has photographically illustrated some of the non-thecate species he observed alive on cruises I and II of this expedition, but unfortunately he has not presented a fully detailed account of these observations, and the taxonomic and quantitative assessment of non-thecate Indian Ocean species must await future studies. In a few samples, even despite inadequate preservation, it could be seen that non-thecate dinoflagellates were abundant. These were from stations 289, 327 and 374, all in coastal regions. Further, SUBRAHMANYAN and SARMA (1965) in a study off the SW

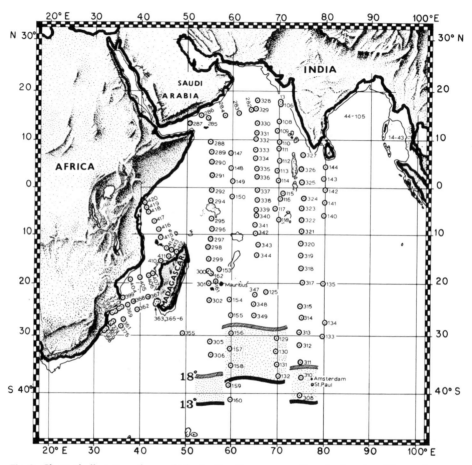

Fig. 2. Chart of all stations from which dinoflagellates were collected other than "Anton Bruun" cruise I. In the southern regions the position of the 18° and 13° C surface isotherms have been plotted at two different times of the year, corresponding approximately to the NE monsoon (southermost) and SW monsoon (northermost)

coast of India have shown that approximately half the nanoplankton fraction which passed through nets consisted of dinoflagellates.

The genus represented by the most species in the material was *Ceratium* with 75 species existing in many varieties and forms. The precise number of species is somewhat meaningless as authors differ in those recognized at the species or infraspecific level. However, this is comparable to the total number included in the monographs by SOURNIA (1968) and SUBRAHMANYAN (1968). Species of *Ceratium* dominated much of the oceanic region whereas the second most strongly represented genus, *Peridinium,* was much more restricted to neritic regions.

Tropical waters are characterized by a great diversity of dinophysoid genera, and it is amongst these that bizarre morphological elaborations are found, particularly within the rarely observed genus *Histioneis* (Figs. 4e, 6e). The most common of the dinophysoid genera in tropical waters is *Ornithocercus,* of which *O. quadratus* (Fig. 5c) is the most widely distributed species.

Various species of the genus *Pyrocystis* (emended by TAYLOR, 1972b) are common, and in particular, *P. pseudonoctiluca, P. fusiformis* and *P. hamulus.* This genus is also interesting because of the strong bioluminescence produced by some of its members

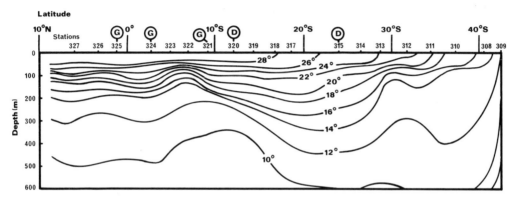

Fig. 3. Profile of isotherms within the upper 600 m from the 75° E meridional stations occupied on "Anton Bruun" cruise V (NE monsoon). G: *Ceratium gravidum.* D: *Histioneis dolon*

(SWIFT and TAYLOR, 1967; ZERNOVA, 1967), making them one of the commonest causes of bioluminescence in oceanic tropical waters.

Some genera usually thought to be rare, such as *Kofoidinium* and *Cladopyxis,* were quite common in the material. In the case of the former, not being thecate in the usual sense, it becomes somewhat deformed by preservation, but not unrecognizably so. However, it has probably been missed in the past, however tempting it might be to attribute its presence to a migration from the Mediterranean from which it has been commonly recorded. It has also been considered to be a "shade genus" (e.g. HALIM, 1967), which might account for its rarity in collections taken from shallow depths.

The "Anton Bruun" material did not contain examples of a rare genus, *Brachydinium,* described from the SW Indian Ocean (TAYLOR, 1963, 1967) which, until recently, might have been considered endemic to the region. LÉGER (1971) has encountered *B. capitatum* quite frequently in the western Mediterranean. Again, it is impossible to attribute this to migration in view of the likelihood of its being overlooked by previous authors.

To this author's knowledge no species of parasitic dinoflagellates have been recorded from the Indian Ocean prior to the present study, due, no doubt, to the fact that no one has looked for them. Although no special attempt to observe them was made nevertheless *Amoebophrya ceratii* was identified from within *Peridinium steinii,* and *Blastodinium spinulosum* was found free in a sample (it typically inhabits the gut of copepods).

Material from the "Anton Bruun" collections was used to supplement the description of a new genus *Discroerisma* (Taylor and Cattell, 1969) and a further new genus related to *Ptychodiscus* will be described in the monograph in preparation.

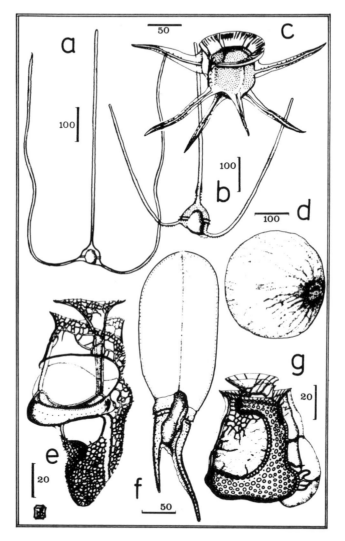

Fig. 4. a *Ceratium trichoceros*. b *Ceratium massiliense* var. *macroceroides*. c *Ceratocorys horrida*. The individual illustrated is a relatively long-spined form. d *Pyrocystis pseudonoctiluca*. e *Histioneis mitchellana*, a representative of the structurally complex dinophysoid species restricted to the tropics and considered a "shade species". f *Ceratium gravidum*, a common member of the subgenus *Archaeceratium*, exhibiting the broad, flattened epitheca found only within the group. This specimen illustrates the most elongate form of the species, others having an almost circular epitheca. g *Citharistes apsteinii*, one of the only two species of this rare dinophysoid genus, illustrating the greatly enclosed, girdle-derived "phaeosome chamber" thought to usually, but not invariably, contain blue-green algal symbionts (dotted outlines). Numbers beside scale lines indicate the length represented, in microns

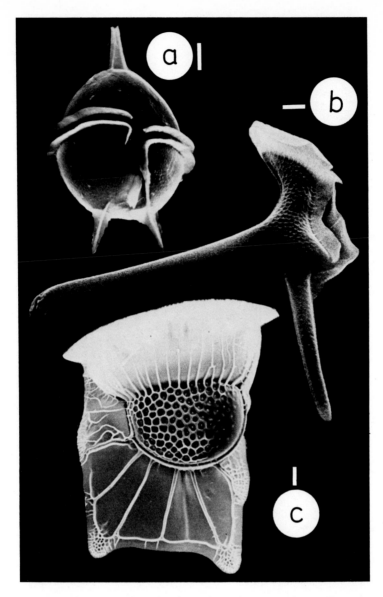

Fig. 5. Scanning electron micrographs. a *Peridinium latispinum* (= *P. africanoides*) with a relatively smooth thecal surface. The small right sulcal list displaced to the proximity of the posterior flagellar aperture is a constant feature and a revelation by scanning electron microscopy. b *Dinophysis miles* var. *schroeteri*, a variety restricted to the vicinity of the East Indies. c *Ornithocercus quadratus*, the most widespread species of the genus. Symbiotic blue-green algae are commonly found within the girdle region of most species of *Ornithocercus*. Scales represent 10 microns in all figures

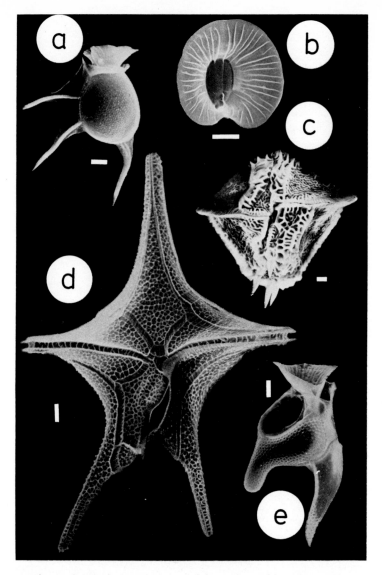

Fig. 6. a *Dinophysis schuettii*. b An apical view of the epitheca of *D. schuettii*. The apical pore is situated close to the ventral (lower) notch. c *Ceratocorys reticulata*. A ventral view of an extremely reticulated specimen. d *Peridinium elegans,* a large, elaborate representative of the genus. e *Histioneis biremis*. Scales represent 10 microns

2. Species Distributions

With such a wealth of species, it is not surprising that representatives of virtually all the types of distributions found by other authors for tropical dinoflagellates (e.g. STEEMANN NIELSEN, 1934, 1939; GRAHAM, 1941, 1942; WOOD, 1964) can be illustrated. Here only a few of the most common or most unusual will be described.

SUKHANOVA (1962a, b; 1964) has recognized the following group of species: *Pyrocystis pseudonoctiluca, Ceratium carriense, C. massiliense* and *C. trichoceros,* as the "basic tropical complex", being the chief tropical component within the tropical Indo-West Pacific region. The present study supports the fact that these are certainly among the commonest species over most of the area studied. However, it should be noted that the "complex" contains dissimilar elements, although *P. pseudonoctiluca* (Fig. 4d) is exceptionally widespread and often abundant (Gulf of Aden, southern India), the other species represent differing preferences. The "Anton Bruun" material tended to support the views of STEEMANN NIELSEN (1934, 1939) and GRAHAM (1941) that of the 3 species of *Ceratium* mentioned *C. trichoceros* (Fig. 4a) is the most highly stenothermal, being incidentally, one of the very few species to show even moderate concentrations in the oligotrophic South Equatorial Current water. *C. carriense* is slightly more thermotolerant, and *C. massiliense* is not only thermotolerant but the var. *macroceroides* (Fig. 4b) dominates in warm temperate waters such as the SW Indian Ocean off South Africa (TAYLOR, MS 1964) and in Australian waters (WOOD, 1964). The variety *armatum* is a cold temperate to subantarctic variety. Consequently it can be seen that although these species are common in the material as a whole, they represent different preferences and degrees of tolerance. In fact, one could add other species which are also common and match the type within the "complex". For example, *Heteraulucus (= Goniodoma) polyedricum* is almost as widespread as *Pyrocystis pseudonoctiluca,* and *Ceratocorys horrida* (Fig. 4c) is as stenothermal and common as *Ceratium trichoceros.*

A cautionary note may be added regarding the genus *Pyrocystis.* It has become evident that this has been a "form genus", being a life-cycle stage of taxonomically diverse dinoflagellate species. Thus although *P. lunula* has a non-thecate motile stage which could be and has been assigned to *Gymnodinium* (KOFOID and SWEZY, 1921), cysts resembling *P. pseudonoctiluca* and *P. fusiformis* give rise to *Gonyaulax* motiles (BALECH, 1962; KOFOID and MICHENER in TAYLOR, 1972b; this material.). Further, as there is so little morphology in the cysts on which to base distinctions (size seems highly variable and can exist in 2 size-stages in the life cycle) there is a strong possibility that cysts termed *P. pseudonoctiluca* may involve several species. For example, DOGIEL (1906) showed that the lunate-cyst species *P. lunula* also has a spherical stage. TAYLOR (1972b) has suggested that species with *Gonyaulax*-like stages be assigned to *Pyrocystis,* and others with gymnodinoid stages be assigned to *Dissodinium.*

The southern boundary of most of the species spread throughout the tropical Indian Ocean is situated close to 30°S where there is an abrupt depletion of dinoflagellates, accompanied by a general sparseness of all protoplankton except for the coccolithophorids. One exception to this is in the southwest where the Agulhas Current represents a southward extension of trophical and subtropical water carrying within its core many tropical species (TAYLOR, 1967; NEL, 1968). The 18°C surface isotherm can be used as a rough approximation of the southern distributional boundary, lying near the northern edge of the Subtropical Convergence region. By comparing the position of the 18° and 13°C surface isotherms on the two meridians of cruise V (55° and 75°E), occupied during the southern summer with the other southern meridional stations, it can be seen that the distance between them varied seasonally and that the 18°C isotherm was situated furthest south during the southern summer (NE monsoon) at approximately 36°S, whereas it was close to 30°S in the southern winter (SW monsoon). It can be noted in passing that SUKHANOVA (unpubl. MS) found that the so-called "tropical convergence" also moved north and south with the seasons, lying between 17° to 20° S during the NE monsoon, and 14° to 16° S in the SW monsoon.

Dinophysis miles represents an extreme morphological modification of the genus *Dinophysis* in that it possesses an elongate dorsal process which can be greatly enlarged (Fig. 5b) so that it exceeds the antapical process in length. It exists in 3 principal forms which differ in the length, shape and angel of the processes, especially the dorsal process (see Böhm, 1935). These forms are here termed *varieties* because 2 can occur sympatrically. The intermediately developed variety, *D. miles* var. *indica,* occurs over the whole Indian Ocean region. In the Red Sea a short-horned variety has been observed which, as it is the type variety, should be named *D. miles* var. *miles* (= *D. miles* var. *maris rubri).* It has never been observed away from the Red Sea-western Araban Sea area. In the vicinity of the East Indies a third variety exists: *D. miles* var. *schroeteri* (Fig. 5b) which possesses the greatest extension of dorsal process and most divergent angle between the dorsal and antapical processes. Despite the currents flowing freely through the various East Indian straits, this variety appears to be completely confined to the eastern Andaman Sea, East Indies and SE Asian waters (see distribution shown on Fig. 1). It co-occurs with the variety *indica* at many stations so that it is not apparently a phenotypic variant caused by an environmental gradient.

Such an unusual phenomenon as this deserves further investigation to fully evaluate it. In fact, many authors may have seen evidence of it but unfortunately this cannot be determined with certainty because of an error in the widely-used taxonomic work by Schiller (1933) in which *D. miles* var. *schroeteri* was included with *D. miles* var. *indica.* Thus the distributional pattern for *D. miles* var. *indica* shown by Sukhanova (1962 a, b) suggests that it was the former variety. Also, the record from the Gulf of Tonkin by Kusjmina (1971) might also be *D. miles* var. *schroeteri.*

In this study no species were found to be particularly associated with the high-salinity water in the northern and western Arabian Sea. The dominant dinoflagellates in that area (*P. pseudonoctiluca,* various ceratia and peridinia) were also found quite commonly elsewhere. In the studies on *Ceratium* distribution carried out by Peters (1932), Steemann Nielsen (1934, 1939) and Graham (1941) no species were found to show a good correlation with salinity *per se* except where the salinities were very low, causing a decline in species.

3. Seasonal Features

Unlike the other major oceans, the tropical and subtropical regions of the Indian Ocean were known, even prior to the IIOE, to be subject to considerable seasonal fluctuations.

Recently Owen and Zeitzschel (1970) have shown marked seasonal variations in the primary productivity of the eastern tropical Pacific. Unfortunately, due to the divergent interests of participating scientists, although the general scheme of longitudinal lines of stations was maintained on the "Anton Bruun" cruises, this seasonal aspect became subordinated to other aims and the resultant plankton samples are difficult to analyse from the seasonal point of view. Ryther et al. (1966), in their presentation of the primary productivity data from the cruises, chose to ignore this aspect in favour of the total point of view. As most of the open-ocean stations were occupied during the SW monsoon or inter-monsoon periods, this may be a reasonable approach for the demonstration of the grossest features. However, as cruises I (Andaman Sea/Bay of Bengal) and V (55° and 75° E meridians and a short line in the northern Arabian Sea from India to the Gulf of

Aden) were undertaken during the NE or post-NE monsoon period (December to April), an attempt is made here to contrast the samples taken on these cruises with the remainder. The reader is referred to RAMAGE (1969) for meteorology and WYRTKI (1973) for physical oceanography. Here the following monthly monsoonal relations have been used: December, January, February – NE monsoon; March, April – post NE monsoon; May, June – early SW monsoon; July, August, September – full SW monsoon; October, November – post SW monsoon.

a) Southwest Monsoon, Intermonsoon/Southern Winter

Although this includes the material from Cruises II (106 – 144), III (147 – 160), VI (328 – 349, 355), VII (358 – 375) and VIII (396 – 420), these stations were not directly situated in the regions of highest productivity associated with the SW monsoon in the nothern Indian Ocean (Somali coast, south Arabian coast and the SW coast of India). Nevertheless, all stations in the northern Indian Ocean, with the exception of cruise VI (65° E meridian), seemed to show a peripheral influence in being generally rich in dinoflagellates. Some stations showed high concentrations of coccolithophorids (157, south of 32° S, and station 336 in the SW Monsoon Current). A dense bloom of the blue-green alga *Trichodesmium thiebautii* (probably = *T. erythraeum*) occured at station 106 off the NW coast of India in May.

The 80° E meridian stations were occupied during the height of the SW monsoon (July) and all stations north of 20° S were rich in dinoflagellates. Station 135 (20° S) was interesting in having a group of species usually considered as deep-water species.

The poorest material of all the cruises was that of cruise VI (June, 65° E), especially south of 10° S.

Cruises VII and VIII were the only cruises undertaken in the Mozambique Channel region. Appararently the season (late winter) is a relatively poor one for dinoflagellates. Coastal stations were higher than central channel stations except those near Tuléar on the SW coast of Madagascar, which were poor. There was a decline from August to September. The richest samples were from the vicinity of Durban and off Kenya (stations 418 – 420). Diatoms were plentiful off Durban, Nosy-Bé (NW Madagascar) and Kenya. Coccolithophorids appeared to be abundant at stations 374 and 417.

b) Northeast Monsoon/Southern Summer

Although only 2 of the cruises, I (Fig. 1, post NE monsoon) and V (stations 282 to 327, Fig. 2), are concerned with this period, they are represented by more samples (118) than the total from the other cruises of the "Anton Bruun". The sampling of the Andaman Sea-Bay of Bengal was more intensive than that of other regions, but cruise I was the only cruise to cover this area and consequently seasonal comparison is not possible. This is a pity, as the material from this cruise was in many respects the most interesting.

Large concentrations of the phagotrophic species *Noctiluca scintillans* (= *N. miliaris*) were present in the vicinity of the Gulf of Martaban and the Irrawaddy River delta in the northern Andaman Sea, and in the NE Bay of Bengal close to the Burmese coast. Throughout the entire Andaman Sea samples were rich in dinoflagellates and also to a lesser extent over most of the Bay of Bengal. The only occurrence of a fresh-water species in the material was also during cruise I with the presence of *Peridinium achromaticum* at station 45 in water with a surface salinity of less than 20‰, presumably situated in a narrow tongue of the Ganges River plume deflected eastwards by the cyclonic circulation in the Bay of Bengal at this time of the year. The presence of many species considered by previous authors to be deep-water "shade forms" in the upper waters in the eastern parts of the Bay of Bengal and adjacent to the Andaman and Nicobar Islands was in contrast to the rest of the material. This aspect will be discussed further later in this paper.

There were striking increases of dinoflagellates in the eastern Bay of Bengal off Vishakhapatnum and particularly off Madras (stations 99 to 103). An exceptionally large number of taxa were present at the latter. At station 103 a total of 88 dinoflagellate taxa were recorded, the highest for a single station in the author's experience. Directly over the narrow shelf the proportion of diatoms increased somewhat and the number of dinoflagellate taxa diminished.

The long cruise V (55° E and 75° E meridians plus an Arabian Sea line to the Gulf of Aden) showed a much more discontinuous distribution of dinoflagellates than was apparent on the other meridional cruises. The Arabian Sea line exhibited only moderate amounts of preservable dinoflagellates, indicating that thecate dinoflagellates played a minor role in the exceptionally high primary productivity recorded by the "Anton Bruun" south of the Arabian coast. Instead, the relevant samples (from stations 284—287) contained large amounts of small, unrecognizably preserved cells, coccolithophorids and amorphous detritus. The dominant dinoflagellate here and in the Gulf of Aden was *Pyrocystis pseudonoctiluca*.

On the 55° E meridian amounts fluctuated greatly with moderate numbers off the Somali coast and an abrupt increase at station 294, immediately to the north of the Seychelles Platform. At the southernmost station on the 55° E meridian, station 306, very large amounts of detritus were present with only low concentrations of net plankton and very few dinoflagellates. Below 30° S all stations had very few dinoflagellates although diatoms were moderately abundant in the Subtropical Convergence Region close to the Islands of Amsterdam and St. Paul. The only dinoflagellates showing moderate increases close to this region were *Cladopyxis brachiolata* and *Ceratium falcatiforme* on the 75° E meridian. Samples rich in dinoflagellates were found to the south of India on the 75° E meridian (stations 325 to 327), dominated chiefly by *Pyrocystis pseudonoctiluca*. The only species showing moderate abundance in the South Equatorial Current was *Ceratium trichoceros*.

In summary, during and immediately following the NE monsoon the Bay of Bengal and Andaman Sea show only a reduced river influence but a rich dinoflagellate flora. In the open Indian Ocean dinoflagellates amounts fluctuated strongly, with maximum numbers close to the Seychelles Platform on the right edge of the Equatorial Counter Current which flows close to the north of the bank during this season. Large numbers were also present to the south of India at stations either in the North Equatorial Current or between it and the Equatorial Counter Current. Southern stations were generally poor in dinoflagellates.

4. Shade Flora

In 1900, in CHUN's book on deep-water marine life, SCHIMPER introduced the idea of a "Schattenflora" in plankton, consisting of certain photosynthetic species living typically below 50 or 100 m, structurally and physiologically adapted to low light concentrations. The data for the theory was derived from the "Valdivia Expedition" material, presented by KARSTEN (1907).

Although the data did not support this theory very well, the idea was taken up by several later authors, particularly those studying tropical and subtropical dinoflagellates (e.g. STEEMANN NIELSEN, 1934, 1939; GRAHAM, 1941). This later work has largely confirmed the tendency of certain dinoflagellate (and some diatom) species to occur consistently at depths below 50 or 100 m except in regions of upwelling (HALIM, 1967). GRAHAM (1941) has stressed that in many species of *Ceratium* thought to inhabit deeper waters the theca is often greatly flattened and extended, either in the epitheca (subgenus *Archaeceratium*, e.g. *Ceratium gravidum*, Fig. 4f.) or in the antapical horns. The latter may have paddle- or wing-like shapes *(C. platycorne)* or the ends may be extended in a resemblance to the fingers of a hand *(C. ranipes)*. The extensions are packed with chloroplasts. GRAHAM considered that the thin walls provided a "window" effect allowing greater penetration of weak light into the cell.

The shade flora phenomenon, if it exists other than under ice, appears to be limited to tropical and subtropical waters. STEEMANN NIELSEN (1934) was unable to observe it in waters south of New Zealand, and HASLE (personal communication) was not able to recognize shade species in her study of cold southern Pacific waters (HASLE, 1969). However, she was also not able to find supporting evidence in her quantitative study of the distribution of equatorial Pacific phytoplankton (HASLE, 1959). It is possible that the small volumes of sample used (an unfortunate but unavoidable consequence of sedimentation counting techniques) were not sufficient to observe the patterns of species in low numbers.

There is also a possibility of physiological adaptation in cells of species also found near the surface. Although deep (below 50 m) chlorophyll *a* maxima have been commonly reported in tropical waters (SAIJO, 1973), there is no conclusive evidence that this is a product of dark adaptation or of the presence of a shade flora.

By sampling from 200 m to the surface on the "Anton Bruun" cruises the material was effectively integrated throughout the depths used by these earlier authors. The depths used by them were usually 200−100 m, 100−50 m, and 50−0 m. The species from these depths were unfortunately termed oligophotic, mesophotic and euphotic by STEEMANN NIELSEN (1939), unfortunate because of the use of the same terms today to designate much greater depths defined by light parameters. In view of the 200−0 m sampling by the "Anton Bruun", it might be expected that the horizontal distribution patterns would reflect the distributions of all three components, completely obscuring the effects of vertical distribution.

In fact, the only reason for raising the question of depth distribution in this otherwise inappropriate context was the picture which emerged from the horizontal plotting of the distributions of several of the so-called oligo- and mesophotic species (determined from the tables of GRAHAM, 1941 and the observations of KAESLER, 1938). For example, in Fig. 1 the distribution of members of the genus *Histioneis* (all considered meso- or oligophotic) and *Ceratium* subgenus *Archaeceratium* (excluding *C. praelongum* which has not been found as selectively deep as the other members of the subgenus) has been plotted. The species concerned are quite noticeably distributed in the western sectors of both the Bay of Bengal and the Andaman Sea. With the exception of the letter stations, they are also in water where the surface salinity is greater than 33‰. At this season the surface and near surface water near the western shore of the Bay of Bengal is derived from coastal upwelling correlated with the NE monsoon and the clockwise circulation within the Bay (LAFOND, 1957; JAYARAMAN, 1965; MOJUMDER, 1968). JAYARAMAN disputed LAFOND's interpretation of upwelling, but MOJUMDER found further evidence for the occurrence of upwelling in the April – June period.

In Fig. 3 the isotherms for the upper 600 m on the 75° E meridian (cruise V) have been plotted. This corresponds also to the NE monsoon period during which the South Equatorial Current is situated at its most southerly latitudes between 10° and 20° S. The eastwardflowing Equatorial Countercurrent is situated at approximately 2° to 6° S, and the westward-flowing North Equatorial Current is also developed close to the southern tip of India and Ceylon. The figure clearly shows a strong subsurface rising of the isotherms within the upper 600 m, reaching to approximaterly 80 m at station 322 and 323. A secondary subsurface upsloping also occurred near 20° S, with the main sloping associated with the northern edge of the Subtropical Convergence region south of 40° S.

Considering only the occurence of *Ceratium gravidum* (G) and *Histioneis dolon* (D), it can be seen that these species occurred at stations to either side of the isothermal "hump" on the right-hand flank of the Equatorial Counter Current and not directly over the upward moving water. Station 315, where *H. dolon* was recorded, showed little direct signs of upwelling.

One of the richest stations for dinoflagellates, station 294 just north of the Seychelles Platform, was situated just south of the Equatorial Countercurrent and here, again, *C. gravidum* was present.

Stations 283 to 287 south of Saudi Arabia, at which very high productivity was recorded, did not reveal any of the "deep" species. Thus the "Anton Bruun" material has some suggestion of an association of the deep species with stations where an upwelling influence might be effective, as well as some contra-indications, even though the sampling extended to the presumed deep range of the species. It may be noted that the most extensive work on the dinophysoid species, including *Histioneis* and *Citharistes,* was based by KOFOID and SKOGSBERG (1928) on samples collected from depths greater than 1000 – 0 m. The relative richness of these rare genera within their Pacific material suggests that for those genera, at least, their normal distribution may extend below 200 m to an unknown depth.

In summary, the position with regard to a tropical "shade flora" of dinoflagellate species is still not entirely unequivocal. The "Anton Bruun" material was not suitable for critically evaluating the problem although the depth of sampling permitted relatively frequent collection of the suspect species. There is a possibility that the rare dinophysoid genera may extend normal distribution below 200 m. One possible application of the established recognition of deep water species would be their use as indicators in shallow samples of deeper subsurface upwelling. HALIM (1967) has employed this principle in the study of the dinoflagellates from the upwelling areas of the Cariaco Trench in the SE Caribbean Sea. He found many of these species in surface samples collected over the trench in October, 1960.

The study has revealed a great richness of dinoflagellates in the Andaman Sea and Bay of Bengal during and after the NE monsoon. This relates well to the observations of ZERNOVA (1962) and ZERNOVA and IVANOV (1964) who also found a great abundance of phytoplankton in the Andaman Sea during the same season. Coverage of this region at other seasons was not made by the "Anton Bruun", although from other studies it can be surmised that the area is much less productive during other seasons when upwelling is not present.

Over the main areas of the central and western Indian Ocean dinoflagellates were more uniformly abundant during the SW monsoon period. During the NE monsoon the distributions were more discontinuous with large quantities present only at a few stations, these being apparently situated in the shear zones between the Equatorial Currents and Countercurrent. The area immediately to the north of the Seychelles Platform was particularly rich in dinoflagellates. BAILEY (1968) has reported that zooplankton is also abundant in this locality during March.

In view of the few observations of north-south shifts in surface features of the southern parts of the Indian Ocean, this requires more detailed evaluation. There is a tendency to ignore this possibility and to combine the results of sampling in the southern parts, assuming that seasonal effects are minimal here. TAYLOR (MS, 1964; 1967) found considerable seasonal differences in the distribution of the phytoplankton in the SW Indian Ocean, apparently correlated chiefly with the formation and breakdown of a strong summer thermocline and variations in the strength of the Agulhas Current.

Finally, mention may be made of the detrital material observed during the analyses for it appears that detritus may constitute a considerable fraction of the particulate carbon in some cases of high productivity in the Indian Ocean, particularly the Arabian Sea (MULLIN, 1965). The stations at which high detrital content was apparent under microscopic observations were also, in general, stations where either diatoms, dino-flagellates of both, were abundant. They were stations 154, 284−285, 291, 294, 297, 300, 306 (very great), 318 and 374.

The Formation of the Chlorophyll Maximum in the Indian Ocean

Y. Saijo

I. Vertical Distribution of Chlorophyll

A typical section of chlorophyll *a* distribution is shown in Fig. 1. As for the surface water, the amount of chlorophyll *a* was 0.1 mg m^{-3} in the nothern area and below 0.05 mg m^{-3} in the southern area. A distinct chlorophyll maximum was found in the layers at

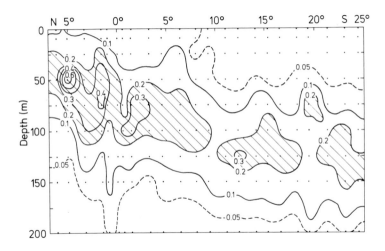

Fig. 1. Vertical distribution of chlorophyll *a* (mg m^{-3}) from samples of the TS "Kagoshima Maru", Dec. 1963 to Jan. 1964, along 78° E longitude. (Data from Endo and Nozawa)

depths of 50 to 75 m in the north near the Equator (0.3–0.6 mg m^{-3}), and at 100 to 125 m in the south (0.2–0.3 mg m^{-3}). In this area the layer of the chlorphyll maximum was generally located in the upper part of the thermocline.

The vertical distribution of chlorophyll *a* and photosynthesis at a station of the same longitude (78° E) is shown in Fig. 2. At this station, the Secchi disk reading was 28 m. The chlorophyll maximum was observed at 100 m, while the maxima of phytosynthesis determined by ^{14}C in *in situ* and tank techniques were found at 75 m and 50 m depth respectively. At the depth of chlorophyll maximum, there is still considerable *in situ* photosynthesis, about one third of that of the maximum value at the 50 m layer, and a minimum in nutrients such as silicate, phosphate and nitrate. This suggests that the

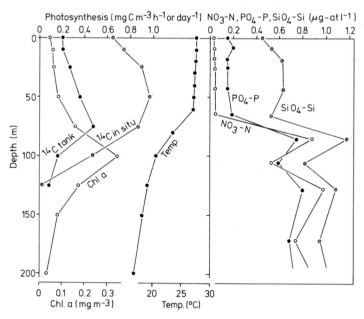

Fig. 2. Vertical distribution of temperatures, chlorophyll *a in situ* and tank photosynthesis and nutrients determined on the TS "Umitaka Maru", Jan. 1963 at 15° 10′ S and 78° 04′ E

chlorophyll maximum is not the result of the passive accumulation of senescent phytoplankton but represents an accumulation of actively growing phytoplankton.

II. Incubation Experiments on Board

To clarify the reason for the occurrence of a chlorophyll maximum in the surface layer, several experiments were carried out by SAIJO, IIZUKA and ASAOKA (1969), in the East China Sea and in the western Pacific Ocean off Japan. The water sample taken from the depth of chlorophyll maximum was transferred into several 250 ml bottles and the bottles were incubated either in a deck tank under natural radiation or in a laboratory tank under fluorescent lamps. The light intensity was regulated to different degrees by white vinyl sheets.

In the East China Sea, the results of a 24 h incubation of samples from the 40 m layer in a laboratory tank showed that under 2000 to 3000 lux the concentration of chlorophyll decreased, whereas under 100 lux it increased to more than twice the initial concentration. These changes might be caused by photooxidation under a strong light and the growth of shade-adapted phytoplankton under a dim light. A similar result was obtained in a deck tank for samples taken from 30 m and 50 m at other stations; the Secchi disk readings were 9.0 m and 13.5 m. Increases and decreases of cell numbers during incubation were observed under higher and lower illuminations respectively.

It is well known that the chlorophyll concentration in an active algal cell which has been exposed to dim light is higher than that in a similar cell exposed to strong light (STEEMANN NIELSEN and JØRGENSEN, 1968 a, b). This phenomenon may also be important in causing the high concentration of chlorophyll pigments in deeper parts of the euphotic layer.

III. Chemical Composition of Particulate Organic Matter

Recently, chemical determinations were carried out for the particulate organic matter taken from the layer of the chlorophyll maximum in Sagami Bay. The chlorophyll maximum was observed in the 100 m layer (Fig. 3) where the light intensity was about

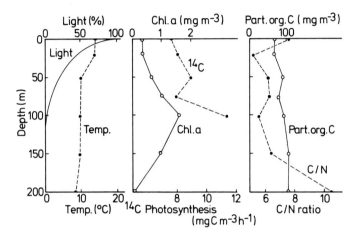

Fig. 3. Vertical distribution of submarine light, chlorophyll *a*, tank photosynthesis, particulate organic carbon and C/N ratio determined on the RS "Tansei Maru", March 1969 in Sagami Bay

1% of that at the surface. The maximum rate of photosynthesis determined by the ^{14}C tank technique and also the highest cell numbers of the dominant phytoplankton, *Skeletonema costatum* were found in that layer. The ratio of C to N showed a minimum (5.6), though the amount of organic C gradually increased from 25 m to 150 m. The C/N ratios of active phytoplankton are generally in the range of 4 to 6, while the C/N ratio of oceanic detritus is 10 or more (SAIJO, 1969). Consequently, the low C/N ratio in the layer of the chlorophyll maximum might be caused by the accumulation of actively growing phytoplankton in that layer. HANDA and YANAGI (1970) found the highest ratio of water-extractable carbohydrate to total carbohydrate for the sample. These results also indicate the existence of active phytoplankton in that layer as has been discussed in detail by HANDA and TOMINAGA (1969). Similar chemical features were observed for the samples taken from the layer of the subsurface chlorophyll maximum in the western Pacific off Japan.

The growth of shade-adapted phytoplankton in the deeper layer and the deterioration of pigments by light in the upper layer are determinative factors causing the subsurface maximum of chlorophyll in the Indian Ocean as well as in other oceanic areas.

2.7

Seasonal Variation of Phytoplankton Pigments and Some of the Associated Oceanographic Parameters in the Laccadive Sea off Cochin

N. M. Shah

I. Material and Methods

Collections were made on board of the RV "Conch" from stations located approximately 7 to 15 km off Cochin (Fig. 1). Most of the monthly collections were made from stations located in area 2, profile studies were made from areas 1, 2 and 3, and one grid

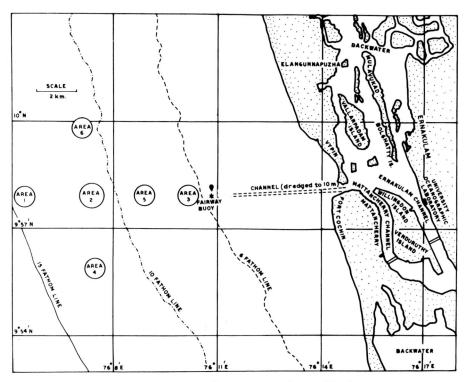

Fig. 1. Map showing collection areas in the sea off Cochin

study from areas 1, 2, 4, 5 and 6. At stations in the depth range 18 to 20 m samples were collected from 0, 5, 10 and 15 m, and at 25 to 26 m deep stations from 0, 10 and 20 m. Collections were generally made between 1000 and 1300 local time. All samples were collected with Nansen reversing water bottles; the usual practice was to operate a single bottle

2 or 3 times at the same depth and empty the water into a plastic bucket. This water was then poured into 2 or 3 one-liter polyethylene screw-cap bottles for determining the amount of plant pigments and nutrients. Samples for pigment determinations were stored in a cool dark place after the addition of 1 ml magnesium carbonate suspension. On reaching the shore laboratory these samples were filtered through Whatman GF/C glass fibre filters, which were then stored in a desiccator in a refrigerator. The analytical procedures for salinity were described in Barnes (1959) and the rest as in Strickland and Parsons (1965 and 1968). Most of the phytoplankton pigment measurements were made with 10 cm path-length, low-volume cuvettes which were specially fabricated for this purpose. Trichromatic equations designated "P.S." were used for calculating the quantity of pigments.

II. Results

1. Variability Studies

The following studies were made to explore the statistical significance of the collections and analyses of seawater samples for phytoplankton pigments.

One quadruplicate and 15 duplicate sets of analyses were made. Combining the results of these, the maximum coefficients of variation were found to be 12% for chlorophyll a and plant carotenoids, and 20% for chlorophyll c. To estimate the extent of sampling variations of individual collections, 2 sets of 7 replicate collections were made alternately from surface and 15 m depth within a 10-minute period in April and October 1968, and 1 set of 4 replicates in April 1969. Each sample of the replicate was treated separately and absorbancies at 750 nm and 665 nm were measured. The coefficient of variation for both surface and 15 m samples was about $10-12\%$. Humphrey (1960) observed greater variation in deeper (30 m and 50 m) samples compared to surface samples. It is concluded that determinations of phytoplankton pigments by a single analysis using mixed water from 2 or 3 Nansen bottle casts in quick succession, as was the practice in most of the cruises, would give values within 12% for chlorophyll a and plant carotenoids, and within 20% for chlorophyll c.

To find out the extent to which the regular station represented the conditions of the area under study, in October 1968, seven collections were made from 5 stations located in a grid in areas, 1, 2, 4, 5 and 6. The first, last and middle collections of the series were taken from the regular station (area 2) so as to eliminate as far as possible, changes in temperature, chlorophylls, tide etc., with lapse of time. Temperature, salinity and O_2 saturation distribution (Fig. 2) show that the general flow in the area was northerly on that day, and that some run-off from the backwaters reached the regular station, mostly in the surface layer, and joined the main flow. However, the regular station does represent the conditions of the area fairly well. The distribution of chlorophyll a also supports this. Profiles of 3 stations located in areas 1, 2 and 3 were worked out in December 1968, and January, February and April 1969. On the basis of the distribution of temperature, salinity and O_2 saturation values, it may be inferred that the 3 stations are more or less alike and are typically marine during these months. However, the influence of backwater run-off can also be seen from the chlorophyll a values, which are higher, and the Secchi disk depths, which are lower, towards the shore.

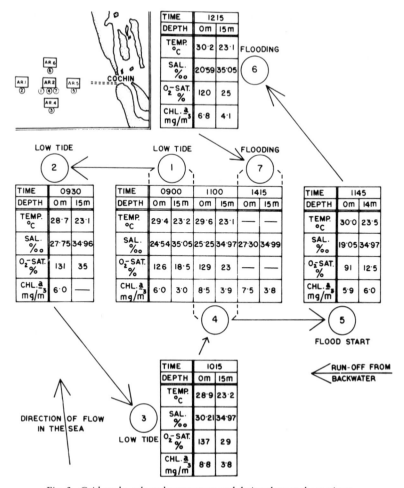

Fig. 2. Grid study, selected parameters and their values at the stations

2. Hydrography

During the annual cycle, the highest and lowest temperatures at surface and 15 m depth are 32.4, 26.2, 30.0 and 21.5° C, respectively. A thermocline with a gradient of more than 2° C in 15 m is present in the upper 15 m during June to October (Fig. 3). Different periods having characteristic distribution of temperature and O_2 saturation have been observed. During June, July and August there is a rapid upward movement in the isopleths indicating upwelling. After October the downward movement in the isopleths, ultimately leading to uniform conditions throughout the water column and lasting till February, is also very clear. During March and April the surface layers warms up, producing weak thermoclines in the upper layers.

Under the influence of run-off from the backwaters, salinity at the surface varies a great deal, especially during the monsoon months, when salinity falls well below 30‰ (Fig. 4); during the rest of the year it remains above 33‰ (maximum 34.99‰). At 15 m depth salinity is above 33.5‰ (maximum 35.34‰), except during December and January when it is around 33.0‰, and in November when it is only 31.8‰. The isohaline distribution in November, soon after the strong haloclines of the previous 6 months, indicates that sinking of the low-salinity surface water has started. Below 5 m depth the water is typically marine throughout the year, thus it may be concluded that the lower salinity at the surface is due to the direct influence of the backwater run-off, which spreads into a thin surface layer by the time it reaches the area under study.

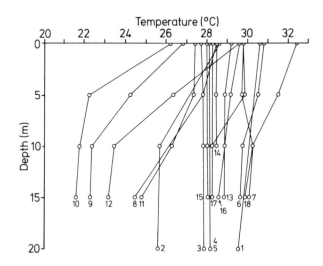

Fig. 3. Vertical distribution of temperature in the Laccadive Sea off Cochin

1	3 May	1967	7	16 May	1968	13	19 Nov.	1968
2	6 June	1967	8	17 June	1968	14	11 Dec.	1968
3	7 Dec.	1967	9	24 July	1968	15	10 Jan.	1969
4	23 Dec.	1967	10	12 Aug.	1968	16	26 Feb.	1969
5	4 Jan.	1968	11	26 Sept.	1968	17	1 April	1969
6	19 April	1968	12	9 Oct.	1968	18	25 April	1969

Dissolved oxygen content in the surface water varies between 3.3 ml l^{-1} and 6.2 ml l^{-1} and at 15 m between 0.7 ml l^{-1} and 4.7 ml l^{-1}. In terms of O_2 saturation values, these figures correspond to a variation between 66% and 129% in the surface and between 12% and 110% at 15 m depth (Fig. 5). The influence of physical and biochemical agencies on the distribution of dissolved O_2 is quite apparent. Though the surface O_2 content differs considerably from that at 15 m during May to October, values are more or less constant from November to March. The reason for the low values at 15 m during May to October is the presence of the cold, high-salinity upwelled water; in the surface layer; however, O_2 is made available by the high organic production that is taking place. On the other hand after November, even when there is a marked drop in the organic production, we find that at 15 m depth O_2 is also present at near-saturation levels. The source of this O_2 could only be the physical agency of diffusion from the atmosphere with subsequent sinking.

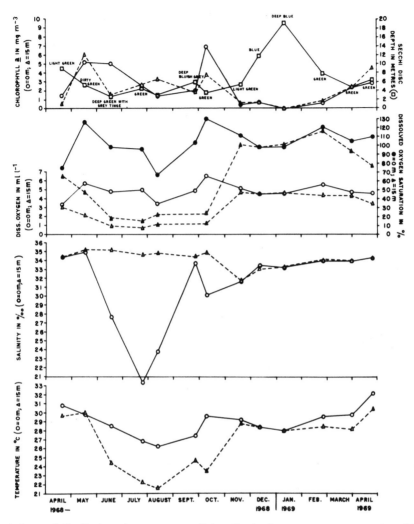

Fig. 4. Seasonal distribution of temperature, salinity, dissolved oxygen, oxygen saturation, chlorophyll *a*, Secchi disk depth and color of the sea

3. Nutrients

In all cases the lowest content was nil and the highest values were 2.7, 2.0, 2.9 and 45.0 µg-at l^{-1} for PO_4^{3-}-P, NO_2^--N, No_3^--N and SiO_4^{4-}-Si respectively. Since the distribution of nutrients does not have a regular pattern, the totals in a column of water $0-16$ m deep are worked out and these values are used in seasonal distribution studies (Fig. 6). The lowest concentration of inorganic phosphate was recorded in January when phytoplankton pigments were also practically nil. While nitrite was present during the SW monsoon months, nitrate was comparatively low throughout the year except in April. Coincident with the higher concentration of both nitrite and nitrate, in April 1969, there was a *Trichodesmium* bloom. Silicate reached its peak value during the SW

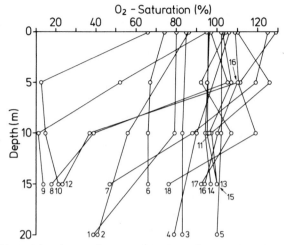

Fig. 5. Vertical distribution of oxygen saturation in the Laccadive Sea off Cochin
(for symbols see Fig. 3)

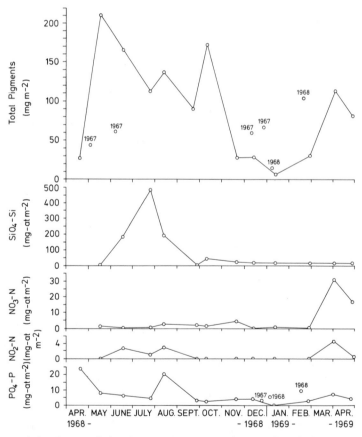

Fig. 6. Seasonal distribution of phosphate, nitrite, nitrate, silicate and total pigments in the upper
16 m of the water column

monsoon when the run-off from the backwaters was also maximum. During the rest of the year there was comparatively little silicate in the water column.

4. Light Penetration

Secchi disk values fluctuate between about 3 m during June, July and August and 19.5 m (20−21 m station depth) in January (Fig. 4). There is a clear inverse relationship

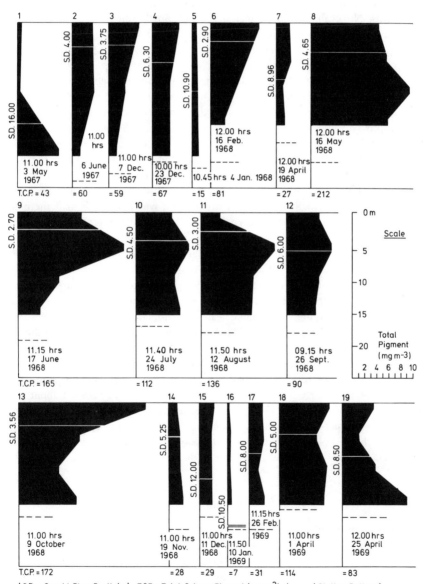

[S.D. = Secchi Disc Depth (m); T.C.P. = Total Column Pigment (mg m⁻²); (−−−−) Station Bottom]

Fig. 7. Vertical distribution of phytoplankton pigments

between Secchi disk depth and phytoplankton pigments. It was also noted that, while the colour tended to be greenish when Secchi depths were less than about 9 m, it was bluish whenever Secchi depth exceeded 9 m.

5. Phytoplankton Population and Pigments

A numerical analysis of the phytoplankton population was made with a view to providing supplementary information on the nature of the population, especially the larger forms. No evaluation of shape, size, chlorophyll content per cell etc., of each species was attempted. The composition of the phytoplankton stock changed considerably with time and depth, the total count being between 1.2×10^3 and 2.9×10^5 cells per liter. The only plankter present throughout the year was *Thalassiosira sp.* and the fluctuation in its abundance was reflected, to a certain extent, in the plant pigment content, both at surface and at 15 m depth. The total pigment content is, of course, the combined contribution of all other organisms, especially the smaller, delicate ones.

Chlorophyll *a* values range between almost nil and about 8 mg m^{-3} at the surface and between 0 and 6 mg m^{-3} at 15 m. If total column (0—16 m) pigments are considered, values range between approximately 5 and 210 mg m^{-2}. Fig. 7 shows the vertical distribution of pigments. Values from 0, 5, 10 and 15 m depth were used in constructing this diagram. Pigments are generally higher in the surface layer, but sometimes the maximum occurs at 5 m. In May 1967, distribution was peculiar in that the pigment content at 20 m depth was much higher than at 10 m off the surface. About 25% of the total at 20 m was phaeopigment. The possibility of *in situ* production contributing towards the pigment content cannot be ruled out because, with the setting in of the SW monsoon, nutrients which have been regenerated in the bottom sediments are likely to be stirred up into the water layer immediately above the bottom and photosynthetic production could take place if light is available. Since the Secchi disk is visible even at 16 m depth, sufficient light is, in fact, available near the bottom. Moreover, diel studies showed a significant increase in pigments at 20 m towards noon, which would indicate the presence of chlorophyll in living cells.

Chlorophyll *c* varies between 0 and about 8 mg m^{-3} in the surface and nil and about 6 mg m^{-3} at 15 m depth. Similarly plant carotenoids also vary between almost 0 and 7 mg m^{-3}. The percentage of phaeo-pigments in the total varies between about 10 and 40% during the SW monsoon; during the other month it is about 10% at 15 m depth while the upper layers have very little. Taking total pigment content, June to October are the rich months and November to March the poor months, average values being about 150 and 20 mg m^{-2} respectively. January is the poorest month with 5—10 mg m^{-2} (Fig. 6).

6. Annual Cycles

A comparison of the distribution of temperature, salinity, O$_2$ saturation and phytoplankton pigments between December 1967 and December 1968 and also between January 1968 and January 1969 (Fig. 8) show, that after undergoing very large changes (Figs. 3 and 5), they more or less revert to their orginal values in the succeeding year. Clearly, the cycles are repeated year after year, thus maintaining a delicate dynamic equilibrium in this complex environment.

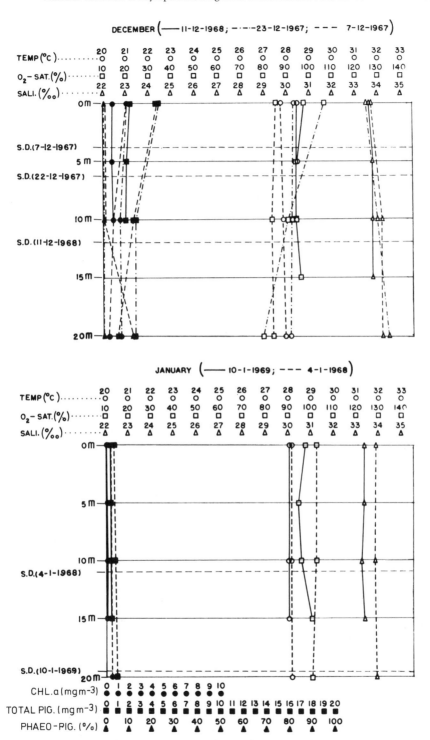

Fig. 8. Comparison of vertical distribution of selected parameters during 2 successive years

III. Discussion

The onset of the SW monsoon in May causes turbulence and increased wave activity in the shallow coastal region and helps to bring the regenerated nutrients into the upper water column; this in turn probably triggers off a new cycle of production, as sufficient light is available down to the sea bottom.

JAYARAMAN and SHESHAPPA (1957) have found high phosphate and plankton content along the coast north of Cochin during the SW monsoon.

A seasonal feature of the sea off Cochin is the alternation between upwelling, which brings up nutrients, and sinking. The present study confirms that, off Cochin, intense upwelling takes place during June, July and August, and the residual effects of upwelling are discernible in September and October. Sinking starts in November and continues until the end of February. Stable conditions are seen in March and April when the upper layers warm up, leading to the formation of weak thermal gradients. Here the upwelling is not, as in most other coastal areas, the direct effect of the wind systems but an indirect effect (BANSE, 1959; SHARMA, 1966). A rough estimate of the rate of upwelling can be made from the vertical movement of the temperature and O_2 saturation curves shown in Fig. 3 and 5. The water at about $22.5°$ C present at 10 m depth on 24 July had moved up to 5 m depth by 12 August; similarly the O_2 saturation curve also seemed to be displaced upwards by about 5 m during this period. This gives a rate of upwelling of approximately 8 m per month.

So far as land drainage is concerned, the sea off Cochin is influenced by backwater run-off. The hydrography of the backwater system, especially of the port area, has been studied by a few workers (SHAH, 1961; RAMAMIRTHAM and JAYARAMAN, 1963; CHERIYAN, 1967; QASIM, 1973).

In the area under study, nitrite, present during the SW monsoon, is absent during the sinking months (Fig. 6). Nitrate, on the other hand, is present in very low concentrations from July to November. Both nitrite and nitrate show abnormally high values in April coincident with *Trichodesmium* bloom; this organism may have the ability to fix nitrogen. Though both nitrite and nitrate occur sparingly and for short periods, nitrogen is unlikely to be a limiting factor. Inorganic phosphate values, which fall almost to nil during January, pick up after February and fairly high concentrations are recorded during the SW monsoon. In culture experiments the rate-limiting concentration has been found to be approximately 0.25 μg-at l^{-1} (GOLDBERG, WALKER and WHISENAND, 1951), so that phosphate may well be the limiting factor since the concentration in the sea falls well below this value. Moreover, the seasonal distribution curve for phytoplankton pigments (Fig. 6) seems to follow the curve for phosphate with a lag of a few weeks, a relationship not seen with the other nutrients studied. Therefore, it is reasonable to assume that the seasonal variations in the phytoplankton pigments are controlled by phosphate concentration in the sea off Cochin.

With regard to the quantity of light available for photosynthesis, bright sunlight is available throughout the year, except on certain days in the monsoon season when the sky may be overcast. Even then, enough sunlight may fall on the sea surface for considerable production to take place in the upper layers. However, the depth of the euphotic zone could be limited by the presence of phytoplankton themselves, or other dissolved and particulate material. A clear inverse relationship between Secchi disk depth and the quantity of phytoplankton pigments has been noted in this study (Fig. 4).

When dealing with phytoplankton pigments, the effect of grazing cannot be overlooked. One of the consequences of grazing would be the production of degraded forms of inactive chlorophyll which would interfere with the spectrophotometric determination of chlorophylls. Off Cochin, during the SW monsoon the percentage of phaeopigments is about 10 to 40% at various depths; during the other months the upper layers have very little, while at 15 m depth there are about 10%. This indicates heavy grazing during the rich monsoon months. However, no data on the seasonal variation of zooplankton in this area are available so that any further interpretation will have to await further studies.

As a general conclusion it may be stated that hydrobiologically 2 distinct periods, "May – October" and "November – April" may be identified. The former is characterized by upwelling and high pigment content and the latter by sinking, followed by stable conditions and low plant pigment content. Now that information on the quantity of plant pigment present during different months in the coastal region off Cochin is available, it is possible to make a rough estimate of the phytoplankton pigments at any given time of the year if the colour of the sea is observed and the Secchi disk measured, provided the influence of the changing hydrographical conditions is also borne in mind.

2.8

Bacteriological Investigations in the Arabian Sea

G. RHEINHEIMER

Bacteriological investigations were carried out during the cruise of RV "Meteor" in the Arabian Sea in March and April 1965. The distribution of bacteria was studied in the northern Gulf of Oman and the Straits of Hormuz, as influenced by the currents flowing out of the Persian Gulf.

Total counts were made by the plate-method on ZoBELL'S yeast extract-peptone agar 2216 E. Numbers of saprophytic bacteria ranged from $8-470$ ml^{-1}, the highest counts being usually obtained along the thermocline at 20 to 30 m. The number of bacteria along the Arabian coast significantly exceeded those along the Persian coast.

Counts of bacteria in the offshore region of the northern Gulf of Oman and the southernmost part of the Persian Gulf are correlated with salinity (Fig. 1). Below the

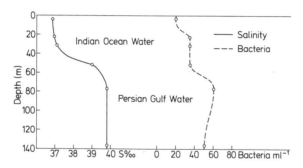

Fig. 1. Vertical distribution of saprophytic bacteria and salinity at station M 373 in the southern Persian Gulf

layer of Indian Ocean water with a salinity of 36.4 to 36.6‰ the Persian Gulf Current, consisting of water of higher salinity, moves SE. The depth of this current increases with increasing distance from the Straits of Hormuz, while salinity and counts of bacteria decrease. The numbers of bacteria approach those of the Arabian Sea, due to the continued mixing of Gulf and Indian Ocean water. Below 200 m the content of bacteria has adjusted to that of the Arabian Sea, while at a depth of 100 m there are significant differences in numbers of bacteria. For instance, at station M 269 with a salinity of 39.1‰, the bacterial count is 93 ml^{-1} whereas the neighboring stations M 253 and M 382 give 27 and 34 ml^{-1} with a salinity of 36.4‰.

The higher content of bacteria of the Gulf water is due to the greater amount of organic material. Repeated vertical profiles during 2 anchor stations, one in March and the other in April 1964, did not show short-term fluctuations of the counts of bacteria.

The proportion of luminous bacteria in the water of the northern Arabian Sea was striking: the average of the total counts was about 10%. As in other parts of the Arabian Sea, the bacterial flora in the northern part was dominated by proteolytic forms with only slight saccharolytic activity.

3. Standing Stock and Distribution of Phytoplankton, Zooplankton and Particulate Matter in Selected Areas

3.1

Agulhas Bank Plankton

A. De Decker

Information on the plankton of the Agulhas Bank has always been scarce and sporadic. We had to rely on occasional collections made at a small number of stations by passing expedition ships. A regular exploration of the Bank from a planktological point of view has never been attempted.

In recent years, the outlook has much improved as far as research effort and available material are concerned. During the International Geophysical Year (IGY), RS "Africa-

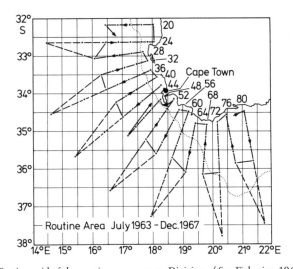

Fig. 1. Station grid of the routine survey area, Division of Sea Fisheries, 1963–1967

na II" worked two lines of stations over the Bank once per quarter. A similar survey was made in 1960. In 1961 the Division of Sea Fisheries, Cape Town, started monthly routine surveys in an extensive area around the Cape, which also covered the western half of the Agulhas Bank. These surveys consisted of oceanographic stations in a dense grid and comprised regular plankton sampling in the upper 150 m (Fig. 1). This routine program was maintained until June 1967. Most of the information contained in the present paper is derived from this source, and most of it is still unpublished.

The eastern part of the Bank was visited much less frequently, chiefly by workers of the Department of Zoology and of Oceanography of the University of Cape Town during IGY and IIOE, when seasonal cruises were undertaken to survey the Agulhas Current. The inshore parts of 1 or 2 of the transects were situated on the Agulhas Bank.

I. Physical Environment

Situated between the lower course of the Agulhas Current (temperature at the core 25° C or more) and the origin of the Benguela Current (surface temperature below 10° C during active upwelling), the water of the Agulhas Bank can display very steep thermohaline gradients, often caused by dynamic or wind-driven upwelling. Vertical gradients of

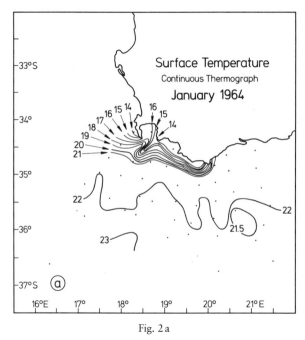

Fig. 2 a

Fig. 2 a – c. Typical surface temperature conditions in austral summer, autumn and winter (° C)

9° C in 10 m (Shannon, 1966) and frontal gradients of 8° C in 5 miles (Bang, 1970) have been recorded. (Fig. 2).

The Agulhas Current does not cross the Bank, but its seasonal and short-term fluctuations must exert a strong influence on the conditions there. Relatively short-lived cyclonic eddies move along the right flank of the current (Bang, 1970) causing intense mixing of Agulhas and Bank waters along their path.

Near the bottom, Central Water, after climbing up the slope, is spread out over the shelf to a variable extent, at times reaching the coast and the surface, or breaking surface over the edge of the Bank in the center of cyclonic eddies.

Strong thermoclines are widespread during summer (Shannon, 1966) and intense coastal upwelling can induce sudden and spectacular drops in temperature, causing

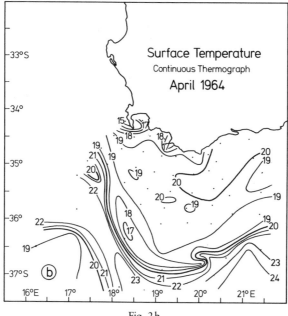

Fig. 2 b

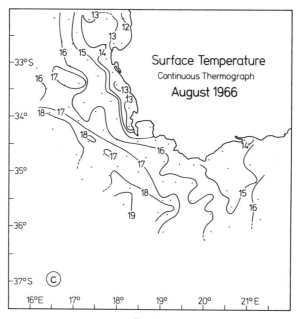

Fig. 2 c

mass mortality of marine life (KORRINGA, 1956). In February 1970, 6° C was measured at the surface, a few miles from the coast, in the neighborhood of Knysna (23° E).

Towards the east, inshore upwelling develops into the cold Counter Current, which is traceable both physically and biologically as far as Durban and beyond.

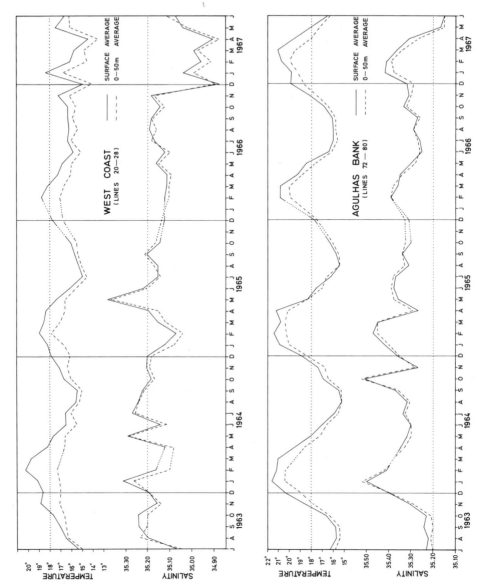

Fig. 3. Monthly averages of temperature and salinity from the west coast of South Africa and the Agulhas Bank

The western side of the Bank appears subject to the most diverse influences, as a result of a shifting dynamic equilibrium between the terminal parts of the Agulhas Current, the upwelling water in the southern fringes of the Benguela Current system and the northward encroachments of the eddy system centered around the Schmidt-Ott Seamount complex.

The main body of water overlying the Bank appears to be a discrete entity with characteristics of its own. The temperature curves (Fig. 3) show a well-mixed water in the upper 50 m, subject to wider seasonal fluctuations than the corresponding layer off the west coast. The salinity fluctuates irregularly in both areas, values over the Bank being as a rule markedly higher. During the 4 years represented in Fig. 3, both areas show a gradual decrease in amplitude of the fluctuations of both temperature and salinity until December 1966, when a sharp and persistent drop occurred off the west coast, followed in May

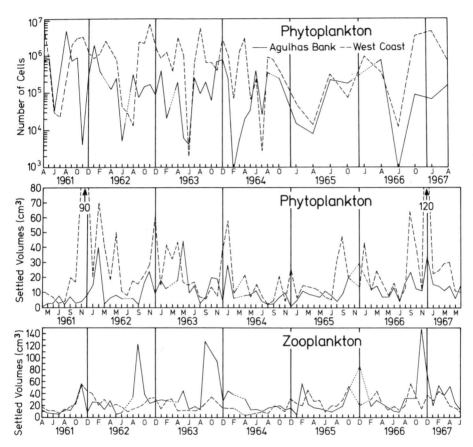

Fig. 4. Monthly averages of phytoplankton cell counts, phytoplankton settled volumes and zooplankton settled volumes off the west coast of South Africa and the Agulhas Bank

and June 1967 by a less abrupt decline of the salinity over the Bank. Such parallelism of physical events is in tune with the biological affinities that will appear between the west coast and large parts of the Bank.

The Agulhas Bank is contiguous with one of the most productive coastal waters in the world — the Benguela Current system. Precise methods for comparing the primary productivity in both areas have not yet been used on a sufficiently large scale, but a rough comparison of the standing stocks of phytoplankton east and north of the Cape of Good Hope can be derived from the routine cell counts on samples taken by means of hydrological bottles at a depth of 10 m, or from the settled volumes of phytoplankton obtained in vertical net hauls with the N 50-net (Kemp, Hardy and Mackintosh, 1929) in the upper 50 m (Fig. 4).

II. Phytoplankton

The unpublished data on phytoplankton given below are from a personal communication by E. A. Coghlan-Nel.

On the average, the cell counts over the Bank are about one tenth of those recorded off the west coast. During 1961−67, cell counts in excess of 10^6 cells per l occurred 53 times over the Bank, as against 126 times off the west coast. The highest single cell count recorded over the Bank was $13 \cdot 10^6$ per l at an inshore station west of Cape Agulhas; off the west coast it was $24 \cdot 10^6$ per l at an inshore station north of Columbine Promontory.

Most of the counts exceeding 10^6 cells per l over the Bank occurred at inshore stations west of Cape Agulhas. They were most frequent in summer (19 times), rarest in winter (7 times).

Among the organisms responsible for the high cell counts were 25 diatom species. Only 5 among them were cosmopolitan or warm-water forms (Chaetoceros compressus, C. costatus, Hemiaulus hauckii, H. sinensis, Nitzschia delicatissima), the others being temperate or cold-water forms occurring abundantly in the inshore belt off the west coast−with the exception of two oceanic forms (Rhizosolenia alata and Chaetoceros decipiens). The most common diatoms over the Bank are Chaetoceros socialis, Leptocylindrus danicus, Nitzschia seriata and N. delicatissima, the latter species being the most common one throughout the whole southwestern sector of the Indian Ocean. (Nel, 1968).

The settled volumes do not necessarily follow the trend shown by the cell counts, due to the large difference in cell size of the different species. In August 1961 the settled volumes were low but the counts exceeded 10^6 cells per l at 6 stations, the dominant species being Nitzschia seriata, a minute diatom. On 5 occasions only the settled volume exceeded 100 ml at stations on the Bank during the period 1961−1967, whereas this happened 29 times off the west coast during the same period. Nevertheless, the largest single volumes recorded in the whole survey area were taken over the Bank west of Cape Agulhas in January 1963: 540 ml and 580 ml respectively at two stations 20 miles apart.

Only one of the 5 high volumes occurred in autumn (April 1962) with Chaetoceros costatus and C. socialis as dominant species. The 4 others were in summer, with the following species in predominance:

Chaetoceros constrictus	Nitzschia pungens var. atlantica
C. curvisetus	Skeletonema costatum
C. debilis	Thalassiosira rotula
C. decipiens	Nitzschia closterium
C. radicans	N. delicatissima
C. socialis	

All the above species are inhabitants of temperate waters and commonly found in large numbers off the west coast, except the cosmopolitan N. delicatissima and the warm-water form C. costatus. Volumes in excess of 50 ml were recorded 35 times over the Bank during the years 1961−1967.

A study of the occurrence and composition of phytoplankton blooms is now in progress. Their seasonal occurrence and predominant components over the Bank are summarized in Table 1.

Table 1. Composition of phytoplankton blooms over the Agulhas Bank (1961 – 1967)

	Spring	Summer	Autumn	Winter
Inshore	*Chaetoceros socialis* most common inshore Other temperate *Chaetoceros* spp., *Nitzschia seriata,* *N. pungens* var. *atlantica* fairly common	*Chaetoceros socialis* *Nitschia pungens* var. *atlantica* inshore every summer from False Bay to Danger Point *Rhizosolenia alata* f. *gracillima* (oceanic) east of Danger Point	*Chaetoceros socialis* *C. curvisetus* most common	*Chaetoceros socialis* most common in False Bay to Danger Point Dinoflagellates *Chaetoceros decipiens* *Thalassiosira subtilis* more abundant further east
Offshore	*Rhizosolenia alata* (oceanic form) is main species in offshore blooms	*Rhizosolenia alata* f. *gracillima* (oceanic) *Ceratium* spp.	Offshore blooms rare	Dinoflagellates

Diatoms blooming exclusively or predominantly over the Bank are the following:

Bacteriastrum hyalinum	*Rhizosolenia alata*
Coscinosira polychorda	*R. alata f. gracillima*
Ditylum brightwelli	*R. alata f. indica*
Nitzschia closterium	*R. hebetata f. semispina*
Planktoniella sol	*R. styliformis*
	R. styliformis f. longispina

Inshore to the east of Cape Agulhas and in the offshore waters all over the Bank, the dinoflagellates increase in numbers and diversity and a shift in the composition of the diatom flora becomes obvious. A closer examination is needed to ascertain whether there exists a typical bank community of phytoplankton. As yet, no clear boundaries between floras have been determined.

The general impression gained from the phytoplankton data is that there is a strong similarity between the inshore floras on either side of the Cape of Good Hope. The diatom flora of the south coast shows predominantly Atlantic characteristics at least as far as Cape Agulhas, and changes its character only gradually further to the East; blooms in which species of the Benguela Current predominated have been recorded from as far as East London (DE DECKER, 1962).

III. Zooplankton

The monthly averages of zooplankton settled volumes show a general tendency towards higher values over the Bank than off the west coast (Fig. 4). This may seem paradoxical, considering the lower production of phytoplankton over the Bank. There are also spectacular peak values in late spring or summer, far exceeding the corresponding maxima off the west coast. The explanation is to be found in the perennial presence of

Thaliacea in variable sizes and quantities over the Bank. This makes any comparison of settled volumes with those in other areas meaningless, unless the catches are broken down into taxonomic groups. These Thaliacea, at the time of their annual peak, can occur in incredible numbers over the central and southern parts of the Bank, their uninterrupted swarms extending over thousands of square miles.

Their maxima closely follow those of the phytoplankton, and their grazing potential probably constitutes an important limiting factor in the development of other consumers within the Bank community. The overwhelming majority among the species present in these swarms belongs to the 2 species *Thalia democratica* and *Doliolum denticulatum* which also predominated in the seas south of Madagascar during the first IIOE cruise "Africana II" in June and July 1961, but in far fewer numbers. Advection by the Agulhas Current and eddy dispersal over the highly productive Bank may initiate their dense swarming. Data from Zoutendyk (1970) on the zooplankton settled volumes in the SW Indian Ocean show high concentrations over the eastern part of the Bank as well. Average volumes in excess of 128 ml per 100 m^3 were recorded throughout the year, except in winter, when they still kept within the range of 65 to 128 ml per 100 m^3.

Apart from the *Thaliacea*, the Bank at times also harbours impressive local concentrations of *Copepoda*, *Cladocera* or *Chaetognatha*.

1. Thaliacea

Van Zijl (1959) identified 11 species of salps and doliolids in material taken monthly over a period of 2 years (1954—56) off the South African west coast. His work was continued by Dowler (unpublished), who examined monthly catches taken over the whole routine survey area from October 1963 to December 1965. The list of species was correspondingly extended to 23, two of which could not be identified beyond the genus (Table 2).

Table 2. *Thaliacea* identified by D. Dowler in the routine survey area of the Division of Sea Fisheries (1964—65)

Thalia democratica	*Cyclosalpa pinnata*
T. longicauda	*C. virgula*
Salpa fusiformis	*C. bakeri*
S. maxima	*Doliolum denticulatum*
S. cylindrica	*D. dentic,* var. *ehrenbergii*
Ihlea magalhanica	*D. mirabilis*
Iasis zonaria	*D.* sp.
Thetys vagina	*Dolioletta gegenbauri*
Ritteriella amboinensis	*D. tritonis*
Traunstedtia multitentaculata	*D. valdiviae*
Pegea confoederata	*D.* sp.

The Agulhas Bank, in spite of its occasionally enormous thaliacean biomass, has in no way contributed to the extension of van Zijl's original list of species. *Thalia democratica* and *Doliolum denticulatum* did not show a consistent difference in the location of their main concentrations, and very often their distribution patterns were very similar.

South of the Cape of Good Hope, in some typical instances the widespread blanket of thaliaceans suddenly narrowed into a ribbon-like strand turning to the North and penetrating the Atlantic along a path parallel to the west coast but well away from the shore, some 40 or 60 miles out to sea. Further north it fanned out again and dispersed, or petered out without dispersing.

Such a pattern is indicative of the presence of 2 water masses between which the water carrying the salp swarms is hemmed in. The inshore water mass is obviously the cold belt of upwelling water, considered as the starting point of the Benguela Current. The offshore water mass appears to be subject to regular seasonal shifts with a pronounced N−S component. This shift is documented by a similar rhythm in the appearance and

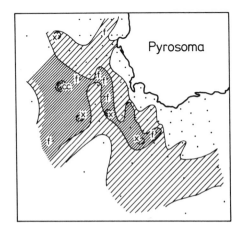

Fig. 5. Distribution of *Pyrosoma sp.* in October 1963

disappearance of a number of plankton organisms, some of which show close connections with Subantarctic or Antarctic species − or are considered as Subantarctic in their general distribution. The patch of *Pyrosoma* in Fig. 5 could be such an indicator. The water mass concerned is considered to be part of the large eddy system centered around the Schmidt-Ott Seamount, some 300 miles SSW of the Cape of Good Hope.

Outside the season of maximal northern advance of this water mass, which precedes the salp maximum over the Bank by one or two months, the salp distribution pattern south and west of the Cape does not show the constriction described above but advances into the South Atlantic over a wide front, while its right flank fans out northward, usually keeping at a greater distance from the cold west coast.

In the typical form of *Doliolum denticulatum*, there was a strong tendency for the gonozoids to avoid the Bank and the inshore stations off the west coast, where the population was mostly composed of phorozoids. No similar tendency could be seen in *Thalia democratica*. This species, however, showed an increase of the solitary form during summer, the aggregates being more common in the other seasons. In *D. denticulatum*, phorozoids were always more widespread than gonozoids, but the latter showed their maximum dispersal in autumn and a minimum in late winter and spring.

Among the less abundant species, only *Doliolum nationale* showed a tendency to keep

Table 3. Occurrence frequency of *Thaliacea* in the routine area

Months		J	F	M	A	M	J	J	A	S	O	N	D
No. of stns occupied:	1963 –	–	–	–	–	–	–	–	–	–	81	80	62
	1964 –	60	74	64	75	70	58	77	66	79	81	74	72
	1965 –	68	73	76	66	73	78	76	68	63	80	–	66
Cyclosalpa pinnata	1963 –											6	11
	1964 –	21	4	4	10	1				1		4	7
	1965 –	10	24	12	16	5	13	7	14				1
Iasis zonaria	1963 –											1	
	1964 –					1							
	1965 –								3	1	2		1
Thalia democratica	1963 –										58	53	46
	1964 –	56	49	40	52	40	31	18	39	52	54	38	47
	1965 –	17	22	50	48	48	42	14	15	40	59		48
Thalia longicauda	1963 –										2	2	
	1964 –	3	1		1	1					1	4	25
	1965 –	29	9	9	1						2		2
Pegea confoederata	1963 –										1		
	1964 –	11	4	2	3								1
	1965 –	3	15	11	9	3		1			1		1
Traustedtia multitentaculata	1963 –												
	1964 –												
	1965 –										2		
Salpa fusiformis	1963 –										7	11	1
	1964 –	3	1	2		2	1	1	1	19	37	14	15
	1965 –	6	6	2	4	11	10	13	19	37	46		18
Salpa cylindrica	1963 –											4	
	1964 –		1	1		5						2	3
	1965 –	1	2							3	13		7
Ihlea magalhanica	1964 –									13	6		2
	1965 –						1	3	2	7	6	4	
Doliolum denticulatum	1963 –										60	47	46
	1964 –	44	57	50	70	61	49	37	47	39	73	39	20
	1965 –	11	20	42	37	61	56	58	54	60	56		21
Doliolum nationale	1963 –										36	5	
	1964 –	1		12	23	2	8	2	1	2	16	7	
	1965 –					1	7	8	7	30	22		2
Dolioletta gegenbauri	1963 –										13	17	
	1964 –				3						6		
	1965 –	1	1	1	4	1					21	4	1

its main concentrations over the Bank. But even at its peak season, its numbers appeared modest in comparison with the 2 former species. A remarkable fact is the absence of gonozoids throughout both years of observation — except for very small numbers in October 1963 at the 2 points of the west coast where inshore upwelling is most frequent (Cape Peninsula and Cape Columbine), and in July 1964 near the southern tip of the Bank, where offshore upwelling occurs regularly.

Doliolum nationale is exceptional among thaliaceans in the area, in having its maximum in winter, when all other species are absent or at a low ebb (except *Ihlea magalhanica* in 1965). In certain periods, its distribution shows a clear preference for areas of upwelling, both in- and offshore. Six other species were found over the Bank for short periods and in small numbers: *Salpa fusiformis* each year mainly in October, but also in June and December — *Cyclosalpa pinnata*, *Pegea confoederata* and *Dolioletta gegenbauri* in March and April — *Dolioletta tritonis* at 5 stations in October 1965 — *Salpa cylindrica* at 6 stations in December 1965.

Cyclosalpa pinnata and *Pegea confoederata* showed a close resemblance in their distribution patterns and displacements during both years. Moving in from the oceanic area in the west, their pattern broke up on reaching the Bank where they soon disappeared completely (January to March 1964; February to April 1965). *Salpa fusiformis* at first appeared at isolated localities closely connected with the areas occupied by the former 2 species, but spread over a large continuous area after these had disappeared (Fig. 6 a−m). A rare species in the area, *Thalia longicauda*, became suddenly widespread in December 1964 and January 1965, declining quickly in February and March before

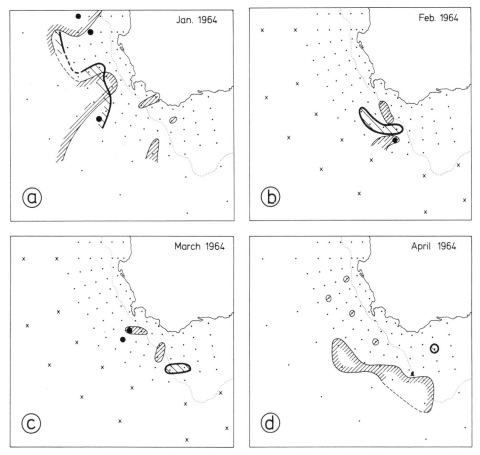

Fig. 6 a−m. Distribution of *Cyclosalpa pinnata* (thin lines), *Pegea confoederata* (thick lines) and *Salpa fusiformis* (black dots and broken lines)

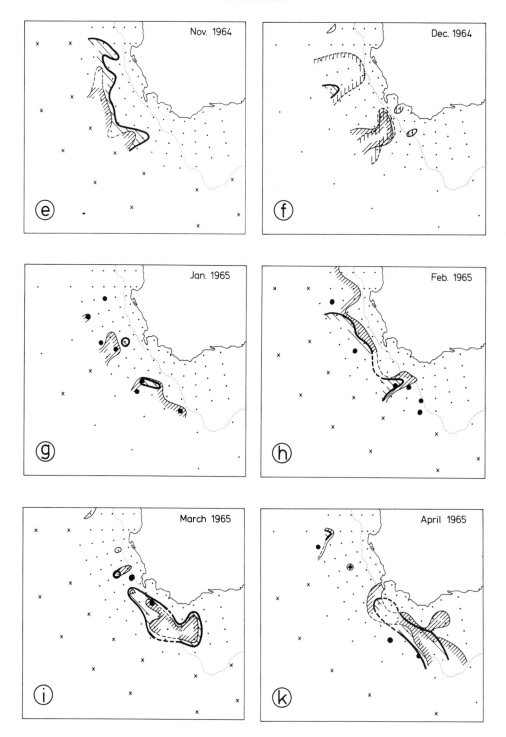

Fig. 6 e–k

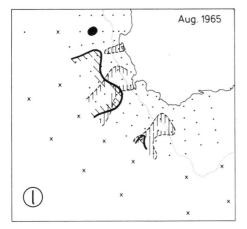
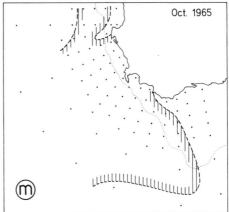

Fig. 6 l and m

dropping back to its usual level of scarcity. It appeared to move in from the NW corner of the routine survey area on the Atlantic side and, in smaller numbers, from the SW slope of the bank. This occurrence might be connected with the unusual conditions prevailing during the summer 1964−65.

Other species listed in Table 2, apart from the above mentioned ones, were recorded in the routine survey area in small numbers only.

2. Appendicularia

This group was studied over the whole routine survey area for 2 years (1964−65) on a quarterly basis by DOWLER; the results are not yet published. 26 species were found, 4 of which could not be identified beyond the genus.

The number of individuals of each species counted over the whole survey area is given for each year separately in Table 4. In many species the total number underwent considerable change from one year to the next. *Oikopleura longicauda,* by far the most abundant species in 1964, as well as the predominant O. *dioica* and O. *rufescens,* decreased by $^2/_3$ or $^3/_4$ in 1965, and so did *Fritillaria formica,* whereas O. *albicans* shrunk from 4 000 to 200 specimens and O. *intermedia* disappeared completely. O. *cophocerca,* however, rose from 700 individuals in 1964 to over 12 000 in 1965. *Fritrillaria pellucida* more than doubled its numbers and O. *fusiformis* also showed a very remarkable increase.

The distribution of the species around the Cape often presents a more scattered aspect than in most other groups. The only way to distinguish geographical trends was by outlining the areas of higher density of population. All species present in sufficient numbers to form a distribution pattern occurred in the Indian and the Atlantic sector of the survey area in one season or another, but in many of them a predilection for one sector or the other was apparent from the population density distribution.

Among the more common species, only the following 3 seemed to avoid the Agulhas Bank: *Oikopleura albicans,* O. *intermedia, Megalocercus huxleyi.* This constitutes a striking difference from other major groups of plankton animals, where the majority of the species tends to disappear from the Bank. A preference for the Bank waters was noticeable

Table 4. *Appendicularia* identified by D. Dowler in the routine survey area of the Division of Sea Fisheries (1964 – 65)

Species in order of abundance of the 2-years total	1964 Total	%	1965 Total	%
Oikopleura longicauda	31 057	38	9 154	16
O. fusiformis	10 616	12	16 293	29
O. dioica	14 863	18	5 232	10
O. cophocerca	701	1	12 042	22
O. rufescens	9 326	11	2 338	4
Fritillaria pellucida	2 457	3	5 644	10
F. formica	4 696	6	1 047	2
Oikopleura albicans	4 092	5	232	0.4
Fritillaria borealis	1 910	2	1 682	3
Oikopleura cornutogastra	547	0.7	416	0.8
Stegosoma magnum	296	0.4	549	1
Fritillaria haplostoma	194	0.2	334	0.6
Tectillaria fertilis	311	0.4	122	0.2
Megalocercus huxleyi	196	0.2	150	0.3
Oikopleura intermedia	230	0.3	0	–
O. parva	107	0.1	13	0.02
Fritillaria sp.	10		32	
F. bicornis	32		0	
F. megachile	16		8	
Oikopleura sp.	1		10	
Fritillaria taeniogona	0		3	
Kowalewskia sp.	3		0	
Appendicularia sicula	3		0	
Folia sp.	0		2	
Fritillaria fraudax	2		0	
Althoffia tumida	0		2	
Total:	81 666		55 305	

in: *Oikopleura cornutogastra, O. longicauda, Fritillaria formica, F. haplostoma.* Both *Fritillaria* species seemed more closely connected with the Atlantic sector, whereas *O. longicauda* showed an increase towards the East in certain seasons.

The following species were generally more abundant in the Atlantic sector beyond the western edge of the Bank, or off the west coast:

    Oikopleura fusiformis   *Fritillaria borealis*

    O. rufescens   *Stegosoma magnum*

    O. dioica   *Tectillaria fertilis*

    O. albicans

A good example of inshore distribution, doubtless connected with upwelling, is seen in *O. dioica*, which is abundant at the inshore stations along the west coast and further east around the Cape towards Cape Agulhas. It tends, however, to scatter over the Bank and is again found in increased numbers at places where offshore upwelling is known to occur, to the SW and S of the Bank (Fig. 7i – m).

The distribution area of *Fritillaria pellucida* (Fig. 7 a – d) and *Oikopleura cophocerca* (Fig. 7 e – h) underwent a seasonal shift from the central part of the Bank towards the Cape and then northward into the Atlantic. This shift took place during both years and

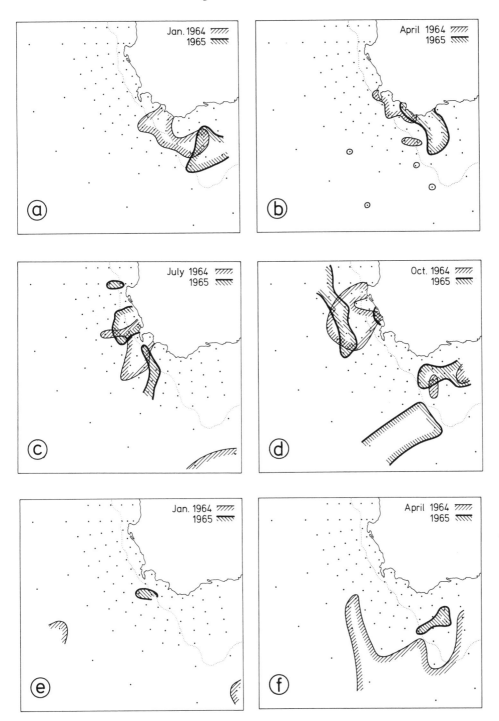

Fig. 7 a—m. Distribution of *Fritillaria pellucida* (a—d), *Oikopleura cophocerca* (e—h), *O. dioica* (i—m) in 1964 and 1965

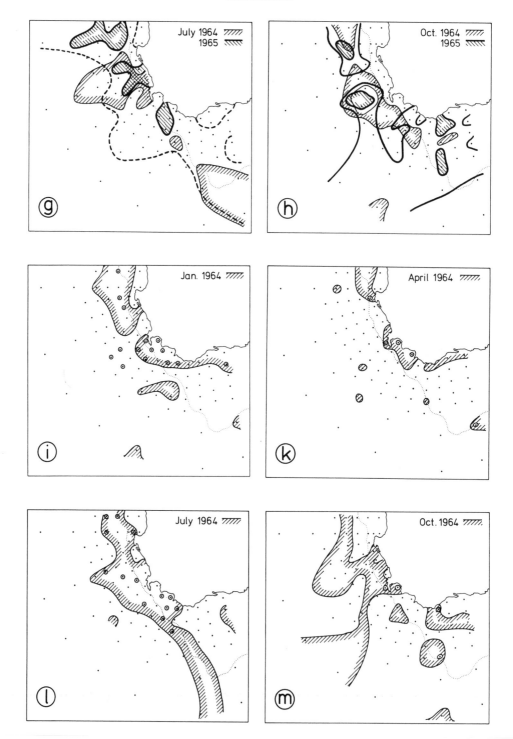

Fig. 7 g–m

for both species in the same period: it started in January from the east and south, and ended up NW of the Cape of Good Hope in October, when a new population would appear also in the east.

Seasonal peaks in abundance are very much in evidence in many species, although they are not always repeated in both years. It is probable that the anomalous conditions of January 1965 affected the cycle of certain species. Only *Fritillaria formica* had its peak in January, in both years. April saw the culmination, mainly over the Bank, of *Fritillaria haplostoma, Stegosoma magnum* and *Oikopleura cornutogastra*, and in the western sector, of *Megalocercus huxleyi* and *Oikopleura rufescens*, all five species in both years; *Tectillaria fertilis* and *Oikopleura intermedia* had a peak in April 1964 only. In July of both years 4 species culminated: *Oikopleura albicans, O. parva, O. cophocerca* and *Fritillaria borealis*. The following 4 species had a peak in October 1964 of 1965, but none in both years, and they also showed more or less important maxima in other seasons, as indicated in parentheses:

Fritillaria pellucida (April 1964, Jan. and Oct. 1965)

Oikopleura dioica (July 1964, Oct. 1965)

O. fusiformis (April 1964, Oct. 1965)

O. longicauda (April and Oct. 1964)

The seasonal maxima observed in SE Australian waters by THOMPSON (1948) for the individual species show very little correspondence with those in South Africa, but analogous hydrological events in Australian and South African waters do not take place at the same time of the year.

3. Chaetognatha

HEYDORN (1959), working on one year's monthly samples which covered most of the area off the west coast between Cape Town and Lamberts Bay, listed 12 species of chaetognaths. STONE (1969) found 18 species in the course of his investigation of the chaetognath community of the Agulhas Current. Among his 34 station positions equally spaced along 8 transects of the current between Durban and Plettenberg Bay, 5 were located on the eastern wing of the Agulhas Bank. His list comprised all the species found by HEYDORN off the west coast.

Chaetognath studies are currently pursued by MASSON and encompass the whole routine survey area, bridging the gap between the regions investigated by HEYDORN and STONE, respectively. Only 6 months' material (May to October 1964) has been examined so far and the results can be summarized as follows.

The species list (Table 5) has been expanded to 24 species, comprising all those found by HEYDORN (1959) and by STONE (1969). The most striking feature so far observed has been the close relationship of the different chaetognaths to the different water masses. *Sagitta friderici*, the most common chaetognath in this region and considered by many authors as a neritic species, was indeed found mainly in inshore waters in May, June and July. A small number were also distributed offshore over the Agulhas Bank, indicating that their distribution may be related to depth. In August, September and October, however, a number of *S. friderici* moved offshore along the west coast, due probably to a corresponding movement of the surface water taking place in conjunction with inshore upwelling. This interpretation is supported by the fact that *Eukrohnia hamata* and *S. decipiens*, both relatively deep-water chaetognaths, were found in the surface water inshore at the time when *S. friderici* was found offshore. These deep-water forms are found near the surface only at times when upwelling occurs and are thus used as indicators of upwelling by several authors.

Table 5.   *Chaetognatha* identified by C. R. Masson in the routine survey area of the Division of Sea Fisheries (May to October 1964)

Sagitta friderici	H, S	S. zetesios	
S. minima	H, S	S. hexaptera	H, S
S. serratodentata	H, S	S. robusta	H, S
S. pacifica		S. neglecta	H, S
S. tasmanica		S. bipunctata	S
S. enflata	H, S	S. bedoti	S
S. regularis	H, S	S. ferox	S
S. planctonis	H, S	S. lyra	S
S. macrocephala		S. decipiens	S
		S. pulchra	
Pterosagitta draco	H, S		
Krohnitta subtilis	H, S	Krohnitta pacifica	S
Eukrohnia hamata	H, S	Eukrohnia fowleri	

H   denotes species identified off the west coast by Heydorn (1959)
S   denotes species identified in the Agulhas Current area by Stone (1969)

S. minima is noted as an indicator of mixed water. The largest concentration of this species was over the Agulhas Bank, a situation agreeing well with the intense mixing occurring in that area. Whenever there was a large concentration of this chaetognath west and north of the Cape of Good Hope, it was found that its presence was caused by influxes of mixed Agulhas water into these parts.

The most obvious association of Chaetognatha with a water mass was evident when water derived from the Agulhas Current rounded the Cape and proceeded up the west coast. In these waters many typically Indo-Pacific Chaetognatha were found. It appears as though in 1964 some Agulhas Current water rounded the Cape each month from May to October. This is indicated by two species: *S. enflata* and *S. regularis*, the latter being an epiplanktonic tropico-equatorial form of the Indo-Pacific region, whereas the former has a more cosmopolitan distribution. Both were found in relatively large numbers off the west coast and their distribution suggested transport by the Agulhas Current. In June, July and August, other typically Indo-Pacific forms were found in smaller numbers in the research area: *S. robusta*, *S. bedoti*, *S. neglecta*, *S. pacifica* and *Krohnitta pacifica*. They were restricted to the offshore stations, probably due to their lesser degree of tolerance to neritic conditions in this area.

Influxes of Atlantic oceanic water into the research area are much harder to define than Agulhas influxes. Four Chaetognatha can possibly be used as indicators of Atlantic water, but none seems entirely satisfactory. A combination of these may prove a better indicator. The species which are of some use are: *S. hexaptera*, *S. bipunctata*, *S. serrato-dentata* and *Pterosagitta draco*. When these Atlantic influxes take place they have a wedge-shaped appearance with the point of the wedge situated SW of the Cape of Good Hope. The Atlantic water seems to have the effect of restricting the Agulhas water to the coastal region on the west coast. This effect was very noticeable in July, when the influx of Atlantic water constricted the Agulhas water to a narrow band off the Cape of Good Hope, which then widened out as it proceeded north. In July the Atlantic water also acted as a block to Agulhas water, because while Indo-Pacific forms were found in great concentrations at the easternmost deep stations beyond the 200 m isobath south of the Bank, they were completely absent from the outer stations further to the west, where Atlantic forms were found.

4. Euphausiacea

The most comprehensive account on the euphausiid fauna of southern African waters, by BODEN (1954), is based on widespread collections in the area between the tropical Indian Ocean (10° S), the Antarctic Convergence (50° S) and the Atlantic waters bordering the African mainland to as far north as Walvis Bay (23° S). This huge area yielded 42 species. NEPGEN (1957) identified 18 species in a restricted area between Cape Town and Lamberts Bay (32° S) on the west coast, where he found *Euphausia lucens* and *Nyctiphanes capensis* as the dominant species. The following summary has been condensed from unpublished data obtained by D. GOW, who analysed two years' monthly samples collected in the routine survey area of the Division of Sea Fisheries (1964 – 1965) (Table 6).

Among the 34 species identified, only 9 were found at one or more stations situated on the Agulhas Bank and only two, *Nyctiphanes capensis* and *Euphausia recurva*, were

Table 6. *Euphausiidae* identified by D. GOW in the routine survey areas of the Division of Sea Fisheries (1964 – 1965)

Euphausia recurva	*Nyctiphanes capensis*	*St. microphthalma*
E. lucens	*Thysanoessa gregaria*	*St. suhmii*
E. similis	*T. parva*	*St. elongatum*
E. similis var. armata	*Nematoscelis megalops*	*St. maximum*
E. diomedeae	*N. microps*	*Nematobrachion flexipes*
E. tenera	*N. gracilis*	*Thysanopoda monacantha*
E. spinifera	*N. atlantica*	*T. obtusifrons*
E. hanseni	*N. tenella*	*T. orientalis*
E. brevis	*Stylocheiron carinatum*	*T. pectinata*
E. mutica	*St. abbreviatum*	*T. tricuspidata*
E. hemigibba	*St. affine*	
E. paragibba	*St. longicorne*	

found there throughout the year. *Nyctiphanes capensis* is a neritic form, known only from the area between SW Africa and East London, until MEIRA (1970) found it in fair numbers off the Cape Verde Islands. *Euphausia recurva* is common in the Indian Ocean. On the Bank, it seems to occupy the place held by *E. lucens* in the offshore waters of the west coast. The latter is seen over the Bank only in the winter months.

Another temporary visitor to the Bank is *Euphausia diomedeae*, also seen in autumn and winter only at the offshore stations, where it is transported by the Agulhas Current; it rounds the Cape and is found in the Atlantic as far north as 32° S. A similar distribution is seen in *E. brevis*. *Thysanoessa gregaria*, although widespread in the whole survey area,

is more common in the north (St. Helena Bay) in winter, generally over deeper water.
It is found over the edge of the Bank in spring and autumn and SW of the Bank in
winter.

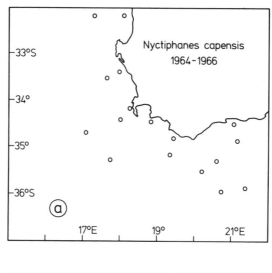

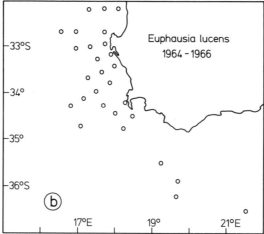

Fig. 8 a—d. Occurrence of euphausiid swarms in 1964—1966

Nematoscelis tenella, normally found in deep water SW of the Cape, also appears at
the southwestern edge of the Bank in winter. *Stylocheiron longicorne* and *S. carinatum*
both appear in autumn at the edge of the Bank. The former, being the more common of the
two, is spread along the southwestern slopes of the Bank and west coast.

Swarming has been observed in 7 euphausiid species in Cape waters, but *Nyctiphanes
capensis* is the only one forming swarms regularly all over the western half of the Bank.

Its concentrations are usually smaller than those of other swarming species. Two other species, *Euphausia recurva* and *E. lucens,* were found swarming over the edge of the Bank on isolated occasions only (Fig. 8 a−d). The limits of temperature, salinity and dissolved

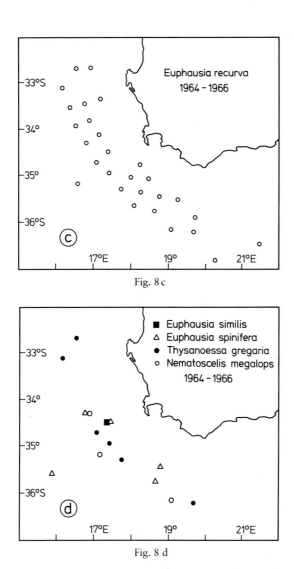

Fig. 8 c

Fig. 8 d

O₂ content within which swarming was observed in 6 species are plotted in Fig. 9. The species swarming over the Bank are those which show the widest tolerance for the three environmental factors considered.

The biomass of euphausiids in comparison with the west coast, is low over the Bank. In winter 1965, the volume of euphausiids ranged from 0.0002 to 0.03 ml m⁻³, in summer from 0.001 to 0.02 ml m⁻³. Off the west coast in the same periods the figures were 0.0001 to 0.26 and 0.0001 to 0.06 respectively.

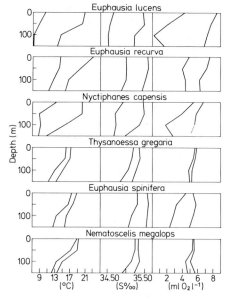

Fig. 9. Vertical distribution of temperature, salinity and dissolved oxygen in the upper 150 m for the
stations where euphausiid swarms were sampled (1964–66)

5. Amphipoda, Hyperiidae

Siegfried (1963) published an annotated list with 77 hyperiid species found in the
150–200 miles wide inshore between Cape Infanta on the south coast and the northern
border of SW Africa. The waters between the Cape of Good Hope and Cape Infanta
yielded only 27 species, as against 40 to 44 for each of the three west coast sectors
distinguished by the author. This may be interpreted as another indication of the restrictive
influence of the Agulhas Bank environment on the diversity of its fauna.

Dick (1970) examined the material taken quarterly from October 1962 to July 1963
in the routine survey area and also the IGY and IIOE samples collected in the Agulhas
Current area and the SW Indian Ocean by SAS "Natal" and RS "Africana II" respectively.
About 9 000 specimens out of 502 hyperiid samples yielded 105 species, 26 of which are
new to southern African seas, 20 species were additions to the west coast fauna, 45 to the
south coast fauna and 39 to the east coast fauna. Keys are given for all genera and species.

From Dick's unpublished notes the following distributional details are apparent.

Parathemisto gaudichaudi has its main area off the west coast and moves east around
the Cape into the inshore waters off the south coast in July; from April, it fanned out over
the Bank and seems to have joined up in July with a small population centered over an area
of offshore upwelling south of the Bank. One unidentified *Hyperia sp.* occurred as
isolated individuals over deep water beyond the southern and southwestern edges of the
Bank in October and April, but in January large numbers were found at many stations
along the SW edge and invaded the shallower waters in the central area of the Bank. Also
in January, *Lycaea pulex* made a similar but less spectacular appearance from the south,
but moved further west over deep water in April.

A similar westward shift from January to April was seen in *Simorhynchotus anten-narius, Tetrathyrus forcipatus, Parascelus typhoides, P. edwardsi* and *Amphithyrus glaber,* whereas *A. similis* underwent the westward displacement between October and January. A remarkable chronological succession of species was seen in the genus *Amphithyrus.* With *A. similis* at its maximum in October and January, and *A. glaber* in January only, *A. sculpturatus* had its widest dispersal in April and *A. bispinosa* in July. A further movement pattern was seen in *Brachyscelus crusculum* and *Vibilia armata,* which were very rare on the Bank but much more common in the western and southwestern parts of the survey area. They tended towards the coast in July and October and kept farther offshore in January and April. The amplitude of this movement was greater in *Vibilia* than in *Brachyscelus.* Their distribution pattern suggests that they may belong to the plankton of the southern eddy system.

6. Cladocera

The Cladocera of the Agulhas Bank have not yet been the object of a formal taxonomic study. The presence of *Evadne spinifera, E. tergestina* and *E. nordmanni,* and of at least one *Podon sp.* has been established. We know that over the western extremity of the Bank *Podon sp.* and *Evadne nordmanni* are common. The latter is present throughout the year in False Bay and had a clear maximum in early spring (September 1959), with lesser maxima at intervals of $2-3$ months (February, May, July, December 1959). *Evadne spinifera* made a sudden appearance in False Bay in December 1959 (444 specimens in one haul), but had vanished completely by the following March. *E. tergestina* appears to be very rare and confined to the summer months. The latter two species seem to be associated with colder water around centres of upwelling.

The dominant cladoceran on the Bank, however, is *Penilia avirostris,* whose center of dispersion appears to be situated in the central area of the Bank. At times in this area *Penilia* by far outnumbers all other zooplankton species caught in the N70-nets, its peak season being summer. Occasionally *Penilia* extends its distribution to the west and rounds the Cape, penetrating northward, both in- and offshore, as far as the latitude of St. Helena Bay (32° S).

The *Penilia* population of the Bank is now under study by DELLA CROCE and his collaborators (DELLA CROCE and ANGELINO, 1968). They found that the Bank was one of very few localities where *Penilia* is present throughout the year and recognized here for the first time that the annual cycle is supported by both parthenogenetic and sexual repro-duction, as in the case of a seasonal cycle. The authors consider that the resting eggs may here accomplish their function in a different way from that observed in the areas where this species shows a seasonal cycle.

7. Copepoda

This group is the only one among the zooplankton for which a reasonable coverage of the whole Bank has been obtained. CLEVE (1904) identified 110 species in a series of 21 vertical hauls taken in inshore waters between Cape Town and Durban. His 4 samples taken west of the Cape Peninsula contained 43 species and 6 samples taken off the east coast yielded 92 species, whereas 17 samples taken over the Bank contained only 27 species. This is another example of the low level of diversity in the plankton groups over the Bank.

Admittedly, CLEVE's hauls over the Bank were taken in much shallower depths than those on either side of it, but this aspect must not be overstressed. A recent survey with vertical nets operated between 100 m and the surface at 9 stations spread over the whole width of the Bank and visited 4 times in one year, yielded 55 species of copepods, as against 71 species found in 7 horizontal surface hauls of 10 minutes made between East London and Durban in July 1965. The coastal belt where CLEVE obtained his material was sampled again 60 years later by means of a plankton pump which allows continuous sampling while the ship is underway (DE DECKER, 1962). The succession of species in E-W direction along the ship's route agreed surprisingly well with that found by CLEVE.

In July 1967, during a similar survey with the continuous pump along the same route, this agreement was found once more. This time, however, the ship also worked 36 oceanographic and plankton stations on the way up and back, the upward leg between Port Elizabeth and Durban following a route at a distance of 60 to 80 miles from the coast in order to sample the core of the Agulhas Current (Fig. 10).

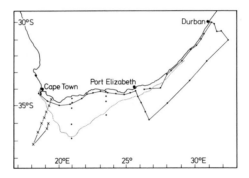

Fig. 10. Sampling grid used for copepod distribution data. Straight lines indicate underway sampling with the continuous pump, dots and crosses indicate vertical net hauls

The general distribution of copepod species over the bank and in its eastern and western approaches, as presented below, is based on the above-mentioned surveys, supplemented by the following.

From April 1960 to January 1961, 2 N-S transects were worked quarterly over the Bank east of Cape Agulhas, starting from St. Sebastian Bay and Plettenberg Bay, respectively, and reaching a point just beyond the 100-fathom line. Vertical net hauls were made down to 100 m. Data on the copepod fauna west of the Bank were obtained from vertical hauls and continuous pump samples along a transect running from Walker Bay in a SSW'ly direction (line 60 in Fig. 1). This transect was done in April 1964 and one particular reason for selecting it was the presence, on its offshore part, of a cyclonic eddy which was likely to—and did— present an interesting plankton content. With the above set of information as a basis, the copepod fauna of the Bank area can be briefly described as follows.

Of major importance, both for dispersal and for abundance, are *Nannocalanus minor, Calanoides carinatus* and *Centropages brachiatus* amongst the calanoids. On the basis of dispersal alone (i.e. number of stations where present) *Rhincalanus nasutus,*

R. cornutus cornutus, and *Centropages chierchiae* come well in front of *C. brachiatus,* and are followed closely by *Acartia danae, A. negligens, Calanus finmarchicus (sensu lato), Paracalanus parvus, Temora discaudata,* and several others, whose names are omitted here because they are mostly found in very small numbers.

The peaks of abundance during 2 separate years were found to be as follows:

	1960−61		*1963−64*
April:	*Centropages chierchiae*	July:	*Centropages brachiatus*
July:	*Centropages brachiatus*	October:	none
October:	*Nannocalanus minor*	January:	*Nannocalanus minor*
	Calanoides carinatus		*Calanoides carinatus*
January:	*Rhincalanus nasutus*		*Rhincalanus nasutus*
		April:	*Centropages chierchiae*

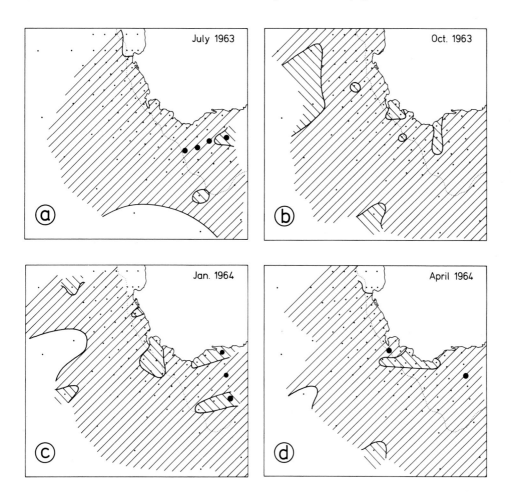

Fig. 11 a−q. Seasonal occurrence patterns of 4 common copepod species. *Nannocalanus minor* (a−d), *Centropages brachiatus* (e−h), *Rhincalanus nasutus* (i−m), *Calanoides carinatus* (n−q). Cross-hatched: total occurrence area of species concerned, thick dots: highest concentration of adults, small areas within cross-hatchings: occurrence of early stages (copedites I and/or II)

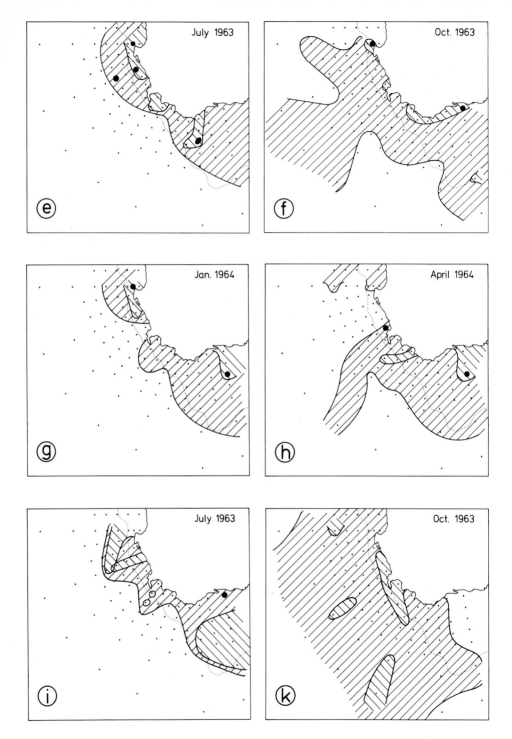

Fig. 11 e–k

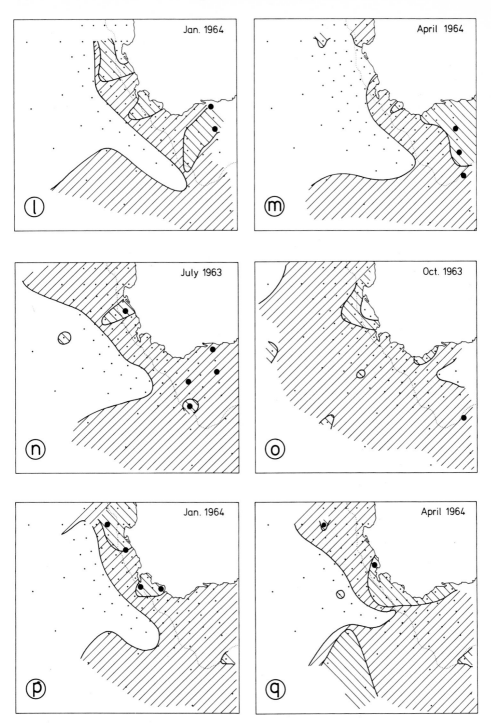

Fig. 11 l–q

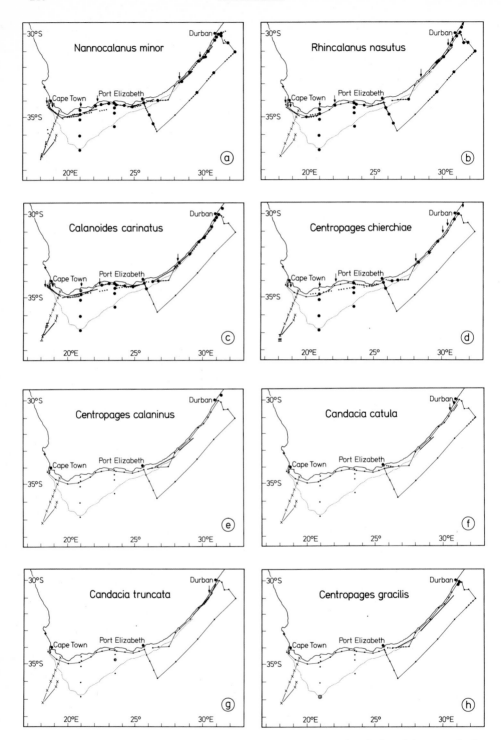

Fig. 12 a—q. Distribution of copepod species (presence indicated by thickened lines or dots)

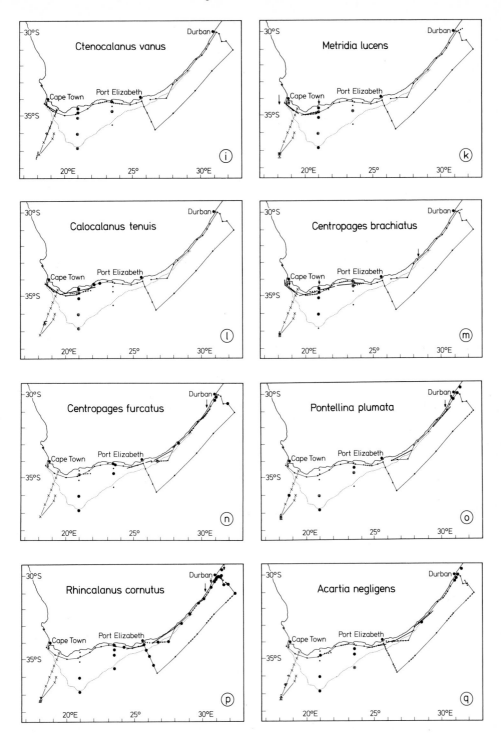

Fig. 12 i–q

Abundant species such as *Calanoides carinatus* or *Centropages brachiatus* were found to have their youngest copepodite stages concentrated in relatively small areas, mostly around centres of upwelling, from where the later stages diverged further afield as they progressed in age. Such "nurseries" were found both inshore and over the shelf edge, the latter position probably denoting cyclonic eddies (Fig. 11 a – q). When comparing the distribution of the various species identified over the Bank, a number of patterns can be distinguished, as enumerated below (Fig. 12 a – q).

a) Species common in regions adjoining the Bank and also present over the latter, without showing a noticeable increase in abundance:

Calanoides carinatus	*Paracalanus parvus*
Centropages chierchiae	*Rhincalanus nasutus*
Nannocalanus minor	

b) Species occurring in adjoining regions, but showing a notable increase in abundance over the Bank:

Calanus finmarchicus s.l.	*Candacia bipinnata*
Ctenocalanus vanus	*Clytemnestra rostrata*
Pseudodiaptomus nudus	*Euterpina acutifrons*

A number of species of groups a and b tend to follow the coastline eastward as far as Durban and beyond, while becoming scarcer with distance from the Bank. They are obviously carried by the cold countercurrent.

c) Species avoiding the Bank but commonly found on the edge of the shelf and beyond:

Neocalanus gracilis	*Pleuromamma abdominalis*
Eucalanus elongatus	*P. borealis*
Eucalanus mucronatus	*P. piseki*
Mecynocera clausi	*P. xiphias*
Undeuchaeta plumosa	

d) Species found only in a relatively narrow inshore belt between the Cape and Durban. Most of them seem to enter the area coming from the Indian Ocean and are listed below in order of westward extension along the coast.

Candacia truncata	*Labidocera acuta*
Clytemnestra scutellata	*Canthocalanus pauper*
Copilia mirabilis	*Temora turbinata*
Candacia catula	*Paracalanus aculeatus*
Centropages calaninus	*Clausocalanus furcatus*
C. gracilis	*Paracalanus crassirostris*

e) Species widespread in the surveyed region of the Indian Ocean and extending westward over the Bank in the inshore belt only (in order of westward penetration):

Acrocalanus monachus	*Calocalanus contractus*
Euchaeta acuta	*Microsetella rosea*
E. wolfendeni	*M. norvegica*

Groups d and e seem to imply longshore transport in the opposite direction from groups a and b.

f) Species widespread in the surveyed part of the Indian Ocean and over the Bank, except in the inshore belt west of Algoa Bay.

Undinula darwini   *Calocalanus plumulosus*
U. vulgaris   *Centropages furcatus*
Eucalanus attenuatus   *Pontellina plumata*
E. crassus   *Acartia negligens*
Rhincalanus cornutus   *Macrosetella gracilis*

g) Species common off the west coast in the Benguela Current system and over the western half of the Bank. They are also found in the offshore cyclonic eddy 100 miles south of the Cape in April 1964.

Metridia lucens   *Calocalanus tenuis*
Centropages brachiatus   *C. styliremis*

In order to gain further confirmation and explanation of the above patterns, many more observations will have to be made. The hydrological data and plankton collections already available may still be too far apart in time (one month) to be capable of catching the crucial processes at work in this very intricate area.

Certain species coming in from the south or SW encroach to a variable extent on the western edge of the Bank, where they can be quite numerous in winter or spring. They are:

Calanus tonsus   *Clausocalanus ingens*
Calanoides sp.   *Euchirella rostrata*

They originate presumably from the southern latitudes and may be carried into our area by seasonal shift of the large eddy system centered around the Schmitt-Ott Seamount.

Plankton Relations of the Red Sea, Persian Gulf and Arabian Sea

B. KIMOR

In this paper I summarize studies on plankton relations in the Red Sea, Persian Gulf and the Arabian Sea. These are mainly contemporary contributions made shortly before, during and following the official closing of the IIOE. Reference to earlier sources of information relating to expeditions or individual taxa is readily available in several bibliographies pertaining to these subjects (PRASAD, 1964; PALDI, 1968) or in synoptic surveys on specific areas such as HALIM's plankton of the Red Sea (1969).

The taxa to be presently considered are those on which the author had most information and which, in his opinion, were of sufficient significance either as biomass formers or as indicators of specific water masses in the three adjacent seas.

I. Specific Aspects of the Environment

The Red Sea is the most northerly part of the Indian Ocean, its deep and narrow basin connected with the latter through the narrow straits of Bab-el-Mandeb leading into the

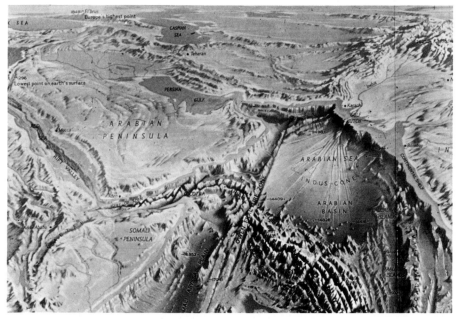

Fig. 1. Bottom topography of the Red Sea, the Arabian Sea and the Persian Gulf. (After the Geographical Magazine, 1967)

Gulf of Aden (Fig. 1). A shallow sill not exceeding 100 m separates the Red Sea from the Gulf of Aden and brings about the partial isolation of its deeper parts from the point of view of its floristic and faunistic characteristics (HALIM, 1969; MORCOS, 1970).

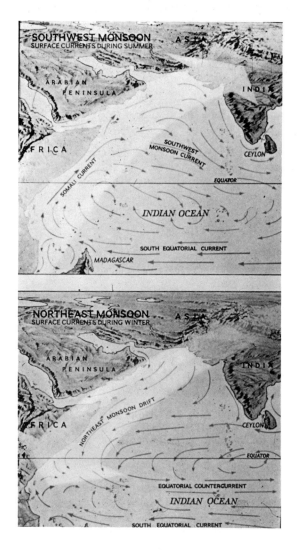

Fig. 2. Surface currents during the SW and the NE monsoons in the NW Indian Ocean. (After the Geographical Magazine, 1967)

In general, most contributors to the biogeography of this specific area concur in their views that only epipelagic species are able to pass over the dividing sill with the surface currents generated by the monsoon winds. This is naturally of special significance in the case of species dependent on the periodic recruitment of individuals by such means for the maintenance of populations (HALIM, 1969).

The direction of flow is determined by the monsoons. In summer, the SW monsoon generates a flow in a clockwise direction along the Somali and Arabian coasts toward the western coast of India. During this period, from May to October, north-westerly winds prevail along the whole of the Red Sea, causing a flow of Red Sea water into the Gulf of Aden. In winter, the NE monsoon generates a current in the opposite direction so that during the months of October to March there is a flow from the Gulf of Aden into the southern part of the Red Sea. During this season the north-westerly winds do not reach further south than the 20° N parallel thus assisting still further the inflow of surface waters into the Red Sea (Fig. 2).

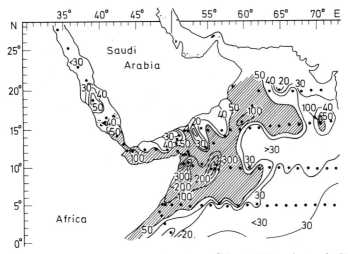

Fig. 3. Distribution of total pigment concentrations (mg m^{-2}) for 0 – 200 m during the SW monsoon period, 1963. (After McGill and Lawson, 1966 and reproduced in Halim, 1969)

Many planktonic organisms are directly influenced by this seasonal change in the direction of the flow. Some of them are not able to survive the higher salinities and temperatures prevailing in the deeper strata of the Red Sea and thus do not survive the northbound migration beyond the immediate reaches of the dividing sill at Bab-el-Mandeb.

The distribution of total pigments concentration, as measured by McGill and Lawson (1966) and quoted by Halim (1969) during the 2 monsoon periods, though in different years, may serve as a good illustration of the monsoon-generated direction of the flow. During the NE monsoon the highest pigment values measured as mg m^{-2} were recorded in the northern part of the Red Sea as well as in two areas at the entrance to the Gulf of Oman. (Figs. 3 and 4).

During the SW monsoon the highest pigment values were recorded in the southern part of the Red Sea, in some areas of the Gulf of Aden and the Arabian Sea.

A similar process in regard to the reaction of planktonic organisms to the prevailing currents is seen in the exchange of waters between the Persian Gulf and the Arabian Sea, and is discussed in a recent paper by Leveau and Szekielda (1968).

In the view of these authors the deeper and more saline waters from the Persian Gulf flow into the Arabian Sea, this being compensated by an inflow of less saline surface waters flowing into the Gulf. Any plankton organisms carried by the latter current towards the Persian Gulf and unable to withstand either its shallowness or its high temperatures and salinities, will die as soon as they reach the steep walls leading towards the narrow and shallow entrance into this Gulf. (Fig. 5).

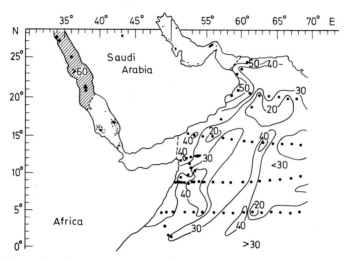

Fig. 4. Distribution of total pigment concentrations (mg m^{-2}) for 0–200 m during the NE monsoon period, 1965. (After McGILL and LAWSON, 1966 and reproduced in HALIM, 1969)

II. Biological Productivity

The assessment of the relative productivity of the three regions under discussion is particularly difficult as the few relevant published data are based on different parameters. BOGOROV and VINOGRADOV (1961); expressing their results in cm^3 of plankton per 1000 m^3, point to the Arabian Sea as one of the most productive areas in the Indian Ocean with over 150 cm^3 1000 m^{-3}. KABANOVA (1961) provides primary production figures expressed as mgC m^{-3} day^{-1} and points to the coastal areas of the Arabian Sea where values of 50–120 mg were recorded as compared with the sea where the values did not exceed 10–30 mg (see also map in the inside of the back cover).

The same author (KABANOVA, 1964) quotes even higher values of primary production expressed as mgC m^{-2} day^{-1} for the Gulf of Aden and the Somali Current region, 88–270 mgC m^{-2} day^{-1} during October–April 1960/61 as compared with more easterly parts of the Indian Ocean such as the Andaman Sea where the values fluctuated between 114–176 and 10–20 mgC m^{-2} day^{-1} in the open parts of the Indian Ocean.

ZERNOVA (1962), studying the quantitative aspects of phytoplankton distribution in the northern Indian Ocean using net samples and expressing her results as numbers of cells m^{-3}, gave the following results: Andaman Sea—6 100, Gulf of Aden—3 600, Arabian Sea—1 200 and the Equatorial Indian Ocean—400. These figures reflect a decreasing trend in phytoplankton biomass from the eastern towards the western parts of the Indian Ocean as well as from the northern towards the equatorial parts.

Working along the same lines, SUKHANOVA (1969) points to a decreasing trend in the concentration of peridinians from the Gulf of Aden through the southern part of the Red Sea towards the northern part, quoting figures of 450−950, 200−350 and

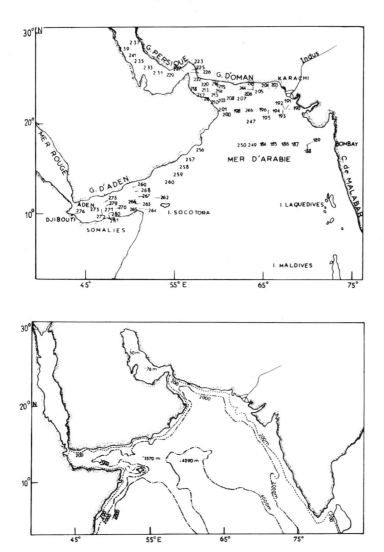

Fig. 5. Bathymetric map of the Persian Gulf, the Arabian Sea and the Gulf of Aden. (After FURNESTIN and CODACCIONI, 1968)

130 cells m^{-3} respectively. Comparable figures were quoted by the same investigator with regard to the distribution of diatoms in the same region.

The same trend is also evident, according to DELALO (1966), in the distribution of zooplankton, with 571, 81 and 48 mg m^{-3} in the Gulf of Aden, the southern and the northern parts of the Red Sea respectively.

Finally, FRONTIER (1963 a) measuring the quantitative distribution of zooplankton by mm^3 per l m of advancing net, points to the NE part of the Arabian Sea as one of the richest with values reaching up to 982 mm^3, while in the main basin of the Arabian Sea the values fluctuate between $25-65$ mm^3. Abrupt differences in zooplankton biomass have been established by the same investigator in different areas of the Persian and Aden Gulf, depending on whether the stations are coastal or more offshore and other factors.

The evidence emerging from these sources, despite the different parameters used, indicates a higher level of plankton productivity in the NW part of the Arabian Sea, more especially in the coastal areas, than in the Red Sea in general and its northern parts in particular.

III. Phytoplankton

From a qualitative standpoint the 3 regions under discussion belong, according to SUKHANOVA (1962 b), to the "Basic Indo-oceanic complex" whereby several species of dinoflagellates common to the whole of the tropical areas of the Indian Ocean constitute an outstanding feature of the phytoplankton. These species are *Pyrocystis pseudo-noctiluca, Ceratium carriense, C. trichoceros* and *C. massiliense.*

In a more recent work SUKHANOVA (1969) established important differences in the diversity of species in the different parts of the Red Sea and the Gulf of Aden. Accordingly the central part of the Red Sea is the poorest in species with more diverse populations in the northern and southern parts.

The dinoflagellates in general seem to be more uniformly distributed in the whole region while the diatoms exhibit a more discontinuous distribution and very rarely produce the water blooms characteristic of other areas of the Indian Ocean (SUBRAH-MANYAN, 1960). Among such cases SUKHANOVA cites *Climacodium frauenfeldianum* as reaching higher numbers in the Gulf of Aden, while in the Gulf of Eilat a one-time occurrence of a waterbloom caused by *Stephanopyxis palmeriana* was noted by the author (KIMOR, 1970) in February 1958.

SUKHANOVA's findings (1969) that many species recorded from the Arabian Sea and other parts of the Indian Ocean (SUBRAHMANYAN, 1958) are not found in the Red Sea, are amply corroborated by WOOD (1963). Out of a total of 452 species of his checklist of dinoflagellates recorded from the Indian Ocean, only 170 are represented in the areas under discussion. Of the 47 genera comprising WOOD's checklist of species for the Indian Ocean as a whole, 14 are not represented at all in its NW parts. From WOOD's records we learn that 130 species are recorded from the Arabian Sea, 88 from the Red Sea and 57 from the Gulf of Aden, but only 2 from the Persian Gulf. The last figure is obviously a result of the lack of information relating to that environment, as will be shown below.

While the pattern of a decrease in the number of species from the Arabian Sea towards the Red Sea is clearly evident in the distribution of phytoplankton, there are a number of species considered as endemic to the Red Sea. Among these, the following may be noted: *Dinophysis caudata, D. maris rubri* and *D. miles* of the dinoflagellates and *Trichodesmium erythraeum* of the filamentous blue-greens, the latter species supposed to occur at times in massive concentrations imparting to the Red Sea waters their charac-teristic coloration.

While the available data regarding phytoplankton relations in the areas under

discussion fit into the pattern outlined above, the information regarding the phytoplankton of the Red Sea is clearly inferior to that for the Arabian Sea.

Most of the data are of a qualitative nature and generally relate to a given season
rather than to a complete year cycle. Nevertheless, some of the basic features of the
phytoplankton of these regions include such features as a dominance of dinoflagellates
as compared with diatoms in the Red Sea, the almost complete absence of diatom blooms
in the Red Sea, and the non-occurrence of certain species in the various areas of this sea
while preserving floristic affiliations with the Indian Ocean as a whole.

Regarding the Persian Gulf and the Gulf of Oman, Böhm (1931) stresses the poverty
in species of dinoflagellates in this region as compared with the Arabian Sea. It is interesting to note that among the 38 species of dinoflagellates reported by this author are
Ceratium carriense and *C. trichoceros,* 2 of the 4 species considered by Sukhanova
(1962) as constituting the "basic Indo-oceanic complex".

IV. Zooplankton

The groups considered in this section will of necessity be those which have received
most attention throughout the years, mainly due to their major role in the total plankton
biomass. Among such groups the copepods and the euphausiids are probably the most
important. The earlier work on the copepods of the Red Sea is summed up by Halim
(1969). He notes that, out of a total of 270 species of calanoid copepods known from
the Indian Ocean, 158 species are recorded from the Red Sea, this being the list compiled
by him from all existing sources to date—primarily Sewell's records (1948) from his
study of the free-living planktonic copepods of this region. In his view, the restricted
copepod fauna of the Red Sea, a large proportion of which is of a deep-water type, is
due to the physical barrier of the sill at Bab-el-Mandeb which prevents the influx of
Indo-Pacific species. This decreasing trend in the number of species continues northward
and there is evidence that still fewer species among those which succeed in settling in
the southern Red Sea actually reach the northern Gulfs of Suez and Eilat.

The seasonal aspect is also of importance in the consideration of this group. According
to Halim (1969), the copepods are represented by the largest numbers of species in
winter, which is clearly a result of the inflow of surface waters from the Gulf of Aden
during the NE monsoon. The subsequent decrease in the number of copepod species
during the summer as noted by Halim may well be caused by the well-known phenomenon
observed by many investigators including the author whereby winter epipelagic species
sink to deeper levels during the hot summer months.

Recently Berdugo (in preparation) made a preliminary study of the calanoid copepods
of the Gulf of Eilat noting the considerably poorer fauna of this region as compared
with that of the southern Red Sea and to an even greater degree with that of the Arabian
Sea.

The question of endemic species is, however, a complex one. While recognizing the
existence of such species which seem to have had their origin in the Red Sea such as
Acartia fossae, Candacia samassae and *Labidocera orsini,* among others, *Candacia
samassae* has since been recorded by Jones (1966 a) in the Arabian Sea and the Bay of
Bengal. It is thus suggested that there should not be hard and fast rules in the drawing
up of zoogeographical boundaries as they may be subject to changes as a result of more

intensive sampling in time and space. At the same time the same author (JONES, 1966 b) notes that geographically remote populations of the same species may have distinct morphological features such as he noted with regard to *Candacia pachydactyla* from the Atlantic and the Indo-Pacific oceans.

The euphausiids of the Indian Ocean have also formed the subject of significant contributions in recent years. The important role of members of this group in the total planktonic biomass of the Arabian Sea and the Bay of Bengal, emphasized by PONOMA-REVA (1964), is contrary to the habits of this group in other tropical areas. In a considera-tion of the euphausiids of the Red Sea, the same author (PONOMAREVA, 1968) discusses the importance of this group for fisheries. Out of 22 species known from the Indian Ocean 10 are known from the Red Sea, most of them being immigrants from the Gulf of Aden. Most of these species are surface forms which could easily pass the Strait of Bab-el-Mandeb. A few endemic species are known from the Red Sea such as *Euphausia sanzoi* and *Pseudoeuphausia colosi*. A more recent work on this group by WEIGMANN (1970) deals with the euphausiids of the Arabian Sea during the NE monsoon. The author defined 5 distinct areas, namely, the Arabian Sea proper with 24 species, the Gulf of Aden with 10 species, the Red Sea with 6 species, the Gulf of Oman with 5 species and the Persian Gulf with 1 species. However, some of the highest concentrations per unit volume of 100 m^3 were recorded in the Persian Gulf and consist of the single species *Pseudoeuphasia latifrons*. Similar patches were also recorded in some parts of the Malabar coast of SW India and in some parts of the Gulf of Aden. These areas of high production are zones of upwelling during the NE monsoon; in the Central Arabian Sea lower concentrations were recorded. (Fig. 6).

According to WEIGMANN, the similarity between the euphausiid fauna of the Red Sea and the Gulf of Aden is due to the fact that during the NE monsoon deep water from the Red Sea flows southward into the Gulf of Aden while the surface current flows into the Red Sea.

The distribution of euphausiids in the Indian Ocean as a whole and the increase in numbers of euphausiids on the western side of the Indian Ocean is emphasized by GOPALAKRISHNAN and BRINTON (1969) who also stress the importance of this group as food for fishes of commercial importance.

WICKSTEAD (1963) mentions 3 species of Cladocera from the Zanzibar area on the East African coast, namely *Evadne tergestina, Podon polyphemoides* and *Penilia avirostris*. These are well-known species, common in all tropical and subtropical regions, including the Mediterranean. WICKSTEAD correlates the sporadic swarming of *Penilia avirostris* with an ample supply of O_2 in the water which may be caused by occasional diatom blooms. In our regular collections in the Gulf of Eilat, the only species so far recorded and perennial in its distribution is *Evadne tergestina* (KOMAROVSKY, 1958). The presence of *Penilia avirostris* was recently reported from the Gulf of Suez during February 1971 (POR, personal information).

GEORGE (1969) discusses the distribution of planktonic ostracods in the Indian Ocean and notes the exceptionally high numbers of some of the species in the northern part of the Arabian Sea, especially in coastal waters. No recent data are, however, available for the Red Sea area although earlier information is reported by HALIM (1969) emphasizing the Indo-Pacific character of the prevailing species.

Further evidence on the selective distribution of species in adjoining seas is provided by FRONTIER (1963 b) reporting on the pteropods of the Arabian Sea, Persian Gulf and the Gulf of Aden. He stresses the poverty in species of the Persian Gulf where only 2−3 species of pteropods were recorded per station, a fact he attributes to the shallow depths of this Gulf which do not exceed 75 m and thus limit the distribution of species to neritic forms. The Gulf of Aden as well as the Gulf of Oman is characterized by a large number of species, although in small numbers, constituting what FRONTIER calls an ecological semblance.

ARAVINDAKSHAN (1969) notes the presence of a group of *Carinaria* species present in the Arabian Sea and the Gulf of Oman and Aden, while absent from the Bay of Bengal.

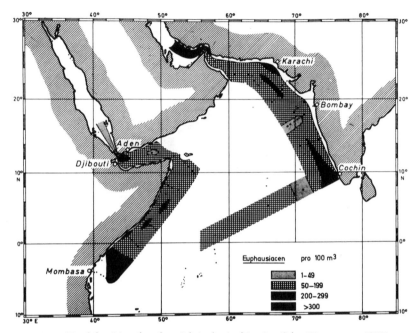

Fig. 6. Total densities of euphausiids in the Arabian Sea.(After WEIGMANN, 1970)

The leading species of Pterotracheidae, typically tropical in character, show a similar pattern of distribution.

The decreasing trend in the number of species from the Arabian Sea through the Gulf of Aden, the Red Sea and its most northerly Gulfs of Eilat and Suez is evident also in the distribution of chaetognaths.

FURNESTIN in a study of the chaetognaths of the Gulf of Eilat (1958) and of the Dahlak Archipelago in the southern Red Sea (1968) drew attention to the predominantly Indo-Pacific character of the species recorded by her in the 2 regions. At the same time she concluded that the Gulf of Eilat is populated by a smaller number of species than the main basin of the Red Sea, but this includes mesopelagic species such as *Sagitta regularis* and *S. hexaptera* which would normally be expected to be found in the Gulf in view of its great depths and other hydrographical features (OREN, 1962). To the chaetognath fauna of the Dahlak Archipelago in the southern Red Sea, which is mainly neritic, she added 2 more species, *Sagitta bedoti* and *S. robusta,* both of Indo-Pacific origin, in addition to *S. pacifica* already reported by her from the Gulf of Eilat (1958). In her view a sporadic and irregular immigration is taking place from the Arabian Sea via the Gulf of Aden and thus adding to the number of species known from the Red Sea.

In a later study of the chaetognaths of the NW Indian Ocean, FURNESTIN and CODAC-CIONI (1968) discuss the geographical distribution of 13 species belonging to this group in the different regions investigated (Gulf of Aden, Arabian Sea, Gulf of Oman and the Persian Gulf) in relation to the bathymetry and the hydrology of the areas. The authors point out that certain mesopelagic species like *Sagitta pacifica* do not penetrate the shallow waters of the Persian Gulf whereas the epipelagic species *S. bedoti,* which is

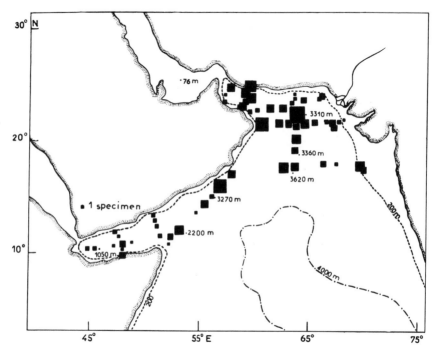

Fig. 7. Distribution of *Sagitta pacifica* in the NW Indian Ocean.(After FURNESTIN and CODACCIONI, 1968)

characteristic of surface waters in general, is quite abundant in this environment and withstands both the high temperatures and high salinities prevailing in the Gulf. (Figs. 7 and 8).

The distribution of pelagic tunicates provides additional information on the plankton relations in the marginal seas of the western Indian Ocean. According to FENAUX (1964) the appendicularians of the Oman and Persian Gulfs represented by 12 and 6 species respectively are considerably poorer in species than those of the Sea of Oman and the Gulf of Aden with 19 species in each environment and a total of 23. The same author (FENAUX, 1966) recorded 14 species in the Red sea proper but only 3 in the Gulf of Eilat (FENAUX, 1960) of which one, *Megalocercus abyssorum* is a new record for the Red Sea, having been considered until then a typical Mediterranean species.

In a note on the *Thaliacea* of the Gulf of Eilat Godeaux (1960) points to several species as new records for the Red Sea of which *Riteriella amboinensis,* a typically Indo-Pacific species, is listed as the most northerly in its distribution in the Indian Ocean area.

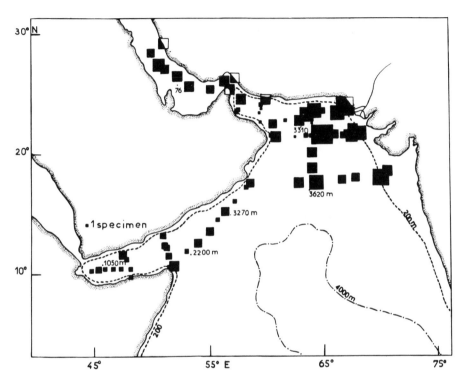

Fig. 8. Distribution of *Sagitta bedoti* in the NW Indian Ocean. (After Furnestin and Codaccioni, 1968)

V. Discussion

The evidence analysed in this review has raised two important points: a) the predominance of tropical Indo-Pacific elements in the plankton of the 3 regions under consideration; b) the decreasing trend in the diversity of species from the Arabian Sea towards the Red Sea and the Persian Gulf.

The immediate causes for the latter characteristic are, however, different in the case of the 2 sea arms embracing, as they do, the Arabian Peninsula from the east and west. While higher temperatures and salinities than in the adjoining Arabian Sea prevail in both areas, the Red Sea, with its great depths, is largely a closed body of water due to the narrow mouth and shallow sill at its southern end, whereas the Persian Gulf is actually a kind of shallow platform also separated from the main basin of the Arabian Sea by a fairly narrow strait but having no sill. In both cases planktonic organisms inhabiting the deeper zones of the Arabian Sea come up against steep walls constituted by narrow continental shelves or a shallow sill as in the case of Bab-el-Mandeb, and are thus barred from reaching the adjacent northern seas, even during the NE monsoon.

The diversity of species is, however, far more reduced in the case of the Persian Gulf, as the shallowness of the latter environment precludes the existence of mesopelagic and bathypelagic species which form important elements of the planktonic communities in the Red Sea. Both seas, although completely different in their bottom topography, are separated from the Arabian Sea by narrow straits which, by imparting to them the character of closed sea arms, may be largely responsible for the more restricted fauna and flora prevailing in these environments. The late THORSON (1957) in his article: "Bottom communities", chapter 17, p. 501, states that in "large fjord areas and in Gulfs with narrow mouths the productivity as well as the weight of the standing stock will gradually decline with increase in distance from the open sea". He refers specifically to the Persian Gulf where in his view the smaller weights per unit area as compared with arctic fjords are compensated for by the faster growth rate of the animals and the much heavier predation in the tropical area.

Although THORSON was writing of bottom communities, this may well be true with planktonic organisms as well. Some of the examples quoted in the present survey tend to confirm this view. Within certain systematic groups considerably fewer species than in the adjoining ocean seem to prevail in the plankton of these closed sea arms. While this is particularly true in the case of the Persian Gulf it also applies to the Red Sea, especially to its northern parts, where the Gulf of Eilat and the Gulf of Suez reveal a still poorer fauna and flora.

This bottle-neck effect apparent in the Persian Gulf, in the Red Sea as a whole, and in the Gulf of Eilat, may well by responsible for the particular plankton features outlined above.

On a wider regional basis significant differences seem to exist between the eastern and the western parts of the Indian Ocean in general and between the various parts of the Arabian Sea in particular. At times, such differences, both in biological productivity and in species diversity, may be seen within comparatively restricted areas such as in some parts of the Gulf of Aden or the Persian Gulf.

The question of speciation apparent in some groups of plankton organisms in the Red Sea stimulates further research. While the hydrographic conditions in the Red Sea seem to favour the evolution of endemic species, or species considered to have had their origin in this sea, the actual boundaries of distribution of such species may be much wider, as proved in a number of cases. Much more work is needed for firm and absolute conclusions, and the results so far available from the IIOE regarding such plankton relations seem to have prepared the road and stimulated the interest for the work still to be done.

3.3

Microbiomass and Detritus in the Upper 50 m of the Arabian Sea along the Coast of Africa and India during the NE Monsoon 1964/65

B. BABENERD, R. BOJE, J. KREY, and V. MONTECINO

This contribution is based on the results of plankton investigations, which were carried out during the German participation in IIOE with RV "Meteor".

The aim of this paper is to relate the amount of plankton and detritus in the upper 50 m of the coastal waters of the Arabian Sea off Africa and India to the hydrographical conditions in this area during time of the NE monsoon.

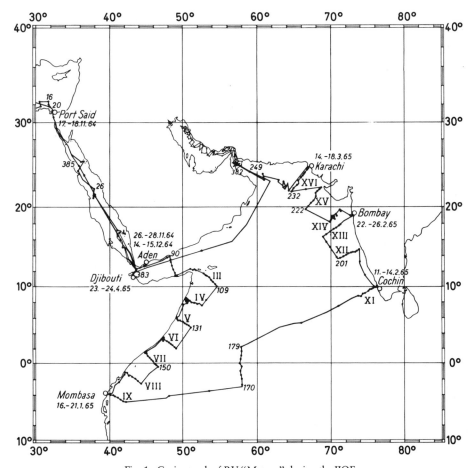

Fig. 1. Cruise track of RV "Meteor" during the IIOE

I. Material and Methods

The observations used in this study are based on sections III−IX and XI−XVI of the "Meteor" cruise (Fig. 1). The African sections were made in December and January, the Indian sections in February and March.

The physical and chemical data were published by Dietrich et al. (1966), the planktological data by Krey et al. (1971).

Water samples from the upper 50 m were taken at 10, 20, 30, 40 and 50 m (sometimes in addition a sample from 2 m is available), and water was filtered for collection of particulate material. Microbiomass was measured as the protein content of particulate matter filtered on paper filters. The procedure used was the Biuret method according to Krey, Banse and Hagmeier (1957). All results are given as albumen equivalents.

The weight of particulate matter (seston) was determined prior to the measurement of protein, using the same filters and a weighing method described by Krey (1950).

From these data detritus was calculated by subtracting the dry weight of microbiomass from seston. According to Hagmeier (1961) albumen data can be converted into dry weight of living material by multiplying with a factor of 4. At some locations of the area investigated the concentration of the properties measured was near the limit of detection of the methods used. Therefore, we felt it appropriate to integrate values for stations and to put the results into only three ranges of concentrations for graphic presentation.

II. Results

1. Microbiomass

Microbiomass is highest at some distance from the African coast near the Equator, in the northern part of the waters at the Indian coast and in the region of Goa (Fig. 2). The total numbers of phytoplankton show a similar distribution with the exception of the area off Goa, where low numbers of phytoplankton are found (Fig. 3). It seems reasonable to assume that most of what is measured as microbiomass in the upper layer of the ocean represents phytoplankton. Therefore, a good correlation between microbiomass and phytoplankton can be expected.

2. Detritus

The shallow waters of the shelf exert a strong influence on the amount of detritus (Fig. 4). This is most obvious near the broad continental shelf of India, but is also indicated along the African coast. There is about the same quantity of detritus and microbiomass present (if calculated as dry weight) but no clear relationship between them can be seen. Probably the differences in turbidity between coastal and offshore waters determine the amount of detritus.

3. Nutrients

As an example of nutrients, the distribution of PO_4^{3-}-P is given (Fig. 5). All values are the means of observations at 2 m, 25 m and 50 m. The regions off the Indian coast where higher values of microbiomass occur, show higher concentrations of PO_4^{3-}-P,

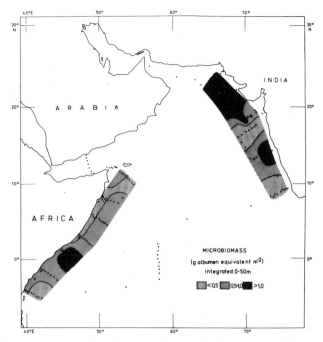

Fig. 2. Microbiomass in the Arabian Sea near Africa and India during the NE monsoon 1964/65.
Filled circles in Figs. 2 – 5 indicate stations where observations were made

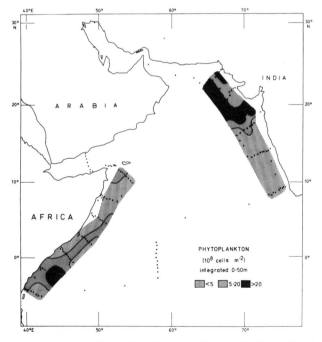

Fig. 3. Phytoplankton numbers in the Arabian Sea near Africa and India during the NE monsoon
1964/65

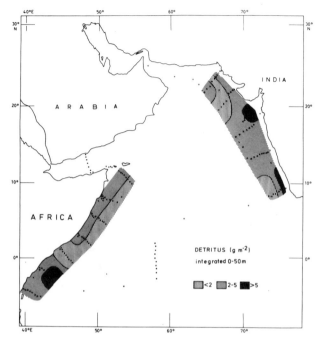

Fig. 4. Detritus in the Arabian Sea near Africa and India during the NE monsoon 1964/65

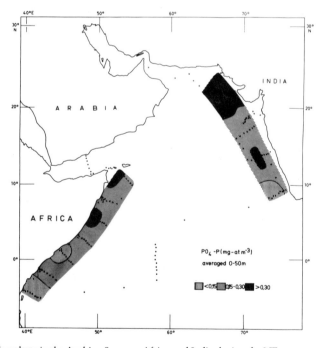

Fig. 5. Phosphate in the Arabian Sea near Africa and India during the NE monsoon 1964/65

but this relationship is not seen off the African coast. The distribution of NO_3^--N and $SiO_3^{4-}-Si$ is similar to that of $PO_4^{3-}-P$.

III. Hydrography

From the hydrographical data of the expedition DÜING (1967) calculated higher vertical velocities between 100 and 200 m south of Socotra, in the African waters near the Equator and in the northern region off the Indian coast. These areas are characterized by a slight uplift of the pycnocline combined with lower values of stability. Mixing is higher in areas of reduced stability, which improves the supply of nutrients. We suggest that this is the reason for the higher amounts of plankton in the northern Indian waters and in the equatorial region near the African coast. Negative effects of mixing because of bad light conditions did not seem to be effective during the time of the investigations. This holds even for the Indian coastal waters, where according to DÜING and KOSKE (1967) stability in general is lower as compared with the coast of Africa. But winds were weaker off the Indian coast (Beaufort 4 from NW was characteristic, while Beaufort 6 from NE prevailed off the African coast), so that this may offset the effect of lower stability.

IV. Discussion

HAGMEIER (1964 a) and NELLEN (1967) reported values of microbiomass for the same latitude of the tropical Atlantic. Our lowest concentrations correspond to the results for the open tropical Atlantic, while these authors found values as high as most of our data only in the region of the African shelf. HAGMEIER (1964 b) gives values for the eastern Indian Ocean, which are comparable to our results.

It seems that in tropical and subtropical waters the amounts of microbiomass and detritus are similar (HAGMEIER 1964 a and b; NELLEN, 1967, our data). The situation is different in the more northern parts of the ocean, where detritus seems to prevail (KREY, 1964).

Certainly the quantity of microbiomass will be much higher in some parts of the Arabian Sea when upwelling occurs. Our results show that even during the time of the NE monsoon the amount of plankton is not as low as one would expect. As RYTHER and MENZEL (1965) point out, one can characterize the Arabian Sea by "the high levels of nutrients and their proximity to the surface", and therefore increased mixing will lead to higher productivity.

3.4

Zooplankton Biomass and its Relation to Particulate Matter in the Upper 200 m of the Arabian Sea during the NE Monsoon

J. LENZ

In investigating food relationships in the sea and the rate of metabolism from the lower to the higher levels in the food web, basic information may be gained from studying the biomass of the main groups of organisms which build up this system of energy transfer in the ocean. Biomass measurements of zooplankton catches, which in most cases are a mixture of herbivores, carnivores and omnivores, mainly cover the second and third links in the common food chain. Regarded in this way, zooplankton biomass studies are important for gaining an insight into the fish production of the oceans.

I. Determination of the Zooplankton Biomass

Although the measurement itself if a fairly simple procedure, there are at present many methodological problems in the determination of the zooplankton biomass; this greatly complicates all attempts for a worldwide comparison of the values obtained. These problems arise from the general difficulty of separating small zooplankton from large phytoplankton organisms, from the varying catching abilities and mesh sizes of the nets used, and from the different methods used to measure the biomass, such as the determination of settling volume, displacement volume, wet weight, dry weight, dry weight of organic matter and carbon content. The 3 last have the advantage of being independent of the very variable water content in plankton animals, which in addition varies with the concentration of the preservative and preservation time. They therefore appear more suitable for productivity studies than the other 3, as the figures obtained are usually more reliable and facilitate comparisons with similar data recorded in standing stock studies such as those for particulate matter. On the other hand, they have the disadvantage of spoiling the sample for further systematic studies.

The biomass of the quantitative zooplankton samples taken by the Indian Ocean Standard Net (IOSN) from the upper 200 m layer during the "Meteor" expedition to the Arabian Sea in 1964/65 (Fig. 1 in BABENERD et al., 1973, this volume) was determined from formalin-preserved samples. A quarter of each sample was analysed for dry weight and organic matter. From the latter, the carbon content of the sample may be estimated by assuming a factor of 0.6 (CUSHING et al., 1958). Altogether 91 samples, including 12 double hauls, were analysed in this way. The data collected have been published by KREY et al. (1971).

II. Zooplankton Biomass

Fig. 1 shows the distribution of the zooplankton biomass in the upper 200 m of the Arabian Sea, the values ranging from 2 to 51 mg m^{-3}, or as integrated values from 0.4 to 10.2 g m^{-2}. Enriched areas are the Gulf of Aden, the lower part of the Somali coast and the Indian coastal region with the exception of the southern part. The highest values were recorded in the NE corner of the Arabian Sea between roughly 20° N and the Gulf of Oman. Areas with greater zooplankton stocks were generally found to correspond to those with high primary production. Approximately the same distribution

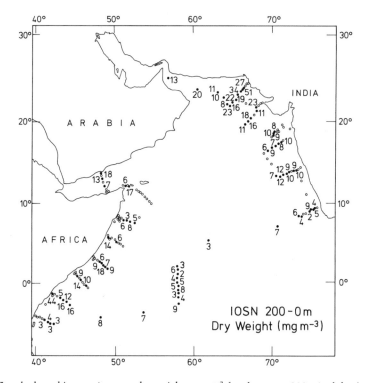

Fig. 1. Zooplankton biomass (average dry weight mg m^{-3} for the upper 200 m) of the Arabian Sea

was found for the microbiomass stock (Babenerd et al., 1973) in the upper 50 m. The IOBC Plankton Atlas reveals a similar abundance of zooplankton (see map on the inside of the front cover).

III. Comparison between Displacement Volume and Dry Weight

Since on "Meteor" double hauls were generally taken at 15 min. intervals at each station, there was an opportunity to compare independently processed parallel samples for displacement volume measured at the IOBC (Brinton and Tranter, 1969) and dry weight. Assuming 1.0 as the specific weight, 61 pairs of samples yielded a mean value of 12.3 ± 5.7 (range 5 − 30) for the ratio of displacement volume to dry weight. This value appears extraordinarily high considering that the average figure usually adopted for this ratio is 6 (CUSHING et al., 1958). The explanation lies in the large proportion of salps and medusae present in many samples.

IV. Organic Matter

In the absence of an exact determination of the calorimetric value, the amount of organic matter in a zooplankton sample may serve as a rough measure for the estimation of energy transfer to the next level in the food chain, small fish, for instance. It indicates how much of the ingested food the predators are able to digest and to convert into energy for the increment of body weight etc. In the 91 samples analysed, dry organic matter ranged from 1.2 to 39.1 mg m^{-3} or 0.2 to 7.8 g m^{-2} for the upper 200 m layer. The percentage of organic matter in the total dry weight has a mean value of $77 \pm 7\%$, ranging from 54% to 93%. As with the ratio of volume to dry weight, this proportion changes with the composition of the samples.

V. Zooplankton Biomass and Particulate Matter

The dry weight of particulate matter, called seston, was measured by filtering 2−4 l of water. Over 90% of the seston usually consists of plankton and detritus particles in the size group approximately 1 to 330 μ. As the mesh size of the IOSN is 330 μ, there is only a slight overlapping of the 2 size fractions. The integrated seston values for the upper 200 m of the area investigated vary between 33 and 281 mg m^{-3} or between 6.6 and 56.2 g m^{-2}. In this layer a mean of 25% of the seston may be ascribed to the biomass of phytoplankton and small zooplankton. On average the amount of seston exceeds the zooplankton biomass by a factor of 11, with a standard deviation of $\pm 60\%$, which means that the biomass of phytoplankton and small zooplankton is about 3 times higher than that of the larger zooplankton. However, there are significant deviations from this ratio in 2 areas. The first area is the section across the Equator in the middle of the Arabian Sea; it represents the open sea with a small zooplankton stock. The ratio of seston to zooplankton is 16:1, this is above average. Because of this low concentration, the grazing effect of the zooplankton on the seston components does not seem high.

In the second area near the Gulf of Oman the zooplankton is on average 4 times as abundant, but the increase of seston is only slight, so the ratio becomes 4:1. It being March and the end of the NE monsoon period in this region, we probably encountered a situation where an originally rich phytoplankton stock had been much reduced by the grazing of a growing zooplankton population. Alternatively the increase of zooplankton in this area may have been due to fish predation being lower than elsewhere, the fish having been repelled by the low O$_2$ concentration in the deeper layers.

4. Standing Stock and Distribution of Zooplankton

4.1

Zooplankton Studies in the Indian Ocean

T. S. S. RAO

There are a number of papers dealing with the distribution of different species and groups of zooplankton from the coastal areas of the Indian Ocean, particularly adjacent to India, Australia and South Africa. However, for many reasons these studies are not comparable to the observations made on the present IIOE collections. Firstly, with a few exceptions, the IIOE collections were taken from the open ocean and secondly they were collected over a period of 6 years (1960–1965) from a wide area of the Indian Ocean. Most of them were collected with the Indian Ocean Standard Net, IOSN (CURRIE, 1963)

Table 1. Indian Ocean Stations (prior to IIOE)

Ship	Date	No. of Stations[a]
1. "Novara"	1857–59	52
2. "Challenger"	Dec. 1873 – Mar. 1874	6
3. "Gazelle"	1874–76	37
4. "Valdivia"	1898–99	67
5. "Gauss"	1902–03	26
6. "Sealark"	1905	23
7. "Planet"	1906–07	57
8. "Möwe"	1912–13	7
9. "Dana"	1928–30	171
10. "Snellius"	1929	25
11. "Discovery II"	1930, 32, 35, 38	124
12. "Mabahiss"	1933–34	80
13. "William Screshy"	1935, 36, 50	60
14. "Albatross"	1947–48	22
15. "Charcot"	1948–49	10
16. "Galathea"	1950–52	48
17. "Umitaka Maru"	1956	32
18. "Guilard"	1961	77
	Total:	924

[a] The information under this column is not complete and does not include stations south of 45° S latitude.

vertically from 200 m depth to the surface. Table 1 shows the work done before the IIOE. Table 2 indicates the density of samples taken during the IIOE for 4 different seasons. Tables 3 and 4 respectively give the seasonal coverage of selected areas and areas of poor zooplankton sampling during the IIOE. Figs. 1–3 illustrate the sampling coverage by area and time.

Table 2. International Indian Ocean Expedition (1960 – 1965), density of samples

Areas	Limit	Total No. of 5° Sq.		Total No. of samples		Poor coverage				Moderate coverage				Good coverage	
						Without samples		1 – 5 samples		6 – 10 samples		11 – 20 samples			
		No. of 5° Sq.	%	No. of Samples [a]	%	No. of 5° Sq.	%	No. of 5° Sq.	%	No. of 5° Sq.	%	No. of 5° Sq.	%	No. of 5° Sq.	%
North Indian Ocean	25° N – 5° S	69	32.1	1. 304	61.3	23	33.3	21	30.4	14	20.3	11	15.9	–	–
	35° E – 105° E			2. 303	61.9	26	37.7	25	36.2	8	11.6	7	10.1	3	4.3
				3. 279	54.9	22	32.0	26	37.2	15	21.7	5	7.2	1	1.4
				4. 261	60.8	30	43.5	19	27.5	12	17.4	7	10.2	1	1.4
Central Indian Ocean	5° S – 25° S	69	32.1	1. 119	24.0	41	59.4	21	30.4	5	7.3	2	2.9	–	–
	30° E – 120° E			2. 120	24.5	42	60.9	21	30.4	1	1.4	5	7.2	–	–
				3. 131	25.8	34	49.3	27	39.1	7	10.2	1	1.4	–	–
				4. 100	23.3	42	60.8	22	31.9	5	7.2	–	–	–	–
South Indian Ocean	25° S – 45° S	77	35.8	1. 073	14.7	53	68.8	20	26.0	3	3.7	1	1.3	–	–
	20° E – 120° E			2. 066	13.6	54	70.2	19	24.7	3	3.9.	1	1.3	–	–
				3. 098	19.3	48	62.4	22	28.5	6	7.7	1	1.3	–	–
				4. 068	15.9	48	62.2	26	33.8	3	3.9	–	–	–	–
Indian Ocean	25° N – 45° S	215	100	1. 496	100	117	54.4	62	28.9	22	10.2	14	6.5	–	–
	20° E – 120° E			2. 489	100	122	56.7	65	30.2	12	5.6	13	6.0	3	1.4
				3. 508	100	104	48.4	75	34.9	28	13.0	7	3.3	1	0.4
				4. 429	100	120	55.8	67	31.2	20	9.3	7	3.3	1	0.4

[a] Numbers in column 5 indicate periods as follows:
1. January – March (NE monsoon)
2. April – June (Transitional)
3. July – September (SW monsoon)
4. October – December (Transitional)

Table 3. The incomplete seasonal coverage of selected areas covered in greater detail during the IIOE

Area	Incomplete months during the period of IIOE
1. West Coast of India and Pakistan 07° 00′ N−25° 00′ N 65° 00′ E−77° 00′ E	January, April, June, July, September and October
2. Somali Coast 06° 00′ N−12° 00′ N 40° 00′ E−55° 00′ E	February, March, April, May, June, September, October and November.
3. South Arabian Coast 12° 00′ N−25° 00′ N 47° 00′ E−65° 00′ E	January, March, April, August and September.
4. West Bay of Bengal 10° 00′ N−21° 00′ N 80° 00′ E−91° 00′ E	February, August, October, November and December.
5. East Bay of Bengal 05° 00′ N−21° 00′ N 90° 00′ E−100° 00′ E	January, February, May, July, October, November and December.
6. Equatorial Zone 06° 00′ N−06° 00′ S 40° 00′ E−100° 00′ E	March
7. West Australian Coast 12° 00′ S−45° 00′ S 104° 00′ E−114° 00′ E	March, June, and November

Table 4. Areas of poor coverage of zooplankton sampling during the IIOE

1. Mozambique Channel	11. East Bay of Bengal

2.   5° S − 50° S
    40° E − 53° E
	16° N 22° N
	    91° E −99° E

3.   5° S − 22° S
    59° E − 64° E
	12. 10° N −12° N
	    82° E −90° E

4.   7° N − 50° S
    72° E − 75° E
	13. 6° N − 8° N
	    83° E −91° E

5.   5° S − 50° S
    80° E − 90° E
	14. Off Sumatra Coast
	    5° N − 7° S

6.   7° S − 50° S
    95° E − 99° E
	15. 5° N −10° N
	    53° E −58° E

7.   7° S − 50° S
    100° E −104° N
	16. 13° N −15° N
	    60° E −70° E

8.   9° S − 20° S
    114° E −117° E
	17. 20° N −25° N
	    61° E −66° E

9. Gulf of Mannar	18. 10° N −13° N 70° E −74° E

10. Coastal areas of Bay of Bengal
    18° N − 22° N
    85° E − 99° E
	19. Persian Gulf
	20. Red Sea

I. Biomass

Plankton biomass distribution in the Indian Ocean formed the subject matter for Vol. I, fascicles 1 and 2, of the Plankton Atlas issued by the IOBC (IOBC, 1968 a, b). PRASAD (1966, 1970) has given a detailed account of the distribution of the biomass

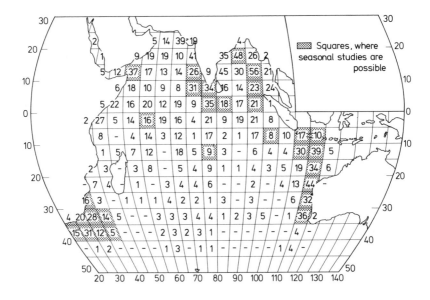

Fig. 1. Number of collections in each 5° square

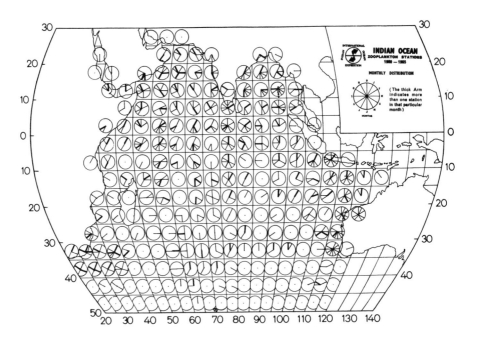

Fig. 2. Monthly coverage of zooplankton stations

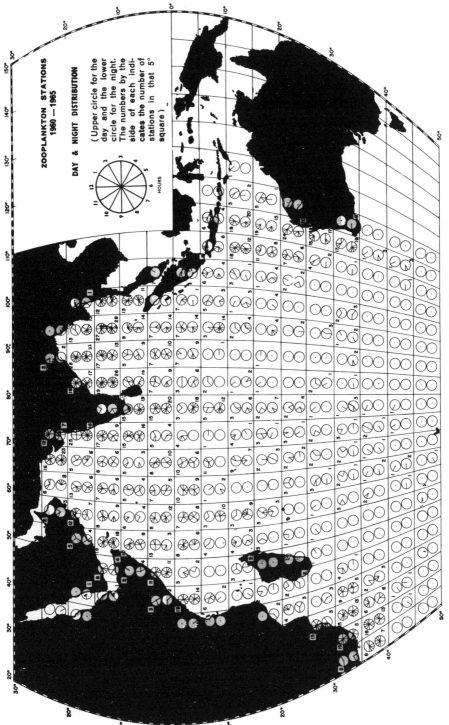

Fig. 3. Day, night and hourly coverage of zooplankton stations

(wet zooplankton displacement volumes expressed as ml per haul taken by the IOSN) in the Indian Ocean based on the data from 1622 samples included in the above atlas (see map on the inside of the front cover).

PRASAD observes that the volumes are highest in the Arabian Sea between lat. 10° to 25° N and long. 50° to 65° E, more particularly in the area off the Somali coast and the coast of Saudi Arabia. Average values as high as 54.7 ml m^{-2} (for 200 m column) were noted off Arabia, with Somali showing 15−35 ml and ± 15 ml all over the south-eastern region of the Indian Ocean and again in the northern Bay of Bengal and South of Java. The rest of the Indian Ocean shows values less than 15 ml per haul.

The data for the atlases mentioned above were based on average values calculated from all the stations in every 5° square. The area was divided into 2 monsoon seasons,

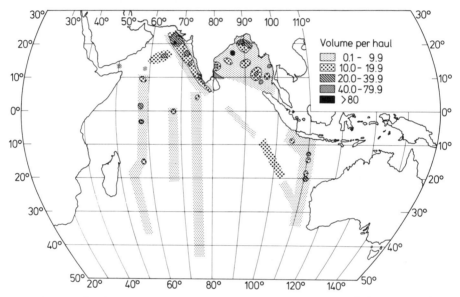

Fig. 4. Biomass distribution in the Indian Ocean, March−April in ml m^{-2} for 200 m column (Premonsoon season with variable conditions)

the SW monsoon extending from 16 April to 15 October, and the NE monsoon from 16 October to 15 April. Day and night treatment was also attempted. During the SW monsoon 3 centres of high biomass (50−60 ml) where noted in the Arabian Sea, located off the Somali, Oman and Kerala coasts. In the Bay of Bengal a similar region was present at the head of the Bay with an average value of around 20−40 ml. During the NE monsoon high values off the Somali coast and Kerala coast were not present, but off the Saudi Arabian coast the peak areas had shifted westward and nearer to 10° N latitude as compared to the situation during SW monsoon when it was in the vicinity of 20° N latitude. The night values were generally higher than day values.

In order to obtain a realistic picture of the biomass, the available data from 1548 standard samples were replotted on 5 different charts (Figs. 4−8) to show the biomass distribution for 5 different periods, as described by DÜING (1970). The different seasons are based on winds and surface currents of the Indian Ocean.

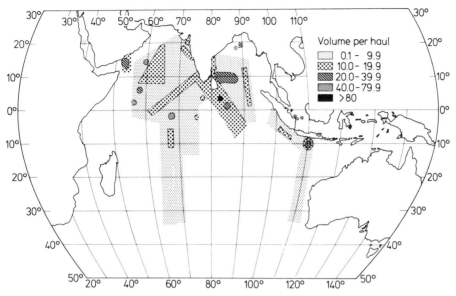

Fig. 5. Biomass distribution in the Indian Ocean, May – June in ml m^{-2} for 200 m column
(Beginning of the SW monsoon)

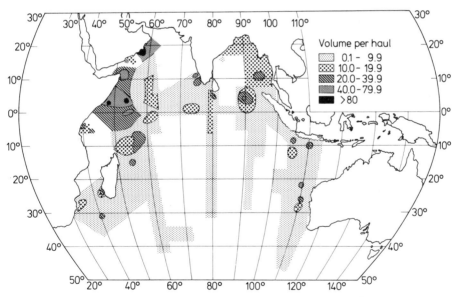

Fig. 6. Biomass distribution in the Indian Ocean, July – September in ml m^{-2} for 200 m column
(SW monsoon, well stabilized all over the area)

During the height of the NE monsoon (December to February) data from 431 samples
indicate the occurrence of $20 - 39.9$ ml m^{-2} biomass in the region of the Gulf of Aden
and north of Mombasa. A few spots indicating highest range, i.e. 80 ml and above, were

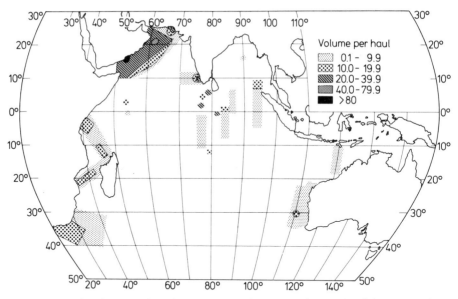

Fig. 7. Biomass distribution in the Indian Ocean, October−November in ml m⁻² for 200 m column
(Postmonsoon season with variable conditions and beginning of NE monsoon)

located off Madras in the Bay of Bengal, off Goa along the west coast of India. The rest
of the area shows low values from 0.1−9.9 ml.

March−April is a transitional period with 238 samples but the Somali and Arabian
coasts are not covered. The west coast of India and the Bay of Bengal are well covered.

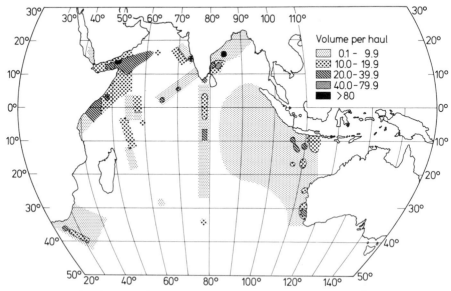

Fig. 8. Biomass distribution in the Indian Ocean, December−February in ml m⁻² for 200 m column
(NE monsoon, well established all over the area)

Both the areas show patches of middle range values (10−39.9 ml) against a background of low biomass (0.1−9.9 ml). Large patches in the central Arabian Sea and eastern Indian Ocean show values from 10−19.9 ml.

The May−June period witnesses the commencement of the SW monsoon. Here also we have no data from the Somali and Arabian coasts nor from the eastern Bay of Bengal. Patches of high values are scattered with a rich patch of biomass (20−39.9 ml) to the east of Ceylon and a similar patch in the Gulf of Aden. Most of the samples out of the 248 for this season exhibit low values (10 ml).

July−August and September are the months when the SW monsoon is fully established all over the north Indian Ocean. There are 451 samples for this season but unfortunately

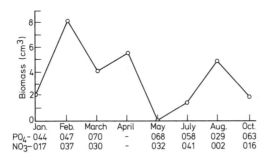

Fig. 9. Biomass, phosphate and nitrate data at the reference station at 32° S and 110° E. Nutrient concentration μg-at l^{-1} 10^{-2}

there are no data for most of the west coast of India north of Mangalore and the Madras coast. High biomass values, 40 ml and above, are found in stations off Somalia (between Garad and Ras Mabber) adjacent to Cape Guardafui and off the Oman coast. Values ranging from 20−39.8 ml are present south of the Andaman Sea, around 5° N and 90° E, off Cochin and south of Ceylon and also on 110° E.

October−November is the transition period and marks the end of the SW monsoon and the beginning of the NE monsoon. There are 180 samples for this period, mostly off the Saudi Arabian coast. This is the only region having biomass values of 20−39.9 ml. The rest of the areas have low values. No data are available for the Bay of Bengal.

From the above account of the seasonal distribution of the biomass, it is evident that the areas adjacent to the Saudi Arabian coast consistently show very high ranges of productivity during the prolonged SW monsoon period. A comparison of the biomass distribution with the surface thickness layer distribution makes clear that high biomass values overlap areas of no surface layer or regions of upwelling. In this respect the Saudi Arabian coast is unique. The persistent easterly component of the currents in the Arabian Sea from May to August (WOOSTER, SCHAEFER and ROBINSON, 1967) creates divergent conditions off the Saudi Arabian coast and thus favours large-scale upwelling. In July, August and September the lowest temperatures on this coast are 23°−25° C. Salinity is high and constant throughout the year. Distribution of nutrients indicates high values for this area. All these circumstances combine to make the Saudi Arabian coast the richest area for secondary production in the north Indian Ocean.

In the southern Indian Ocean the number of samples available for analysis are few. There are 2 exceptions, the seasonal repetitive cruises along 110° E (TRANTER, 1973)

and the "Africana" cruises off South Africa (DE DECKER , 1973). At 32° S 100−112° E
there are 14 observations made by Australian scientists covering 8 months of the year.
The biomass at this station is very low and shows a bimodal fluctuation, high values
being observed during February and August (Fig. 9).

In the "Africana" collections the biomass values are higher than at the 32° S−100° E
station, and variable (0.9−21.7 ml for 100 m^3). Most of the stations here are located
on the continental shelf and the data here are excellent for correlation with hydrographical
parameters. A clear relationship exists between the prevailing current and the plankton
populations. Both copelata and chaetognaths come from the east and drift westwards
and southwards with the Agulhas Current.

II. Distribution of Copepoda

As the copepods form a good percentage of the zooplankton both in volume and
numbers, the pattern of distribution of biomass already described (IOBC, 1970 a),
reflects to a large extent the distribution of copepods and in fact many other groups
such as amphipods, chaetognaths, cladocerans, fish eggs and larvae, etc. In the Bay of
Bengal there is a high-density region in the head of the Bay during the SW monsoon
(April 16−October 15) which disappears during the NE monsoon season. It is also clear
from these charts that the area of high density of the copepods spreads out from the area
of upwelling in the direction of the prevailing currents. *Gaussia princeps* (T. SCOTT)
studied by SARASWATHY (1973) reveals that this bathypelagic species exists in areas of
the Indian Ocean where intermediate waters come up within 200 m of the surface.
Haloptilus acutifrons (GIESBRECHT) studied by ROSAMMA and SARALADEVI (personal
communication) considered to be a deep water species, presents a pattern of distribution
suggesting that it is euryphagous, eurythermal and euryhaline and was taken in stations
where the O_2 was not less than 1.5 ml l^{-1} and seems to avoid salinities higher than 36‰.

III. Decapod Larvae

The total distribution of decapod larvae (IOBC, 1970 a) shows the interesting feature
that while off the Somali, Indian and Burmese coasts high numbers (301−900 per haul)
occur adjacent to the coast, off Saudi Arabia they occur at a great distance (150−200
miles) from the shore. They are also distributed much more extensively during the SW
monsoon than in the NE monsoon. The occurrence of a dense patch of larvae south of
Java (over 2,700 per haul) and a large patch of high value (300−2,700) south of the
Andaman is noteworthy.

Very high concentrations of the larvae are met with at one station each in the western
and eastern Indian Ocean, off Port Elizabeth and south of Java respectively, and 3 stations
off the west coast of India (mostly brachyuran larvae). In the central Indian Ocean south
of 10° S latitude there is very little representation of these larvae in the plankton.

The larvae of penaeid prawns show a maximum concentration around the southern
extremity of the Indian peninsula and off the Somali coast. Similar patterns of distribution
are found for other families of decapod larvae.

IV. Fish Eggs and Larvae

Taking the distribution of fish eggs as an indication of spawning areas, the IOBC Atlas (IOBC, 1970 b) reveals that such centres are located adjacent to the Saudi Arabian coast and the northeastern Bay of Bengal. These areas are consistently rich and show a high range (100 per haul) throughout the monsoons and also in the day and night distribution of eggs and larvae. PETER (1967) has recorded for the first time early stages of the mackerel at 3 stations, one at the head of the Bay of Bengal, the other off Madras and a third in the Gulf of Oman. It is clear that the IOSN samples have not shown the existence of a sufficient number of larvae to distinguish the breeding grounds of commercially important fisheries, particularly sardines and mackerel. While the oceanic zone is dominated by the larvae of bathypelagic fishes such as gonostomids, stomiatids, myctophids, etc., the intermediate zone towards the coastal areas is found to be the richest for fish larvae of economic importance. The families *Thunnidae, Scomberomoridae, Carangidae,* etc. are all well represented here.

In conclusion it may be stated that the emergence of the northeastern Bay of Bengal as an area of fish spawning is an important discovery of the IIOE. The poor catches of fish in the Bay of Bengal should not mislead us and make us overlook the possibilities of finding rich fishery resources here as indicated by IIOE data on fish eggs larvae and biomass distribution.

V. Mollusca

The family *Cavolinidae (Clio, Creseis, Styliola, Hyalocylix* and *Cuvierina)* seems to be densely distributed off the Somali coast, in the Red Sea, off the south of Java, the southwest coast of India and the northern part of the Bay of Bengal; the highest peak is in the Red Sea, the maximum number being 3160 at "Discovery" station 5002 A. The same station is noted for its peak abundance of *Limacinidae, Peraclidae* and *Cymbulidae* (the highest number is 6920). This is also true in the case of meroplanktonic gastropods (the maximum number being 3360). *Limacinidae, Peraclidae* and *Cymbulidae* are abundant in the Red Sea and western Arabian Sea off Mauritius, including the Mozambique Channel to the Persian Gulf. During the NE monsoon rich areas of *Limacinidae, Peraclidae* and *Cymbulidae* extend to the west coast of India and also along the meridians between 75° E and 85° E for a long distance in the central Indian Ocean.

Bivalve larvae are densely distributed around the Somali coast and the southern coast of Arabia, the SW coast of India, north of Sumatra and south of Java with dense patches scattered in these areas. Maximum abundance was in the Gulf of Aden. Bivalve larvae are sparse along the coastal areas of Australia and South Africa and the east coast of India.

In the case of cephalopod distribution, the areas of highest abundance were observed in the northern part of the Bay of Bengal and also on the western half of the Bay off the Madras and Andhra coasts. In addition, they are well distributed off the Somali coast, Arabian coast, Kutch and south of Ceylon. Here again the Bay of Bengal is outstanding for the abundance of cephalopod larvae.

VI. Other Groups

Amphipods, cladocerans, euphausids, chaetognaths, medusae, copelates, salps, and doliolids, ostracods, and polychaetes are all under study at the IOBC. The distribution of most of these groups follows the same pattern as that of the copepods, fish eggs and larvae, the richest region being the Saudi Arabia and Somali coasts. For example, amphipods show a great abundance along the coasts of Oman, Somalia, west coast of Burma and off the southern coast of Java, increasing in general towards the northern part of the Indian Ocean. Their numbers decrease southwards.

Chaetognaths, too, show a similar distribution. The highest density was recorded in the western part of the Arabian Sea and their numbers also decrease southwards. It should be noted, however, that the concentration of these groups overlaps and also radiates from the areas of upwelling. This would be expected because the development of maximum populations of carnivores or omnivorous groups of plankton takes some time in the sequency of biological events in the sea. Firstly, there is local enrichment due to upwelling and as the surface waters get fertilized and spread under the influence of the local currents, the development of the phytoplankton population is displaced in space and time, and by the time copepods and their predators begin their population explosion, they may be located quite some distance from the area of upwelling. This is precisely what happens in the case of distribution and abundance of copepods, fish larvae and chaetognaths, amphipods and other groups in the northern Arabian Sea and the Bay of Bengal (see Plankton Atlases Vols I and II, IOBC, 1968, 1970).

VII. Numerical Distribution

Assuming that each IOSN sample of zoplankton represents the optimal distribution and occurrence in the 192 m^3 of water strained through the net, Table 5 was prepared in order to see whether any relationship exists between the different kinds of plankton. A 5° Marsden square (067−4) where we have data for about 5 months was arbitrarily selected and the numerical data were tabulated. Ecologically, the copepods are the major grazers and next come the copelates. The rest of the groups listed are mostly carnivorous or omnivorous; they are also capable of devouring each other or may even be cannibalistic in some cases. The order of dominance appears to be, barring copepods

Table 5. No. of zooplankters % of the total. Marsden square: 067 (4)

Station No.	ABA 3	D1 5251	D1 5012	D1 5089	AB 4A 170	Average Value
Months	Feb.	Mar.	June	Aug.	Oct.	
Copepoda	69.74	73.47	76,91	72.30	75.53	75.59
Chaetognaths	8.41	12.30	3.63	4.06	10.08	6.41
Copelata	0.07	1.13	1.89	2.76	0.66	1.09
Medusa	0.22	0.30	0.13	0.66	0.27	0.26
Polychaeta	0.59	0.62	1.04	1.97	0.39	0.77
Thecosomata	1.97	1.32	2.11	1.37	0.34	1.18
Euphausiacea	1.45	0.92	2.89	5.24	3.20	2.30
Amphipoda	0.54	0.35	0.18	0.17	0.16	0.23
Ostracoda	15.70	7.65	7.01	6.45	1.84	6.44
Decapoda	0.59	1.81	0.91	1.00	0.81	0.85
Salps	0.41	0.35	0.59	3.00	6.33	1.78
Fish larvae	0.30	0.22	0.63	0.82	0.19	0.36
Biomass						
Total No.	75629	54884	29683	19514	55456	39194

which numerically form nearly 70% of the total samples, ostracods, chaetognaths, euphausids, thecosomates and the rest.

The pattern of distribution of the major components of zooplankton including fish eggs and larvae clearly indicates that some of the Indian Ocean areas, such as Saudi Arabia and the Somalia coasts and the head of the Bay of Bengal are extraordinarily productive and the question uppermost in our minds is how much of this secondary production gets converted into exploitable resources of fish and how much of it goes to waste. PRUTER (1964) and PRASAD (1966) have discussed the potential yield of fisheries in the Indian Ocean. PRASAD estimates that the level of organic production in the Arabian Sea is at least 3 times that of the Bay of Bengal and in the actual fish yield the former is 2.4 times more than the latter. Such estimates are not possible for other areas of the Indian Ocean for want of sufficient data. However, it should be noted that rich patches of zooplankton occur at many places in the Indian Ocean as indicated by the IOBC samples.

4.2

The Distribution and Abundance of Zooplankton along the Coast of Pakistan during Postmonsoon and Premonsoon Periods

S.M. Haq, J. Ali Khan, and S. Chugtai

Zooplankton samples were collected on 4 cruises with PNS "Zulfiquar" with the IIOE net, except for cruise 1 where a smaller net (standard net 13) with a 30 cm mouth diameter was employed. Some further results of RV "Machera" from a cruise in Nov./Dec. 1964 are also included (Fig. 1). On each occasion vertical hauls were taken and cosine depths

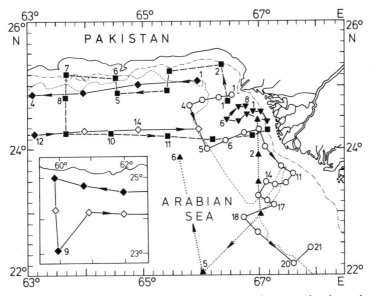

Fig. 1. Tracks of all cruises off the coast of Pakistan: Cruise I October 1962 (rhomb, no observations open rhomb); cruise II November 1964 (open circle); cruise III March 1967 (squares); cruise IV March 1968 (upright triangles); "Machera" cruise December 1964 (inverted triangles)

were computed from wire angle. Zooplankton biomass was measured in wet volume by the displacement method. All samples were preserved in 4% neutral formalin.

Each sample was analyzed from aliquots after ensuring homogeneous distribution of organisms by stirring. The fraction used for the counting of aliquots varied from $1/4$ to about $1/120$ depending on the density of the plankton in the samples. The number of individuals counted in each aliquot varied from about 400 to 800.

Species of copepods were identified according to Giesbrecht (1892), Sars (1924 to 1925), Mori (1937), and many others pertinent to the subject. Siphonophores and chaetognaths were identified with the help of Alvariño (1967), Totton and Bergmann (1965), and Sears (1953), and where later confirmed by Alvariño of the Scripps Institution of Oceanography, U.S.A.

I. Abundance of Major Groups

The quantitative study of various major groups for the 58 stations used in the cruises has yielded massive data. The areas covered by each cruise have been divided into sectors, based on differences in ecological conditions as well as topographical features. The average number per m² of each major group was computed from the values obtained for all the stations in a particular sector. Table 1 shows the scheme of division into various

Table 1. Division of areas into ecological sectors covered by each cruise

Cruise	Sectors	Stations
Cruise I Oct. 1962	Slope water	61/1 − 5, 7, 9, 12
Cruise II Nov. 1964	North of Swatch	64/1 − 10, 14, 15
	Swatch	64/13, 16, 18
	South of Swatch	64/11, 12, 17 − 21
Cruise III March 1967	Shelf	67/1 − 7, 12 − 14
	Slope water	67/8 − 11
	Western sector	67/7 − 9
	Eastern sector S. Astola Island	67/1 − 6, 10 − 14
Cruise IV March 1968	Shelf	68/1 − 3
	Slope water	68/4 − 6

sectors and the stations occupied. On the southern shelf 3 sectors have been established, i.e. the Swatch, and the areas north and south of it. In general, all other areas were divided into slope and shelf sectors. The area along the west coast covered in March 1967 is divided into a western sector, represented by stations 67/7 to 67/9 south of Astola Island and an eastern sector represented by all other stations. Figs. 2−7 show the distribution of the total number of zooplankton organisms and the distribution of biomass for various cruises. Fig. 8 shows the average values per m² of sea surface for each major group.

Copepods formed the bulk of the zooplankton stock. Comparison between various sectors shows maximum abundance in October from the slope water region along the western coast. The second largest abundance was found in the slope water region, but very low values in March 1968 from the shelf. In March 1967, the highest number was found in the western sector near Astola Island. Comparison between various sectors for this month shows very low values on the shelf as well as in the entire eastern sector including the slope water. In fact, there was a very high concentration of copepods in the western sector of the slope water region which apparently accounted for high values of the entire slope water region; this high abundance coincided with a reduced isothermal

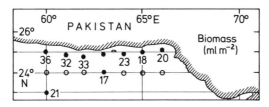

Fig. 2. Distribution of biomass; open circles represent stations where no zooplankton samples were collected

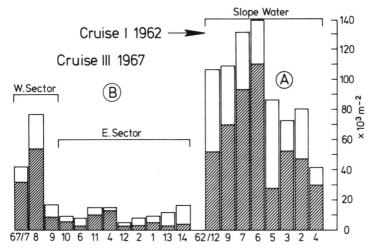

Fig. 3. Total number of zooplankton m^{-2} at different stations off the west coast of Pakistan; shaded part represents total number of copepods

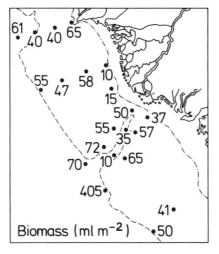

Fig. 4. Distribution of biomass on the southern shelf of Pakistan during November (cruise II, 1964)

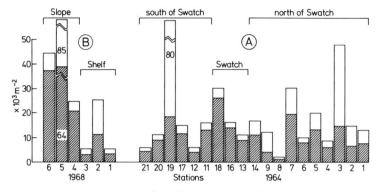

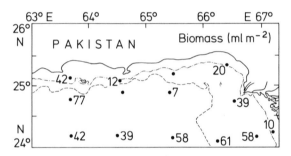

Fig. 5. Total number of zooplankton m^{-2} at different stations off the coast of Pakistan; shaded part represents total number of copepods. A: Cruise II, November 1964; B: Cruise IV, March 1968

Fig. 6. Distribution of biomass (cruise III, 1967)

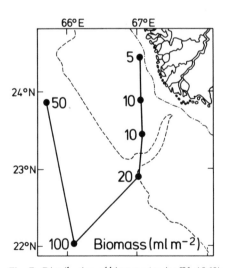

Fig. 7. Distribution of biomass (cruise IV, 1968)

surface. Comparison between various sectors within the southern shelf in November indicates the highest values in the area of the Swatch and the lowest in the northern sector. The total number of copepods in November was 2 to 3 times that obtained on the shelf in March.

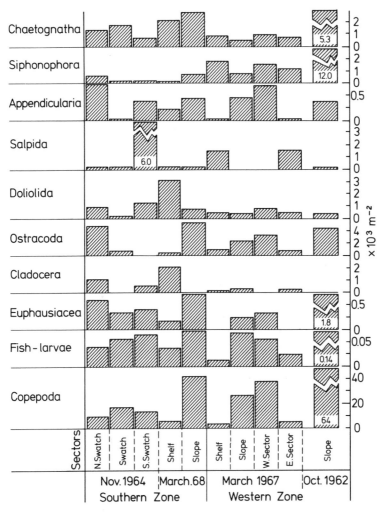

Fig. 8. Abundance of major groups of zooplankton in different ecological sectors covered by cruises I—IV along the coast of Pakistan

Fish larvae yielded the highest abundance in areas of rich zooplankton stocks. Their largest concentration was found in October and in March in the slope water. During November they were abundant on the southern shelf in areas close to the continental margin. They were most abundant in the southern sector; in the sector north of the Swatch they were largely confined to the area near the continental margin but were mostly absent or poorly represented from the shelf. The highest number 164 per m^2 was recorded for station 64/18 at the head of the Swatch.

The euphausids were found in large numbers in areas where oceanic influence predominated. A comparison shows the largest numbers in the slope water regions during October and March 1968. A somewhat higher number in the southern shelf during November is presumably associated with penetration of oceanic water into this region. They were completely absent during March from the west coast but were present in small numbers on the southern shelf. The cladocerans, on the other hand, were found to be restricted to the shelf. A comparison between various sectors indicates the largest concentration on the shelf during March 1968 and fair abundance in the area north and south of the Swatch. They were completely absent in the Swatch area itself.

Among micro-crustaceans, the ostracods at times formed the significant fraction of the plankton in both the shelf and slope water sectors. Their highest concentrations were restricted to small areas as in October and March in the slope water regions. They formed a significant fraction of the plankton in the sector north of the Swatch, particularly close to the continental margin. The highest number (28,730 per m^2) was recorded from station 64/3. Surprisingly, they declined to almost rare occurrence in the southern sector.

The doliolids were common in all sectors. They were most abundant in March in the shelf area of the southern region. In all other sectors they were less. As compared to this, the salps were highly restricted in distribution and an occasional dense swarm accounted for a high biomass value. They were generally confined to the shelf in vicinity of the continental margin. The highest concentration of salps (27,000 per m^2) was found in the sector south of the Swatch which contributed the bulk of the biomass (405 ml m^{-2}). In March 1967 the largest number of 6 613 per m^2 was found at station 67/13, contributing the bulk of the biomass (Fig. 6; Stn 67/13).

At times the siphonophores formed a significant part of the plankton, the number being largest during March and October in the western region. In March they were the dominating feature of the plankton biomass in the shelf and most of the eastern sector. The appendicularians were abundant in both the slope and shelf sectors in association with rich zooplankton. The largest number was found in the western sector in March 1967 but they were very rare in other parts of the shelf and the eastern sector. A similar trend was seen in March 1968. In November they were most abundant north of the Swatch, rare in the Swatch and south of the Swatch. The chaetognaths were the most widely distributed group, the largest numbers being associated with areas rich in zooplankton in October and March 1968. They were present in large numbers in the shelf during November. In March 1967 they were less variable in all the sectors.

Composition and Abundance of Copepods

Of all the major groups found, the copepods formed the bulk of the zooplankton stock. As the principal source of energy in the building of higher trophic levels, their numerical abundance at different stations in different periods provides a better measure of productive areas than other groups. The species have been studied and their quantitative abundance determined. In this paper the copepods are divided into 2 groups: the epiplanktonic species which are largely confined to the surface area on the shelf and slope water, and the mesopelagic species living in subsurface oceanic waters. The criteria for categorization of species into one or the other group were based on the work in this region of SEWELL (1947), VERVOORT (1946), and VINOGRADOV (1968). Out of some 82 species of copepods identified (from the area of present studies) a relatively small number constitutes a significant fraction of the whole copepod stock. Table 2 gives the most common species arranged in order of frequency of their occurrence at all stations occupied during all cruises. The epiplanktonic species, with the exception of *Oncaea conifera*, *Clausocalanus arcuicornis* and *Acartia amboensis* which appeared in large

Table 2. The frequency of occurence of the most common species of copepods on the shelf and adjacent areas off Pakistan

	Cr. I	Cr. II	Cr. III	Cr. IV	Machera Cr.	% of all stations
Epilanktonic spp.						
Eucalanus pileatus	88	90	50	83	87	79.6
Acrocalanus longicornis	88	72	50	66	100	75.0
Paracalanus aculeatus	78	20	57	100	100	71.0
Oithona plumifera	66	73	86	100	100	65.0
Canthocalanus pauper	88	61	72	0	100	61.6
Temora turbinata	22	66	35	83	100	61.0
Eucalanus crassus	88	53	42	66	50	59.2
E. subcrassus	56	90	28	50	50	55.0
Corycaeus crassiusculus	33	98	50	100	74	53.2
Eucalanus subtenuis	56	47	42	83	25	50.6
Acartia amboensis	56	100	–	–	83	47.8
Undinula vulgaris	44	9	42	50	100	49.0
Acrocalanus gracilis	89	19	7	–	100	43.0
Euchaeta concinna	44	–	14	66	50	34.8
Oncaea conifera	88	33	–	–	50	34.2
Corycaeus flaccus	66	18	21	100	74	31.0
Clausocalanus arcuicornis	–	–	64	33	50	28.8
Oceanic spp.						
Pleuromamma indica	89	90	28	50	25	56.4
Euchaeta wolfendeni	56	66	64	50	37	54.6
E. marina	89	57	14	50	–	42.0
Eucalanus mucronatus	44	38	–	50	25	31.4
Rhincalanus nasutus	22	28	73	16	13	17.4
Clausocalanus farrani	–	9	42	33	–	18.8

numbers only in certain months, seem to be common and widespread in the shelf and the slope water areas during the postmonsoon and the premonsoon periods. The oceanic species, on the other hand, are relatively few and largely dominated by *Pleuromamma indica* and *Euchaeta wolfendeni*. *Euchaeta marina*, *Clausocalanus farrani* and *Eucalanus mucronatus* were found in substantial numbers in some areas.

Fig. 9 shows the abundance per m² in different sectors of 16 important species representing 63 to 90% of the average values of the total copepod number as shown for different sectors in Fig. 8.

In the southern zone during November the epiplanktonic species formed the bulk of the copepods. The most abundant species were *Acrocalanus longicornis*, *Canthocalanus pauper*, *Eucalanus pileatus*, *Tempora turbinata*, *Paracalanus aculeatus*, *Eucalanus crassus*, *Acartia amboensis*, *Oncaea conifera* and *Corycaeus flaccus*. In the sector of the Swatch where oceanic conditions dominated, all other species were present except *Temora turbinata*. This species was mostly confined to the shelf and in small numbers to areas where oceanic influence predominated. Among oceanic species *Pleurormamma indica* and *Euchaeta wolfendeni* were present in considerable numbers in various sectors.

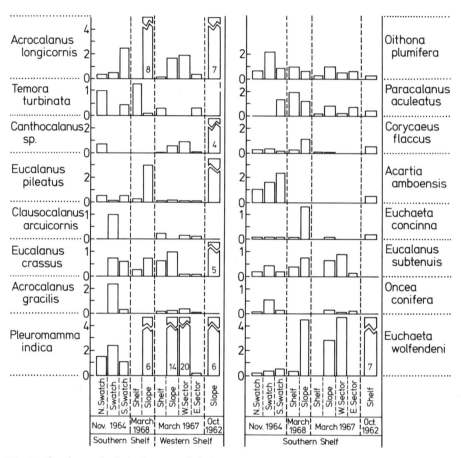

Fig. 9. Abundance of principal species of planktonic copepods in different ecological sectors covered by cruises I—IV along the coast of Pakistan. Numbers represent averages per m²

Observations made in March near the continental margin and the slope water, showed that the epiplanktonic copepods dominated only at stations 62/1 to 3, whereas at all other stations the oceanic species formed the bulk of the copepods. Among the epiplanktonic species of this sector, the most abundant were *Acrocalanus longicornis*, *Eucalanus pileatus*, *E. crassus*, *E. subtenuis* and *Canthocalanus pauper*. All these species tend to diminish in number in the slope water region. Among the oceanic species, *Pleuromamma indica*, *Euchaeta wolfendeni* and *E. marina* formed the bulk of the copepods. In March 1967 when copepods were few in the shelf and most of the slope water region, *Temora turbinata* and *Eucalanus subcrassus* formed the bulk of the former area while

Acrocalanus spp. predominated in the latter. In the most productive area near Astola Island the oceanic species formed the bulk of the copepods and were largely represented by *Pleuromamma indica, Clausocalanus farrani,* and *Euchaeta wolfendeni.* The epiplanktonic species in this sector were of the same order of magnitude noted in other sectors during the period. They were largely dominated by *Acrocalanus longicornis,* and *Eucalanus crassus.*

To summarize, the epiplanktonic species dominated the bulk of the copepod stock in the shelf and adjacent area during October and November, while the oceanic species, largely represented by mesopelagic forms, formed the bulk of the slope water population in October and at places where a reduced surface isothermal layer was the predominant feature. On the shelf they were substantially represented during November but were absent in March.

II. Distribution of Oceanic Species in Relation to Hydrographic Conditions

Evidence has been obtained that hydrographic factors affect the distribution of oceanic species principally inhabiting the subsurface region of the oceanic zone and the surface waters of the slope area and the shallow region of the shelf, in this case the

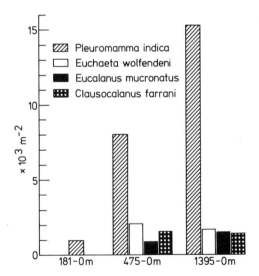

Fig. 10. Vertical distribution of oceanic species (No. per m²)

copepods *Pleuromamma indica* and *Euchaeta wolfendeni* and the chaetognath *Sagitta decipiens.* For a better understanding of their distribution pattern, one needs to know the environmental conditions which determine their normal habitat.

Observations on the vertical distribution of *Pleuromamma indica* and *Euchaeta wolfendeni* are available from two stations in March 1967 and 1968. Fig. 10 shows the vertical distribution of these species together with 2 others for station 67/10. This station was located about 30 miles east of station 67/9 where high abundances of the above species were found in the surface haul of the 180−0 m column. Vertical hauls were taken from 3 different depth ranges. Fig. 11 gives the physical data collected from standard depths as the same station. *Pleuromamma indica* was least frequent in the top range of 181−0 m, increasing with depth. *Euchaeta wolfendeni, Eucalanus mucronatus,* and *Clausocalanus farrani* were present only at the intermediate depth; their numbers

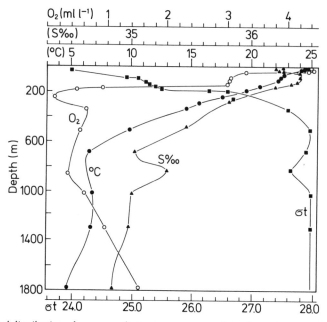

Fig. 11. Vertical distribution of oxygen, salinity, temperature and density at deep stn 67/10 (cruise III, 1967)

remained the same at depth ranges 475−0 m and 1395−0 m. An examination of physical conditions indicates the presence of cool water (23°C) at about 65 m (top of the thermocline), falling to about 20°C at 181 m, and 6.5°C at 1375 m depth. The O_2 content had a minimum of about 0.16 ml l^{-1} at 250 m but tended to increase slightly with increasing depth, though remaining much below 1 ml l^{-1} for almost the whole of the deepest haul. Observations made at station 68/6 in March 1968 (Figs. 12 and 13) about 65 miles SE of station 67/10 indicate a similar trend except that all species were more abundant than at station 67/10. The hydrographic conditions at station 68/6 were marked by the presence of reduced isothermal surface. Below this layer the water was highly deficient in O_2. At the level of the deepest haul (700 m) the O_2 content was about 0.5 ml l^{-1} and the temperature had declined. Although none of the observations established a precise limit for their vertical distribution, it is reasonable to assume that the species referred to above, and particularly *Pleuromamma indica*, thrive at temperatures between 6° to 23°C and at O_2 contents much below 1 ml l^{-1}. In the case of *Euchaeta wolfendeni*, the conditions present at the intermediate depths are probably optimal.

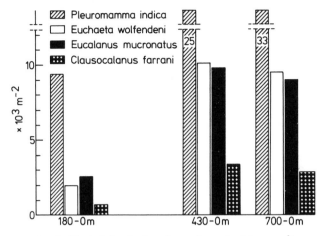

Fig. 12. Vertical distribution of oceanic species (No. per m²)

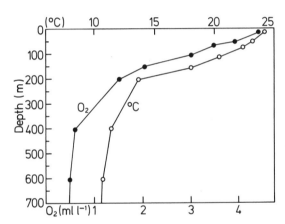

Fig. 13. Vertical distribution of temperature and oxygen at deep stn 68/6 (cruise IV, 1968)

Figs. 14 and 15 shows the horizontal distribution of *Pleuromamma indica* and *Euchaeta wolfendeni* in the area covered by the present studies. In the southern shelf area *P. indica* was found at almost all stations during November. The highest concentration of this species was found near the continental margin and inside the area of the Swatch where deep penetration of cool and O_2-deficient water was seen. The interesting aspect is the deep penetration of *P. indica* at the coastward end of the Swatch where it was found in considerable numbers at shallow stations (Stns 64/11, 64/12). Observations made in December at 8 stations near Karachi about 3 weeks after the November observations failed to record this species at most stations. Only at 2 stations further offshore were 3 specimens recorded. In March this species was completely absent in the southern shelf where homogeneous water was found, but it was abundant in the 200 m haul in the slope water region. Along the western shelf in October, it was

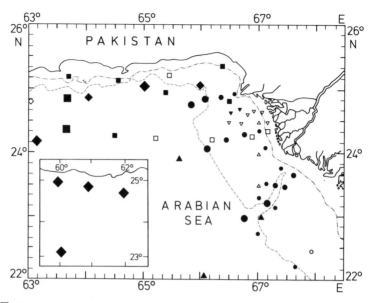

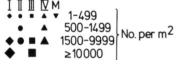

Fig. 14. Distribution and numerical abundance of *Pleuromamma indica* (cruise I—IV and "Machera" cruise)

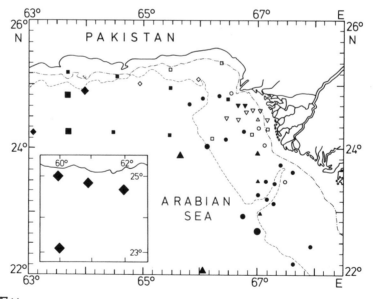

Fig. 15. Distribution and numerical abundance of *Euchaeta wolfendeni* (cruise I—IV and "Machera" cruise)

most abundant in the slope water region at all stations except station 62/4, and in March in the western sector near Astola Island where a reduced surface isothermal layer was present. An almost similar picture was obtained for *Euchaeta wolfendeni* except that numbers were much less than of *P. indica*.

The distribution of *Sagitta decipiens* is shown in Fig. 16. This species is essentially mesopelagic and is reported in the Indian Ocean below 200 m (ALVARIÑO, 1965; RAO and GANAPATI, 1958). Large concentrations of this species were found during November

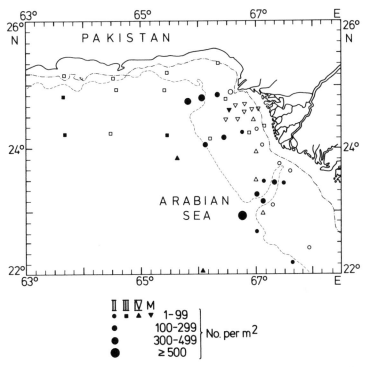

Fig. 16. Distribution and numerical abundance of *Sagitta decipiens* (cruise I−IV and "Machera" cruise)

along the continental margin as well as in the area of the Swatch, even at the shallow (21 m) station 64/12 where the bottom temperature was 23.9°C. It was probably transported by ascent of oceanic water into the shallow region of the shelf. This species and the others referred to above seem to provide biological evidence of subsurface water upwelling in the area.

III. Discussion

The observations reported in this paper for the area adjoining the coast of Pakistan are confined to the postmonsoon (October through December) and premonsoon (March) periods. The considerable variations in zooplankton abundance may be regarded as temporal and spatial in nature. The months of October through December in the area of the present studies are periods of high zooplankton abundance, while in March a period of low zooplankton abundance is found particularly in the main area of the shelf. The results obtained during these periods may be compared with those obtained from other parts of the Indian Ocean. Recently the Indian Ocean Biological Centre at Cochin published the IIOE Plankton Atlas (IOBC 1968, 1970), which provides the best source for comparison. Our observations on the zooplankton biomass for various months referred to earlier fall within the period of the NE monsoon (October through April) as shown in the atlas. The average biomass based on day and night samples recorded for the NE sector of the Arabian Sea shows the values $15-25$ ml m^{-2} for a water column of 200 m. This is much lower than the average biomass computed for the 53 stations (55 ml m^{-2}). The values obtained for this area are very close to those recorded from the coast of Arabia. Comparison with other regions of the Indian Ocean including the coast of Somalia, SW coast of India and the Bay of Bengal show values from present studies to be 3 to 4 times as high as those recorded for these regions. On the other hand, the results are of the same order of magnitude as those recorded during the SW monsoon from the above region. The point worthy of mention here is the spectacularly high zooplankton production during November and December, noted earlier. The December records, averaged over 6 stations from the area immediately south of Karachi, showed a value of 166 ml m^{-2} for a water column ranging up to 80 m depth, which to the author's knowlegde is the highest ever recorded from the Indian Ocean. Earlier records for March from the open sea of the northern Arabian Sea by BOGOROV and VINOGRADOV (1961) show a value 100 ml per 1000 m^3 for a column of water 100 m deep which translated into values per m^2 were lower (10 ml) than those obtained for this month (37 ml m^{-2}) in the entire area including the shelf and slope water. Because of different nets employed, some discrepancies might be expected in this comparison. The various aspects of studies so far carried out tend to suggest a close relationship between zooplankton abundance and hydrographic conditions. Some insight into this may be derived from other work done in this region. The months of November and early December are generally calm. The zooplankton abundance noted in these months is associated with the presence of cool water highly deficient in oxygen water which has penetrated into the shelf as a part of a large-scale movement under the influence of the SW monsoon (BANSE, 1968). The dissolved phosphate contents recorded from various depths in this area (Cruise Report "Zulun" I, 1964) have values ranging from 1 to 1.2 μg-at l^{-1} at 50 m or above at most of the stations. This nutrient-laden water near the surface would account for the high organic production, as noted in other areas (RYTHER and MENZEL, 1965; BRANDHORST, 1958). This is supported by earlier studies of KABANOVA (1964) who recorded high phytoplankton production rates (30.6 to 83.3 mgC m^{-2} day^{-1}) during October and November on this shelf. The spectacular increase in zooplankton noted in December must have been supported by increased primary production. Similarly the observations carried out along the western shelf in October 1962 showed very high numbers of microcrustaceans. RYTHER et al. (1966) found a very high organic production rate (more than 1 gC m^{-2} day^{-1}) in November 1963 in the area extending from the coast of Arabia to that of Pakistan. Perhaps this is a regular annual feature.

During November and March the phytoplankton production is probably too low to support the larger zooplankton due to deepening of the thermocline, and consequently of the fertile water, as a result of withdrawal of subsurface water from the shelf (BANSE, 1968).

The biomass values recorded by FRONTIER (1963a) from stations RG 203 and RG 204, which were close to our station 67/4 in March, when converted into values per m^2 yielded 128 and 72 ml for a 50 m column of water for the respective stations. These were much higher than those obtained in March from 67/4 (7 ml m^{-2}).

There is some evidence of marked spatial variations in zooplankton abundance in geographically limited areas. For instance, notes of high zooplankton abundance in shallower areas along the southern bank of the Swatch (Stns 64/11, 64/12, 64/17) are confirmed by records (Cruise Report "Zulun" I, 1964) of a rich phytoplankton bloom in this area, as well as a high phosphate content. These and the presence of aerated water in the southern region would offer ideal conditions for zooplankton production. ELIZAROV (1968) reported ascent of deep oceanic water inside the Swatch in January and excluded any possibility of wind-induced upwelling. How far this phenomenon is a regular feature of the area is not known. A further example was found near Astola Island (western sector) on the west coast, where rich zooplankton was associated with a reduced surface isothermal layer. Similarly, in the slope water in March 1968, rich zooplankton coincided with reduced surface isotherms. Such a situation is reported by BRANDHORST (1958) from the eastern Pacific.

Total zooplankton expressed in numerical terms has often shown lack of agreement with the corresponding values of biomass. This may be accounted for by the presence or absence, or restricted distribution, of certain large organisms such as siphonophores, salps, medusae etc., reported to be responsible for the depletion of phytoplankton and copepods (FRASER, 1961; TRANTER, 1962).

Most of the early work on copepods of the shelf and slope water area in the Indian Ocean deals only with taxonomy. The principal species referred to here are also reported from other parts of the Indian Ocean (MENON, 1945; SEWELL, 1947; VINOGRADOV, 1968), but there is a lack of quantitative data. Comparative studies of various sectors show that, whereas epiplanktonic species formed the bulk of the copepod stock in the shelf and neighboring waters, the oceanic species occupied a significant fraction of the sub-surface region both in the slope water and on the shelf, and therefore may contribute substantial food energy for higher trophic levels.

The composition of oceanic species is distinguished by the numerical abundance of relatively few species, principally *Pleuromamma indica* and *Euchaeta wolfendeni,* the former far exceeding the latter. VINOGRADOV and VORONINA (1961) reported vertical distribution of a few species in April 1960 in a transect extending from the Seychelles, off the African Coast, to Bombay. They describe 6 species which include 3 members of the genus *Pleuromamma (P. gracilis, P. xiphias* and *P. indica).* According to these workers, whereas other species are limited in their distribution by higher O_2 content (0.5 ml l^{-1}), *P. indica* is associated with an O_2 content of less than 0.1 ml l^{-1}. This is supported by our present study. Oxygen depletion immediately below the surface thermocline is probably the rule in the Arabian Sea (RYTHER and MENZEL, 1965; BANSE, 1968). Where there is vertical ascent of this layer, as during the SW and NE monsoon, or in areas of divergence (RYTHER and MENZEL, 1965) and when massive displacement of surface water results in reduced surface isothermal layers, *Pleuromamma* and other oceanic species may form a significant fraction of the subsurface plankton. This is borne out by our studies where these species formed the bulk of the copepods during October in the slope water region as well as in areas of reduced surface isothermal layers. There are some indications that diurnal migration (VINOGRADOV and VORONINA, 1961) may play some part in the vertical distribution in the upper strata (night Stn. 67/8), but this was not true of other night stations (67/11) in the same area.

The area of the southern bank of the Swatch and that situated near Astola Island is well known for its high fishery yield, a fact supported by present studies on zooplankton abundance and environmental conditions.

4.3

Distribution of Hydromedusae in the Indian Ocean

M. Vannucci and D. Navas

We have endeavoured in this work to characterize the various oceanographic systems of the Indian Ocean at different depths, using the medusae as indicators of the prevalence of plankton at the trophic level of obligate carnivores.

I. Material and Methods

We chose hydromedusae as our example because:

a) most species are in good taxonomic order and we use the species as the basic biological unit; b) all medusae are exclusive carnivores, and most fish passively for their food by the hook and line technique and thus fall into a single ecological category with regard to food acquisition habits; c) they are too sluggish to actively avoid the plankton sampler, thus sampling bias brought about by avoidance behaviour is minimized and the numbers in the samples should adequately represent the association at sea. Here the main source of error lies in the very great fragility of many species; vulnerability varies between species, so they are not numerically comparable except in a gross manner; however, this error is minimized by considering each species separately and disregarding those that for various reasons did not provide reliable information. Special difficulties arise when the juveniles cannot be determined to species level and when they are specially abundant, as for instance in the genus *Aequorea,* a group of slow-growing species.

Given the rarity of hydromedusae, all specimens in each sample were sorted, determined and counted. About 150 species were found in about 900 samples from the Indian Ocean, which were made available for study from the Smithsonian Institution.

Some of the samples are duplicates or insufficiently labelled, and some of the specimens are doubtful or undeterminable because they are young stages, new species, or damaged beyond recognition. About 45000 specimens were determined and counted; 34 species were not previously recorded for the Indian Ocean and were dealt with separately (Navas, 1971), 1 new species *Halistaura bruuni* (Navas, 1969) is, as far as known, endemic in the Bay of Bengal.

II. Results

Two species predominate (45%): *Aglaura hemistoma* ($^2/_3$) and *Lyriope tetraphylla* ($^1/_3$), both warm-water, holoplanktonic, frequent, surface-water species; their abundance in the collection is due to the geographic distribution of the stations, mostly oceanic and far from land. The scarcity or absence of inshore and coastal species is noteworthy. Fig. 1 shows frequency distribution with depth, and the identical behaviour of the two species: both are euryhaline and eurythermal and *Aglaura* is more abundant in tropical oceanic samples (Vannucci, 1957; 1963). *Lyriope* feeds on larger animals than *Aglaura* and this

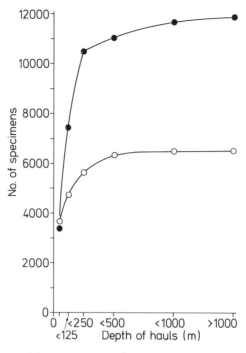

Fig. 1. Cumulative curves of frequency versus depth distribution of *Aglaura hemistoma* (closed circles) and *Lyriope tetraphylla* (open circles). The curves were obtained by plotting the sums of all the specimens taken with open nets from the depths indicated to the surface

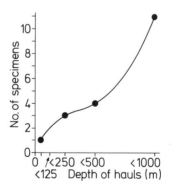

Fig. 2. Cumulative curves of frequency versus depth distribution (obtained as in Fig. 1.) of *Euphysora furcata*

may help to keep the 2 species separate. Fig. 2 shows the different depth distribution pattern of *Euphysora furcata*, a cold-water species found to sink at the sub-Antarctic convergence.

Few species were found to be euryhaline, eurythermal and widely tolerant for dissolved O_2 and some of these are rare, e.g. *Vannuccia forbesi* which is eurytopic for salinity temperature and dissolved O_2. The species has a benthic hydroid stage and its distribution may be limited by the bottom-living stage, or some ecological factor not considered here. The 8 specimens taken in $33.0-35.9‰$ salinity, $16-27.4°C$ temperature and $0.8-4.5$ ml l^{-1} dissolved O_2 occurred in many different water masses: Bay of Bengal surface and subsurface waters, Arabian Sea surface and subsurface waters, South Central surface water and South Tropical surface water; perhaps also in Indian Ocean central water. The species seems to require waters rich in zooplankton standing stock.

The fact that species were new records for the Indian Ocean and one was a new species, probably reflects the paucity of earlier studies. Two species have migrated into

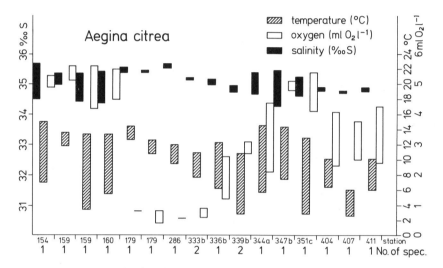

Fig. 3. Example of the distribution of a stenohaline, eurythermal and oxygen-tolerant species, *Aegina citrea*, in relation to these parameters

the Indian Ocean via the Suez Canal; this is certain for *Koellikerina fasciculata* but less so for *Bougainvillia maniculata* (SCHMIDT, 1973). Many species were closely associated with one or two water masses and were not found in others. Thus, 20 species were taken in surface and/or subsurface Bay of Bengal waters and 10 species only in surface and/or subsurface Arabian Sea waters. Some 20 were Antarctic species taken in cold waters or in water of Antarctic origin, but their presence north of the Equator in the Indian Ocean does not mean they had been bodily transported from south of the subtropical or subantarctic convergence, it merely means that their distribution is dependent on temperature. The species have had ample time to populate gradually those bodies of water that have suitable temperature conditions. Sixteen species belong to the Indian Ocean central water system and 13 to the equatorial surface water and southern gyre systems (Fig. 3). Between species tolerance differs for different parameters; divergent adaptation to different environmental conditions in ecological closely related species is evident. Therefore, neither the geographical nor the ecological range of distribution is the same

Table 1. Distribution of selected species of hydromedusae in different areas of the ocean

Species / Environmental factors	Salinity controlled	Temperature controlled	Oxygen controlled	Boundary layer	Only in Bay of Bengal	Only in Arabian Sea	Indian Ocean Central Water System	Tropical Equatorial System	Upwelling	Antarctic & Sub-Antarctic
Ectopleura sacculifera	+					+			+	
Euphysilla pyramidata	+						+			
Euphysora annulata	+	+								
E. bigelowi	+		+		+			+		+
E. furcata		+								
Vannuccia forbesi	+	+		high + food						
Zanclea costata			+				+			
Z. dubia				high + food						
Z. orientalis				+				+	+	
Zancleopsis tentaculata		+	+	+				+		
Z. gotoi	+	+	+		+					
Cytaeis tetrastyla	widely, distributed, tropical, subtropical, temperature, surface							+		
Bougainvillia falva			+							
B. playtygaster	widely, distributed, tropical, subtropical, surface							+		
Koellikerina octonemalis	+			+	+					
Amphinema rugosum	+	+		+	+		+			
Leuckartiara octona	+	+		+			+			
Merga violacea			+							
Pandea conica			+					+		
Pandeopsis scutigera			+		+					
Protiara tropica				+			+			
Heterotiara minor			+	+			+			
Laodicea fijiana	+	+						+		

Species	1	2	3	4	5	6	7	8
L. indica								
Halistaura bruuni	+	+	+	+	+		+	
Eucheilota menoni	+	+	+	+	+			
Lovenella cirrata	+	+	+		+			
Octophialucium indicum	+	+	+		+			
Phialucium carolinae	+	+	+	+	+			
P. multitentaculatum	+				+			
Eirene elliceana				+	+			
E. hexanemalis			+	+	+		+	
E. viridula	+		+		+		+	
Aequorea aequorea	+		+		+		+	
A. coerulescens	+	+	+					
A. conica			+					
A. macrodactyla	+			+			+	
A. pensilis	+		+	+	+	+	+	
Olindias singularis	+	+						
Proboscidactyla ornata	+			+			+	
Geryonia proboscidalis	+	+	+	+			+	
Botrynema brucei	+	+	+	+				+
Halicreas minimum	+	+	+			+		+
Halisceras racovitzae	+	+		+		+		
Halitrephes maasi	+	+				+		+
Aglantha elata				+		+		+
Amphogona apicata				+		+		
Colobonema sericeum	+		+					+

for any 2 species. Table 1 shows the basic distribution of some of the species studied. Fig. 4 shows the distribution of a sub-Antarctic species.

The greatest number of species and specimens comes from boundary zones, the discontinuity layer, perhaps the deep scattering layer, and front or areas of mixing; probably this is due to greater food availability in such areas. Fig. 5 shows the distribution of *Zanclea dubia* and its aggregation at the boundary layers.

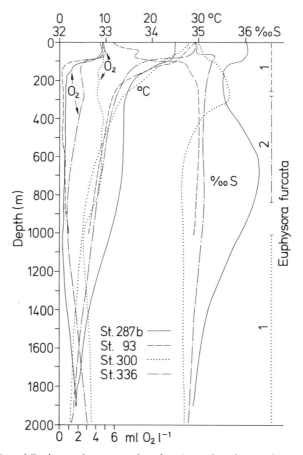

Fig. 4. Distribution of *Euphysora furcata*, at selected stations, plotted over salinity, temperature and oxygen distribution with depth, at the same stations. Vertical lines indicate depth of hauls at which the species was found. Stn 287b, 10°21′N, 54°17′E; Stn 93, 15°58′N, 84°27′E; Stn 300, 17°14′S, 54°38′E; Stn 336, 02°01′N, 65°03′E

III. Discussion

In seeking patterns in the interaction between the environment and the animals and their numbers, it must be remembered that density-dependent factors may become as important or even more important than physical and chemical factors. By density dependent factors we mean food and its availability, the presence of predators and their density and reproductive rate, as well as intra- and interspecific competition for space and food, determined by population density. The idea that meaningful patterns of species distribution exist among plankton is linked to two ancillary ideas that we considered in the analysis of the data: 1) species distribution is regulated by environmental parameters, while population density at any given time or place is regulated by the amount of food available and the age of the ecosystem; 2) in the world of plankton, patterns of higher

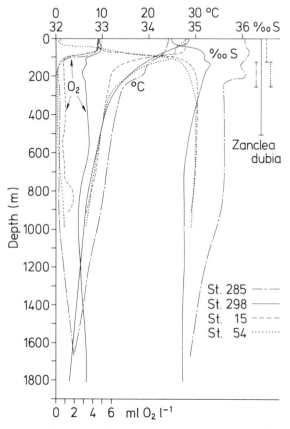

Fig. 5. Depth distribution of *Zanclea dubia*, at selected stations plotted over salinity, temperature and oxygen distribution with depth, at the same stations. Stn 15, 07°27′N, 95°18′E; Stn 54, 18°24′N, 90°45′E; Stn 285, 14°22′N, 54°18′E; Stn 298, 12°33′S, 54°33′E

order are probably superimposed on the patterns of the distribution of the species. There are indications that primary producers, grazers, secondary producers, active hunters and all such ecological categories that are not taxonomic categories, have patterns of distribution peculiar to themselves.

From the examples cited and the detailed study of the other species we draw some general conclusions that appear to be corroborated by studies of species belonging to other taxonomic groups made by the staff of the Indian Ocean Biological Centre at Cochin.

1. Bay of Bengal

Although we would not go as far as to say that the Bay of Bengal is nothing more than a large estuary, it has many of the features of an estuary: its surface waters have high temperature and low salinity, the latter decreasing northward and, together with the subsurface water, have twice as many species restricted to them as the surface and subsurface waters of the Arabian Sea. About half are neritic species, elsewhere confined to coastal areas of greater or lesser extent. They are found in the Bay of Bengal as far out to sea as their longevity and the velocity of the current permit. All are metagenetic species, and therefore dependent on available substratum for the benthic-living hydroid stage; all have a long life span and are restricted to salinity lower than 35‰ associated with temperature higher than $19-20°$ C.

2. Arabian Sea

The Arabian Sea surface system has temperatures higher than $19-20°$ C, associated with salinity higher than 35,8‰. Vannucci and Santhakumari (in press) have listed 14 species that are new records for the Arabian Sea, 4 of them already known from the Bay of Bengal. The other 10 species add to the known difference in the hydromedusan fauna in the surface layers of the Arabian Sea and Bay of Bengal. The species common to the surface layers of both are found in restricted coastal and estuarine areas in the Arabian Sea, except for a few very euryhaline species.

3. The Indian Ocean Central Water

This system, for the present purpose, comprises waters with temperatures lower than $19-20°$ C and salinity of about $34.5-36.0$‰. The species found therein occur also in Arabian Sea subsurface water, but only species that can tolerate lower salinity are found in the Bay of Bengal subsurface water too (salinity $34.1-35.0$‰). These species are geographically widely distributed and may include some preferring cold water as well as Antarctic species, either in upwelling areas or at the lower boundary.

4. Upwelling

Examples are scarce, but some species such as *Ectopleura sacculifera* appear to be restricted to upwelling areas. However, we cannot yet generalize on the correlation between upwelling and particular species.

5. Deep and Intermediate Waters

There are deep- or intermediate-water species that do not appear to be of Antarctic origin, like *Merga reesi* and *Amphogona apicata*. There are also several Antarctic species that sink at the convergences and spread north via Antarctic intermediate water or Antarctic deep water and thence into Indian Ocean central water, Arabian Sea intermediate water, Arabian Sea subsurface water and Bay of Bengal subsurface and deep water, as far as their limits of tolerance will permit. These include *Euphysora furcata*,

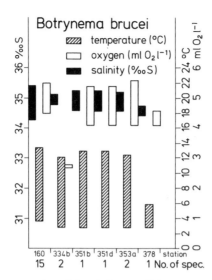

Fig. 6. Distribution of *Botrynema brucei*, in relation to salinity, temperature and dissolved oxygen, showing its stenotopic properties

Botrynema brucei, Halicreas minimum, Halitrephes maasi, Colobonema sericeum, Crossota alba (Fig. 6).

Divergent adaptation of species, especially congeneric species, is noteworthy. Thus, *Koellikerina fasciculata*, an immigrant from the high-salinity Mediterranean, is found in the Arabian Sea while *K. constricta, K. elegans, K. multicirrata* and *K. octonemalis* occupy different low-salinity niches in the Bay of Bengal. A similar situation arises between *Euphysora annulata* (restricted to the Arabian Sea), *E. furcata* (an Antarctic species), and *E. bigelowi* (widely distributed). Other examples may be quoted for the genera *Zanclea*, *Aequorea* (Table 1), *Bougainvillia* and others.

Biogeographical Problems of the Red Sea Area Exemplified by Hydroids

H.-E. Schmidt

There is at present very little information available concerning Red Sea faunistic regions; this makes it impossible to draw any certain conclusions about hydroid distribution. On the other hand, it becomes increasingly interesting to consider the origin of the species found in the Red Sea. A fair number of species recorded from there are widely distributed throughout the Atlantic, Pacific and Indian Ocean and the Mediterranean. They are restricted to tropical and subtropical waters or are cosmopolitans and could be divided into 3 groups: Indo-Pacific-Atlanto-Mediterranean (IPAM) species, Indo-Pacific (IP) species, and Atlanto-Mediterranean (AM) species.

I. The Indo-Pacific-Atlanto-Mediterranean (IPAM) Species I
(Table 1)

We do not know when or how hydroids belonging to this group reached the Red Sea. There are no records from the Suez Canal, and if they had reached the Red Sea during the periods when the Red Sea was linked with the Tethys, they must have survived the Glacial Age. This theory will not meet with general acceptance. Penetration through

Table 1. Indo-Pacific-Atlanto-Mediterranean (IPAM) species and their distribution

Species	Red Sea	Suez Canal	Mediterranean Sea	Atlantic Ocean (excl. South Africa)	South Africa	Indian Ocean (excl. South Africa)	Pacific Ocean	Red Sea immigrants in Mediterranean Sea	Mediterranean immigrants in Red Sea
Halecium sessile Norman	+	−	+	+	+	+	+	−	−
Clytia hemisphaerica (Linné)	+	−	+	+	+	+	+	−	−
Hebella calcarata (Agassiz)	+	−	+	+	+	+	+	−	−
Filellum serratum (Clarke)	+	−	+	+	+	+	+	−	−
Antenella secundaria (Gmelin)	+	−	+	+	+	+	+	−	−
Plumularia setacea Ellis	+	−	+	+	+	+	+	−	−

the ancient canals is impossible due to the freshwater barrier, so that they must have penetrated from the Indo-Pacific waters after the Glacial Age. Of course, it is possible that specimens penetrated the Suez Canal in both directions, but this cannot be confirmed unless we have records of them from the Canal.

II. The Indo-Pacific-Atlanto-Mediterranean (IPAM) Species II

(Table 2)

These species differ from the first group in that they do occur in the Suez Canal (Billard, 1926). Billard distinguishes 3 groups: hydroids which penetrated from the Mediterranean, those which originated from the Red Sea, and those which may have entered from either end. His decision was definitely influenced by lack of information.

Table 2. Indo-Pacific-Atlanto-Mediterranean (IPAM) species and their distribution (species recorded from the Suez Canal)

Species	Red Sea	Suez Canal	Mediterranean Sea	Atlantic Ocean (excl. South Africa)	South Africa	Indian Ocean (excl. South Africa)	Pacific Ocean	Red Sea immigrants in Mediterranean Sea	Mediterranean immigrants in Red Sea
								According to Billard (1926)	
Bougainvillia ramosa muscus (Allman)	−	+	+	+	+	+	+	+	+
Eudendrium capillare Alder	−	+	+	+	+	+	+	+	+
Laomedea geniculata (Linné)	−	+	+	+	+	+	+	+	−
Dynamena cornicina McCrady	+	+	+	+	+	+	+	−	+
Ventromma halecioides (Alder)	+	+	+	+	+	+	+	+	−
Lytocarpus philippinus (Kirchenpauer)	+	+	+	+	+	+	+	−	+

The species mentioned above have now been recorded from all 3 oceans, so it is not possible to confirm Billard's opinion.

Eudendrium capillare (Alder), *Laomedea geniculata* (Linné) and *Bougainvillia ramosa muscus* (Allman) have not been previously recorded from the Red Sea due to the fact that less work has been done in this area. *Bougainvillia ramosa,* for example, occurs in the Gulf of Tadjoura (Billard, 1904). We cannot be so certain, as in the case of the first group, that they penetrated from the Indo-Pacific waters because they could have originated in the Mediterranean. From this viewpoint Billard's opinion might be correct, but it is probably too late to confirm it. That *Eudendrium capillare* (Alder) and *Lytocarpus philippinus* (Kirchenpauer) occur more frequently in the southern Canal, *Laomedea geniculata* (Linné) in the north, and the others are well distributed throughout the Canal makes it more difficult to solve the problem. Besides the zoogeographical viewpoint, we have to consider the ecological conditions in the Canal and the behaviour of the hydroids.

III. The Indo-Pacific (IP) Species

(Table 3)

The IP species undoubtedly penetrated into the Red Sea through the Bab-el-Mandeb. They do not normally occur in the Atlanto-Mediterranean waters. *Thyroscyphus fruti-*

Table 3. Indo-Pacific (IP) species and their distribution

Species	Red Sea	Suez Canal	Mediterranean Sea	Atlantic Ocean (excl. South Africa)	South Africa	Indian Ocean (excl. South Africa)	Pacific Ocean	Red Sea immigrants in Mediterranean Sea	Mediterranean immigrants in Red Sea
Halocordyle disticha (GOLDFUSS) var. *australis* (BALE)	+	+	+?	+?	+	+	+	+?	−
Thyroscyphus fruticosus (ESPER)	+	−	+	−	−	+	+	+	−
Hydractinia kaffraria MILLARD	+	−	−	−	+	−	−	−	−
Campanularia gravieri BILLARD	+	−	−	−	−	+	+	−	−
Gymnangium gracicaulis (JÄDERHOLM)	+	−	−	−	+	+	+	−	−

cosus (ESPER) migrated through the Suez Canal into the Mediterranean and was recorded in the Adriatic (MARKTANNER-TURNERETSCHER, 1890). According to STEINITZ (1967, 1968), *Halocordyle disticha* (GOLDFUSS) var. *australis* (BALE), mentioned as *Pennaria disticha australis* BALE, followed the same route. This opinion appears to be correct although we have a doubtful record of this variety in the Atlantic Ocean. To confirm the migration of this species, discussion of the species problem is necessary. The variety *australis* of the widely distributed *Halocordyle disticha* may differ from the typical species by its production of free medusae. The typical form is assumed to have fixed gonophores (STECHOW, 1924). The variety *australis* shows variable annulations at the origin of the branches bearing the polyps. Only a comparison of all the material will allow a valid decision about the migratory route of the species and its variety. *Hydractinia kaffraria* MILLARD, *Campanularia gravieri* BILLARD and *Gymnangium gracicaulis* (JÄDERHOLM), which seem to be restricted to the Indo-Pacific waters, do not raise any such problems.

IV. The Atlanto-Mediterranean (AM) Species
(Table 4)

The AM group is the most interesting. The record of *Tubularia larynx* (ELLIS and SOLANDER) from the Suez Canal is doubtfull because BILLARD (1926) probably described *Tubularia mesembryanthemum* ALLMAN. This, however, has no important influence on the results we can draw from this group. It is certain that these 5 species have been transported into the Red Sea through the Suez Canal, but we have to consider some further viewpoints. *Tubularia larynx* ELLIS and SOLANDER is recorded from the southern part of the Canal, *Laomedea dichotoma* (LINNÉ) from the northern part and the other 3 are not recorded from this region. BILLARD considered them as deriving from the Mediterranean. Both *Tubulariidae* occur in the colder Pacific waters and they might also be found in the Indian Ocean. The records of *Tubularia larynx* ELLIS and SOLANDER, *Laomedea dichotoma* (LINNÉ), *Sertularella mediterranea* HARTLAUB and *Kirchenpaueria*

Table 4. Atlanto-Mediterranean (AM) species and their distribution

Species	Red Sea	Suez Canal	Mediterranean Sea	Atlantic Ocean (excl. South Africa)	South Africa	Indian Ocean (excl. South Africa)	Pacific Ocean	Red Sea immigrants in Mediterranean Sea	Mediterranean immigrants in Red Sea
Tubularia larynx Ellis and Solander	+	+	+	+	+	−	+	−	+
Tubularia mesembryanthemum Allman	+	−	+	+	−	−	+	−	+
Laomedea dichotoma (Linné)	+	+	+	+	+	−	−	−	+
Sertularella mediterranea Hartlaub	+	−	+	+	+	−	−	−	+
Kirchenpaueria pinnata (Linné)	+	−	+	+	+	−	−	−	+

pinnata (Linné) from South Africa show that the low temperature in most parts of this area is no barrier for them. The coasts of South Africa are discussed separately because this region is better investigated by Millard (1958, 1967, 1968) than the other parts of the Indian Ocean. All 5 species have been found in the harbour of Eilat, Gulf of Aqaba, in 1970, 3 years after the closing of the Suez Canal. Ships from all parts of the world coming from East Asia through the Indian Ocean and from Europe around the Cape of Good Hope could have brought the species on their hulls. If we had more results from the east coast of Africa, from Arabia, India and from the Red Sea, the above-mentioned opinion could be confirmed.

So far there are not enough results concerning *Hydromedusae*. Some publications on the eastern Mediterranean, the Red Sea and the Arabian Sea are in preparation by different authors. Two remarkable records should be mentioned in this paper. Vannucci and Navas (1973) recorded *Koellikerina fasciculata* (Peron and Lesueur) a species restricted to the Mediterranean and the adjacent Atlantic waters from the Arabian coast. This species belongs to the AM group and seems to have been transported through the Red Sea. The IP species *Euphysora bigelowi* Maas and *Laodicea fijiana* Agassiz and Mayer were found by the author in plankton collected near Cyprus (Schmidt, in press).

V. Discussion

Certain knowledge exists of less than 50 species of hydroids from the Red Sea area, including the Suez Canal and the Gulf of Aden. The hydrographical situation in the Red Sea is unique. A temperature of $21°C$ exists at a depth of more than 2000 m. The average salinity is 40‰, $4-6$‰ higher than in the open ocean. The small entrance in the north does not allow a significant exchange of water masses. The Bab-el-Mandeb is narrow and not more than 200 m deep. That the number of species found is so small, is due to lack of investigations and absence of records of hydroids below 50 m depth. It is interesting that no endemic hydroid has been found—a proof that the Red Sea entrances have been no barrier for these hydroids.

In the tables only some typical species are mentioned which do not normally necessitate systematic discussion. The number of species in each group will increase with further studies. On the other hand, these results could reduce (esp. the AM species) or increase the number of known Suez Canal migrants in both directions. In future, if the faunistic regions are more intermingled, it will become increasingly difficult to determine the migratory route of a hydroid.

Zoogeographers are frequently confronted with the decision to divide species and (local) varieties. Often literature gives no certain help and it is necessary to study the available material. The synonymy in the case of the hydroids is rather complicated and makes decisions difficult. A further problem occurs when it is stated that a species is well distributed. How often must it be recorded and from how many regions of an area? Thus the author's division into different groups may not be accepted without reservations.

The present results show 5 Mediterranean species which have been transported into the Red Sea and only 2 which penetrated the opposite way, a proportion which is normally reserved (STEINITZ, 1968). This might be caused by the absence of coral reefs and of any extensive rocky substrata in the eastern Mediterranean. At a radius of some 200 km, NE of Port Said the bottom is covered almost exclusively by sediment which provides good conditions for only a few species of hydroids.

4.5

Meroplanktonic Stages of Anthozoa in the Indian Ocean

T. BALACHANDRAN

The international collection of 1927 zooplankton samples lodged at the Indian Ocean Biological Centre (IOBC) forms the basis for the present study. The geographical names used in the present report follow those adopted by the International Hydrographic Bureau (IHB) (Sp. Publ. 23, 1953). An aliquot of the catch, equalling about 3 to 4 ml of the plankton irrespective of sample size, was fractionated either with a Lea's fractionator (WIBORG, 1955) or with a Folsom plankton splitter (MC EVEN, JOHNSON and FOLSON, 1954) and sorted. From this aliquot the catch per unit haul is estimated and this is used for comparison of collections. Abundance indicates population density, the term population being used not in the ecological sense but in a statistical sense. Biomass is used here to mean wet zooplankton displacement volume.

I. Salient Features in the Distribution of Anthozoa Larvae

Numerical abundance — When compared to the copepods that constitute roughly 70% of the zooplankton, the percentage of *Anthozoa* larvae is negligible. From Table 1 it can be seen that 61% of standard samples and 33% of nonstandard samples contained anthozoan larvae.

Out of a possible total of 220 5° squares, collections are available from 170; of these, 39 squares (22% of total squares) were devoid of larvae; 79 squares (47%) contained only 1 to 3 larvae; 29 squares (17%) contained 4 to 6 larvae; 16 squares (10%) contained 7 to 9 larvae; 4 squares contained 10 to 12 larvae; one square contained 12 to 25 larvae and only 2 squares had more than 18 larvae. This extensive dispersal of anthozoan larvae by currents indicates a long life span or extended larval life for most species.

Numbers ranged from 0 to 190 per haul. The maximum average representation in a 5° square is 20, and that of a 10° zone of latitude 16. Of the 1065 samples which contained anthozoan larvae, only 71 samples had more than 20. The 71 samples had 2858 larvae, i.e. 40 per unit sample, while the other 994 samples had 4891 larvae, hence an average of 5 per sample. Most of the samples had about the same number of larvae.

Areas of greater larval abundance are (Fig. 1) a) along the West Australian coast. The sampling in this area was done along the longitude 110° E from 12° S to 32° S. Night hauls show a slightly bigger catch; b) between the Red Sea and the Gulf of Aden and off the Arabian coast; c) in the central and western Bay of Bengal, to the northwest and south of the Andaman and Nicobar Islands; d) along the Mozambique coast, east of 30° E and 30° S; e) the Malabar coast, the Laccadive Sea and SW of the Maldive Islands; f) the coast of Kenya and Somalia, 5° S to 7° N.

In addition, isolated places in the north and central Indian Ocean, such as the SW coast of Sumatra, the southern tip of India, the northern and SW coasts of Ceylon, off Visakhapatanam 13° N and 80° E, and around the St. Brandon group of islands.

Outside these regions the average catch is much smaller, i.e. below 25%. The central south Indian Ocean is almost devoid of larvae except in the coastal areas. A gradual reduction is noticed from north to 40° S in the oceanic region. Larvae are more abundant in the neritic areas than in the oceanic areas. Minimum numbers have usually been recorded in areas far from land. An exception, however, is the area adjoining the Kerguelen Islands, represented by 9 larvae. There is a relation between numbers of larvae and proximity to land. The trend of distribution in general shows comparable high values towards the western and eastern sides of the Indian Ocean and along the coasts of India.

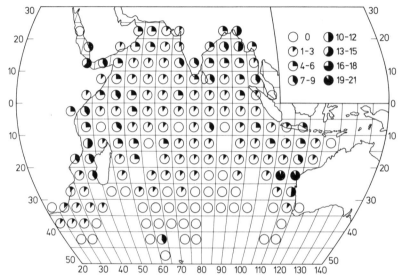

Fig. 1. Distribution of anthozoan larvae in the Indian Ocean
No. of individuals under 1 m², averaged for 5° squares

Off the Gujarat coast between 15° N and 24° N in the mouth of the Gulf of Cambay and Kutch there were poor catches. Very low density areas were found along the South African coast between 30° S and 40° S, 20° E and 40° E. Collections made in this area in January, April, July and October produced negligible catches. Below 30° S along the west coast of Australia density is low. Anthozoan larvae were completely absent in between 33° S to 46° S and 59° E to 114° E where the "Patanela" collections were obtained.

The mean biomass of zooplankton in the Bay of Bengal is less (15.5 ml) than that in the Arabian Sea (19.2 ml per haul), yet the anthozoan population is higher. The Arabian Sea yielded 25% of the total larval collections. Similarly, though the mean plankton biomass value of the SE Indian Ocean is less (7.6 ml) than that of the SW Indian Ocean (9.5 ml), the anthozoan population has a higher density.

II. Diurnal and Hourly Variation in the Catch of Anthozoan Larvae

Larvae are present in 61% of night hauls and in only 50% of day hauls (Table 1). The catch per night haul is 0−9 and per day haul 1−4 (Table 2), depending on area

Table. 1. Occurrence of anthozoan larvae according to category of sample

Category of samples	Number of samples	% of total No. of samples	Larvae present No. of samples	%
Total	1927	100.00	1065	55
Standard	1548	81.00	943	61
Nonstandard	379	19.00	122	33
Day	1028	53.50	621	61
Night	892	46.50	444	50
SW monsoon	987	51.00	563	57
NE monsoon	939	49.00	502	54.5

Table 2. Time and area of zooplankton sampling of 11 cruises in the Indian Ocean

Stn No.	Ship and Cruise	No. of hauls	Average catch per haul	% of hauls without larvae	Time hour	Period	Area
1.	"Diamantina" 1/65	19	1	47	19.00 – 24.00	18.4.65 to 12.5.65	7° N – 32° S, 76° E – 110° E
2.	"Kagoshima Maru" 3	31	2	35	19.30 – 21.00	26.11.63 to 9.1.64	5° N – 24° S, 69° E – 80° E
3.	"Diamantina" 1/64	11	1	64	20.00 – 23.00	1.2.64 to 17.2.64	21° S – 33° S, 113° E – 114° E
4.	"Anton Bruun" 2	38	2	22	06.12 – 14.10	23.5.63 to 17.7.63	17° N – 37° S, 69° E – 80° E
5.	"Anton Bruun" 5	45	3	44	08.00 – 12.45	29.1.64 to 30.4.64	16° N – 42° S, 50° E – 75° E
6.	"Anton Bruun" 6	23	1	60	08.10 – 19.00	17.5.64 to 12.7.64	18° N – 37° S, 64° E – 65° S
7.	"Umitaka Maru" 23, 24	28	1	80	Day	21.11.63 to 22.1.64	4° S – 25° S, 99° E – 112° E
8.	"Diamantina" 3/64 and 5/64	23	4	30	Day	5.5.64 to 15.5.64 11.8.64 to 8.9.64	9° S – 32° S, 105° E – 112° E
9.	"Koyo Maru" 14 and 16	47	2	40	Night	23.11.62 to 15.1.63 23.11.63 to 25.1.64	5° N – 32° S, 94° E – 110° E 8° N – 22° S, 94° E – 100° E
10.	"Patanela"	25 Surface hauls	0	100	Night	6.12.64 to 21.2.65	33° S – 46° S, 59° E – 114° E
11.	"Pioneer"	40	9	31	Night	16.4.64 to 21.4.64	20° N – 6° S, 81° E – 102° E.

of catch and season and probably other factors that interfere with vertical migration, such as stratification of the water.

Hauls during "Diamantina" cruises 1/64 and 1/65 and "Kagoshima Maru" cruise 3, "Anton Bruun" cruises 2 and 5 indicate that the hour of collection is less important than the area of collection (Table 2).

Of the hauls having more than 20 larvae, 43 night hauls (1725 larvae) averaged 40 per haul, and 28 day hauls (1133 larvae) averaged 40 per haul. This probably shows some diurnal effect. The hauls made at 2000 to 2100 h, 0100 to 0600 h, 0800 to 1200 h, 1500 to 1800 h, and 2200 to 2300 h had fairly good catches, probably indicating an absence of hourly effect on larval catch. While one haul at 2100 h had 190 larvae, one haul at 0900 had 112, indicating patchiness. There was no relation of catch to plankton biomass.

III. Effect of Structure of Water Column on Bathymetric Distribution of Larvae

On "Discovery" cruises 1 and 3, additional hauls were made at 62 stations from the thermocline to the surface (Table 3).

Table 3. Bathymetric distribution of zooplankton samples from "Discovery" cruises 1 and 3

Serial No.	"Discovery" Stn No.	Time of sampling	No. of samples 200−0 (m)	No. of samples from other depth ranges	Depth range (m)	Depth of thermocline (m)
1	5292	Night	10	2	70−0	125 Not clear
2	5307	Day	16	0	50−0	98 and 118 not clear
3	5310	Night	26	6	40−0	No therm.
4	5336	Day	7	0	45−0	100−125 not clear
5	5340	Day	8	1	40−0	75−95
6	5348	Day	8	0	50−0	75−85
7	5363	Night	10	0	70−0	
8	5381	Night	15	2	80−0	100
9	5429	Day	13	0	70−0	94
10	5488	Night	8	0	70−0	100
11	5502	Day	17	4	75−0	50
12	5505	Night	18	2	55−0	91
13	5516	Day	17	0	80−0	95
14	5267	Night	3	12	100−0	99
15	5367	Night	0	2	85−0	94
16	5491	Night	3	5	70−0	84
17	5514	Night	0	9	70−0	75
18	5515	Day	0	10	80−0	75
19	5520	Night	8	10	75−0	114
20	5521	Night	5	32	95−0	141

A comparison of hauls taken at the same station with the same net from 200 m to the surface and from a lesser depth to the surface, shows very clearly that the larvae are most abundant below the thermocline and are seldom found in the upper layer when a thermocline is present. When there is no thermocline, the larvae occur higher up ("Discovery" Stn 5310). Night also seems to influence upward movement of the larvae. On the other hand when the stations were in upwelling waters, larvae were commonly found in the upper layer.

4.6

Chaetognaths of the Arabian Sea

V. R. NAIR and T. S. S. RAO

During the IIOE (1959−1965) the Indian Ocean Biological Centre (IOBC) received 1927 zooplankton samples, of which 1548 are standard ones (IOBC, 1969). Of these, 614 samples belong to the area extending from 10°S to 25°N lat. between 20°E and 80°E long. The chaetognaths identified from these 614 samples form the basis of the present study. The figures given refer to catch per unit standard haul.

I. Distribution of Species

A total of 19 species belonging to 4 genera *Eukrohnia, Krohnitta, Pterosagitta,* and *Sagitta* are present in the collections analysed.

Table 1 represents the total counts, percentage and maximum density of the different species. The seasonal differences for the different species are shown in Table 2.

Table 1. Total counts, percentage and maximum density of the different chaetognaths species from the IIOE collections

Species	Total abundance Number	Percent-age	Range of abundance per 5° Sq. %	Maximum observed density (No. per std. haul) SW monsoon	NE monsoon
E. fowleri	7	negligible	negligible	−	4 (Laccadive Sea)
K. pacifica	10 847	1.0	0− 5.7	250 (near Kenya)	425 (Red Sea)
K. subtilis	3 780	0.3	0− 3.1	400 (off Somalia)	100 (off Ceylon)
Pt. draco	48 319	5.1	0−19.1	1 940 (off Somalia)	810 (Gulf of Aden)
S. bedoti	94 709	8.3	0−35.8	4 160 (off Somalia)	2 960 (near Kenya coast)
S. bipunctata	48 815	4.3	0−23.6	3 620 (off Somalia)	735 (off Arabia towards north)
S. bombayensis	2	negligible	negligible	−	2 (off the northwest coast of India)
S. decipiens	26	negligible	negligible	−	16 (off South Arabia)
S. enflata	697 810	61.0	31.6−86.3	9 000 (off Somalia)	18 585 (Red Sea)
S. ferox	23 654	2.1	0−31.0	2 221 (South eastern part at 10°S−75°E)	820 (off Somalia)

Table 1 (continued)

Species	Total abundance		Range of abundance per 5° Sq. (%)	Maximum observed density (No. per std. haul)	
	Number	Percent-age l		SW monsoon	NE monsoon
S. hexaptera	6 228	0.5	0−2.4	192 (off Somalia)	140 (off Somalia)
S. lyra	10	negligible	negligible	10 (mouth of Gulf of Aden)	−
S. minima	4 837	0.4	0−10.5	800 (southwestern part at 3° S lat. and 54° E long.)	500 (southwestern part at 8° S lat. and 54° E long.)
S. neglecta	12 700	1.1	0−8.3	640 (off Arabia towards north)	820 (near Arabia towards north)
S. pacifica	119 049	10.4	0.3−38.3	4 400 (near Arabia towards north)	2 440 (off Somalia)
S. pulchra	5 022	0.4	0−1.2	280 (near Somalia)	200 (Gulf of Aden and off Somalia)
S. regularis	41 495	3.6	0−17.1	1 600 (off Somalia)	1 004 (Gulf of Cambay)
S. robusta	16 774	1.5	0−8.3	730 (near Arabia towards north)	606 (off Somalia)
S. zetesios	10	negligible	negligible	−	10 (off Arabia towards north)

Table 2. Numerical abundance of the different epiplanktonic species of chaetognaths during the two monsoon periods

Species	SW monsoon		NE monsoon		Total No. irre-spective of seasons
	Total	Average No. per haul	Total	Average No. per haul	
K. pacifica	5 481	23	5 366	23	10 847
K. subtilis	2 492	10	1 288	6	3 780
Pt. draco	27 444	114	20 875	92	48 319
S. bedoti	45 639	190	49 070	217	94 709
S. bipunctata	26 068	109	22 747	101	48 815
S. enflata	371 291	1 547	326 519	1 445	697 810
S. ferox	20 395	85	3 259	14	23 654
S. hexaptera	3 645	15	2 583	11	6 228
S. minima	3 651	15	1 186	5	4 837
S. neglecta	5 342	22	7 358	33	12 700
S. pacifica	76 622	319	42 427	188	119 049
S. pulchra	2 179	9	2 843	13	5 022
S. regularis	27 582	115	13 913	88	41 495
S. robusta	8 721	36	8 053	36	16 774
Total:	626 552	2 609	507 487	2 272	1 134 039

1. Krohnitta pacifica (Aida, 1897)
(Figs. 1 a and 1 b)

This species is occasionally encountered in the collections and the range of abundance is 0−5.7% of the total chaetognaths. The general pattern of distribution shows a scattered representation of the species with isolated areas of high values. The maximum value is at

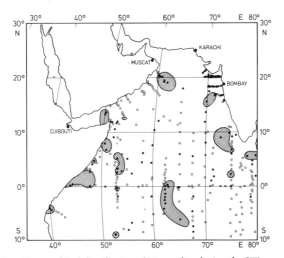

Fig. 1 a. Geographical distribution of *K. pacifica* during the SW monsoon
No. of specimens per standard haul. For symbols see Fig. 14, p. 310

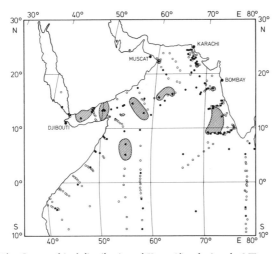

Fig. 1 b. Geographical distribution of *K. pacifica* during the NE monsoon

the mouth of the Red Sea (425 per std. haul). The distribution of the species for the 2 monsoon periods does not show much variation, except that the Somalian region is better populated during the SW monsoon, otherwise it seems to have a patchy distribution and the position of the patches is comparable in both periods. The average number of specimens per standard haul is the same in both seasons (Table 2). This suggests that on average the abundance of the species in the surface layer is not directly affected by the monsoons.

2.Krohnitta subtilis (Grassi, 1881)
(Figs. 2 a and 2 b)

This species is occasionally represented in the samples, the range of abundance being 0−3.1% of the total chaetognaths in the samples. *K. subtilis* has higher representation in the western Arabian Sea, particularly near Somalia (400 per std. sample), but is very scarce in the collections taken off the coasts of India and in the SE part. The SW monsoon

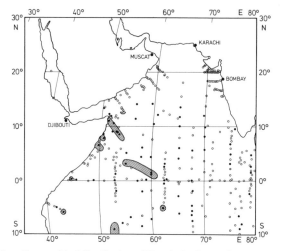

Fig. 2a. Geographical distribution of *K. subtilis* during the SW monsoon

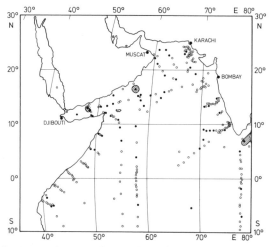

Fig. 2b. Geographical distribution of *K. subtilis* during the NE monsoon

period shows higher representation of the species along the western half of the Arabian Sea excluding the northern part. The maximum values are in the Somalia region. However, during the NE monsoon this species is encountered in the north Arabian Sea. The distribution is totally different during the 2 seasons, and during the SW monsoon the species is found to be on average 1.7 times more abundant per haul. The distribution tends to show that it is limited to highly productive waters.

3. Pterosagitta draco (KROHN, 1853)
(Figs. 3 a and 3 b)

Comparatively small mature individuals (length at maturity 5.4 mm) are encountered in a few samples taken from the Laccadive Sea. The species is common in the Arabian

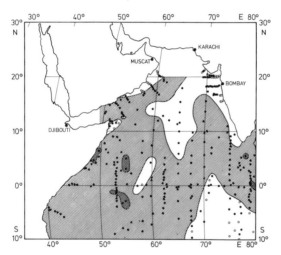

Fig. 3 a. Geographical distribution of *Pt. draco* during the SW monsoon

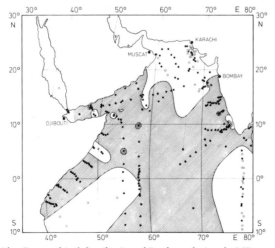

Fig. 3 b. Geographical distribution of *Pt. draco* during the NE monsoon

Sea. The range of abundance of the species is 0—19.1%. The maximum values are represented by small patches near and off Somalia (1940 per std. haul), off Kenya, off Ceylon and far south of Ceylon. *Pt. draco* is poorly distributed in the northern and southeastern part. The general pattern of distribution for both periods is roughly the same. The Somalian region has high values of *Pt. draco* during the SW monsoon which is not so marked in the other season. The average number per haul during the SW monsoon is 1.2 times more abundant than that in the NE monsoon period.

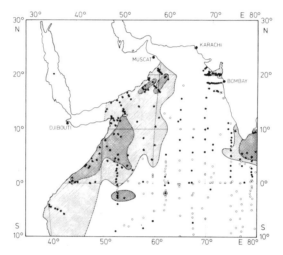

Fig. 4a. Geographical distribution of *S. bedoti* during the SW monsoon

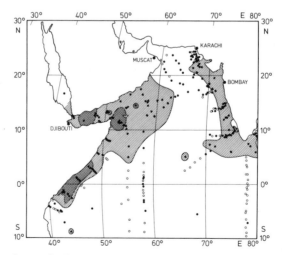

Fig. 4b. Geographical distribution of *S. bedoti* during the NE monsoon

4. Sagitta bedoti (BÉRANECK, 1895)
(Figs. 4a and 4b)

This is a very common species, constituting 0−35.8% of the total chaetognaths in the samples. In one "Varuna" sample (20° 19′ N and 72° 29′ E) they are dominant. The general pattern of distribution of the species shows that they are more abundant in the areas adjacent to continents. The western side of the Arabian Sea shows almost uniform high density population. The maximum number is along the Somali coast (4160 per std. haul). Scattered patches of high values are observed particularly in the Gulf of Aden, near Arabia, in the Gulf of Mannar and off Tanganyika. The western coast of India and Ceylon also maintain a comparatively high concentration. Most of the northern, central and southern parts are poor in the representation of the species. The pattern of distribution for the different periods is more or less the same except that the maximum density at Somalia extends over a wider area during the SW monsoon period. Comparatively better representation of the species is seen along the west coast of India during the NE monsoon period. This species is 1.14 times more abundant during the NE monsoon. It seams to avoid poor waters but is not tied to specially productive waters.

5. Sagitta bipunctata (QUOY and GAIMARD, 1827)
(Figs. 5a and 5b)

This is another common chaetognath from the Arabian Sea. The abundance ranges from 0−23.6%. This species exhibits scattered distribution with localized concentrations. Maximum number is seen off Somalia (3620 per std. haul) and off the Bombay coast. The central part of the ocean is poorly populated, while the northern and southwestern parts are moderately represented. The 2 monsoon periods show differences in the distribution pattern of the species. The SW monsoon has higher density off and along the coast of Somalia and Kenya, while the NE monsoon sustains a higher population along the western coasts of India. During the SW monsoon a few patches of high values are found that are absent during the NE monsoon. Although S. bipunctata is absent or rare in zones

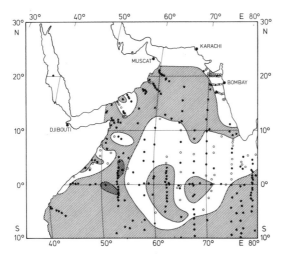

Fig. 5a. Geographical distribution of S. bipunctata during the SW monsoon

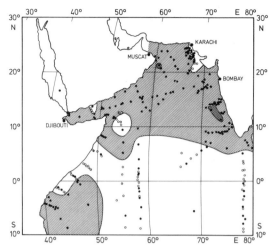

Fig. 5 b. Geographical distribution of *S. bipunctata* during the NE monsoon

of low production, it also seems to avoid the areas of maximum zooplankton abundance. The average catch per haul is about the same during both seasons. This species shows a special type of widespread distribution which was called "anti-equatorial" (Bieri, 1959). It was found to be less abundant in most of the stations occupied in the equatorial region, similar to some of the observations for the Pacific (Bieri, 1959).

6. Sagitta bombayensis (Lele and Gae, 1936)
(Fig. 15)

Two specimens were obtained from a single station in the Gulf of Cambay (20° 20′ N and 72° 00′ E) during the cruise of "Varuna" in 1963. The species is considered to be endemic to the west and east coasts of India (Tokioka, 1962). The hydrographical data relating to these stations show shallow depth (30 m), temperature 28.7—28.0° C, salinity 35—35.4‰ and high O_2 values of 5.2 ml l^{-1}. The available data suggest that this is a rather rare species in the Arabian Sea and it seems to prefer shallow waters with relatively low salinity.

7. Sagitta enflata (Grassi, 1881)
(Figs. 6 a and 6 b)

When fully mature the size ranges from 8—24 mm. The gonads in this species may mature periodically (Michael, 1919; Thomson, 1947). As Alvariño (1965, 1967) and Furnestin and Balança (1968) pointed out, this species seems to have more than one sexual cycle in the course of its life. This phenomenon is met with in the present collections also. Usually 2 forms occurred, one with short and the other with long ovaries. However, the long ovary forms appeared in comparatively small numbers. Occasionally intermediate forms are also encountered.

S. enflata is the dominant species in all except a few samples. It constitutes about 32–86% of the total chaetognaths in the sample. The distribution shows a nearly uniform population density along the western half of the Arabian Sea during the SW monsoon, while the eastern part has relatively poor concentrations of *S. enflata*. The maximum

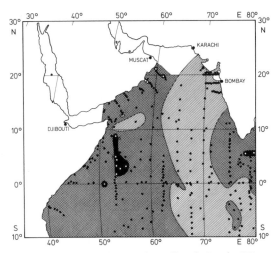

Fig. 6 a. Geographical distribution of *S. enflata* during the SW monsoon

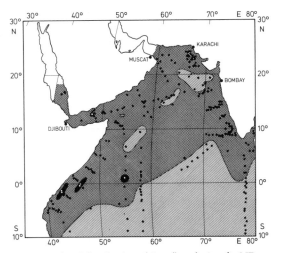

Fig. 6 b. Geographical distribution of *S. enflata* during the NE monsoon

density is off the Somali coast and small areas of maximum density are observed in the vicinity of Somalia (9 000 per std. haul), mouth of Red Sea (18 585 per std. haul), Gulf of Aden, Arabian coast and near Ceylon. The lowest representation of *S. enflata* is seen during the SW monsoon period and is restricted to a small area near Gujarat. Compared to the NE monsoon period the SW monsoon period shows a greater representation of the species. However, the average number of specimens per unit haul is about the same for both periods. The 2 seasons have maximum density of *S. enflata* towards the western part of the Arabian Sea off Somalia and Kenya. During the NE monsoon low values extended along the southern part and in the SW monsoon low density spreads uniformly from the SE part towards the Indian coast.

8. Sagitta ferox (Doncaster, 1903)
(Figs. 7a and 7b)

Fairly common in the Arabian Sea. They constitute about 0−31.0% of the total chaetognaths in the sample. This species shows a higher density along the Equator. The

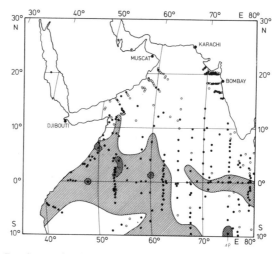

Fig. 7a. Geographical distribution of *S. ferox* during the SW monsoon

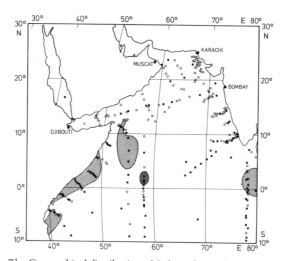

Fig. 7b. Geographical distribution of *S. ferox* during the NE monsoon

maximum observed density is in the SE part (2221 per std. haul). The whole of the northern part of the Arabian Sea has low values for *S. ferox*. The SW monsoon period sustains a 6 times higher population and an almost uniform value prevails along the equatorial region. The NE monsoon period has moderately high values near and off Somalia, and off the southern tip of the Indian peninsula. A single patch of high density is present near the Equator at about 58° E during the NE monsoon period.

9. Sagitta hexaptera (d'ORBIGNY, 1843)
(Figs. 8 a and 8 b)

Even though this species is found in many of the samples, its numerical representation is usually low. In the collections it ranges from 0 − 2.4%. This species is represented

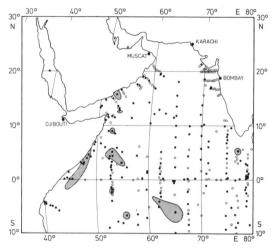

Fig. 8 a. Geographical distribution of *S. hexaptera* during the SW monsoon

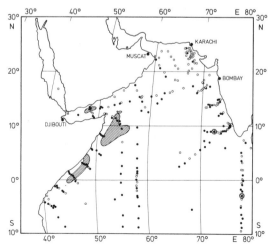

Fig. 8 b. Geographical distribution of *S. hexaptera* during the NE monsoon

by patches along the western part of the Arabian Sea in the equatorial area, off the Somalian and Arabian coasts and in the SE part. Higher values are restricted to the western part of the Arabian Sea, particularly off the Somali coast (192 per std. haul). The average number per haul is 1.4 times greater during the SE monsoon.

10. Sagitta minima (GRASSI, 1881)
(Figs. 9a and 9b)

This species is only occasionally encountered in the samples, its range of abundance varied from 0−10.5%. Maximum density is seen along the southern part of the Arabian

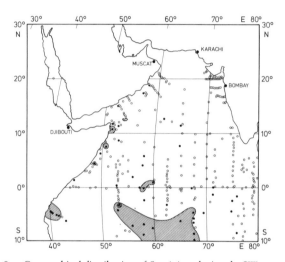

Fig. 9a. Geographical distribution of *S. minima* during the SW monsoon

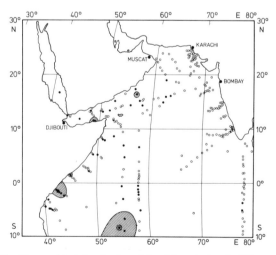

Fig. 9b. Geographical distribution of *S. minima* during the NE monsoon

Sea (800 per std. haul), at the mouth of the Gulf of Aden and off and near Somalia, Kenya and Tanganyika. *S. minima* is absent near and off the coasts of India except for a single station near the SW coast of India. It is found to be 3 times more abundant during the SW monsoon.

Several authors considered this to be a coastal species (THOMSON, 1948; FURNESTIN, 1952, 1953; PIERCE, 1953). However, the present distribution shows a different pattern since a large population seems to be fairly stable south of the Equator from about 50° to about 70° E and includes the highest densities found. ALVARIÑO'S interpretation (1965) of it being a boundary species seems to be confirmed.

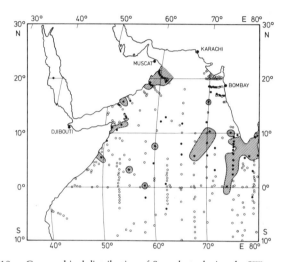

Fig. 10 a. Geographical distribution of *S. neglecta* during the SW monsoon

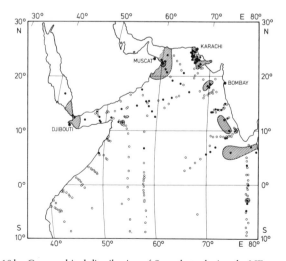

Fig. 10 b. Geographical distribution of *S. neglecta* during the NE monsoon

11. Sagitta neglecta (AIDA, 1897)
(Figs. 10 a and 10 b)

This species is moderately common, having a range of 0−8.3% of the total chaetognaths. The distribution of the species shows an affinity towards the coastal region. Highest density is noticed on the southern part of the Indian Peninsula and near Arabia and Persia. The maximum number (820 per std. haul) of specimens is obtained from a station near Arabia. They are very scarce south of the Equator. Better representation of the species was noticed during the NE monsoon when the average number of the specimens per haul is 1.5 times higher. During the NE monsoon high values are found near Arabia and Persia, at the mouth of the Red Sea and off the coast of India. The SW monsoon period has a greater density near and off Somalia and Arabia, the southern part of India and isolated patches north of the Equator. In the "Sealark" material (BURFIELD and HARVEY, 1926) *S. neglecta* was scarce, probably because the collections were taken far away from the coast.

12. Sagitta pacifica (TOKIOKA, 1940)
(Figs. 11 a and 11 b)

S. pacifica reported from the Pacific (ALVARIÑO, 1961) South China Sea and Gulf of Thailand (ALVARIÑO, 1967) has ovaries reaching the level of the ventral ganglion, and even to the neck region in fully mature specimens. In the present specimens the ovaries are found to extend up to the middle of the anterior fin, rarely up to the ventral ganglion, and never beyond that.

S. pacifica is very common in the Arabian Sea and comes second to *S. enflata* in the order of abundance. The percentage range of abundance in the sample is 0.3−38.3. Numerical representation of the species is greater south of 10° N. Maximum densities observed are near Arabia (4400 per std. haul) and the Somalia region (2440 per std.

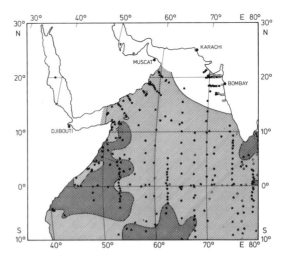

Fig. 11 a. Geographical distribution of *S. pacifica* during the SW monsoon

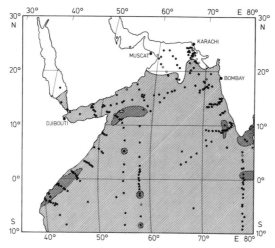

Fig. 11 b. Geographical distribution of *S. pacifica* during the NE monsoon

haul). Central parts of the southern and eastern Arabian Sea also have high values. On average the SW monsoon period has a population density 1.7 times greater than in the NE monsoon period. The maximum density of *S. pacifica* during the SW monsoon covers large areas, while during the NE monsoon maximum density was noted as isolated patches. In both periods the values were very low in the northern Arabian Sea.

13. Sagitta pulchra (DONCASTER, 1903)
(Figs. 12a and 12b)

This is not a very common species, the percentage range of abundance being 0 − 1.2. Isolated patches are observed near Somalia (280 per std. haul), Gulf of Aden, near Arabia

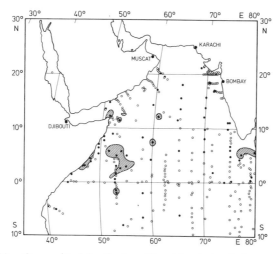

Fig. 12a. Geographical distribution of *S. pulchra* during the SW monsoon

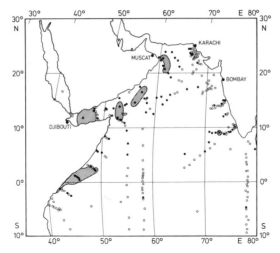

Fig. 12b. Geographical distribution of *S. pulchra* during the NE monsoon

and south of the Indian Peninsula. It is rarely represented near the coasts of Indian and central and south eastern part of the surveyed area. The NE monsoon period has higher numerical values for the species off the Arabian coast. On the whole the average number per haul is 1.4 times greater during the NE monsoon.

14. Sagitta regularis (AIDA, 1897)
(Figs. 13a and 13b)

Size at maturity varies from 4.8 − 6.0 mm. Stumpy forms of this species (3.2 − 3.6 mm) are encountered in a few samples. Such stumpy forms were obtained from 14 stations, all located towards the coast (south of the Indian Peninsula, west coast of India, near

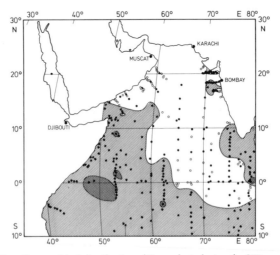

Fig. 13a. Geographical distribution of *S. regularis* during the SW monsoon

Somalia and Gulf of Aden). These samples were taken mostly during the NE monsoon period (11 samples) and a few (3 samples) in the later part of the SW monsoon period (August – September – early October).

S. regularis is among the most common species in the Arabian Sea, represented in most of the samples and the abundance ranged from 0 – 17.1%. The general pattern of distribution of the species shows an almost uniform concentration along the southwestern part of the Arabian Sea and western coast of India and Ceylon. The maximum density is

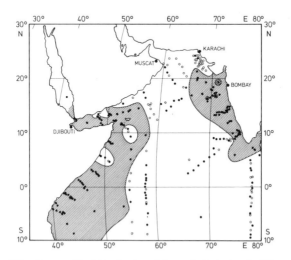

Fig. 13 b. Geographical distribution of *S. regularis* during the NE monsoon

near Somalia and Kenya (1600 per std. haul) with small areas of high density at isolated areas in the Arabian Sea but a poor representation in the northern and central parts. The species is found to be 1.4 times more abundant during the SW monsoon than in the NE monsoon period. During the SW monsoon period the whole of the south and southwestern part extending to the Somalian region and western coast have relatively better population density. The NE monsoon period sustains a better representation of the species along the west coast of India.

15. Sagitta robusta (DONCASTER, 1903)
(Figs. 14 a and 14 b)

Size at maturity varied from 9.8 – 14.2 mm. However, comparatively short mature forms (8.5 – 8.8 mm) were obtained from 4 samples taken between 5 – 20°N lat. and 60 – 76°E long. Of the 4 samples, 2 were taken during SW monsoon and the other in NE monsoon period.

This species is moderately common in the Arabian Sea, representing 0 – 8.3% of total chaetognaths. The general pattern of distribution shows a steady population occupying a large area along the coasts of Arabia, northern Somalia and the Gulf of Aden, otherwise the distribution is patchy. The southern part of the Indian Peninsula has high population during the SW monsoon period. The maximum representation is near the

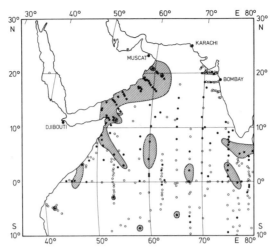

Fig. 14a. Geographical distribution of *S. robusta* during the SW monsoon

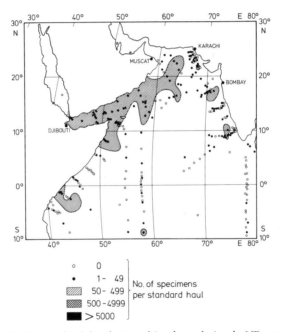

Fig. 14b. Geographical distribution of *S. robusta* during the NE monsoon

Arabian coast (730 per std. haul). This species is sparse in the stations south of the Equator. The 2 monsoon periods show the same numerical representation with regard to average numbers per haul. The northern half of Somalia and the coast of Arabia maintained a uniform high density for both seasons.

While the above-mentioned species are all known to be epiplanktonic, the following

4 are known to inhabit greater depths. They are; *Eukrohnia fowleri* described as a bathyplanktonic form and 3 other species—*Sagitta decipiens, S. lyra* and *S. zetesios*—reported as mesoplanktonic chaetognaths. All of them are cosmopolitan forms in temperate and warm oceanic regions (ALVARIÑO, 1965). Tables 3 and 4 show the data for these species.

16. Eukrohnia fowleri (RITTER – ZÁHONY, 1909)
(Fig. 15)

This species was found at 2 stations, located off the southern coast of India and worked on 2 successive days (Table 3). Three specimens were taken at "Varuna" station 2009 on November 5, 1963, at 09° 04′ N and 74° 00′ E where the temperature at 200 m depth was 16.5° C, salinity 34.9‰ and O_2 content 4.5 ml l^{-1} (Arabian Sea subsurface water mixed with Indian Ocean equatorial water). Four specimens were taken on the following day at "Varuna" station 2014 at 09° 10′ N and 70° 40′ E at 200 m; 14° C temperature, salinity 35.2‰ and 0.45 ml l^{-1} O_2 indicate Arabian Sea subsurface water.

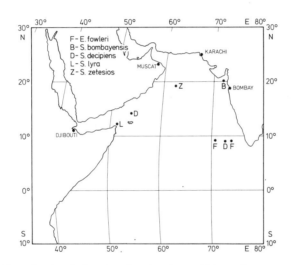

Fig. 15. Chart showing the location of stations from which rare forms were obtained

17. Sagitta decipiens (FOWLER, 1905)
(Fig. 15)

S. decipiens was encountered in 2 stations (Table 3), one off Saudi Arabia and the other off the southern coast of India. The first sample was taken by "Anton Bruun" cruise A, station 5, 27 February off Socotra in upwelling waters at 14° 03′ N and 54° 00′ E. At 200 m the water was Arabian Sea Subsurface Water and temperature was 15.1° C. More specimens were obtained from this haul. The second was "Varuna" station 2011 at 09° 00′ N and 72° 40′ E occupied on November 5, the water at 200 m depth was also Arabian Sea Subsurface Water and the temperature was 13.48° C. At both stations the dissolved O_2 content at 200 m depth was low, the values being 0.6 and 0.5 ml l^{-1} respectively.

Table 3. Station data for the rare species

Ship	Cruise No.	Station number	Latitude	Longitude	Date	Time	Depth m	Species Name	No. per hauls
"Varuna"	104	2 009	09° 04' N	74° 00' E	5 — 11 — 63	11.10	200	E. fowleri	Juvenile — 3
"Varuna"	104	2 014	09° 10' N	70° 40' E	6 — 11 — 63	20.10	200	E. fowleri	Juvenile — 4
"Varuna"	30	1 793	20° 20' N	72° 00' E	10 — 5 — 63	12.02	25	S. bombayensis	Stage IV — 2
"Anton Bruun"	A	5	14° 03' N	54° 00' E	27 — 2 — 63	04.47	200	S. decipiens	Stage I — 2 Juvenile — 7
"Varuna"	104	2 011	09° 00' N	72° 40' N	5 — 11 — 63	02.00	200	S. decipiens	Stage I — 2 Juvenile — 4
"Anton Bruun"	4A	170	12° 04' N	51° 31' E	9 — 10 — 63	06.16	200	S. lyra	Stage I — 2 Juvenile — 5
"Anton Bruun"	4A	198	19° 17' N	62° 29' E	5 — 11 — 63	01.26	200	S. zetesios	Stage I — 1 Juvenile — 5

Table 4. Environmental data for the chaetognaths described as meso- and bathyplanktonic forms

Species	Previous data Temperature °C	Salinity S‰	Present data Tempera- ture °C	Salinity S‰	Depth from which recorded in the Indian Ocean
E. fowleri	13.4−14.5 (OWRE, 1960)	34.65 (SUND, 1961)	13.99 16.51	35.23 34.90	600 and below to 1300 m. (SILAS and SRINIVASAN, 1969) Mainly below 450 m (BURFIELD and HARVEY, 1926)
S. decipiens	8.9−18.0 (SUND, 1961)	34.4−34.9 (SUND, 1961)	15.14 13.48	35.54 34.99	Maximum at 405 Spread at 720 m (BURFIELD and HARVEY, 1926)
S. lyra	14.7−24.2 (PIERCE and WASS, 1962)	35.8−36.8 (PIERCE and WASS, 1962)	15.51	35.41	225, 270 (BURFIELD and HARVEY, 1926) 100 or 200 to the surface (TOKIOKA, 1956) 0−50 m (TSURAT, 1963) 300 and below to 1300 m (SILAS and SRINIVASAN, 1969)
S. zetesios	12.4 (FAGETTI, 1958)	34.6 (SUND, 1961)	16.05	35.85	−

18. Sagitta lyra (KROHN, 1853)
(Fig. 15)

Seven specimens were obtained from a single station near the mouth of the Gulf of Aden (12° 04′ N and 51° 31′ E) in Oct. 1963. The hydrographical data indicate up-welling at the time of collection. Comparatively cold water (22.88° C) was present at 40 m. The recorded temperature at 227 m was 13.6° C, salinity 35.6‰ and dissolved O_2 0.89 ml l^{-1} (Arabian Sea Subsurface Water mass).

19. Sagitta zetesios (FOWLER, 1905)
(Fig. 15)

Six specimens of this species were found in a sample taken in the North Arabian Sea (19° 17′ N lat. and 62° 29′ E long.) in November 1963. The data show the presence of upwelling waters at the time of sampling. Temperature at 40 m was 23.4° C and O_2 content was low from 75 m (0.70 ml l^{-1}) downwards. The temperature and salinity at 199 m were 16.05° C and 35.85‰ respectively while dissolved O_2 content was 0.40 ml l^{-1} (Arabian Sea Subsurface Water).

II. Discussion

The collection includes 15 epiplanktonic species, 3 mesoplanktonic and 1 bathy-planktonic species, the 2 latter groups being very rare and represented by a few stray individuals. S. enflata is the dominant species in this area, constituting 32−86% of the total chaetognaths. S. pacifica, S. bedoti, Pt. draco, S. bipunctata and S. regularis are the other

common species in the order of their numerical abundance (Table 1). *S. ferox, S. robusta,*
S. neglecta and *K. pacifica* are moderately common, while *S. hexaptera, S. pulchra,*
S. minima and *K. subtilis* are occasionally encountered, *S. bombayensis* is endemic to the
coasts of India but specimens were obtained only from a single collection taken from the
Gulf of Cambay.

The Arabian Sea is in the NW of the monsoon area of the Indian Ocean and its surface
currents and upwelling systems are regulated by the monsoonal regime. The western
Arabian Sea, especially the Somalian and Arabian areas, has the maximum density for all
abundant and frequent species excluding *S. ferox* and *S. minima* (Table 1). During the
SW monsoon upwelling occurs along the east coast of Africa and west coast of India.
According to PANIKKAR and JAYARAMAN (1966), upwelling is prevalent along the coast
between $7-10°$ N lat. during August to early October. Even during the NE monsoon
period, the western Arabian Sea and coast of India are rich in most of the chaetognath
species. Investigations made during the IIOE indicate that the Arabian Sea has a very high
concentration of nutrients (BEZRUKOV, 1961; RYTHER and MENZEL, 1965). The western
side of the Arabian Sea is more productive (LA FOND, 1965; WOOSTER, SCHAEFER
and ROBINSON, 1967) and hence it is no wonder that the chaetognaths, which occupy a
high level in the food web, also have maximum abundance in this part of the Arabian
Sea. The region $40-60°$ E between the Equator and northern limit of the ocean is
richest in chaetognaths during both seasons (NAIR, 1969). The IIOE data on zooplankton (IOBC, 1968 a, b) suggest that primary production is able to support a good
standing stock of higher organisms in the northern and western part of the Arabian Sea,
with a peak during the SW monsoon upwelling season. The biomass values (IOBC,
1968 a, b) for both monsoon periods show the highest values along Somalia, Arabia and
SW coast of India. However, during the NE monsoon period the areas of highest values
for biomass are located further south than in the SW monsoon period.

In attempting to determine the primary cause or causes of abundance it is important
to compare the distribution with that of zooplankton. Examination of the stomach content
of the chaetognaths in the IIOE samples indicates that copepods form the main food
item (see also VARADARAJAN and CHACKO, 1943; THOMSON, 1947; REEVE, 1966).
Chaetognaths feed mainly on calanoid copepods, the commonest forms being *Cen-*
tropages, Eucalanus and *Lucicutia,* and cyclopoid copepods like *Corycaeus, Oithona*
and *Oncaea.* Rarely harpacticoid copepods and other groups like fish larvae, ostracods,
euphausiids and polychaete larvae were found inside the gut. The IIOE data on copepod
distribution for the NE and SW monsoon periods show maximum population along
the Somalian coast of Africa extending northwards to the Arabian coast (IOBC, 1970 a).
Lowest population density for both monsoon periods was observed in the central part of
the Arabian Sea. Most of the chaetognath species except *S. enflata, S. pacifica* and
Pt. draco also have sparse representation in the central part of the Arabian Sea. In general,
the abundance and scarcity of different chaetognath species corresponds to the pattern of
distribution of copepods.

Although the distribution of each species is different in itself, based on the distribution
pattern, the various species can be grouped by their regional dominance as follows:

    a) Widely distributed: *S. enflata, S. pacifica;*
    b) Localized areas: *S. bedoti, S. bombayensis, S. neglecta, S. robusta;*
    c) Patchy: *K. pacifica, K. subtilis, S. bipunctata, S. hexaptera, S. pulchra;*
    d) Equatorial: *S. ferox;*

e) South of the Equator between 50 — 68° E: *S. minima;*

f) Southwest Arabian Sea and western side of India and Ceylon: *Pt. draco, S. regularis;*

g) Deep and subsurface waters: *E. fowleri, S. decipiens, S. lyra* and *S. zetesios.*

The distribution of certain species shows seasonal variation (Table 1 and Figs. 1 — 14). Tables 1 and 2 show that maximum density is to be found in areas and seasons where secondary production is high, such as the western boundary area, the equatorial upwelling off India. The exceptions are few and apparently not too significant. They are *S. ferox* and *S. minima* (Table 1) during the SW monsoon, and *E. fowleri, K. subtilis, S. ferox, S. minima* and *S. regularis* during the NE monsoon. The numerical distribution of chaetognaths as shown in these tables illustrates that numerical abundance is correlated to food availability, while species presence or absence may be attributed to suitability of the environment and tolerance of the species.

Table 2 shows that the average number per haul is higher during the SW monsoon for nine species. In 2 species (*K. subtilis* and *S. pacifica*) the average number per haul during the SW monsoon is 1.7 times that of the NE monsoon, while *Pt. draco, S. bipunctata, S. enflata, S. hexaptera* and *S. regularis* showed an increase in number per haul by a factor of 1 to 1.4. *S. ferox* is 6 times and *S. minima* 3 times more abundant during the SW monsoon period. The average numbers per haul for the 2 species (*S. robusta* and *K. pacifica*) are equal in both seasons. *S. bedoti, S. neglecta* and *S. pulchra* have more numbers per unit haul in the NE monsoon period by a factor of 1.14 to 1.5 although 2 of them showed highest density during the SW monsoon. This indicates that patterns of distribution and swarming can be due to factors other than food availability. Species like *E. fowleri, S. decipiens* and *S. zetesios* are obtained in small numbers only during NE monsoon. *S. lyra* was found in small numbers at a single station in the SW monsoon period. *K. pacifica, S. enflata* and *S. neglecta* showed maximum density (measured as number of specimens per haul) during the NE monsoon. Further detailed studies on the individual species should clarify the ecological factors involved.

It is significant that 2 of the 3 species showing affinity for the coastal area (*S. bedoti* and *S. neglecta*) have an average number per haul greater during the NE monsoon, while the other (*S. robusta*) has the same average number, because coastal species are more affected by local factors other than large-scale upwelling.

There is remarkable similarity in the Indo-Pacific chaetognath fauna (TOKIOKA, 1952; 1965; HYMAN, 1959). In the present collections all the 15 epiplanktonic species are common to the Indo-Pacific and 7 of them (*S. bedoti, S. ferox, S. neglecta, S. pacifica, S. pulchra, S. regularis* and *S. robusta*) are endemic to this region. A critical study of earlier work dealing with the Indo-Pacific reveals the fact that it sustains a variety of species and many species are exclusive to this region. The maintenance of the Indo-Pacific fauna may be due to the pattern of circulation in the Indian Ocean. The main part of the Agulhas Current flowing along the SE coast of Africa is directed towards Australia across the southern part of the Indian Ocean. During the NE monsoon there is a strong flow of water from the Pacific to the Indian Ocean through the straits of Malacca into the Andaman Sea and then to the Bay of Bengal (SEWELL, 1948). During the SW monsoon the direction of the currents is reversed and there is a westward flow between the Malay Archipelago and Australia (SEWELL, 1948). Recent studies based on IIOE data also indicate the influx of Pacific Ocean water through the Indonesian Archipelago (WYRTKI, 1973). There is much interchange of water between the 2 oceans, resulting in a wide distribution of chaetognaths in the Indo-West-Pacific. Thus the similarity of the fauna can naturally be expected.

There is a distinct difference in the distribution of chaetognaths in the Arabian Sea and the Red Sea. There are 2 samples available from the Red Sea, 5 from the Bab-el-Mandeb and 12 from the Gulf of Aden. All the epiplanktonic forms (excluding *S. bombayensis*) recorded from the Arabian Sea are found in the Gulf of Aden. *S. enflata*, *S. bedoti*, *S. robusta* and *Pt. draco* are the common forms in these samples. At Bab-el-Mandeb all the species found in the Gulf of Aden (except *K. subtilis*) are encountered. In these samples *S. enflata*, *S. regularis*, *S. bedoti* and *K. pacifica* are the common species and *S. hexaptera*, *S. pulchra* and *S. ferox* are sparse. In the Red Sea samples *S. enflata*, *S. pacifica*, *S. bipunctata*, *S. regularis*, *S. neglecta*, *S. ferox*, *S. heraptera*, and *S. bedoti* are found. These collections from the Gulf of Aden and Red Sea are comparable since they cover the NE monsoon period, except the one located towards the northernmost part. Along with the reduction in specific number, there is a general lowering of population density of the different species of chaetognaths from the Gulf of Aden into the Red Sea. The hydrographic conditions prevailing in the Red Sea are high salinity (36.66−40.50‰) and high temperature (21.96−29.53°C) down to 200 m depth, and thus may not be congenial for all the species which occur in the Arabian Sea and Gulf of Aden. FURNESTIN and BALANÇA (1968) have commented on the sporadic transportation of chaetognaths from the Gulf of Aden into the southern section of the Red Sea. STUBBINGS (1938) has reported mass mortality of pteropods entering the Red Sea from the Arabian Sea. The hot, highly saline waters of the Red Sea, and perhaps other unfavourable physical and chemical factors, are a barrier to the survival of many chaetognath species. The species which are able to withstand this peculiar environment might have maintained the population due to lack of competition from other species and availability of abundant food, as is evidenced by the copepod distribution in the area (IOBC, 1970a).

All the samples from which mesoplanktonic and bathyplanktonic chaetognaths were taken belong to the upper 200 m. The $0-200$ m water column includes the Arabian Sea surface water (ASSW), extending from the surface to $100-150$ m depth, and the Arabian Sea subsurface water (ASSSW) extending from a depth below the ASSW. At "Varuna" station 2009, where *E. fowleri* is found, the surface water is diluted by run-off from the Cochin backwater system down to $30-40$ m depth and O_2 content is high down to 200 m depth. ASSSW has an unusually high dissolved O_2 content.

According to GALLAGHER (1966) the ASSSW has a temperature range of $10-19°C$, salinity varies from 35.0−36.0‰ and O_2 content from 0.21−2.09 ml l^{-1}. The lowest level in the column sampled in the present collection had temperatures 13.5−16.5°C. These features may explain the presence of species described as meso- and bathyplanktonic at depths as low as 200 m.

At the stations from which *S. decipiens* (station AB5 only), *S. lyra* and *S. zetesios* were taken, upwelled waters were present; however, since these species were not taken when and where upwelling was at its peak intensity, or in upwelled waters only, other factors must have been involved. Temperatures at 40 m at stations 170 and 190 were 22.88°C and 23.41°C, respectively. At the station at which *S. decipiens* occurred, temperature was low even at the surface (25.32°C). Previous records of these species from the Indian Ocean are from depths below 200 m except for *S. lyra* (Table 4) which has already been reported from the upper 200 m (TOKIOKA, 1956; TSURUTA, 1963). *E. fowleri* is considered to be bathyplanktonic and BURFIELD and HARVEY (1926) found it mainly below 450 m. According to ALVARIÑO (1965), it is abundant at depths below 800 m. SILAS and SRINIVASAN (1969) noted its occurrence at 600 m and down to 1300 m.

These meso- and bathyplanktonic species are known to be cosmopolitan. The earlier relevant records, summarized with the present data in Table 4, show that the temperature range varies little, while the difference in the salinity pattern may indicate a certain tolerance to salinity changes associated with habits of vertical migration.

All hauls except for "Varuna" station 2009 (Table 3) were made at night or in the early morning and all specimens are either juvenile or stage I. Diurnal migration is well known in chaetognaths (MICHEL, 1911; MOORE, 1949; HAMON, 1956 and others), and it is likely that at dawn the young follow the adults in this downward migration. The specimens may be late migrants caught in the top layer of the population range, or those brought up to a shallower depth by the upwelling of deep water.

Chaetognaths from the Laccadives with the New Record of *Spadella angulata* (TOKIOKA, 1951)

V. R. NAIR and T. S. S. RAO

This paper is based on the material collected in 1968 during cruises 2 and 5 of the National Institute of Oceanography to Kavaratti and Kalpeni, 2 atolls in the Laccadives (Fig. 1).

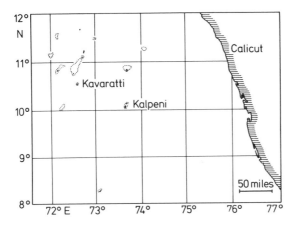

Fig. 1. The Laccadive Archipelagoes off the west coast of India, showing the relative position of Kavaratti and Kalpeni atolls

I. Material and Methods

Plankton was collected at Kavaratti on 20–22 October and Kalpeni on 21–27 December, 1968, collections being made at the surface within the lagoon and around the atoll. The Kavaratti stations (Fig. 2) were worked on 2 successive nights. Two series of 20 plankton samples were taken, the first series (Oct. 20) while the tide was rising, and the second (Oct. 21–22) while the tide was falling (TRANTER and GEORGE, 1969). In the Kalpeni survey (Fig. 3) 36 plankton samples were taken exclusively at night in 3 series, within the lagoon (Dec. 21), round the atoll (Dec. 24) and on 2 seaward traverses (Dec. 27) 5 miles to NE and 5 miles to SW of the atoll (TRANTER and GEORGE, 1969). A modified WP 2 net (UNESCO, 1968) of nylon gauze was used, for the Kavaratti survey with a 0.2 mm mesh, and for the Kalpeni cruise with 0.33 mm mesh. It is assumed that this did not influence the numbers of chaetognaths caught. Plankton samples were

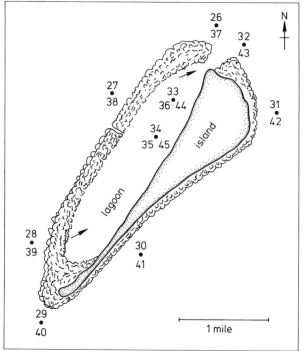

Fig. 2. Kavaratti atoll showing the relative location of island, lagoon and reef. Numbers indicate stations worked

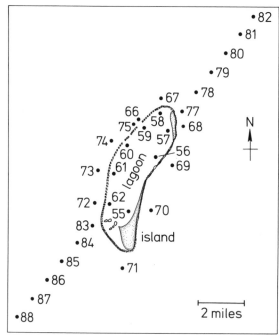

Fig. 3. Kalpeni atoll showing the relative location of island, lagoon and reef. Numbers indicate stations worked

fixed in 4% seawater formaldehyde buffered with 1% hexamine. In the laboratory, each sample was divided into half, one sub-sample for biomass determination and the other for taxonomic studies. From the latter, chaetognaths were sorted out and classified into species. Each species was again subdivided into 5 maturity stages, taking into consideration the growth of the gonads.

II. Results

Thirteen species belonging to 4 genera *Krohnitta, Pterosagitta, Sagitta* and *Spadella* were obtained from the collections (Fig. 6).

The species were:

Krohnitta pacifica (AIDA, 1897)
Pterosagitta draco (KROHN, 1853)
Sagitta bedoti (BÉRANECK, 1895)
Sagitta bipunctata (QUOY and GAIMARD, 1827)
Sagitta enflata (GRASSI, 1881)
Sagitta ferox (DONCASTER, 1903)
Sagitta hexaptera (d'ORBIGNY, 1843)
Sagitta neglecta (AIDA, 1897)
Sagitta pacifica (TOKIOKA, 1940)
Sagitta pulchra (DONCASTER, 1903)
Sagitta regularis (AIDA, 1897)
Sagitta robusta (DONCASTER, 1903)
Spadella angulata (TOKIOKA, 1951)

Of these, *S. ferox* and *Sp. angulata* were encountered only in the Kalpeni collections.

1. Krohnitta pacifica

Moderately common in the waters surrounding the atolls. Highest number from Kavaratti: 211 per 100 m³, from Kalpeni: 719 per 100 m³. Very rare in the Kavaratti lagoon (average number 1 per 100 m³), comparatively better represented in the Kalpeni lagoon (average number 25 per 100 m³). Maturity stage IV was dominant in almost all collections.

2. Pterosagitta draco

More abundant at the Kavaratti (maximum number 39 per 100 m³), at Kalpeni present at only a few stations, the maximum number being 48 per 100 m³. Totally absent in the Kavaratti lagoon, while in the Kalpeni lagoon the average number was 2 per 100 m³. Stage IV was not represented in any of these collections and most of the specimens were immature.

3. Sagitta bedoti

Common in the waters surrounding the atoll. Maximum at Kavaratti was 1213 per 100 m³, at Kalpeni 718 per 100 m³, but only at 2 stations. In the Kavaratti lagoon it was poorly represented (average number 5 per 100 m³) whereas at Kalpeni lagoon it was third in abundance (167 per 100 m³). Most of these were immature forms and stage IV was moderately represented.

4. Sagitta bipunctata

Both at Kavaratti and Kalpeni it was present at 2 stations only, maximum 11 per 100 m³ and 18 per 100 m³, respectively. At Kavaratti mature specimens at stages I and II were taken while at Kalpeni all the specimens were immature.

5. Sagitta enflata

The dominant species in most of the samples taken around the lagoon except at stations 28 and 30 at Kavaratti and station 67, 68, 72, 73 and 74 at Kalpeni. Maximum was 8531 per 100 m³ at Kavaratti and 6462 per 100 m³ at Kalpeni (highest densities at both atolls). Within the Kavaratti lagoon the species was second in abundance; present at stations 36, 44 and 45. Comparatively higher representation at Kalpeni lagoon where it was absent only at station 61. *Sagitta enflata* was the dominant species in the Kalpeni lagoon (average number 414 per 100 m³) but at Kavaratti 53 per 100 m³. All 5 maturity stages, especially stage IV and immature forms were very common. In a few samples taken around the atoll representatives of 3 different maturity cycles were encountered. The size at maturity varied from 7−21 mm and the ovary extended to about ²/₃ of the extent of the posterior fins on the trunk in the first cycle, slightly beyond the posterior fin in the second cycle and to the posterior part of the anterior fin in the third cycle. The length range was: 7−9 mm for the first cycle, 13−16 mm in the second and 18−21 mm in the third cycle. There were also specimens about 11 mm in length having one ovary extending upto about the anterior part of the posterior fins, and 17 mm specimens with ovaries reaching just behind the anterior fins.

6. Sagitta ferox

Present in most of the samples taken around the Kalpeni lagoon (maximum 217 per 100 m³). Three of the lagoon collections also contained this species (average number 11 per 100 m³). Mature specimens were encountered in only a few collections and the majority were immature forms.

7. Sagitta hexaptera

Not very common around the atolls, the maximum number at Kavaratti being 13 per 100 m³ and at Kalpeni 32 per 100 m³. It was taken only from the Kalpeni lagoon (average number 9 per 100 m³). Stage IV predominated at Kavaratti, at Kalpeni, immature individuals.

8. Sagitta neglecta

Very common in the seas around Kavaratti and Kalpeni. At Kavaratti it dominated the samples at station 30 (821 per 100 m³), the maximum number at Kalpeni was at station 65 (2154 per 100 m³). The species was represented at only 2 lagoon stations (33 and 34) at Kavaratti, but more abundant at Kalpeni, even dominating the collections at stations 57 and 58. The average number in Kavaratti lagoon was 14 per 100 m³ and in Kalpeni lagoon 282 per 100 m³. All maturity stages were present.

9. Sagitta pacifica

Very common in the waters at Kavaratti and Kalpeni: maximum representation at Kavaratti 1511 per 100 m³ and at Kalpeni 2226 per 100 m³. At Kalpeni they dominated at stations 67, 72, 73 and 74. Rare in Kavaratti lagoon, average number at Kavaratti atoll

23 per 100 m³ and at Kalpeni 70 per 100 m³. All the different stages were present. Immature and stage I were predominant.

10. Sagitta pulchra

Very scarce: at Kavaratti present only at station 38 (14 per 100 m³) and at Kalpeni at 3 stations (maximum number 3 per 100 m³). At Kalpeni lagoon encountered at station 56 (2 per 100 m³). Only stages III and IV were present at Kavaratti. At Kalpeni immature specimens and stage I were also encountered.

11. Sagitta regularis

A common species around the atoll, particularly at Kavaratti (maximum 800 per 100 m³). At Kalpeni the maximum was 718 per 100 m³ and the species was absent in the samples from stations 67, 68 and 74. Common in the Kavaratti and Kalpeni lagoon stations; at Kavaratti dominant at station 36. Average number at Kavaratti 57 per 100 m³ at Kalpeni 39 per 100 m³. At Kavaratti they were well represented by different stages, especially stage IV; at Kalpeni the different stages were not well represented.

12. Sagitta robusta

Moderately common around the atoll. The maximum number at Kavaratti was 316 per 100 m³, at Kalpeni 257 per 100 m³. Poorly represented in the Kavaratti lagoon, being present only at station 44. At Kalpeni lagoon it was moderately represented and was absent only at stations 55 and 59. Average number at Kavaratti 1 per 100 m³, at Kalpeni 49 per 100 m³. At Kavaratti the different stages were not well represented whereas at Kalpeni a better representation of stage IV and immature stage was noticed.

13. Spadella angulata

This species was recorded only at station 55 at the southern part of the Kalpeni lagoon. A total of 100 specimens was obtained out of which 52 were stage IV of maturity and the rest stage II. Previously it has been recorded at Nanao Bay as *Sp. cephaloptera f. angulata* (TOKIOKA, 1951), in the coastal waters of Malay as *Sp. angulata* (TOKIOKA and PATHANSALI, 1964) and west of Penang Island as *Sp. angulata* (PATHANSALI, 1968).

14. Quantitative Evaluation

The mean representation of Chaetognatha in and around the atolls are given below:

	Kavaratti no per 100 m³	Kalpeni no per 100 m³
Average number of chaetognaths inside the lagoon	154	1 068
Average number of chaetognaths outside the lagoon	3 121	3 175

At Kavaratti the water coming through the reef into the lagoon was found to be improverished of its chaetognath fauna by a factor of 20, while the water coming into the Kalpeni lagoon loses about 67% of its chaetognaths.

The abundance of chaetognaths at the Kavaratti atoll is represented in Fig. 4. Two series of samples were taken, one during the rising tide and the other during the falling tide, at the stations shown in Fig. 2, in time sequence. The curves representing the abundance of chaetognaths outside the lagoon do not indicate a tidal cycle. However,

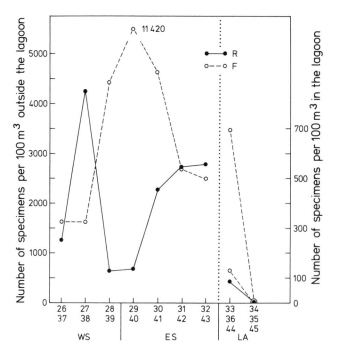

Fig. 4. Abundance of chaetognaths in the Kavaratti atoll. ES: eastern side, F: falling tide, LA: lagoon,
R: rising tide, WS: western side

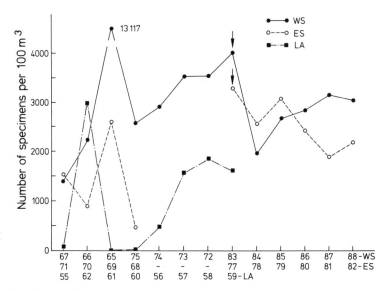

Fig. 5. Abundance of chaetognaths in the Kalpeni atoll. ES: eastern side, LA: lagoon, WS: western
side. The arrows on the curves indicate the place from where stations were worked towards the sea.
The left part of these curves refers to the stations worked along the reef on either side of the atoll

the stations with similar and small numbers (26, 37; 31, 42; 32, 43) are all located at the northern end of the atoll, presumably in waters that have been partly washed through the reefs. All the other stations were outside the atoll. The main stream of the current is from south to north. The maximum density at station 40 (11 420 per 100 m³) was due

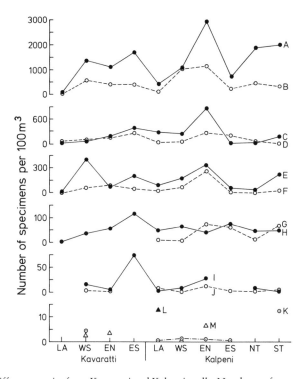

Fig. 6. Different species from Kavaratti and Kalpeni atolls. Numbers refer to mean values

A:	*S. enflata*	B:	*S. pacifica*
C:	*S. neglecta*	D:	*S. regularis*
E:	*S. bedoti*	F:	*K. pacifica*
G:	*S. robusta*	H:	*S. ferox*
I:	*Pt. draco*	J:	*S. hexaptera*
K:	*S. pulchra*	L:	*Sp. angulata*
M:	*S. bipunctata*		
EN:	entrance	ES:	eastern side
LA:	lagoon	NT:	northeast traverse
ST:	southwest traverse	WS:	western side

to a dense patch of *S. enflata* and *S. pacifica*. In the Kavaratti lagoon chaetognaths seem to be concentrated in the main stream leaving the lagoon from the entrance (stations 33, 36, 44). Stations 34, 35, 45 located towards the central part of the lagoon yielded very scanty numbers of chaetognaths. Fig. 5 shows the population density of chaetognaths at the Kalpeni atoll. The stations are arranged along the atoll towards the sea (Fig. 3) from NE to SW on the western side and SW to NE on the eastern side. The NE and SW traverses were worked on one day, and the similarity of the curves indicates that the same water is flowing on both sides. The western side of Kalpeni showed a higher density, the maximum was observed at station 65 and it was due to patches of *S. enflata, S. neglecta* and *S. pacifica*. The eastern side of Kavaratti where a greater abundance of chaetognaths was found, and the western side of Kalpeni are the same part of the ocean surrounding these atolls. The number of chaetognaths is reduced in the Kalpeni lagoon, but not as drastically as in the Kavaratti lagoon. Relatively large swarms were found at stations 62, 57, 58 and 59, suggesting that occasionally rather undisturbed parcels of water penetrate the lagoon, either over the reef or through some incoming channel. A similar but much smaller patch was found in the Kavaratti lagoon at station 44.

III. Discussion

DONCASTER (1903) described the chaetognaths in the Laccadive and Maldive Archipelago based on the collections made in the years 1899 and 1900. He reported 15 species, of which the validity of only 11 was accepted (ALVARIÑO, 1964). All the species recorded by DONCASTER were present in the material studied except *S. septata. S. bipunctata* and *S. angulata* are new records for the Laccadive area. Only 2 specimens of *K. pacifica* were present in DONCASTER'S collections, whereas in the present material it was common. In DONCASTER'S collections, *S. regularis* occured in small numbers and *S. pulchra* in moderate numbers. The present work showed that, next to *S. enflata*, *S. regularis* was the most abundant form at Kavaratti atoll, and that it was moderately common in the Kalpeni atoll. *S. pulchra* was sparse in all the collections. SILAS and SRINIVASAN (1969) reported on the occurrence of 14 species from the Laccadive Seas and off the west coast of India. Their collections include the mesoplanktonic species *S. decipiens* and *S. lyra* and bathyplanktonic species *Eukrohnia fowleri* and *E. minuta*.

It is of interest to see how the species composition of chaetognaths in our collections compares with that of the samples taken from the Laccadive Seas (between 08° 45' − 09° 09' N and 71° 30' − 74° 30' E) during the IIOE (1959 − 1965). Ten standard samples (IOBC, 1969) collected by "Meteor" in February 1965 (4 samples), "Discovery" in May 1964 (1 sample), "Kistna" in August 1963 (1 sample) and "Varuna" in November 1963 (4 samples) are available. Of these, the "Varuna" and "Meteor" samples, like ours, were taken during the NE monsoon. *S. enflata* was the dominant chaetognath in all these samples. The other common forms occuring in the IIOE samples were *S. pacifica, Pterosagitta draco, S. bedoti* and *S. bipunctata* in decreasing order of abundance. In the IIOE samples better representation of *Pt. draco, S. bipunctata, S. hexaptera* and *S. pulchra* were noticed while *S. neglecta, S. regularis* and *S. robusta* were rare. *Krohnitta subtilis* (GRASSI, 1881) was represented in these samples and is an addition to the list of species from the Laccadive Seas.

The present collections include only epiplanktonic species except for *Sp. angulata. K. subtilis, Pt. draco, S. bipunctata, S. enflata* and *S. hexaptera* are all cosmopolitan forms of warm and temperate oceanic waters (ALVARIÑO, 1965). *K. pacifica* is also widely distributed but only in the equatorial belts of the Atlantic, Pacific and Indian Ocean (ALVARIÑO, 1965). *S. bedoti, S. neglecta, S. ferox, S. pacifica, S. pulchra, S. regularis* and *S. robusta* are Indo-Pacific forms. The presence of *Sp. angulata*, a bottom dwelling species inside the lagoon at Kalpeni suggests that it breeds there and that it may be a permanent inhabitant of the lagoon. *Sp. angulata* is a new record from the Arabian Sea. Apart from the record of this species from the west of Penang Island (PATHANSALI,

1968) there is no other record from the Indian Ocean. BURFIELD (1950) reported the occurrence of 12 species from the Barrier Reef Expedition and all except *S. lyra* were found in the present collections. The commonest forms at the Great Barrier Reef were in order of abundance *S. enflata*, *S. neglecta*, *S. robusta*, *S. bedoti*, *S. pulchra* and *S. pacifica* (reported as *S. serratodentata*). The difference noticed in the Laccadive collections is the occurrence of *K. pacifica*, *S. ferox* and *Sp. angulata*, the abundance of *S. regularis* and the scarcity of *S. pulchra*.

A comparative study of the present collections from the lagoons with those of the chaetognaths reported from the Palao Islands (TOKIOKA, 1942) and New Caledonia (TOKIOKA, 1960) also shows similarities in the species composition. In the Palao Islands 10 species were present and New Caledonia sustains 4 species already recorded from the Palao Islands. The species include *K. pacifica*, *S. bedfordii*, *S. enflata*, *S. ferox* (reported as *S. ai*), *S. neglecta*, *S. oceania*, *S. pacifica* (reported as *S. serratodentata*), *S. regularis*, *S. robusta* and *S. tropica*. All these except *S. bedfordii* and *S. tropica* were encountered in the lagoon collections of Kalpeni. The similarity between the chaetognaths of the Laccadive lagoons and the Pacific lagoons indicates the identity of the Indo-Pacific tropical fauna, a fact already pointed out by earlier authors (TOKIOKA, 1952, 1962; HYMAN, 1959).

In almost all the collections taken outside the lagoons different maturity stages of the dominant species were encountered; this indicates that breeding was taking place. It has been assumed that chaetognaths die after egg laying (KUHL, 1938). However, periodic maturation of ovaries in *S. enflata* has already been reported (MICHAEL, 1919; THOMSON, 1947; ALVARIÑO, 1965, 1967; FURNESTIN and BALANÇA, 1968). We found 3 different size groups of *S. enflata* in the same sample, apparently representing 3 consecutive cycles of maturity, although it could also indicate the presence of different populations which attain maturity at different lengths. DONCASTER considered the bigger forms of *S. enflata* to be a new species: *S. gardineri*, but as ALVARIÑO (1967) concluded, our work confirms that his specimen was *S. enflata* at the third maturity cycle. Differences in meristic characters cannot be considered reliable, since they show considerable overlapping and variation with age, season and geographic localities (JOHN, 1933; ALVARIÑO, 1967).

Compared to the samples taken outside the atoll, the lagoon samples showed a general impoverishment in chaetognaths. There were no significant changes in salinity and temperature in and around these atolls. Hence the lowering of the population density of chaetognaths inside the lagoon cannot be attributed to variation in salinity and temperature. According to TRANTER and GEORGE (1969) zooplankton is lost "in transit across the reef into the lagoon and is probably utilized by the reef community". Corals are believed to be specialized carnivores living primarily on zooplankton (RUSSELL and YONGE, 1963; YONGE, 1963). This is probably the reason for the lower population density of chaetognaths inside the lagoon.

4.8

Cumacea of the Indian Ocean

C. V. KURIAN

The cumacea are essentially benthic forms which live in the bottom deposits. They are rarely caught in plankton hauls. The cumacea dealt with here were obtained from 54 stations in the Indian Ocean and adjacent regions collected during the IIOE (1961–1965) in plankton nets and in the benthos samples.

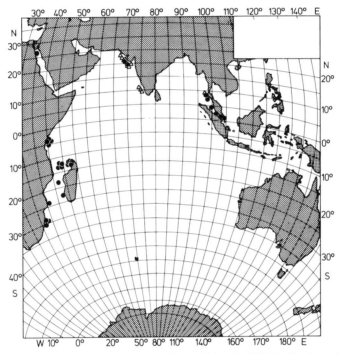

Fig. 1. Distribution of *cumacea* in the Indian Ocean. Triangles IOBC collections, filled circles collections of the Smithsonian Institution

The specimens in the plankton collections were received from the Indian Ocean Biological Centre (IOBC) after being sorted out from the samples taken by the Indian Ocean Standard net (IOSN) from 200 m to 0 m. Of the 1927 plankton samples in the IOBC, only 11 samples showed the presence of cumacea. Altogether 28 specimens have been separated. This number seems very low compared to the number of specimens which are usually observed in the surface plankton samples collected from the inshore waters. It is also remarkable that all the specimens of the IOBC collection come from the stations near the coast—7 of the stations located off Gujarat, 3 off the SW coast of India and 1 near the Malayan coast (Fig. 1). The specimens belong to the families *Bodotriidae, Holostylidae, Diastylidae, Pseudocumatidae* and *Nannastacidae.*

The second series of specimens were received from the Smithsonian Institution having been collected by RV "Anton Bruun" and RV "Te Vega" during the period 1963—1965, from the Indian Ocean and adjacent seas. This collection consists of 43 samples and a total of 502 well-preserved specimens. These specimens were collected from the intertidal region to a depth of 2125 m and from a variety of substrata ranging from clay to rock. While some of the specimens were collected by hand, others were obtained by using rock dredge, shrimp trawl, Agassiz trawl and Menzies trawl. The specimens vary in length from 1.2 mm to 15 mm and belong to the families *Sympodammatidae, Bodotriidae, Leuconidae, Diastylidae, Holostylidae, Nannastacidae* and *Campylaspididae.* Most of the shore collections are represented by very small specimens belonging to the genus *Nannastacus* BATE. While mud and clay deposits yielded very few specimens, the rich collections came from sand deposits. It is interesting to note that both series of collections recorded cumacea specimens off the Gujarat coast. The systematics of the species collected are dealt with separately.

From the study of the ecology of the specimens obtained during the IIOE the following conclusions can be drawn: All cumacea specimens obtained in the Indian Ocean samples were from the nearshore waters. The 11 stations of the IOBC collections were located on the west coast of India and Pakistan and the Malaya coast. The specimens of the Smithsonian collections which were obtained mostly from benthos samples were also obtained from the nearshore waters on the east coast of Africa, Red Sea, west coast of India and Singapore strait. The IOSN samples were taken from 200 m upward and so they actually missed the cumacea in the deeper water layers.

The IIOE collections have definitely shown that the cumacea are essentially benthic organisms and that their appearance in the open water is accidental. However, some of the plankton nets which reached very near the bottom caught a few of the specimens. The mass migration of cumacea as reported by JONES (1955, 1956) along the west coast of Africa and their occurrence in large numbers in the plankton is attributed to low oxygen concentration in the bottom water. Experiments conducted in the laboratory show that *Gigacuma halei* KURIAN, the large species of cumacea that occurs in the inshore waters of India, could tolerate very low oxygen content and that they migrate from the bottom only when the dissolved oxygen content of the bottom water falls below 0.6 ml l^{-1}.

The total absence of cumacea in the IOSN samples taken in the open sea during the day or during the night clearly shows that they are incapable of surviving in the upper waters for any considerable length of time and that they usually remain on the bottom or near the bottom of the sea. The cumacea are capable of living at great depths and in the present collections 2 specimens of *Campylaspis sp.* were obtained from a depth of 2125 m off Madagascar with the Menzies trawl. However, cumacea are abundant on a fine sandy bottom with a small percentage of silt, and rare in coarse sand and clay deposits. Like many other benthic organisms they are more prevalent at shallow depths and as depth increases their number decreases. The collections from Nosy-Bé are mostly very small specimens of 1.2 to 2.5 mm belonging to the genus *Nannastacus* BATE.

4.9

Distribution of Copepoda in the Indian Ocean

L. R. Kasturirangan, M. Saraswathy, and T. C. Gopalakrishnan

The present paper deals with the distribution of the group *Copepoda* in the Indian Ocean. This group includes mostly species of planktonic habits, besides demersal species which are excluded from this account. The group is treated as a whole, without reference to the constituent species or families. The paper is based on numerical data derived from the zooplankton samples collected during the International Indian Ocean Expedition (IIOE) and processed at the Indian Ocean Biological Centre (HANSEN, 1966; IOBC, 1969).

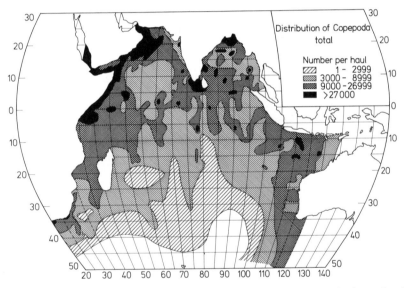

Fig. 1. Distribution of *Copepoda* (total) in the Indian Ocean form 1548 standard samples. (After IOBC, 1970a)

Fig. 1 to 3 are reproduced, with some simplification, from the original maps which were published in the IIOE Plankton Atlas, Volume II, fascicle 1 (IOBC, 1970a). These maps must be regarded as visual aids, giving only a general picture of the geographical pattern of the distribution of numerical abundance. Areas of high copepod populations correspond in general with areas of high zooplankton standing stock. In Fig. 1 the total distribution of copepods is given. The areas of highest population density (27 000 and above) are mostly close to the land masses. The areas of high density which occur in mid-ocean are smaller and fewer. In general, they are greater in extent in the northern

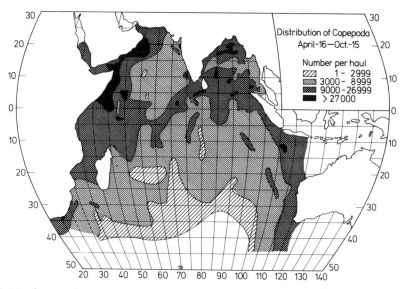

Fig. 2. Distribution of *Copepoda* (16 April to 15 October) in the Indian Ocean from 836 standart samples. (After IOBC, 1970 a)

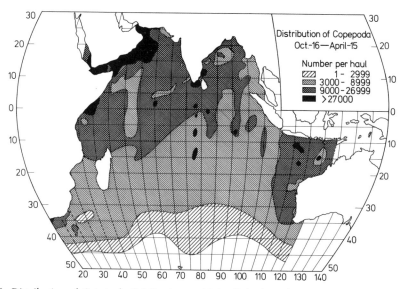

Fig. 3. Distribution of *Copepoda* (16 October to 15 April) in the Indian Ocean from 712 standard samples. (After IOBC, 1970 a)

Indian Ocean as compared to the southern, and more extensive in the Arabian Sea than in the Bay of Bengal. The largest of the areas of high population density is located in the northwestern border of the Arabian Sea. It is shown in the northern winter map (Fig. 3) as well as in the northern summer map (Fig. 2), but it is broken into 2 sections in Fig. 3 and the bigger section is located a little further north as compared to Fig. 2.

In Fig. 2 the comparatively low-density area in the Arabian Sea (3 000 to 8 999) is quite large; it is, in the main, centrally located but it abuts over the greater part of the west coast of India. In contrast to this, the northern winter map (Fig. 3) shows the low-density area (3 000 to 8 999) to be smaller in extent and located more to the south and to the west.

The lowest population density (1 to 2 999) extends over greater areas in the southern Indian Ocean as compared to the northern. It is more noticeable over the central oceanic areas, not extending to the western borders close to Africa or the eastern borders close to Australia.

Copepods from day and night samples show a remarkable difference in their abundance. In the following description of day night distribution patterns we refer to Figs. 4 and 5 of the IIOE Plankton Atlas (IOBC, 1970a). In Fig. 4 of the Atlas, depicting day stations, the lowest density of 1 to 2 999 is fairly extensive over the southern and central parts of the ocean but in Fig. 5 (IIOE Atlas), depicting night station, this density is reduced to a few small patches; there is a compensating increase in the area covered by the next higher density of 3 000 to 8 999. In comparison to Fig. 4, Fig. 5 (night stations) shows that the area covered by the highest density (27 000 and above), is nearly doubled and the area covered by the density, 9 000 to 26 999, is also distinctly greater. From this, the conclusion is drawn that the night samples of the IIOE, by and large, contain more copepods than the day samples.

The copepods form the dominant element of the zooplankton. By *Copepoda*, in this context, is meant the *Calanoida*, which are extremely numerous; the *Harpacticoida* and the *Cyclopoida* also occur in the IIOE plankton but they are quite subordinate to the *Calanoida* in number and bulk.

The lowest population density (1 to 2 999) extends over great areas of the southern Indian Ocean (Figs. 1 to 3) and corresponds to the centre of the anticlockwise gyre with the predominance of conditions of convergence. It may be pointed out that in all the 5 figures in the Atlas, a gradual increase in numerical abundance of copepods is evident as we proceed northward from lat. 40° S. This has also been remarked upon in relation to biomass by PRASAD (1969). Comparing Fig. 4 (day stations) with Fig. 5 (night stations) of the IIOE Plankton Atlas, we assume that the replacement of numerical density 1 to 2 999 by the next higher values of 3 000 to 8 999 in the night stations is related to vertical migration in several species of copepods (CLARKE, 1933). The movement of the copepods either upward or downward within the upper 200 m of the ocean would not alter the population figures calculated for the standard hauls, but if the species that stay below 200 m during the daytime migrate upwards during the night hours, there would be an augmentation of the population density in the upper 200 m stratum. The genus *Pleuromamma* is an example. It is represented by at least 6 species in the IIOE collections. It has been observed during subsorting of the *Copepoda* that individuals of *Pleuromamma* species are abundant in the night samples only, whereas in the day samples they are very sparse and include mostly juvenile stages.

The areas of greater density of copepod populations are the same as areas of rich overall zooplankton production. The southern borders of the Indian Ocean are poor in copepods but a gradual northward increase in population is observed, and the extensive border areas of the northwestern Indian Ocean are rich in copepods. The fact that in some areas night stations show higher numbers of copepods than day stations, is thought to be due to circadian rhythms which cause the copepods to migrate to the upper 200 m of the sea at night.

4.10

Distribution of Gaussia (Copepoda, Metridiidae) in the Upper 200 m in the Indian Ocean

M. Saraswathy

This paper is based on specimens of the genus *Gaussia* sorted during analyses of the 1927 zooplankton samples received at the Indian Ocean Biological Centre (IOBC). The sampling coverage by area and time is given by Rao (1973) this volume. Only

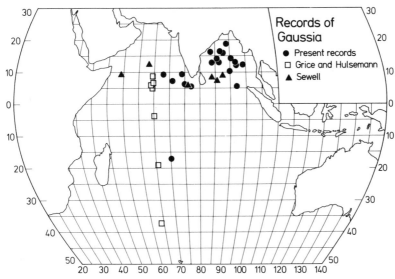

Fig. 1. Available records of *Gaussia* in the Indian Ocean (present records, Grice and Hulsemann, 1967; Sewell, 1932, 1947)

19 revealed the presence of *Gaussia*, all except 1 from stations located north of the Equator: 13 in the Bay of Bengal, and 5 in the Arabian Sea (Fig. 1). Most of these are from the upper 200 m of water, collected in a uniform manner with the Indian Ocean standard net (IOSN) (Currie, 1963). Table 1 lists the 19 stations, date and time of collection, depth of haul and number of specimens obtained from each sample.

I. Distribution and Density of the Species

The 66 specimens of *G. princeps* obtained from the samples include males, females and copepodites 5, 4, 3, and 2 (Table 1). About 20% of the specimens, all of them copepodite stages, were collected from the only station in the southern hemisphere at about 17° 18′ S, 70° 05′ E. The remaining 80% were collected from the 18 stations

Table 1. Collection data (AB. "Anton Bruun"; Di. "Discovery"; Ki. "Kistna"; Pi. "Pioneer"; Vi. "Vitiaz")

Station identification	Location Lat.	Long. E	Date	Time	Collection depth	wire angle	Adults Male	Female	Copepodites 5	4	3	2	Total Specimens
AB. 1. 32	12° 52′ N	94° 13′	28– 3–63	2 230	200	–	1	–	1	–	–	–	2
AB. 1. 58	18° 11′ N	88° 04′	9– 4–63	0 012	200	–	–	–	2	1	–	–	3
AB. 1. 70	15° 17′ N	87° 50′	16– 4–63	2 129	200	–	2	–	2	2	1	–	7
AB. 1. 73	14° 02′ N	90° 08′	17– 4–63	2 233	200	–	2	3	1	1	1	–	8
AB. 1. 76	12° 56′ N	92° 10′	18– 4–63	2 304	200	–	–	–	1	1	–	–	2
AB. 1. 92	16° 40′ N	83° 58′	29– 4–63	0 249	200	–	–	–	3	2	–	–	5
AB. 1. 95	14° 22′ N	85° 20′	30– 4–63	0 144	200	–	–	–	1	–	–	–	1
AB. 1. 97	13° 08′ N	86° 12′	1– 5–63	0 450	200	–	–	3	–	–	–	–	3
AB. 1. 99	13° 02′ N	84° 22′	1– 5–63	2 229	200	–	–	1	–	–	–	–	1
AB. 2. 123	17° 18′ S	70° 05′	10– 6–63	0 635	200	–	1	–	6	2	2	2	12
Di. 5 381 B	09° 57′ N	74° 27′	19– 5–64	2 255	200	–	–	–	2	2	2	–	5
Di. 5 383 A	09° 58′ N	67° 32′	21– 5–64	2 055	200	–	1	–	1	–	–	–	1
Ki. 7. 189	16° 30′ N	87° 15′	16– 3–63	2 330	200	–	–	1	–	–	–	–	1
Ki. 13. 294	07° 00′ N	71° 30′	20– 8–63	2 235	200	–	1	1	–	–	–	–	2
Ki. 13. 308	06° 00′ N	75° 00′	26– 8–63	0 035	200	–	–	1	–	–	1	–	2
Ki. 14. 352	13° 00′ N	92° 00′	15– 9–63	2 232	200	–	2	1	1	–	–	–	4
Ki. 15. 362	10° 00′ N	90° 00′	13– 6–64	0 835	200	40°	–	1	–	–	–	–	1
Pi. 35	05° 02′ N	92° 00′	13– 6–64	2 030	200	45°	–	–	1	1	2	–	3
Vi. 5 249	05° 05′ N	77° 07′	1–10–62	0 229	283	45°	1–	1	1	–	–	–	3

located between $5° - 19°$ N and $67° - 95°$ E (Table 1). The Indian Ocean north of the Equator comprises the monsoon region, characterized by seasonal reversal of the surface currents. Most of the specimens of *Gaussia* were collected during the SW monsoon period. Even typical upwelling areas have not shown the presence of the species in the upper layer.

II. Discussion

The fact that 20% of the total number of specimens was collected from the single positive station south of the Equator may indicate that the species occurred in this

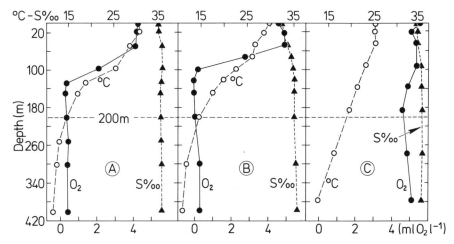

Fig. 2. Hydrographic data at selected stations in the Arabian Sea (A); Bay of Bengal (B); and southern Indian Ocean (C)

locality in maximum number at the time of sampling. The absence of any adult specimen in the catch from this apparently rich area may be due to vertical migration or may be the result of different environmental preferences by adults and young. CUSHING (1951), reviewing the vertical migrations of planktonic *Crustacea*, observed that migration can be modified by weather, sunlight, temperature and phytoplankton density, and further masked by differences in behaviour of groups of animals. On the basis of previous work on the distribution of juveniles and adults of different species of copepods, he concluded that surface-living species have younger stages which prefer greater depths while deep-water species have the juveniles towards the surface.

From Fig. 1 it can be seen that, though the typical upwelling areas were well sampled during the IIOE, specimens of *Gaussia* were usually absent from these regions. In connection with these negative results, it may be interesting to recall the observations on the distribution of bathypelagic copepods in the equatorial Pacific by GUEREDRAT (1969). He recorded a difference in behaviour according to the structure of the water column, with a wider vertical migration in areas where upwelling is weak, and more restricted migration in regions of intense upwelling. Dealing with latitudinal distribution in the area 20° S to 4° N along 170° E, GUEREDRAT found an equatorial increase of the species in upwelling areas where there is enrichment of the upper layer. The pattern of distribution in the Indian Ocean is seen to be different from that noted in the Pacific, the positive stations being located mostly north of 5° N and south of 4° S (Fig. 1).

Our findings on the distribution pattern of the species in the Indian Ocean are not inconsistent with the observations of SEWELL (1948). There may well be a population of *Gaussia* in the southern areas of the Indian Ocean at deeper levels than towards the north. This speculation is supported by records of the species at 3 stations south of the Equator, the southernmost at 37° 59′ S (GRICE and HULSEMANN, 1967). Samples at all these stations were taken with the Isaacs-Kidd mid-water trawl from 350−2 394 m depth at the southernmost station. The actual number of specimens collected from these stations is not given. Further, as quoted by GRICE and HULSEMANN (1967), IVANENKOS and GUBIN (1960) observed that "in the area between 10° and 16° S, the upper part of the southward flowing North Indian Deep Water mixes with northward flowing Sub-Antarctic Intermediate Water and the lower part of the North Indian Deep Water mixes with the Antarctic Bottom Water. This mixing results in the formation of two water masses: the South Indian Deep Water (1 500−3 500 m) which flows southward and North Indian Bottom Water (a layer of 200−700 m) which flows northward. The North Indian Deep Water, formed in the northern Arabian Sea, is centered between 400 and 1 500 m north of the Equator and between 800 and 2 000 m south of the Equator". This supports the view that cold water is encountered nearer the surface in the northern Indian Ocean than in the southern.

It can be seen from Table 1 that at 2 stations the net had fished only above 200 m depth, as evidenced by the wire angle; Fig. 2 shows water of 19° C temperature or lower in the Bay of Bengal at approximately 130 m.

The hydrographic data available for water depths at every one of the stations from which *G. princeps* was collected, indicate the presence of cold water at subsurface levels. This, considered along with time of collection and the inherent tendency of the species to diurnal vertical migration, would explain the presence of this bathypelagic species at depths of only 200 m. Moreover, latitudinal differences in temperature are insignificant in deep-water layers as compared to the surface; hence bathypelagic fauna commonly have a more extensive distribution than epigelagic fauna (EKMAN, 1953). Speciation declines with increase in depth; it is, therefore, of interest that only 1 species of *Gaussia* is known from all the oceans.

Relationship of Indian Ocean Epiplanktonic Calanoids to the World Oceans

A. Fleminger and K. Hulsemann

Circumglobal distributions are widely accepted as commonplace among epiplanktonic species of zooplankton and especially for those copepods occurring in warm oceanic waters (Sewell, 1948). Nevertheless, the warm-water belt lying roughly between latitudes 40°N and 40°S is not a continuous circle. Interruptions include a virtually perfect warm-water barrier, the Americas, separating the Atlantic and Pacific Oceans, the extensive Afro-European barrier separating the Atlantic from the Indian Ocean as far south as latitude 35°S and the mosaic of land masses and shallow seas comprising the Austral-Asian boundary intervening between the Indian and Pacific Oceans. These barriers appear a priori to be formidable deterrents to panmixis and in all likelihood they have prevailed in their relative positions at least since the end of the Tertiary (Darlington, 1965).

Dahl (1894) was among the first to suggest that the circumglobal warm-water belt is not faunistically homogeneous. On exceedingly limited evidence Dahl noted the existence of many differences among the species of copepods known at the time from the Atlantic Ocean on one hand and from the Indian and Pacific Oceans on the other. Appropriate support for his view has been scanty and largely unnoticed. One source is Schmaus' (1917; Schmaus and Lehnhofer, 1927) discovery that the equatorial epiplanktonic species, *Rhincalanus cornutus,* is geographically polytypic and actually consists of 2 distinctively different populations, one restricted to the Atlantic Ocean and the other ranging through the Indian and Pacific Oceans. Equally significant is Jones' (1965) observation that the equatorial epiplanktonic species *Candacia pachydactyla* parallels *R. cornutus* in having constant morphological differences distinguishing the Atlantic form from the form found throughout the Indian and Pacific Oceans. In addition, Lang (1967) presents evidence that within the *Eucalanus elongatus* species group, *E. inermis* is found only in the eastern equatorial Pacific and it is replaced to the west in the Indo-Pacific region by *E. elongatus* s.s.

Drawing upon his admirable efforts to document the limits of diversity in the genus *Calanus* s.l., Brodsky (1965) argued at length on the need to analyze and compare epiplanktonic populations systematically from the vantage point of a world-scale view. Judging by the perspectives of warm-water distributions obtained from such a view of the genus *Clausocalanus* (Frost and Fleminger, 1968) in addition to the others mentioned above, Brodsky's points are well taken. Frost and Fleminger found 2 categories of warm-water distribution within *Clausocalanus.* One pattern is circumglobal and apparently sustained by warm-water epiplanktonic species capable of breeding effectively to about 40° north and south latitudes. The second pattern is non-circumglobal and the breeding range is apparently restricted to lower latitudes between the Equator and perhaps 30° north and south.

Additional evidence of different categories of distribution among warm water copepods may be found among the more numerous studies on copepod distribution restricted to a single ocean or sea [e.g., *Calanus tenuicornis* and *C. lighti:* BOWMAN (1955), MULLIN (1969); *Eucalanus elongatus* complex: LANG (1967); pontellid copepods: FLEMINGER (1957), HEINRICH (1960, 1964, 1969), VORONINA (1962, 1964), SHERMAN (1963, 1964)].

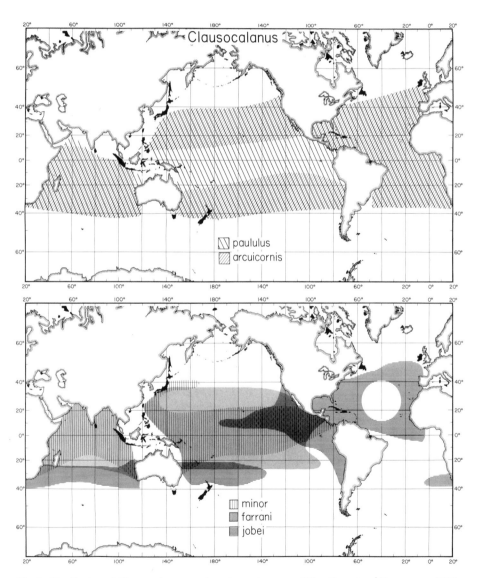

Fig. 1. Distribution of *Clausocalanus arcuicornis* species group. (After FROST and FLEMINGER, 1968; and FROST, 1969)

I. Distribution of Epiplanktonic Calanoids

Fig. 1 shows the distribution of the 5 species of the *Clausocalanus arcuicornis* species group, the only group in the genus with species restricted to equatorial latitudes. The two species represented in Fig. 1 (top) *(arcuicornis* and *paululus)* are both circumglobal and occur roughly between 45° N and 45° S. *C. arcuicornis* is absent from the equatorial region in the Pacific. Fig. 1 (bottom) shows the distribution of 2 equatorial species, *minor*

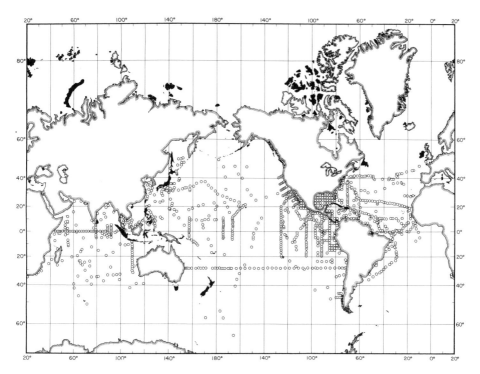

Fig. 2. Localities from which one or more samples were examined for all species of the following calanoid genera: *Eucalanus, Pontellina, Centropages,* and *Temora.* For readability, replicate samples and stations too close to others have been omitted

and *farrani.* In contrast to the circumglobal forms, *minor* and *farrani* are restricted to lower latitudes and appear only in the Indian and Pacific Oceans. *C. jobei,* a cognate of the closely related *farrani,* is somewhat unusual and seems to inhabit the cooler segments of boundary currents especially in the Southern Hemisphere.

Our objective in the remainder of this paper is to call attention to new evidence of geographic variation among populations of warm-water epiplanktonic calanoids and to take note of some obvious patterns in their geographical distributions. The evidence has been drawn freely from a number of geographical analyses being carried out on *Eucalanus, Pontellina, Centropages,* and *Temora,* genera with oceanic and neritic species and varying from fine grain filterers to rapacious predators. We have utilized plankton collections from a variety of institutions including Scripps Institution of Oceanography, Woods Hole Oceanographic Institution, and the Indian Ocean Biological Centre. Grouped together and omitting seasonal and other replication, the geographical array of samples examined by us is shown in Fig. 2. Most of these samples were obtained with nets 1 m in diameter at the mouth which were towed obliquely from 150 or 200 m to the surface. A typical sample represents the straining of about 400 to 500 m^3 of water. Routine examination of these samples consists of sorting and identifying specimens of the genera from randomized subsamples ranging from 2% to 10% of the total catch.

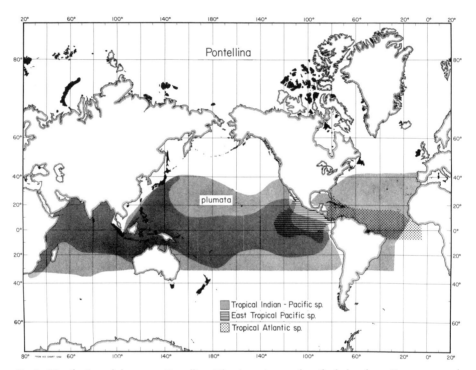

Fig. 3. Distribution of the genus *Pontellina*. The 4 species are described elsewhere (FLEMINGER and HULSEMANN, in press). Approximate limits are based solely on our records

Our taxonomic analyses utilize available material from all geographical sectors yielding specimens. Diagnostic features used to distinguish populations at the species level include morphological characteristics that appear with the completion of sexual maturity. Constant differences in secondary sexual characters among otherwise morphologically similar forms are assumed to express the existence of pre-zygotic mating barriers, and therefore completion of the evolutionary process of speciation.

Fig. 3 presents the generalized distributions we have determined for the genus *Pontellina* (FLEMINGER and HULSEMANN, in press). *P. plumata,* represented by vertical hatching, is common circumglobally though in modest numbers roughly between latitudes 40° N and 40° S. Close inspection of *Pontellina* revealed three additional species with mutually exclusive distributions that tend to replace *plumata* in lower latitudes. One species is restricted to the eastern tropical Pacific. Its sibling occupies the lower latitudes throughout the remainder of the Pacific and Indian Oceans. The most dissimilar of the 3 is restricted to the lower latitudes of the Atlantic Ocean and shows stronger morphological affinity to the true *plumata*.

Fig. 4 illustrates the generalized distributions estimated for the 5 species of the *Eucalanus elongatus* species group. The species of immediate concern are the 3 inhabiting

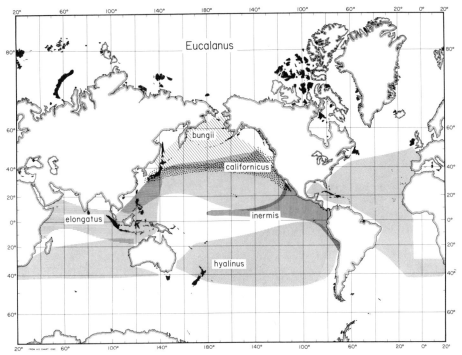

Fig. 4. Distribution of the *Eucalanus elongatus* species group. The group, modified from LANG (1967), consists of *E. elongatus* s.s., restricted to the tropical Indian and Indo-Pacific regions, *E. hyalinus* s.s., circumglobal subtropical with postero-lateral margins of fifth thoracic segment extended as a pointed conical process, *E. inermis*, *E. bungii bungii* and *E. bungii californicus*. Approximate limits are based solely on our records

the warm waters between 40° N to 40° S. *E. hyalinus*, shown by vertical hatching, is, like *Pontellina plumata*, common and relatively abundant north and south of the Equator to the latitudes of the westerly winds. Populations in the Atlantic, Indian, and Pacific Oceans are morphologically indistinguishable. In contrast, the 2 more equatorial forms, *elongatus* and *inermis*, showing restricted distributions, one being confined largely to the Indian Ocean and the other to the eastern equatorial Pacific. No equatorial form of this species group appears in the Atlantic Ocean. The remaining 3 species groups comprising the genus *Eucalanus* show parallel patterns, the tropical or equatorial species lacking circumglobal distributions while those species ranging through the subtropics or central water gyres are circumglocal (FLEMINGER and LANG, in preparation).

Fig. 5 shows that equatorial provincialism may also prevail among offshore neritic species. Within the genus *Temora*, shown in vertical hatching, *discaudata* and *stylifera* comprise a morphologically related pair that differs markedly from the remainder of the genus (see Figs. 6e–j, 7a–i). Though they may occur on occasion well beyond 40° of latitude, typically in regions dominated by a western boundary current, their effective breeding range does not ordinarily appear to extend beyond 35° from the Equator. Our

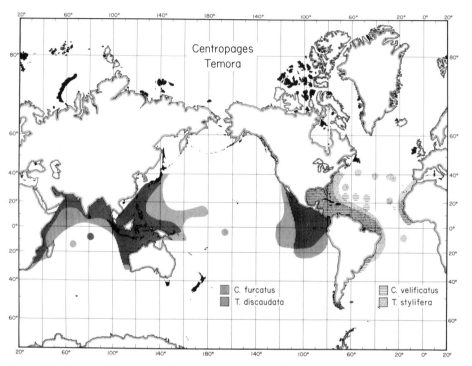

Fig. 5. Distribution of *Centropages furcatus* species group and the *Temora discaudata* species group. Approximate limits are based solely on our records

laboratory has found that *stylifera* is endemic to the Atlantic Ocean and its adjacent seas, while *discaudata* replaces it in the Indian and Pacific Oceans.

A parallel situation prevails in the genus *Centropages*, represented by horizontal hatching in Fig. 5. *C. furcatus* and its Atlantic cognate, *C. velificatus*, formerly regarded as conspecific with *furcatus*, replace one another in equatorial latitudes. Previously *C. furcatus* s.l. was treated as a homogeneous, circumglobal species. In actuality, it is polytypic and shows morphological and geographical discontinuities (FLEMINGER, unpublished data) paralleling the 2 *Temora* species above. The Indian and Pacific Ocean populations appear to enjoy genetic continuity in that diagnostic features are similar and relatively constant throughout the 2 oceans. The appearance of these diagnostic features in the Atlantic is also constant but significantly different in certain details (Fig. 6a–d). No intermediate individuals have been observed among the hundreds or the thousands examined from the African coasts and the American coasts, respectively. There are a number of advantages to separating the 2 geographical forms as distinct species and we have utilized the senior available synonym, C. *velificatus* (DE OLIVEIRA, 1947), to refer to the Atlantic population; in our view C. *furcatus* s.s. should be restricted in application to the Indian and Pacific populations, the original specimens of C. *furcatus* (DANA) having been collected in straits (Selat Bangka) between the islands of Bangka and Sumatra.

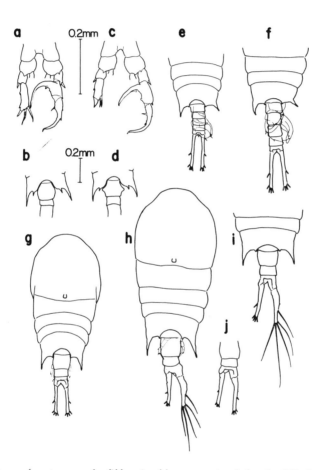

Fig. 6. *Centropages furcatus:* a male, fifth pair of legs, posterior; b female, fifth thoracic segment and genital segment, dorsal; specimens from Gulf of Panama off Panama City. C. *velificatus:* c male, fifth pair of legs, posterior; d female, fifth thoracic segment and genital segment, dorsal; specimens from Gulf of Mexico off Galveston, Texas. *Temora*, males: e *stylifera*, thorax and abdomen, dorsal; f *discaudata*, thorax and abdomen, dorsal. *Temora*, females: g *stylifera*, dorsal; h—j *discaudata*, dorsal, i and j showing variation in the furca. T. *stylifera* specimens from Caribbean Sea off Colon, Panama; T. *discaudata* specimens from Gulf of Panama off Punta Mala f, h; Mombasa Harbor, Kenya i; and Manila Bay, Philippines j

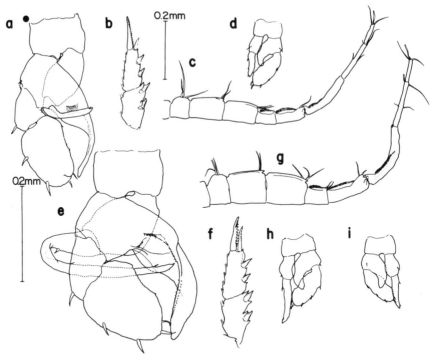

Fig. 7. *Temora* males. *T. stylifera:* a fifth pair of legs, posterior; b second leg, exopod, posterior; c right first antenna, dorsal; d stage V, fifth pair of legs, anterior; specimens from Caribbean Sea off Colon, Panama. *T. discaudata:* e fifth pair of legs, posterior; f second leg, exopod, posterior; g right first antenna, dorsal; stage V, fifth pair of legs, h anterior, i posterior; specimens from Gulf of Panama off Punta Mala e — h and the Indian Ocean off Ceylon i

II. Discussion and Conclusions

EBELING (1967), largely on the basis of bathypelagic fishes of the genus *Melamphaes*, concluded that pelagic deep-sea animals in general follow 2 main geographical patterns: one group is associated primarily with equatorial (tropical) water masses and the other with central (subtropical) water masses. He found relatively few circumtropical species. Further, within strongly equatorial species groups, the regions occupied by individual species varied from group to group. For example, 3 essentially circumtropical groups (*typhlops* spp., *suborbitalis* spp., and *spinifer* spp.) show different geographical patterns of species succession. Similar features emerge from GIBBS' (1969) account of the bathy-pelagic fish genus *Stomias*. Phronimid amphipods (SHIH, 1969) do not appear to show 2 main warm water patterns of distribution but species of euphausiids do, at least in the Pacific and Indian Oceans and intervening seas (BRINTON, 1962).

Our results suggest that epiplanktonic warm water copepods have distribution patterns essentially similar to those of bathypelagic fish and euphausiids. Circumglobal warm-water species occur regularly in central (subtropical) waters up to the subtropical convergences, often penetrating deeply into the temperate waters comprising the transition zones. Thus the likelihood of circumglobal gene flow is high for species with a meridionally broad (extensive) warm water distribution and concurs with our noting an absence from such species of appreciable morphological variation between oceans. In contrast, epiplanktonic copepods occurring mostly in the lower equatorial latitudes, i.e. with northern and southern limits falling roughly between the 20th and 30th parallels, tend to show regional provincialisms. Moreover, geographical patterns of species succession within a species group appear to be more similar among the copepods than among bathypelagic fish, although this may reflect a more restricted depth range represented by the copepod groups discussed above. Thus the tropical (equatorial) copepods tend to be restricted to either 1) the Atlantic Ocean, 2) the Indian Ocean and western portion, or more, of the Pacific Ocean, or 3) the eastern tropical (equatorial) Pacific Ocean. The existence of oceanic species of copepods apparently restricted in distribution to the eastern tropical Pacific is in accord with similar endemics in other pelagic organisms, e.g. melamphaid fishes (EBELING, 1962) and euphausiids (BRINTON, 1962).

The distributions noted among the 5 calanoid genera suggest 2 generalities of biogeographical significance to the epiplankton of the Indian Ocean:

a) warm water species that breed regularly up to mid-latitudes tend to be circumglobal in distribution and probably maintain gene flow around South Africa;

b) warm water species that breed regularly only in low latitudes are provincial and may have one or more tropical cognates elsewhere in the other oceans.

4.12

Distribution and Abundance of Planktonic Amphipods in the Indian Ocean

K. K. C. NAIR, P. G. JACOB, and S. KUMARAN

This report is to our knowledge the first to describe the quantitative and qualitative distribution of amphipods in the Indian Ocean, with special emphasis on the dominance of various families within the sub-order. Detailed studies at the species level are in progress.

I. Material and Methods

The data presented here arise from the basic sorting and subsorting of the IIOE samples carried out at the Indian Ocean Biological Centre (IOBC). Out of 1927 samples processed (IOBC Handbook 1, 1969), only 1548 standard samples have been taken into account in preparing the figures.

The year is divided into 2 periods: April 16–October 15 SW monsoon and October

Table 1. Composition of pelagic amphipods in the IIOE collections, total number of specimens, percentage and number of stations

Suborder *Hyperiidea*	No. of specimens	Percentage	No. of stations
Family			
Hyperiidae	56 426	45.18	1 589
Anchylomeridae	19 897	15.93	1 306
Pronoidae and Lycaeidae	13 514	10.89	1 227
Platyscelidae and Parascelidae	9 640	7.71	1 083
Phronimidae	8 593	6.88	880
Vibiliidae	3 920	3.14	598
Oxycephalidae	2 853	2.28	555
Lycaeopsidae	2 762	2.21	485
Scinidae	2 101	1.69	541
Paraphronimidae	1 012	0.81	194
Lanceolidae	36	0.03	15
Mimonectidae	28	0.02	14
Dairellidae	2	0.002	2
Suborder Gammaroidea	4 116	3.30	514

16–April 15 NE monsoon. In the preparation of the figures, the data from each Marsden 5° square have been averaged. Blank squares indicate that no samples were collected from that area. A table shows the percentage composition of the catches (Table 1) and the figures give latitudinal and longitudinal variations (Figs. 6–9), both standard and nonstandard collections being taken into consideration.

II. Results

Amphipods were few in the southern central Indian Ocean and central Arabian Sea (Fig. 5). Fair numbers were noted in the east and west of the southern Indian Ocean, which can be compared with the equatorial area. The Somali and Arabian coasts showed average to good density, comparable to that of the Bay of Bengal where a high concentration was noted towards the northern part of the Bay. The highest concentration was recorded in the northern part of the Arabian Sea.

In order to study the seasonal fluctuation and vertical migration of these animals, we made a seasonal analysis of the data.

1. April 16 to October 15

Day collections (Fig. 1) show a general north-to-south decrease in abundance. Low values were noted in the southern central Indian Ocean and central Arabian Sea. Relatively few amphipods were found at the eastern and western sides of the Indian Ocean, with

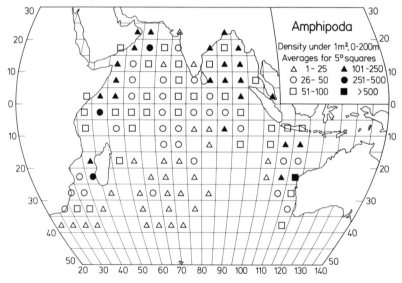

Fig. 1. Distribution of pelagic amphipods in the Indian Ocean during the period from April 16 to October 15 (day collections)

areas of comparative abundance along the Somali coast, off and around the Andamans. Patchy areas of high concentration were recorded along the SW coast of Madagascar, towards the west of the equatorial area, and off Saudi Arabia. Maximum abundance was towards the northern part of the west coast of Australia.

Night collections (Fig. 2) show greater abundance in most of the samples than day collections. This may be due to vertical migration, which is quite common among hyperiid amphipods. Fairly high values are noted from the Somali coast, the northern part of the Bay of Bengal, south of the Andamans and off the south coast of Java.

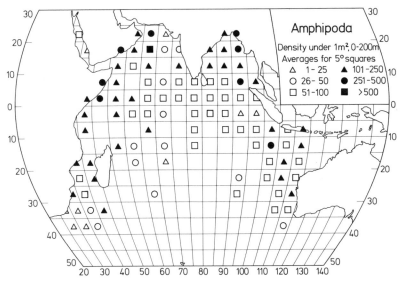

Fig. 2. Distribution of pelagic amphipods in the Indian Ocean during the period from April 16 to October 15 (night collections)

2. October 16 to April 15

Day samples (Fig. 3) show in general that in the south central Indian Ocean, central Arabian Sea and southern Bay of Bengal values are minimal, as in the SW monsoon period. Average to good density values were seen to the east and west of the southern Indian

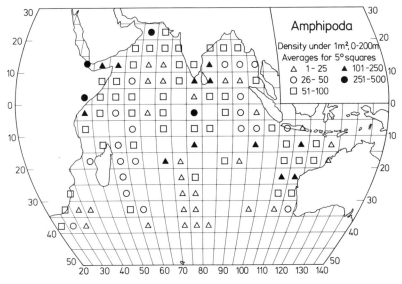

Fig. 3. Distribution of pelagic amphipods in the Indian Ocean during the period from October 16 to April 15 (day collections)

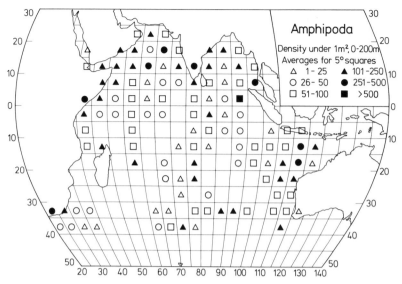

Fig. 4. Distribution of pelagic amphipods in the Indian Ocean during the period from October 16 to April 15 (night collections)

Ocean, Somali coast, and the west and east coasts of India. Patchy areas of high concentration were noted in the central part of the equatorial area, south of the Somali coast, in the Gulf of Aden and the north Arabian Sea.

Values for night samples (Fig. 4) were higher than for day samples. Areas of high concentration were recorded in the Andaman Sea, Arabian Sea, off the Somali coast, Agulhas Bank and to the south of Java. The maximum abundance was found off the west coast of Sumatra.

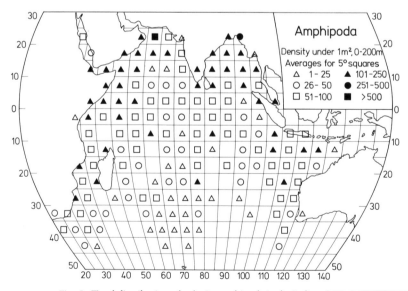

Fig. 5. Total distribution of pelagic amphipods in the Indian Ocean

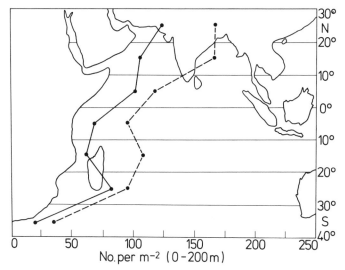

Fig. 6. Day and night variations in the distribution of pelagic amphipods under 1 m² (200−0 m) in each 10° zone of latitude for the period April 16−October 15 (solid line: day, dotted line: night)

In general, the numerical abundance of amphipods is higher in areas of upwelling, off South Africa (pronounced, especially during the southern summer), the Somali coast, South Arabia, the west coast of India, the head of the Bay of Bengal, the Andaman coast, and the east coast of India (maximum during the SW monsoon). In the equatorial zone there are moderately high peaks in patches of abundance throughout the year. Low-density areas were noted round the year in the south central Indian Ocean, in the central Arabian Sea and in scattered areas.

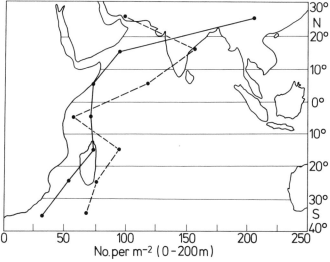

Fig. 7. Day and night variations in the distribution of pelagic amphipods under 1 m² (200−0 m) in each 10° zone of latitude for the period October 16−April 15 (solid line: day, dotted line: night)

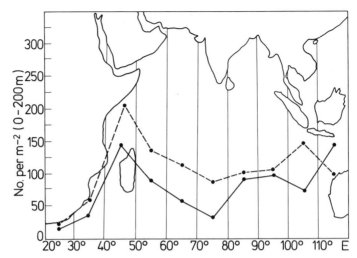

Fig. 8. Day and night variations in the distribution of pelagic amphipods under 1 m² (200−0 m) in each 10° zone of longitude for the period April 16−October 15 (solid line: day, dotted line: night)

Latitudinal variation (Figs. 6 and 7) shows a general decrease in numbers of amphipods from north to south in both seasons reaching a minimum in the belt from 30° to 40°S. Likewise, the number of families and species also decreases from north to south. The highest peaks for both seasons occur along the belt between 20° and 30°N, due to the high values found in the northern part of the Arabian Sea and the Bay of Bengal. In general, night values were much higher compared to day except in areas within 20−30°N and 0−10°S (Fig. 7). The high day values for the former area were

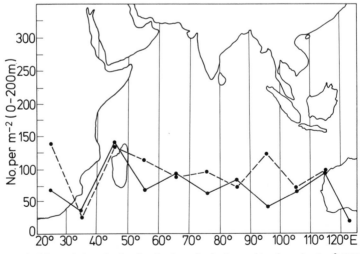

Fig. 9. Day and night variations in the distribution of pelagic amphipods under 1 m² (200−0 m) in each 10° zone of longitude for the period October 16−April 15 (solid line: day, dotted line: night)

contributed by 2 collections which sampled through a dense patch of amphipods, while for the latter area night samples were generally lower.

Longitudinal variations show their highest peak between $40° - 50°$ E for both seasons (Figs. 8 and 9). Other peaks occur between $90° - 100°$ E (Fig. 9) and $110° - 120°$ E (Fig. 8) and are due to the areas of upwelling off the Somali coast, and rich areas in the Bay of Bengal and off south of Java. During the southern summer, minimum values are noted between $20°$ and $30°$ E for both day and night, while the same area shows fairly high values during the southern winter (Fig. 9), the low-density areas being shifted to $30° - 40°$ E. These 2 areas are under the dominance of the Agulhas Current and the changes may be related to seasonal displacement of the areas of upwelling in this area. Night values were slightly lower than day values (Fig. 9) between $30° - 40°$ E, $40° - 50°$ E, $60° - 70°$ E and $80° - 90°$ E; this may be due to chance.

Table 1 shows the percentage composition by families represented in the catches and the number of stations from which they were collected. The family *Hyperiidae* contributed the most individuals and *Dairellidae* the least, being recorded from only 2 stations at $17° 30'$ N, $68° 00'$ E (central Arabia Sea) and $06° 51'$ N, $75° 02'$ E (to the southwest of Cape Comorin). The family comprises only one genus of 2 species and of these only *Dairella latissima* had been recorded from the Indian Ocean (BARNARD, 1937).

III. Discussion

The total data, irrespective of seasons and times of collection, show a higher concentration of pelagic amphipods towards the northern part of the Indian Ocean, especially in areas enriched by upwelling and land drainage, or regions adjacent to them. Pelagic amphipods were thought to be more abundant in high latitudes (BOWMAN, 1960) but our data indicate high concentrations towards the tropical and sub-tropical regions as well, associated with highly productive waters.

The overall picture of distribution and abundance of pelagic amphipods (Fig. 5) on the scale of the IOBC maps (1970 a, b) closely resembles that of copepods and fish larvae with minor variations here and there. Amphipods are abundant (> 501) in the northern part of the Arabian Sea, whereas the copepod maxima extend south to the Gulf of Aden and along the Somali coast. The high values of copepods over a wide area may be due to their varied feeding habits. Fairly high concentrations of amphipods noted towards the northern part of the Bay of Bengal also coincide with the great abundance of copepods and decapod larvae. Areas of minimum concentration of copepods also show low values of amphipods.

A comparison of amphipod distribution in relation to zooplankton biomass distribution (IOBC, 1968 a, b), in the Indian Ocean for the whole year reveals that the peaks of both are located towards the northern part of the Arabian Sea and head of the Bay of Bengal. However, at the station level no clear correlation was found between the areas of high primary production and the areas of abundance of amphipods (see maps on the inside of the front and back cover).

Studies of the gut content of members of the family *Phronimidae* show that they are omnivorous (SHIH, 1969). This is probably true for other hyperiid amphipods as well. Young hyperiids generally occur towards the surface, probably due to the abundance of food in the surface layers. Vertical migrations are known in hyperiid amphipods (SHIH,

1969). The greater abundance of amphipods in night hauls in the upper 200 m layer may well be due to diurnal vertical migration.

Formation of swarms is also noted among pelagic amphipods. During an oceanographic cruise of "Blue Fin" (April, 1970) a swarm of hyperiid amphipods mostly constituted by a single genus, *Hyperia* (family *Hyperiidae*) was observed extending for more than 20 miles along the coast of Kerala; flying fishes in large numbers were seen feeding on them.

4.13

The Distribution of Indian Ocean Euphausiids

E. BRINTON and K. GOPALAKRISHNAN

The present account includes charts of the distribution of 26 of approximately 36 species of Euphausiacea considered to have been representatively sampled during the IIOE. For the most part, these are the species occupying the upper strata of the sea. Inasmuch as the Indian Ocean Standard Net (IOSN) typically fished from a depth of 200 meters to the surface, the species best represented in the samples are those having a) young stages which regularly live above 200 m depth and b) adults which occupy nearsurface waters at least during the night. Mention will be made of the more irregularly sampled species, but plotting of their distributions will await completion of analysis of the full complement of samples.

Charts are not included here of several of the widely ranging species – those which appear throughout most of the tropical and subtropical waters of the Indian Ocean. This presentation emphasizes the species ranges which are bounded within the ocean, and is intended to illustrate what appear to be faunistic areas. Most of these distributions will be nonquantitative, though for 6 of the species estimates of abundance are given. Details of the quantitative aspects of distribution, including the occurrences in space and time of the many developmental stages, will be provided in a more definitive IIOE euphausiid atlas.

In order that some general features of seasonality may be considered, distributions are plotted for 2 time periods, May – September (corresponding to the SW monsoon in the northern half of the ocean) and November – March (corresponding to the NE monsoon period). Data within a season, but for the several years of the expedition, are plotted together.

More detailed consideration of seasonal change in distributions is probably not yet justified for the ocean as a whole, in view of the limited temporal-geographical coverage presented by even this extensive collection of samples. Time series are available from waters east of South Africa, and west of Australia along 110° E. *Thysanopoda* euphausiids sampled by the Isaacs-Kidd Midwater Trawl during the 6 cruises along 110° E, 1962 – 63, have been the subject of an ecological study by ROGER (1966). Study of the IOSN samples from the same cruises and from the South African cruises is not yet complete.

I. Material and Methods

The material upon which these charts are based was obtained by 16 of the vessels participating in IIOE.

The bulk of the samples are classified as standard. That is, they were obtained using a net of 1 m² mouth opening and 0.33 mm mesh width (CURRIE, 1963; UNESCO, 1968) hauled vertically from a depth of approximately 200 m. Though 0° wire-angle was rarely attained, we assume, here, that a volume of approximately 200 m³ of water was strained by the net. Errors in estimated abundance introduced by this assumption are considered small in relation to the abundance intervals plotted, which differ by factors of 10.

The collection procedure appears to have been well suited for sampling euphausiids. For most species, the full range of postnaupliar developmental stages is captured by the IOSN. The smaller calyptopises (< 2 mm length) and the larger adults (> 15 mm length) are undoubtedly underestimated, as are the vertically-migrating forms in the daytime collections, but we have felt justified in applying only a general correction. A comparison

Table 1. Samples used in May 7 — September 28 charts

Vessel	Cruise	Stations
"Anton Bruun"	2	106 — 144
	3	145 — 160
	4A	161 — 164
	6	328 — 355
	7	358 — 389
"Argo"	Dodo	25 — 84
	Lusiad	1 — 96
"Diamantina"	2/62	46 — 104
	3/62	104 — 125[a]
	3/63	90 — 122
"Discovery"	1	5 002 — 5 094
	3	5 380 — 5 573
"Kistna"	11	256 — 258
	13	292 — 314
	14	317 — 351
	15	353 — 378
	16	383 — 410
	17	427 — 443
	19	511 — 522
	20	526 — 539
"Natal"	4	58 — 94
"Pioneer"	442	7 — 43[b]
"Varuna"	30	1 769 — 1 793
	31	1 797 — 1 814
"Vitiaz"	35	5 184 — 5 216, 5 222, 5 229, 5 231

[a] (Stations 110 — 125, September 29 — October 5)
[b] (Stations 7 — 14, April 17 — May 6)

of day versus night catches of total euphausiids led us to conclude that night estimates are 50% higher than day estimates on the average (Gopalakrishnan and Brinton, 1969). In the quantitative distributions included here, abundances at stations occupied in the daytime are increased by 50%. Counts include all developmental stages sampled.

The list of plankton samples is contained in a handbook to the international collection (Indian Ocean Biological Centre, 1969). This list provides the station data (locality, time, depth), together with the displacement volumes and the fraction of each sample that was sorted into its constituent major taxa. The sorting procedure is described by Hansen (1966).

Of the 1927 samples processed at IOBC, 1231 have been examined in the preparation of this report. Six hundred and eleven were used for the May—September charts (Table 1), and 620 for the November—March charts (Table 2). In some instances where a significant

Table 2. Samples used in November 1—March 31 charts

Vessel	Cruise	Stations
"Anton Bruun"	A	1— 13
	1	14— 55[a]
	4 A	172— 200[b]
	5	282— 327[c]
	8	395— 420[d]
"Argo"	Monsoon	13— 24
"Diamantina"	1/64	31— 61
"Discovery"	3	5 265— 5 355[e]
"Gascoyne"	1/63	1— 34
"Kagoshima Maru"	3	1— 32
"Kistna"	4	102— 123
	7	187— 194
	21	541— 566
	22	570— 612
	25	652— 667
"Koyo Maru"	14	17— 23
	16	2— 20
"Meteor"	1	49— 229
"Natal"	6	142— 178
"Oshoro Maru"	1	1— 34, 49—50
	7	1— 13
	11	1— 23
"Patanela"		4— 56
"Umitaka Maru"	24	6 301— 6 328
"Varuna"	104	2 009— 2 014
"Vitiaz"	31	4 641— 4 642
	33	4 883— 4 905
	35	5 279— 5 289
	36	5 313— 5 369[f]
"Zulfiquar"	Zulun	1— 22

[a] (Stations 43—55, April 1—8)
[b] (Stations 172—188, October, 15—31)
[c] (Stations 308—327, April, 3—15)
[d] (Stations 395—415, September, 26—October, 31)
[e] (Stations 5 310—5 355, April, 1—25)
[f] (Stations 5 304—5 306, October, 24—28)

geographical area was sampled only during an "inter-monsoon period", October or April, those samples have nevertheless been incorporated into one or the other of the seasonal pictures. For example, the eastern half of the Bay of Bengal was sampled by "Anton Bruun" only very late in the NE monsoon period, March 19—April 8. However,

data collected up until April 8 are included in the November — March chart. The several
instances in which we have used samples from inter-monsoon periods are designated by
indices in Tables 1 and 2.

A number of non-standard samples were included for the same reason — to fill
geographical gaps. In cases where depth-of-haul was standard but a different net was
used, useful estimates of abundance may still be made. Where sampling was by means of
surface tow only (i.e., "Patanela"), useful qualitative information has been deduced.

The following non-standard material, not part of the international collections, has
also been used: "Argo" Monsoon Expedition, stations 7 — 24 (Snyder and Fleminger,
1965) (Station 7: 9° 12′ N, 127° 34′ E, and station 8: 7° 47′ N, 121° 17′ E in the Timor
and Banda Seas are included together with the Indian Ocean stations); Baker's 1965 data
for *Euphausia* species caught along 90° E by "Discovery II", 1950 — 51 (a region not well
sampled by IIOE); "Anton Bruun" Isaacs-Kidd midwater trawl samples from all stations,
cruises 3 and 6. The latter samples, processed at the Smithsonian Institution's Oceanographic Sorting Center (SOSC), proved of use in determining presence or absence of
species at a number of relatively barren localities where the standard samples were
particularly sparse in euphausiids. In our continuing study, fuller use is being made of
these samples and of the rest of the large "Anton Bruun" collection processed at SOSC,
particularly in the study of bathymetric distribution.

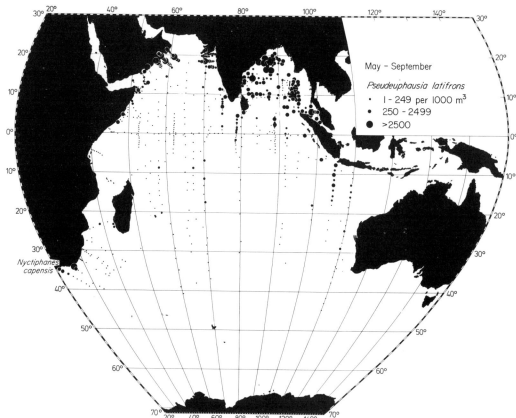

Fig. 1 a. *Pseudeuphausia latifrons* and *Nyctiphanes capensis* distribution, May — September

II. Results

1. The Distribution of Euphausiids

Pseudeuphausia latifrons is an abundant coastal species in the northern part of the Indian Ocean. During May – September (Fig. 1a) high densities were commonest off the coast of Arabia, both coasts of India, and in the Andaman Sea. This is the only euphausiid

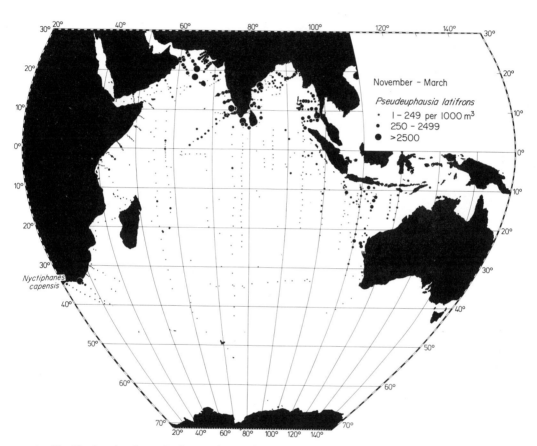

Fig. 1 b. *Pseudeuphausia latifrons* and *Nyctiphanes capensis* distribution, November – March

occurring in the shallow Strait of Malacca (WICKSTEAD, 1961), where it was sampled during cruise 19 of "Kistna". Evidently this neritic waterway is not an inter-ocean path for other euphausiid species (BRINTON, 1963).

Moderate densities of *P. latifrons* were found close to shore in the Somali Current during the SW monsoon, but only scattered individuals occured there, and more offshore, during November – March (Fig. 1b). Similarly, this species was not abundant off Arabia or in the northern part of the Bay of Bengal during November – March, as compared with May – September.

Weigmann (1971) describes a geographical variant of *P. latifrons* living in the Persian Gulf, and points out that *Pseudeuphausia colosii* Torelli, 1934, described from the Red Sea, and recorded there by Ponomareva (1968), is synonymous with *P. latifrons* G. O. Sars (1883).

Essentially a neritic euphausiid, *P. latifrons* was nevertheless caught sporadically

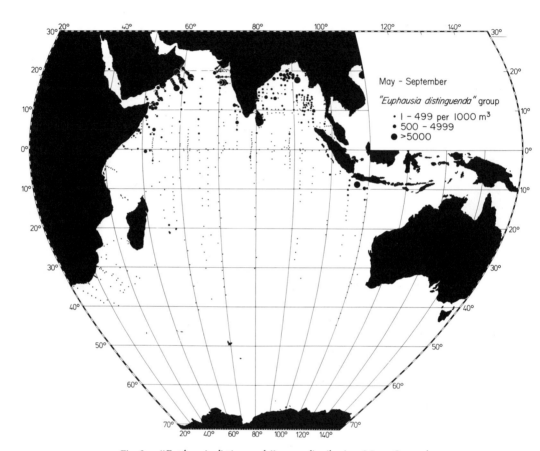

Fig. 2a. "*Euphausia distinguenda*" group distribution, May – September

throughout the oceanic part of the tropical zone, but usually near islands (Fig. 1a, Seychelles and Chagos Archipelagos; Fig. 1b, Tromelin Island, Nazareth Bank, Chagos Archipelago). Occurrences south of Java and to the north and west of Australia appear to be typical parts of the distribution, adjacent to the extensive neritic waters of the Sunda shelf and Arafura Sea.

A second Indian Ocean euphausiid with neritic affinities, *Nyctiphanes capensis,* has a limited range off South Africa (Fig. 1a, b).

Euphausia distinguenda Hansen, *sensu strictu,* is known from the eastern tropical Pacific (Hansen, 1911; Brinton, 1962). A sibling species, *E. sibogae* Hansen occurs in the Philippine – Celebes region, but not in the South China Sea, Gulf of Thailand, or

Java Sea. As has been pointed out (SEBASTIAN, 1966; JONES, personal communication) the form in the northern Indian Ocean more nearly resembles *E. sibogae* than *E. distinguenda,* though it has heretofore been reported only under the latter name (e.g., TATTERSALL, 1939; BRINTON, 1962; WEIGMANN, 1970). Until the taxonomy within this complex is better understood, we shall refer to the Indian Ocean populations as the *E.*

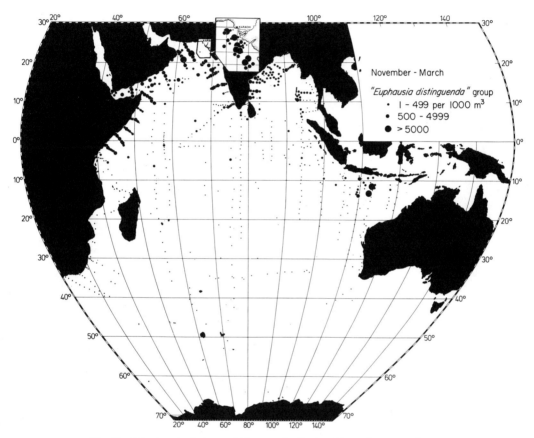

Fig. 2b. "*Euphausia distinguenda*" group distribution, November – March

distinguenda group. We are not at present clear as to the relationship of the population south of Java (Fig. 2a, b) to either *E. sibogae* or *E. distinguenda* to the north. This is not a neritic species, though it is evidently dependent upon coastal processes. The Bay of Bengal and south Java populations of *E. distinguenda* are more clearly disjunct than comparable populations of the neritic *P. latifrons* which merge along both coasts of Sumatra.

The May – September distribution of *E. distinguenda* (Fig. 2a) closely resembles that of *P. latifrons* (Fig. 1a), particularly off Somalia and Arabia. However, while *P. latifrons* was sparse in these regions during November – March (Fig. 1b), *E. distinguenda* was then common as far south as 5°S off Africa. Neither species showed seasonality in the Andaman Sea region.

Euphausia diomediae (Fig. 3a, b) is a third characteristic species of the northern part of the ocean. It is more typically oceanic, ranging along the full extent of the tropical belts of the Pacific and Indian Oceans. It nevertheless achieves abundance in the fertile Somalia and Arabian regions, and occasionally in the Bay of Bengal. Occurrences of this species

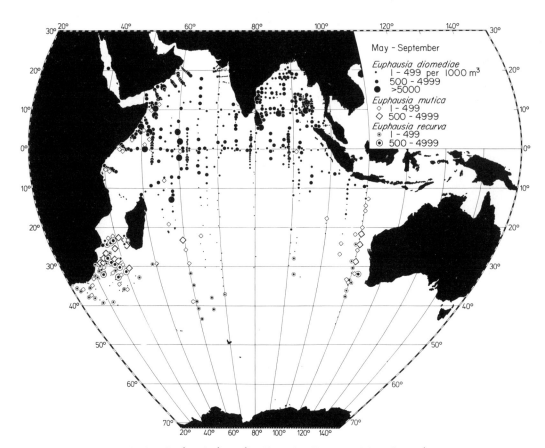

Fig. 3a. *Euphausia diomediae, E. mutica, E. recurva,* May—September

taper off to the south of 10°S, but there were 6 records in the Natal Basin during May—September.

Toward the south, *E. diomediae* tends to be replaced by *Euphausia brevis* at 0°−10°S (Fig. 4a, b). *Euphausia mutica* appears in the zone of 10°−20°S (Fig. 3a, b), and *Euphausia recurva* in the zone of 25°−40°S. Subantarctic *Euphausia* species (e.g., *E. spinifera, E. lucens*) were not well represented in the IIOE collections, occurring to the south of 35°−40°S.

Ranges of species of the genus *Nematoscelis* are comparable to the ranges of *Euphausia* species, just discussed. *Nematoscelis gracilis* (Fig. 5a, b), like *E. diomediae*, is a northern species in this ocean. However, as in the Pacific (BRINTON, 1962), *N. gracilis* has a relatively broader range than *E. diomediae*, extending southward to 20°S in midocean and to 30°S along the eastern margin. It is the predominant *Nematoscelis* species in the Arabian Sea and Bay of Bengal.

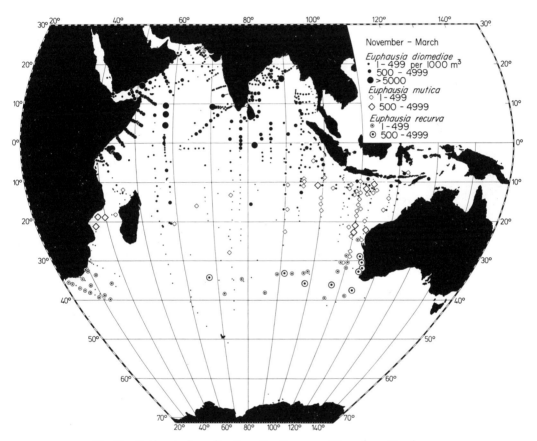

Fig. 3b. *Euphausia diomediae, E. mutica, E. recurva,* November — March

Nematoscelis atlantica (Fig. 5a, b) is typical of the zone of 10° — ca. 34°S, although there were no records in midocean, 10° — 20°S, during November — March.

Nematoscelis microps and *N. tenella* occur together throughout the tropical-sub-tropical oceanic regimes (Fig. 6a, b). Both penetrate the Arabian Sea and the Bay of Bengal at their western and eastern sides, respectively. Whereas *N. tenella* provides most of the Arabian Sea records, *N. microps* provides the bulk in the Bay of Bengal and Andaman Sea. Both species were lacking in the coastal waters of India and Pakistan. The southernmost species in the genus, *N. megalops,* was sparsely sampled. Most occurrences were in the zone of 35° – 40° S during both seasons.

All of the 11 recognized species of *Stylocheiron* were found in the Indian Ocean. *Stylocheiron indicum* Silas and Matthews (1967) is evidently endemic to the Arabian Sea – Bay of Bengal region, *S. microphthalma* is equatorial, as in the Pacific, while *S. suhmi* lives mainly between 10° S and 30° S (Fig. 7 a, b).

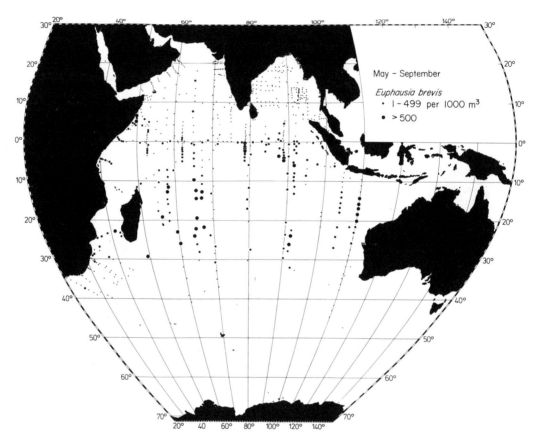

Fig. 4 a. *Euphausia brevis,* May – September

Stylocheiron insulare Hansen (1910) appeared at 4 "Anton Bruun" localities in the Andaman Sea and at one "Vitiaz" locality south of Java. These are the only Indian Ocean records for this species. Curiously, it did not appear in the "Kistna" cruise 14 samples from the Andaman Sea. The entire known range of *S. insulare* is shown in Fig. 12. Year-round sampling in the Gulf of Thailand – South China Sea region by Naga expedition (Brinton and Watanaprida, 1963) and the Strait of Malacca (Wickstead, 1961) did not yield this species. This supports the possibility that *S. insulare* is actually restricted to the regions illustrated.

Of the 7 *Stylocheiron* species not mapped in this paper, 6 have broad ranges, extending across the tropical and subtropical zones of all oceans (MAUCHLINE and FISHER, 1969). These include *S. longicorne* (bounded on the north by closely-related *S. indicum* in the Indian Ocean), *S. affine*, and *S. carinatum* (both occur from 35°S to the northern limit of the Indian Ocean), *S. abbreviatum* (lacking only in the Arabian Sea and Bay of Bengal),

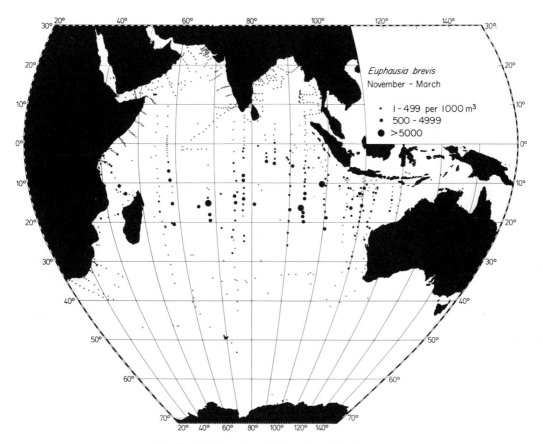

Fig. 4b. *Euphausia brevis*, November — March

and the typically mesopelagic species, *S. maximum* and *S. elongatum*. The seventh species, *S. robustum*, was caught at 5 localities, all within the zone 19°S – 30°S.

Three of the 4 species comprising the "*Euphausia gibba*" group occur in the Indian Ocean. The fourth, *E. gibba*, is restricted to the central South Pacific. *E. hemigibba*, known from both the Atlantic and North Pacific, lives in the southern Indian Ocean, 10° – 40°S (Fig. 8a, b), the zone comparable to that occupied by *E. gibba* in the Pacific. There are records of *E. hemigibba* to the north of 10°S only at the western edge of the Indian Ocean, but during both seasons.

In the equatorial belt *Euphausia paragibba* is the predominant species of this group. During May—September the axis of its distribution lay along the Equator, and there were records northward to Arabia and southward to Natal. During November—March *E. paragibba* was found north of the Equator only to the west of 60° E.

E. pseudogibba occurs in the zone 0°—10° N, ranging somewhat farther to the north in the Andaman Sea. This species is rare in the western half of the ocean. November—

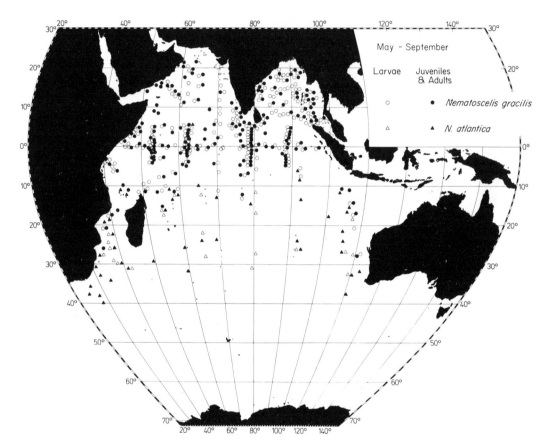

Fig. 5 a. *Nematoscelis gracilis, N. atlantica,* May—September

March records south of Java (Fig. 8 b) suggest that the Indian Ocean populations of *E. pseudogibba* may communicate with those occupying the deep waters of the East Indian Archipelago to the east. Such communication is probably via the Timor Sea, inasmuch as *E. pseudogibba* is known from the Flores and Molucca Sea, but not the Java Sea or the Sunda shelf (HANSEN, 1910; BRINTON, 1962).

The ranges of 2 *Thysanopoda* species, *T. aequalis* and *T. subaequalis* show parallels to those of the *E. gibba* group just discussed. The *aequalis—subaequalis* composite range extends from near 35° S northward to the southern limits of the Arabian Sea and the Bay of Bengal (Fig. 9a, b). Again, more northward occurrences are near the Andaman Islands, though some immature individuals were found on the Indian coast. *T. aequalis* lives mainly in the 0° − 10° N zone, to which *Euphausia pseudogibba* was seen also to be restricted, save for the records south of Java. *T. subaequalis* is found from the Equator southward, occupying the combined ranges of *Euphausia paragibba* and *E. hemigibba*.

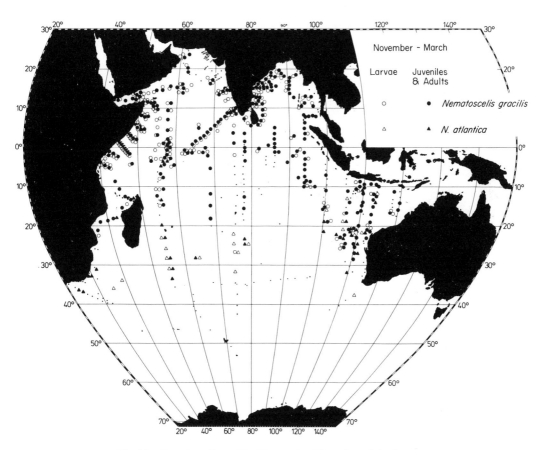

Fig. 5b. *Nematoscelis gracilis, N. atlantica,* November − March

A species of the *Euphausia gibboides* group living in the western part of the Indian Ocean is now recognized as *Euphausia sanzoi* Torelli (1934) (Brinton, 1962; Ponomareva, 1969; Weigmann, 1970). The IIOE collections show *E. sanzoi* to occur along the full latitudinal extent of the western side of the Indian Ocean, 25° N − 30° S (Fig. 10a, b). Even where *E. sanzoi* was consistently caught (off Kenya, Pakistan), there were few specimens per sample. The sampling was evidently inadequate for describing more than the gross aspect of the range of this species.

A second species of the *E. gibboides* group, *Euphausia fallax*, is known from the western Pacific: the Philippines, the South China Sea and waters east of Australia (HANSEN, 1916; BRINTON, 1962). This distribution is included in Fig. 10 b.

What may prove to be another species of the *E. gibboides* group occurs in the Andaman Sea. Records from cruise 14 of "Kistna" (September, 1963) and Cruise 1 of "Anton Bruun" (March, 1963) place consistent limits on its distribution, excepting a

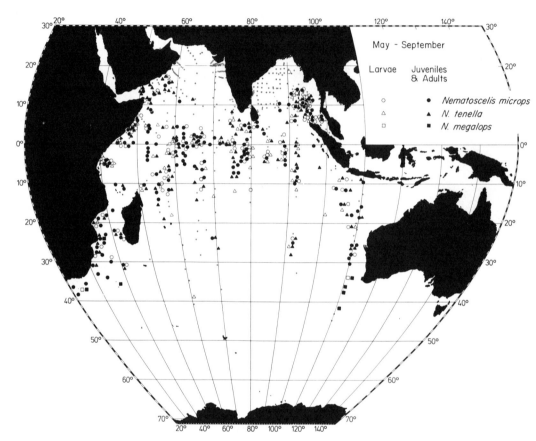

Fig. 6 a. *Nematoscelis microps, N. tenella, N. megalops,* May — September

specimen found off the tip of India (Fig. 10 a, b). As yet, this population is known only on the basis of larvae, but in densities up to 120 specimens per sample. Presumably, the juveniles and adults live deeper than 200 m. The larvae show morphometric differences from larvae of the other 3 species of the *E. gibboides* group, though they appear to belong to this group (KNIGHT, in prep.).

A juvenile specimen found south of Java in January, 1963, and a larval specimen found there in September, 1962, are more similar to *E. sanzoi* and *E. fallax* than to the Andaman Sea form.

The distribution of *Euphausia similis* is anomalous (Fig. 11). Known chiefly as a circumglobal subantarctic species (JOHN, 1936) and as whale food off southern Japan (NEMOTO, 1959) *E. similis* would be an unlikely resident of the tropics. Its occurrence in the East Indian Archipelago was reported by HANSEN (1910, 1916), the South China Sea by BRINTON (1962), and the Indian Ocean, 9° N–9° S, by TATTERSALL (1912, 1939), ILLIG (1930), and WEIGMANN (1970).

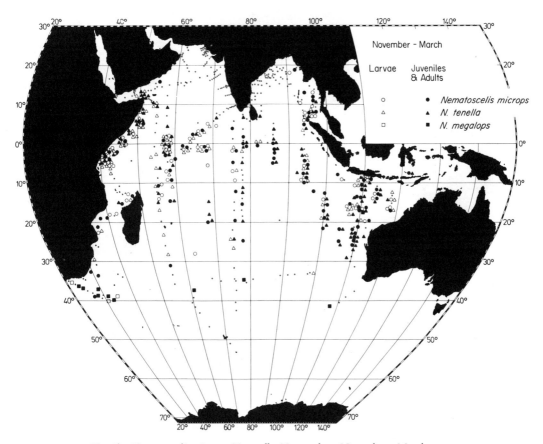

Fig. 6b. *Nematoscelis microps, N. tenella, N. megalops,* November – March

Though *E. similis* is not known to live in the Pacific except for the nearshore records shown in Fig. 11 (and the subantarctic zone), the IIOE material confirms that its range extends across much of the Indian Ocean, excepting the Arabian Sea and the Bay of Bengal. It lives primarily in the zones 0° – 10° S and 28° – 50° S. Evidence that this species is virtually lacking between 10° S and 28° S is provided by the midwater trawl collections of "Anton Bruun" cruises 3 and 6, along the 60° E and 65° E meridians respectively. Along both transects, *E. similis* was present in the trawl samples only to the north of 9° 58′ S and to the south of 28° 30′ S. In midocean a single juvenile was caught at 16° S, 81° E on the "Argo" Monsoon Expedition.

Both the tropical and southern populations of *E. similis* are breeding populations. Larvae were present in the tropical zone throughout the year; gravid, spermatophore-bearing females were observed in September, October, December, and January, — all

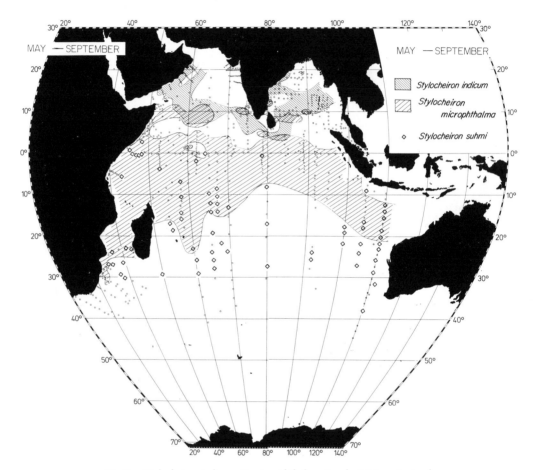

Fig. 7a. *Stylocheiron indicum, S. microphthalma, S. suhmi,* May — September

between the Equator and 5° S. Larvae were observed in the southern zone during June, September, and December.

As yet, we have no evidence that the tropical population lives deeper than that to the south. Of 33 samples of *E. similis* from standard 0 — 200 m collections made at night withing the tropical zone, 16 contained adults and 12 more contained juveniles. (Daytime records were all of larvae.)

Variety *armata* of *E. similis* was found only in the subantarctic zone (Fig. 11), together, however, with the typical *E. similis*.

14 additional euphausiid species occurred in the IIOE collections:

Euphausia tenera ranges from 15°N to 25°S in midocean, and southward to near 30°S off Africa. This is a regularly occurring, abundant species.

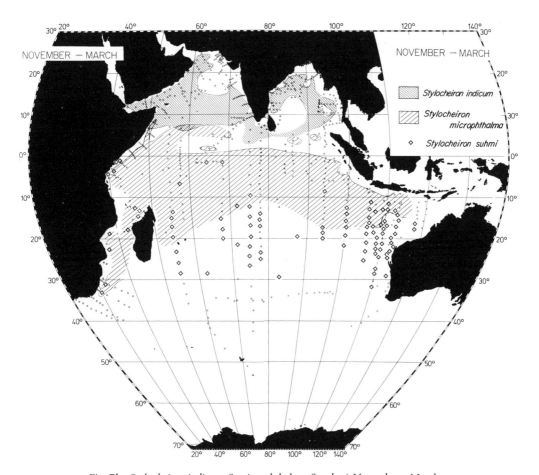

Fig. 7b. *Stylocheiron indicum, S. microphthalma, S. suhmi,* November – March

Nematobrachion flexipes lives from 15°N to 45°S, but is sparse and irregular in occurrence.

Nematobrachion sexspinosum is rare (only 11 records), occupying the zone 0° – 30°S, with one record at 4°N, 65°E.

Thysanopoda tricuspidata and *Thysanopoda monacantha* have similar distributions, ca. 10°N to 25°S. Both range to at least 30°S near Africa. Larvae of both species occurred regularly in the IOSN samples. *T. tricuspidata* was present in 509 of the 1231 samples examined, but adults of this species were present in only 46 samples. *T. monacantha* was present in 441 samples, though adults were found in only 32.

Thysanopoda obtusifrons occupies the zone of 0° − 30° S. The scattered records are based mainly on larval specimens.

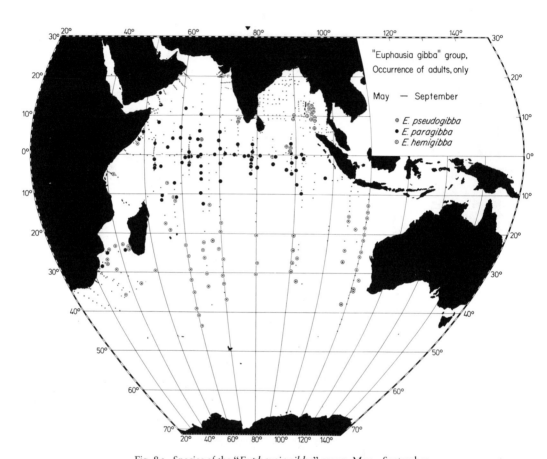

Fig. 8 a. Species of the "*Euphausia gibba*" group, May − September

The following are relatively deep-living species, the north-south ranges of which are based on the midwater trawl sampling by "Anton Bruun" along 60° E and 65° E:

Thysanopoda pectinata, 10° N − 41° S;
Thysanopoda orientalis (possibly including *T. microphthalma*) 10° N − 45° S;
Thysanopoda cristata, 0° − 30° S;
Thysanopoda spinicaudata, only found at 13° 36′ N, 65° 03′ E in the Arabian Sea;
Thysanopoda cornuta, 12° N − 45° S;

Thysanopoda egregia, 3° S — 45° S;
Nematobrachion boopis, 10° N — 45° S.

The genus *Thysanoessa* is represented in the collections mainly by *T. gregaria*. This epipelagic species occupied the east-west zone of 30° S — 41° S, ranging northward to 22° S between Africa and Madagascar.

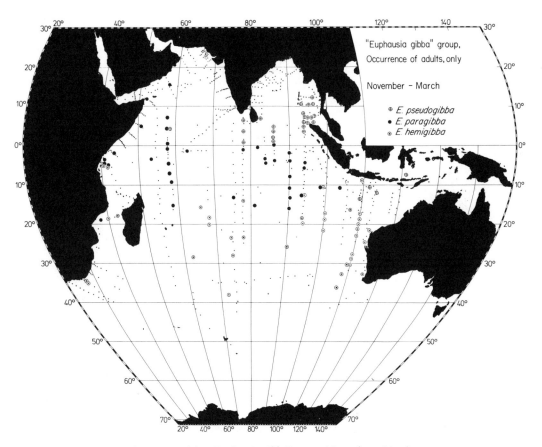

Fig. 8 b. Species of the "*Euphausia gibba*" group, November — March

2. Zoogeographical Groupings

The euphausiid faunistics show zonal characteristics in oceanic regions, and meridional characteristics in the boundary regions. The zonal characteristics appear less subject to seasonal change than the meridional.

a) Zonal Distributions

The zonal characteristics relate primarily to these parallels of latitude: 10° N, 0°, 10° S, 25° — 30° S, and 40° — 45° S.

a) 10° N

This corresponds to the southern part of the region dominated by coastal forms *Pseudeuphausia latifrons* (Fig. 1a, b) and *Euphausia distinguenda* (Fig. 2a, b). This region consists of the Arabian Sea and Bay of Bengal — the tropical, paired semi-enclosed basins peculiar to the Indian Ocean. The abundance there of *P. latifrons* and *E. distin-*

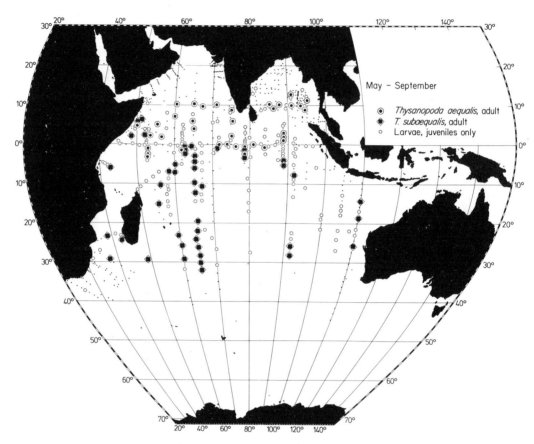

Fig. 9a. *Thysanopoda aequalis, T. subaequalis*, May — September

guenda indicates that these waters are coastal in quality. *Stylocheiron indicum* (Fig. 7a, b) is a third species essentially limited to the northern region, where it replaces *S. longicorne.*

The list of euphausiid species in the Arabian Sea — Bay of Bengal is small, as compared with that in the tropical and subtropical ocean to the south. In addition to the above three species, only the following are important in the north: *Euphausia diomediae* (Fig. 3a, b), *Nematoscelis gracilis* (Fig. 5a, b), *Stylocheiron carinatum* and *Stylocheiron affine.* Of these, *E. diomediae* and *N. gracilis* are also identified with the region of the equatorial water mass in the Pacific (Brinton, 1962; Sverdrup, Johnson, and Fleming, 1942).

That is, they extend over the full breadth of the Pacific, including particularly the eastern equatorial Pacific characterized by high productivity and a strong oxygen minimum above 500 m depth. (The eastern equatorial Pacific is also the habitat of *E. distinguenda*, mentioned in the preceding paragraph). These 2 environmental properties also characterize the Arabian Sea and Bay of Bengal, through which the equatorial ranges of *E.. diomediae* and *N. gracilis* extend.

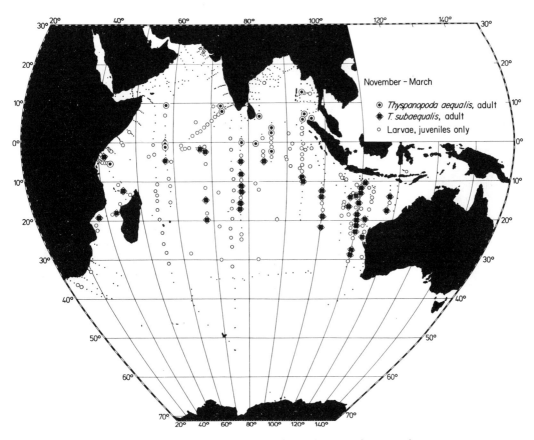

Fig. 9 b. *Thysanopoda aequalis, T. subaequalis,* November – March

A number of tropical-subtropical circumglobal species are bounded on the north in the Indian Ocean by the region of the 10° N parallel – the southern limit of the Arabian Sea – Bay of Bengal. These are:

Euphausia tenera
Thysanopoda monacantha
Thysanopoda tricuspidata
Nematoscelis microps (Fig. 6 a, b)
Nematoscelis tenella (Fig. 6 a, b)

Nematobrachion flexipes
Stylocheiron abbreviatum
Stylocheiron longicorne

All of these species except *Euphausia tenera* are scarce or lacking in both the eastern equatorial Pacific and the Arabian Sea — Bay of Bengal.

The northern limits of the 2 other species restricted to the Pacific and Indian Ocean, *Stylocheiron microphthalma* (Fig. 7a, b) and *Euphausia paragibba* (Fig. 8a, b), are near 10° N but these limits are not distinct. Both species occur regularly only to the

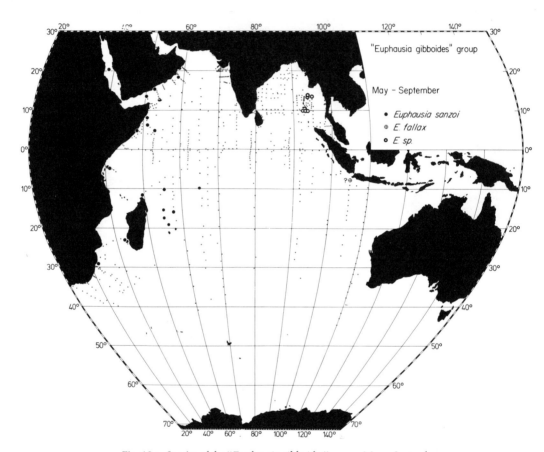

Fig. 10a. Species of the "*Euphausia gibboides*" group, May — September

south of the Equator, 0 — 10° S. During November — March when the North Equatorial Current, 0 — 8° N, is westerly (Taft and Knauss, 1967; Wooster, Schaefer and Robinson, 1967) both species are scarce in that zone. During May — September, when flow north of the Equator reverses, then deriving in part from the north-easterly Somali Current, both *E. paragibba* and *S. microphthalma* are more widespread north of the Equator.

Euphausia pseudogibba (Fig. 8a, b) and *Thysanopoda aequalis* (Fig. 9a, b) occupy the zone of 0−10° N, including the Andaman Sea. Here, both tend to replace more southern cognates, *E. paragibba* and *T. subaequalis*. It may be noted that while *E. pseudogibba* and *T. aequalis* occupy the same habitat in the Indian Ocean, they do not in the Pacific. *E. pseudogibba* more consistently co-occurs with *T. subaequalis* in the Pacific, where *T. aequalis* is a central water mass species (BRINTON, 1962).

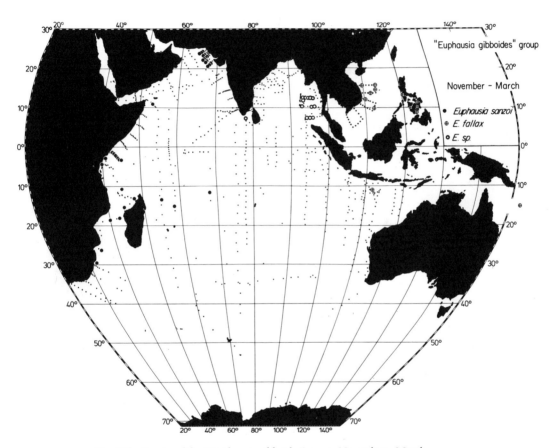

Fig. 10b. Species of the "*Euphausia gibboides*" group, November − March

β) 0°

The Equator, along which the southern edge of the North Equatorial Current lies, is the southern limit of *Thysanopoda aequalis* and *Euphausia paragibba,* just discussed. *Euphausia diomediae* (Fig. 3a, b) tends to taper off in a southerly direction as the Equator is crossed. The Equator is the northern limit of *Euphausia brevis* (Fig. 4, b) and *Thysanopoda subaequalis* (Fig. 9a, b).

E. pseudogibba and *E. paragibba* tend to be separated at the Equator during November—March (Fig. 8b), but co-occur to the north of it during May—September (Fig. 8a) when the north equatorial flow is easterly.

Records for *Euphausia similis* also taper off sharply to the north of the Equator (Fig. 11).

γ) 10° S

This is the southern edge of the easterly Equatorial Countercurrent during November—March (NE monsoon). During May—September the northern edge of the westerly

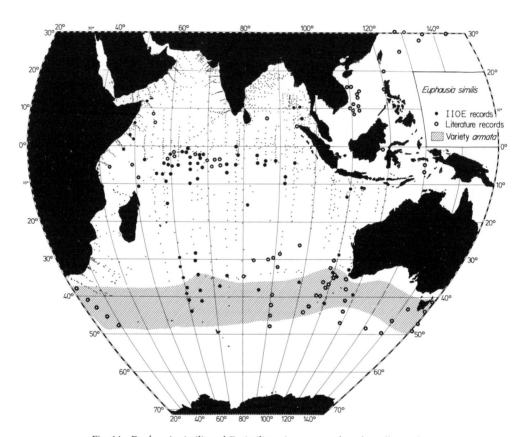

Fig. 11. *Euphausia similis* and *E. similis* variety *armata*, based on all samples

South Equatorial Current is 6° S—10° S. The equatorial species tend to sharply diminish to the south of 10° S, i.e., *E. diomediae* (Fig. 3a, b), *Nematoscelis gracilis* (Fig. 5a, b), *Stylocheiron microphthalma* (Fig. 7a, b), and *Euphausia paragibba* (Fig. 8a, b).

Euphausia diomediae is evidently replaced by *E. mutica* as well as by *E. brevis*, *Nematoscelis gracilis* by *N. atlantica*, *Stylocheiron microphthalma* by *S. suhmi*, and *Euphausia paragibba* by *E. hemigibba*.

δ) 25° S – 30° S

This is the region of the southern boundary of certain subtropical species that occur to the south of the Equator in the Indian Ocean: *E. brevis* (Fig. 3 a, b), *E. mutica* (at least during November – March, Fig. 3 b), *Stylocheiron suhmi* (Fig. 7 a, b), and *Thysanopoda subaequalis* (Fig. 9 a, b). It is also a generalized southern limit for a number of more widely ranging tropical-subtropical species: *Euphausia tenera; Nematoscelis microps* and *N. tenella* (Fig. 6 a, b); *Thysanopoda tricuspidata, T. monacantha,* and *T. obtisifrons* (ROGER, 1966); and the three rare species *T. cristata, Stylocheiron robustum,* and *Nematobrachion sexspinosum.* 25° S – 30° S is also the northern limit of the southern population of *Euphausia similis* (Fig. 11), and of *Thysanoessa gregaria.*

ε) 40° S – 45° S

This may be regarded as the boundary region between the subtropical and temperate zones in all oceans. It is the southern limit of *Euphausia recurva* (Fig. 3 a, b), *Nematoscelis megalops* (Fig. 6 a, b), and *Euphausia hemigibba* (Fig. 8 a, b). The enigmatic *E. similis* ranges southward to 50° S.

b) Meridional Distributions

A feature of the zoogeography of both the western and eastern sides of the Indian Ocean is the extensive north-south ranges of coastal species. In the west, *Pseudeuphausia*

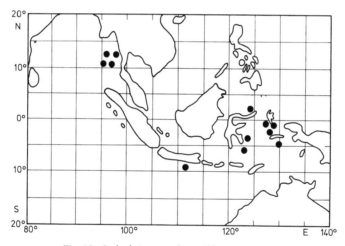

Fig. 12. *Stylocheiron insulare,* all known localities

latifrons ranges from the Persian Gulf to waters off Madagascar. *E. distinguenda* is more tied to the north, less so in November – March than May – September, but there is one record east of Madagascar (Fig. 2 a). *Euphausia sanzoi* (Fig. 10 a, b) occurs from 25° N to 30° S, again with records to the east of Madagascar. Seasonal change in the range of *E. sanzoi* is not evident.

Coastal species on the eastern side of the ocean range from the Bay of Bengal to waters south of Java. *E. distinguenda* is abundant at both extremes of its distribution. As in the west, *P. latifrons* ranges farther southward than *E. distinguenda,* as far as the coast of SW Australia. *Stylocheiron insulare* occurred in the Andaman Sea and south of Java (Fig. 12).

The following more oceanic species range northward into the Bay of Bengal, evidently by way of the Andaman Sea: *Nematoscelis tenella* and *N. microps* (Fig. 6a, b), *Euphausia pseudogibba* (Fig. 8a, b), *Thysanopoda aequalis* (Fig. 9a, b), and *Euphausia similis* (Fig. 11). Again, no seasonality is evident in these penetrations. The peculiar place of the Andaman Sea in the zoography of the Bay of Bengal is further emphasized by the occurrence there of the apparently distinct species of the *E. gibboides* group (Fig. 10a, b) and of *Stylocheiron insulare.*

On the western side of the ocean, a number of subtropical oceanic species are found to the north of the Equator along the Somali Coast, particularly during May — September when the northerly Somali Current is developed. These include *Euphausia mutica* (Fig. 3a), *E. brevis* (Fig. 4a), *Nematoscelis microps* and *N. tenella* (Fig. 6a, b), *Stylocheiron suhmi* (Fig. 7a, b), *Euphausia hemigibba* (Fig. 8a), *Thysanopoda subaequalis* (Fig. 9a), and *E. similis* (Fig. 11). These species do not become abundant in the Somali region and do not replace its assemblage, which is consistently characterized by *E. distinguenda, E. diomediae, E. tenera, Nematoscelis gracilis, Stylocheiron affine, S. carinatum,* and *Thysanopoda tricuspidata.*

Records from the South African samples supplement the findings of Boden (1954), emphasizing the southerly occurrences in the Agulhas Current region of tropical and subtropical species, particularly during May — September. The tropical species include:

Euphausia diomediae, to 31° S (Fig. 3a)

Nematoscelis gracilis, to 27° S (Fig. 5a)

Stylocheiron microphthalma, to 33° S (Fig. 7a, b)

Euphausia paragibba, to 29° S (Fig. 8a)

Tropical-subtropical species ranging southward include:

Euphausia brevis, to 38° S (Fig. 4a)

Nematoscelis microps, to 38° S (Fig. 6a, b)

Nematoscelis tenella, to 32° S (Fig. 6a, b)

Euphausia tenera, to 31° S

Thysanopoda tricuspidata, to 31° S

Studies on *Limacina inflata* d'Orbigny (Thecosomata, Gastropoda) in the Indian Ocean

M. SAKTHIVEL

This paper deals with the seasonal and diurnal variations in spatial abundance, the annual variations along 78°E, latitudinal and seasonal variations along 110°E and also the distribution in relation to the thermocline. This study is based on the identification of the sorted fractions of Euthecosomata from 1927 zooplankton collections of the IIOE and 180 collections of the seasonal biological cruises of the Division of Fisheries and Oceanography CSIRO Australia. Because of remarkable diurnal changes of *Limacina inflata* only night collections were taken into consideration for studying seasonal variations.

I. Present Observation on Geographical Abundance

Out of 1927 samples, *Limacina inflata* was present in 1040, of which 438 were day hauls, and 602 night hauls. The day distribution (Fig. 1) shows that a large number of stations in the central water mass of the southern Indian Ocean and the areas which fall away from the zones of upwelling and divergence either caught none of this species or very few (<10 per haul). This species has been caught in moderate numbers in the areas where coastal upwelling or divergence is reported, for example, the coasts of Kenya and Somalia, the Gulf of Aden, the south Arabian coast, the SW coast of India, a part of the western Bay of Bengal, near Andaman, off Sumatra, off Java and in isolated areas in the equatorial zone. The areas of greater abundance are restricted to small areas off the Kenya and Somali coast, off Goa, off Cochin and off Madras. The night distribution (Fig. 2) shows that the range B (10 – 100 per haul) covers about $^{3}/_{4}$ of the area of the Indian Ocean, whereas the same range of abundance was found mainly in the North Indian Ocean during the day. Except in a few coastal areas (West Australian coast, Malaya and Burmese coast, NE coast of India) and a large area off South Africa, Gulf of Oman, the eastern Bay of Bengal, east of Ceylon, a few areas in the equatorial zone and the area near West Java, *Limacina inflata* is more common at night in the entire area of the Indian Ocean. The area of greater abundance (range C, 100 – 1 000 per haul Fig. 2) is comparatively many times larger than during the day; it covers almost the entire western half of the Indian Ocean from Madagascar to the south Arabian coast, off Goa, off Cochin, a meridional zone along 78°E, specified areas in the equatorial zone, off Madras, a part of the northern Bay of Bengal, Andaman Sea and off Java. The areas of highest abundance (range D, > 1 000 per haul) were noted in the form of patches off the Somali coast, near Socotra, off Goa, off Madras and near the Equator at 82°E. The average number of organisms in the day hauls is 39 and night hauls 105.

The distinct variation in spatial abundance of *Limacina inflata* clearly indicates that

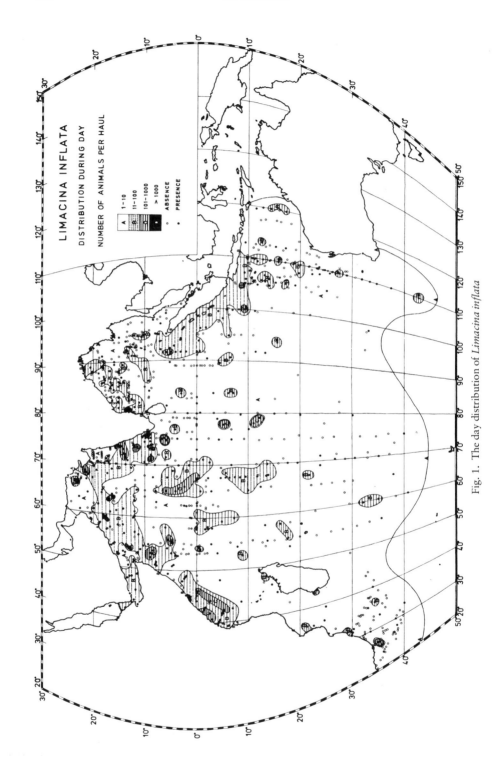

Fig. 1. The day distribution of *Limacina inflata*

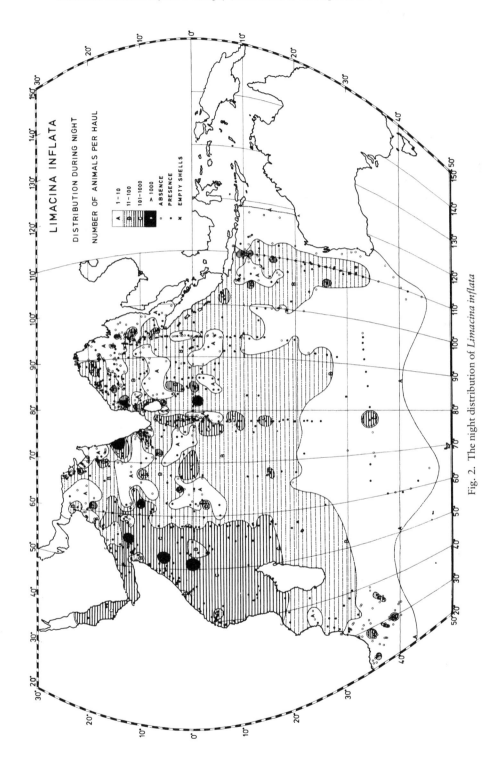

Fig. 2. The night distribution of *Limacina inflata*

it undergoes vertical migration and avoids surface waters during the day. The mean level of this species might be around 200 m in the areas of coastal upwelling and divergence where, in general, light penetration is less. In clear waters where light penetrates deeply, this species lives mainly below 200 m. This is evident from its occurrence in the night hours in the central water mass of the South Indian Ocean where it is absent in the daytime. The ascending migration at night is for the purpose of feeding on phytoplankton, generally most abundant at 75 m (HUMPHREY and KERR, 1969). The areas of greater abundance of *Limacina inflata* are approximately the areas of the vertical extension of monsoonal effects, as reported by DÜING (1970). As this result almost coincides with the similar finding of MCGOWAN (1960) in the North Pacific, *Limacina inflata* could be considered an indicator of environments where the nutrient-rich, deep water is brought up, in the form of upwelling, divergence or other vertical mixing processes.

II. Seasonal Variation in Spatial Abundance

From mid-April to mid-October, a large area in the western Indian Ocean between Madagascar and the south Arabian coast and a large area in the eastern Indian Ocean, especially the western Bay of Bengal, the Andaman Sea, the areas around Ceylon, off Sumatra and the areas between Java and Australia, show abundance (range B) of *Limacina inflata* (Fig. 3). The areas of greater abundance (range C) are found off Kenya, NE of Madagascar, the Somali coast, the south Arabian coast.

The highest abundance (range D) was seen only in the area off the Somali coast. A large area off South Africa, part of the central and eastern Bay of Bengal including the Malacca Strait, a few areas in the equatorial zone and a large area in the southern Indian Ocean are poorly populated. From mid-October to mid-April (Fig. 4), the areas of abundance (range B) are seen off Kenya and Somali coast, the Gulf of Aden, the west coast of India, a meridional zone along 78° E, the areas around Ceylon, a part of western Bay of Bengal, a few areas in the equatorial zone and the NW Australian Sea. The areas of greater abundance (range C) are found in the areas off the Kenya and Somali coast, near Socotra, the Gulf of Aden, off Kathiawar, the SW coast of India, a meridional zone along 78° E, off Madras and off Java. The highest abundance (range D) is noted in the area near Socotra, off Goa, off Madras, and a patch near the Equator at 82° E. The area off South Africa, the Gulf of Oman, the central and southern Arabian Sea, the eastern Bay of Bengal, the west coast of Australia and a large area in the western half of the Indian Ocean are poorly populated by *Limacina inflata*. The fact that the period from mid-April to mid-October which is dominated by the SW monsoon shows greater abundance than that from mid-October to mid-April; that might be due to the different intensities and duration of the SW and NE monsoons which bring about a number of changes in the properties of the environment according to the vertical extension.

The finding of a large number of well-preserved empty shells of *Limacina inflata* off the eastern part of the Somali coast (Table 1 and Fig. 2) could indicate mass mortality of this species, due to the toxic effects of phytoplankton blooms or other unknown environmental factors. The subsurface O_2 minimum is also recorded.

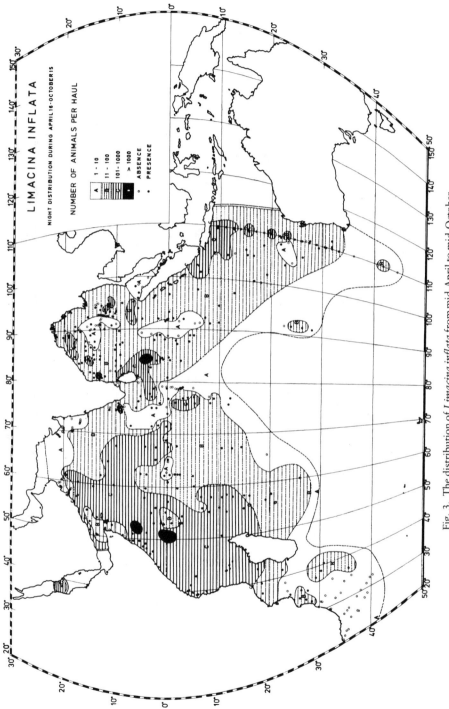

Fig. 3. The distribution of *Limacina inflata* from mid-April to mid-October

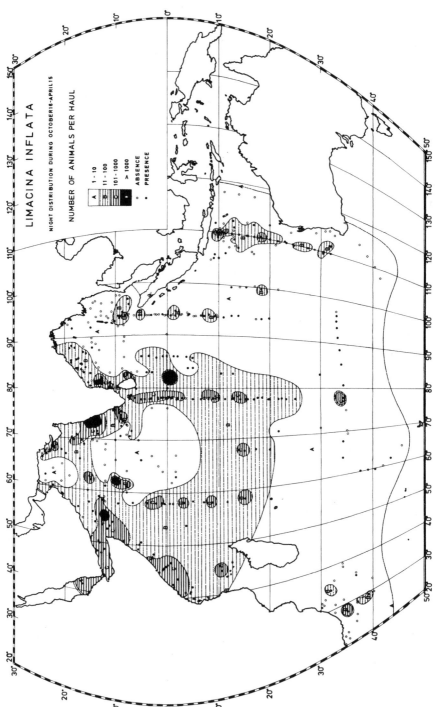

Fig. 4. The distribution of *Limacina inflata* from mid-October to mid-April

Table 1. Hydrographic details of stations where a large number of empty shells of *Limacina inflata* were found

Ship	Cruise	Station	Date	Gear	Position	O₂ range 200 m layer (ml l⁻¹)	Temperature range 200 m layer (°C)	Salinity range 200 m layer (‰)	No. of L. inflata 200 m layer
INS "Kistna"	2	78	9. 11. 62	Organdie	12°00′ N 55°00′ E	0.32 – 4.47	15.52 – 27.5°	35.43 – 36.31	3195
INS "Kistna"	3	95	2. 12. 62	Organdie	08°00′ N 60°00′ E	1.95 – 4.31	14.05 – 27.8	35.21 – 36.22	522
INS "Kistna"	3	96	2. 12. 62	Organdie	10°00′ N 62°03′ E	2.06 – 4.74	15.72 – 27.4	35.40 – 35.96	2126

III. Annual Variation of *Limacina inflata* along 78° E

"Umitaka Maru" and "Kagoshima Maru", 2 Japanese research vessels, during the IIOE took a series of collections along the meridian 78° E during December to January 1962 — 1963 and December to January 1963 — 1964. Twenty zooplankton collections during the first year and 23 during the second year were made along the track between

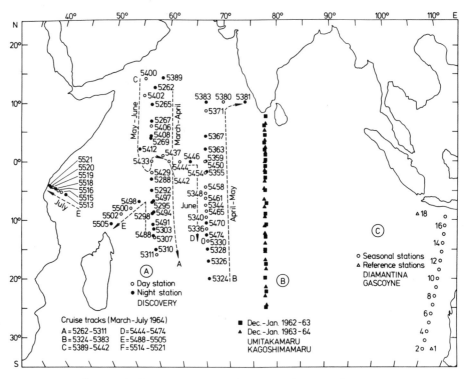

Fig. 5. Stations for special observations, A Distribution in relation to the thermocline, B Annual variation, C Seasonal variation

8° N and 25° S, almost all between 1900 and 2400 h, the majority between 2000 and 2100 h. The position of these stations is given in Fig. 5 B. The data collected from these stations for chlorophyll *a*, zooplankton displacement volume and numbers of *Limacina inflata* are plotted with temperature (Figs. 6 and 7). The station list and sampling details are given in the IOBC Handbook (1969). On the basis of vertical temperature gradients approximately 3 zones were selected for latitudinal comparison. The vertical temperature gradient in the upper 100 m was very narrow at the Equator during both years. From 15° S to 25° S temperatures at 0 m, 75 m and 100 m were falling and the temperature at 200 m was rising (Fig. 6). The stations up to the Equator were taken as track A, stations between the Equator and 15° S as track B, and the stations between 15° S and 25° S as track C. The data collected from each zone in the form of mean values for chlorophyll *a*,

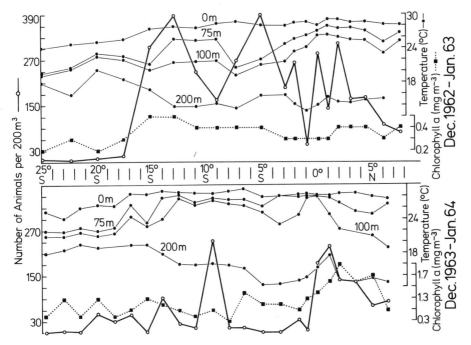

Fig. 6. Annual variation of *Limacina inflata* along 78° E with chlorophyll *a* and temperature

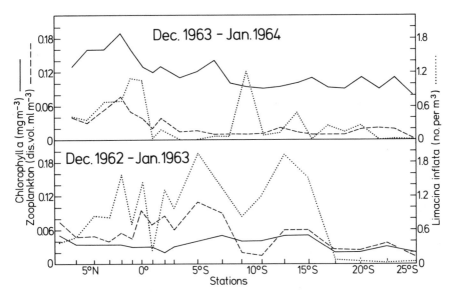

Fig. 7. Annual variation of *Limacina inflata* in comparison with chlorophyll *a* and zooplankton
displacement volume along 78° E

zooplankton displacement volume and *Limacina inflata* are given in Fig. 8. The mean annual variation is given in Table 2.

Table 2. Mean annual variation in chlorophyll *a*, zooplankton displacement volume and *Limacina inflata* along 78° E

Year	Mean chlorophyll *a* mg m⁻³	Mean zooplankton displacement volume ml m⁻³	Mean number of *Limacina inflata* No m⁻³
Dec. 1962 – Jan. 63	$0 \cdot 034$	$0 \cdot 053$	$0 \cdot 85$
Dec. 1963 – Jan. 64	$0 \cdot 118$	$0 \cdot 025$	$0 \cdot 32$

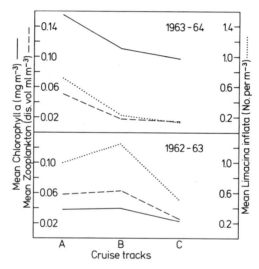

Fig. 8. Mean annual variation of *Limacina inflata*, chlorophyll *a* and zooplankton displacement volume in 3 selected tracks along 78° E

From Table 2 it is clear that chlorophyll *a* is low in the first year, but zooplankton and numbers of *Limacina inflata* are high. In the second year, chlorophyll *a* is more than 3 times as abundant, zooplankton is less than half as abundant and *Limacina inflata* about 3 times less abundant when compared to the mean values of the first year. In the first year, track B shows high abundance in all 3 values while track A shows slightly less abundance and track C poor abundance (Fig. 8). Whereas in the second year, all the 3 mean values are high along track A with a decrease along track B and C, the decrease in chlorophyll *a* in the first year and increase in zooplankton and *Limacina inflata* suggests that the secondary producers have established themselves after a long period of grazing. In the second year, primary producers are abundant and secondary producers are less abundant, giving an impression that the secondary producers have just started grazing, following the bloom of phytoplankton. As *Limacina inflata* is predominantly a herbivore, this follows closely the general trend of increase or decrease of zooplankton. This year-to-year change in the cyclic changes of the ecosystem might probably have been introduced by the earlier or later setting in of the NE monsoon.

IV. Latitudinal, Seasonal and Diurnal Variations of *Limacina inflata* along 110° E

In 1962–63 the Division of Fisheries and Oceanography, CSIRO Cronulla, with the collaboration of the oceanographic laboratory, ORSTOM New Caledonia, undertook 6 seasonal biological cruises, at 2-month intervals along 110° E meridian between 32° and 9° S. The aim of these cruises and other details have been published by ROCHFORD (1969 and TRANTER (1973) this volume).

Duplicate collections from these cruises were sent to IOBC and utilized for comparison. The data collected for the identification of thecosomes are being worked out; only the species *Limacina inflata* is presented here. The number of *Limacina inflata* from each collection was converted to log 10 and a contour was drawn at different grades of density; figures were prepared for day and night (Fig. 9 a, b).

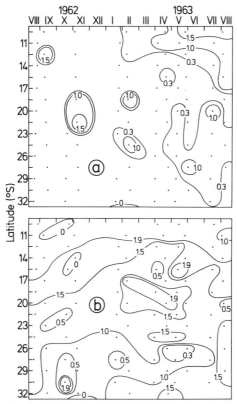

Fig. 9. Latitudinal, diurnal and seasonal variations of *Limacina inflata* along 110° E Contours: log of individuals per 200 m³ a Day b Night

Limacina inflata is abundant in the northern latitudes (between 9 and 12° S) almost throughout the year (Fig. 9b). The area of abundance extends spatially up to 20° S between August and November in 1962 and May to August in 1963. The central latitudes between 15° and 26 °S show less abundance and southern latitudes in general between 26° and 32°S are poor. This follows the results on the latitudinal variation of biomass well (TRANTER, 1969). The absence of *Limacina inflata* in many collections in the southern latitudes and periodical occurrence in certain months might be due to the scarcity of this

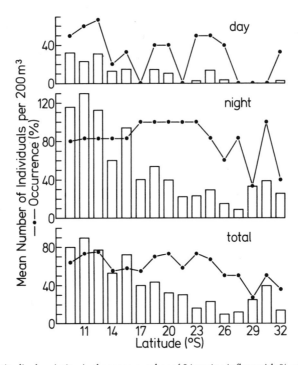

Fig. 10. Latitudinal variation in the mean number of *Limacina inflata* with % of occurrence

species in an area where water conditions are stable. The central latitudes in general show less abundance but in the period of summer divergence, as reported by ROCHFORD (1969), *Limacina inflata* undergoes a significant increase, as in northern latitudes. As a whole this species is in maximum abundance during August, following the peak period of chlorophyll, reported as maximum during June to August (HUMPHREY and KERR, 1969). The maximum abundance of *Limacina inflata* in the northern latitudes might be due to the upwelling during the SE monsoon as described by WYRTKI (1962) followed by high biological productivity. The absence of this species in 4 of the collections in the northern latitudes during September — October 1962 might be due to the different type of gear used. Out of 18 night tows using the Clarke-Bumpus Sampler (CBS) during September and November *Limacina inflata* was present in only 8 samples, whereas this species was present in all 12 Indian Ocean Standard Net (IOSN) night tows in August and October. As CBS and IOSN samples were not available from the same station, no definite conclusion can be drawn as to the efficiency of the gear. However, in the southern latitudes IOSN samples, too, lack this species.

The diurnal variation of this species is remarkable (Fig. 9a). There are a few records of small numbers of specimens, especially during April−August, but most of the day collections do not contain this species, whatever the latitude and season. Only collections

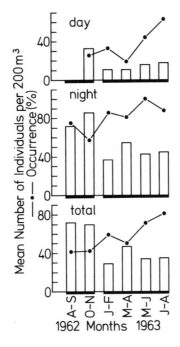

Fig. 11. Seasonal variation in the mean number of *Limacina inflata* with % of occurrence

from the northern latitudes between 9° and 13°S and another at 21°S show greater abundance. This shows that *Limacina inflata* for most of the year lives below 200 m during the day in many stations along 110°E.

The mean number of *Limacina inflata* and its percentage of occurrence with respect to latitude and month are shown in Figs. 10 and 11, day and night values being shown separately. In determining the average, either for each latitude or each cruise, single records of occurrence were omitted in day values, but included in the total. Of all the latitudes between 9° and 32°S, the maximum number of this species was found at 11°S and minimum at 26°S. Of all 6 cruises, the highest percentage was found in July − August 1963, the highest mean number in August−September 1962 and the lowest in January− February 1963 (Fig. 11).

V. The Distribution of *Limacina inflata* in Relation to Thermocline

During the IIOE RRS "Discovery" collected zooplankton samples from 62 stations in the area of the western half of the Indian Ocean for the study on distribution of plankton in relation to the thermocline (Fig. 5 A). Fig. 12 shows that *Limacina inflata* is abundant at night above and below the thermocline in the 200 m water column. During the day the population of this species is very poor above the thermocline and less abundant below the thermocline (Fig. 12). The mean number of organisms above and below the thermocline in terms of unit haul and in terms of number per m³ are given in Table 3.

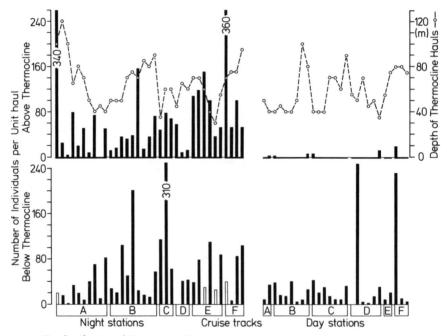

Fig. 12. The distribution of *Limacina inflata* in relation to the thermocline (in terms of unit haul). For cruise tracks see Fig. 5

Table 3. Diurnal variation in the mean number of *Limacina inflata* in relation to the depth of thermocline in terms of unit haul and number m⁻³

Limacina inflata	Day		Night	
	Thermocl. −0 m	200 m− Thermocl.	Thermocl. −0 m	200 m− Thermocl.
Mean number per unit haul	3.83	34.96	72.17	+ 52.06
Mean number per m³	0.07	0.16	1.12	− 0.55

Of the 6 cruise tracks, tracks C, E and F show relatively high abundance of *Limacina inflata* which perhaps might be due to the influence of the SW monsoon during June and

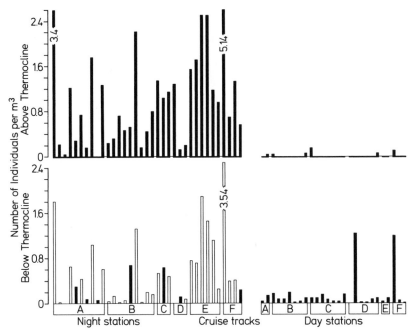

Fig. 13. The distribution of *Limacina inflata* in relation to the thermocline (in terms of number per m³)

July. As *Limacina inflata* is an eurythermic form inhabiting tropical to polar waters, the temperature may not act as a barrier to the up and down migration of this species. As diurnal variation is remarkable, light may be the major factor in the vertical distribution of *Limacina inflata*.

Even though no correction factor was applied to the varying depth of thermocline hauls (30–120 m), the occurrence and abundance of *Limacina inflata* above and below the thermocline show more or less the expected vertical distribution. When the data were converted in terms of number per m³ (Fig. 13), 28 of the 35 night stations below the thermocline show negative values, giving the impression that no organisms are present. This might be due to the non-random distribution of the organisms, the population of *Limacina inflata* being more dense above than below the thermocline at night, or it might be an artefact of the method used.

4.15

Distribution and Ecology of *Pterotrachea coronata* (FORSKÅL)

P. N. ARAVINDAKSHAN

The genus *Pterotrachea* comprises 4 species, *Pt. coronata* being the largest. This paper reports an attempt to find out how this species is distributed in the Indian Ocean. Most of the IOBC samples were collected in a uniform manner from $200-0$ m with the Indian Ocean Standard Net (IOSN) (CURRIE, 1963; RAO, 1973). All the larg specimens

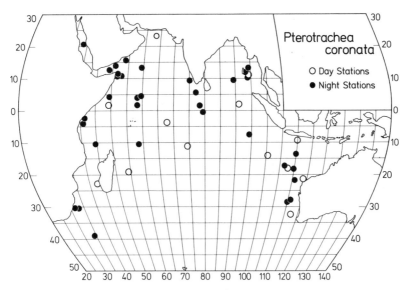

Fig. 1. Stations in which *Pterotrachea coronata* was present

were removed from the plankton samples before splitting and the smaller specimens were sorted from the subsamples.

The present study revealed that the sucker a secondary sexual character, is undoubtedly confined to the male sex only.

A total of 55 specimens was examined. 34 specimens were females and 13 were males. Eight specimens could not be identified as to sex because they were badly damaged. OKUTANI (1957) noted that females were 3.5 times as numerous as males in his collections from Japanese waters. DALES (1952) also reported that the females were more numerous than the males.

The largest specimen measured only 104 mm and the smallest 7 mm in length. The Indian Ocean specimens were smaller than those recorded elsewhere.

I. Food Habits

Gut contents of 21 specimens from 21 different stations were examined. The principal food includes copepods, chaetognaths and ostracods. Inside the oesophagus of a 73 mm female *Pt. coronata* numerous copepods of fairly large size (4 mm) were observed. In another 13 mm specimen, a 5 mm copepod *Rhincalanus cornutus* was noted. In all cases examined the species was exclusively carnivorous and had a varied diet in accordance with the relative abundance of the food species available.

II. Distribution

The distribution of *Pt. coronata* in the Arabian Sea, the Andaman Sea and the western Indian Ocean was discussed in a preliminary study (ARAVINDAKSHAN, 1969). The present observation is that the species was present in only 49 samples of the 1927 examined from the epipelagic zone, with a total number of 63 specimens. Fig. 1 shows the total number of stations where *Pt. coronata* occured. It was absent in the eastern Arabian Sea, in the northern and western parts of the Bay of Bengal and in the central zone of the southern Indian Ocean. It was common around the mouth of the Gulf of Aden, in the eastern African waters, in the eastern part of the Andaman Sea, and off the NW of Australia.

The species were caught at 38 out of 920 night stations and 11 out of 1001 day stations. Therefore, vertical diurnal migration is usual in this species.

Pt. coronata was found in almost all the water masses of the upper layer of the Indian Ocean at different seasons of the year. Comparing the stations where the net sampled a single water mass, it is seen that the species must be euryhaline and eurythermal; the range of tolerance appears to be $33-40‰$ and $12-30°$ C respectively. It seems likely that the species requires a relatively high O_2 content since it was not taken in waters with less than 2.0 ml l^{-1} dissolved oxygen.

Most specimens come from stations where the net fished through different layers, whether the boundary between the two watermasses was shallow or deep, whether a thermocline was present or not. This suggests that the species lives mostly at the boundary between surface and subsurface water zooplankton aggregates as a deep scattering layer. A similar distribution was found by NAVAS (1969) for a hydromedusa, *Halistaura bruuni*, that is also a zooplankton feeder. Therefore, although *Pt. coronata* has been described as a warm-water epipelagic species, the present data suggest that it is a warm-water, widely tolerant species that performs vertical migrations following the copepods on which it feeds. For this reason it is common in some upwelling areas, although very few specimens were caught in the center of upwelling. The scattered and wide distribution of the species and its comparatively greater abundance in enriched areas may be explained by its eurytopic capacity and its euryphagous habits.

Biogeographical Change in the Latitudinal Boundary of a Bisubtropical Pteropod *Styliola subula* (QUOY et GAIMARD) in the Indian Ocean

M. SAKTHIVEL

The geographical distribution and relative abundance of the bisubtropical pteropod *Styliola subula* is given in Fig. 1. This species has a wide range of distribution from 10°N to 40°S and is very rare or absent in the Indian Ocean north of 10°N and south

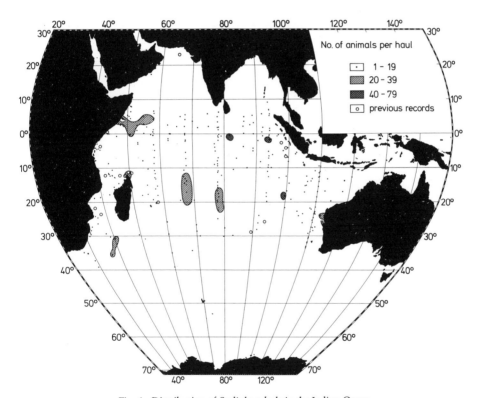

Fig. 1. Distribution of *Styliola subula* in the Indian Ocean

of 40°S. The sparse occurence of this species between 5°N and 10°N, and 30°S and 40°S is noticed in the present study. There were 579 collections from north of 10°N: except for a single record of a single specimen from AB 175 at 17° 26′N and 56° 57′E, none of them contained this species. Therefore, the extreme scarcity of *S. subula* in the

northern part of the Arabian Sea is borne out by previous and present findings. There
were also 268 zooplankton collections from north of 10° N in the Bay of Bengal, none
of which contained this species. The southern boundary of *S. subula* in the South Indian
Ocean further supports previous findings in all 3 oceans. Clearly, the boundary of
subtropical convergence which runs for the most part between 38° S and 40° S acts as a
thermal barrier to the distribution of *S. subula* further south than 40° S.

 S. subula is more common between 5° N and 30° S, especially in the subtropical gyre,
the Mozambique Channel and along 110° E in the Indian Ocean. It is abundant off the
Somali coast, and in 2 isolated patches in the eastern equatorial area and another at

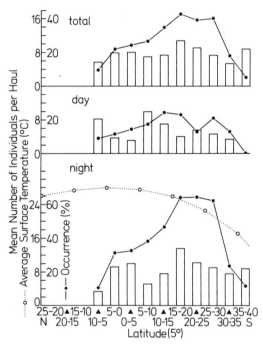

Fig. 2. Latitudinal and diurnal variation of the occurrence of *Styliola subula* in the Indian Ocean

19° S and 100° E, also in the areas between 66° E and 80° E, and 10° S and 25° S (Fig. 1).
The 3 larger areas of abundance are known to have mild climatic conditions.

    Even though the area of abundance near the Somali coast is very close to the Equator,
it is subject to upwelling which reduces the temperature to the subtropical level. The
other 2 large areas are between 10° and 25° S. The availability of adequate food in
association with mild climate must provide a suitable habitat for the breeding and
spawning of this species.

    From the records of *S. subula* in the IIOE collections an attempt was made to evaluate
the latitudinal variation in the occurrence of this species. The percentage occurrence
at each 5° interval was calculated by dividing the number of records by the number of
collections. The abundance in the form of arithmetic mean at each 5° interval was
estimated by dividing the total number of individuals by the number of records. As this

species is subject to marked diurnal fluctuations in abundance, 3 graphs were prepared (Fig. 2) based on day, night and total distribution to minimize any error in the estimation of abundance.

Fig. 2 shows that the latitudinal variation in occurrence of *S. subula* is almost uniform. This species is absent in the northern latitudes (except for a single record) between 25° N and 10° N and sparse (10%) between 10° N and 5° N, rising to 22% between 5° N and the Equator. From the Equator to 15° S there is a gradual increase in percentage occurrence (22 to 35%) with the peak (40%) between 15° S and 20° S and maintaining more or less the same percentage up to 30° S. Between 30° S and 35° S there is a sudden decrease to 18% with a further reduction (5%) beyond 35° S and total disappearance beyond 40° S. The peak percentage occurrence between 15° and 30° S indicates clearly that *S. subula* flourishes in the subtropical zone rather than in the tropical zone of the Indian Ocean. The unique feature in the distribution of *S. subula* is the change in occurrence with latitude. The absence of this species in the northern latitudes and its continuous occurrence from 10° N to 40° S suggests a possible change in the bisubtropical distribution of a subtropical species in a unipolar ocean.

The diurnal variation of *S. subula* is clearly seen in Fig. 2. A distinct rise in percentage occurrence is observed during the night, especially between 5° N and 30° S. The largest difference in the percentage between day and night is found between 15° S and 30° S. This diurnal variation is attributed to the position of the sun at different latitudes in different months of the year, the intensity of light, the transparency of water and other local environmental conditions which determine the vertical division of the hydrosphere into photic, dysphotic and aphotic zones.

From the present state of knowledge of the hydrography of the Indian Ocean it is really difficult to define the exact barrier to the distribution of *S. subula* in the northern part of the north Indian Ocean. It is probably due to the combination of several factors caused by the land barrier in the north.

With regard to surface salinity, the waters of the Bay of Bengal are less saline than the waters of the Arabian Sea. The average values are 30 — 33‰ for the Bay of Bengal and 34 — 37‰ for the Arabian Sea (PANIKKAR and JAYARAMAN, 1966). Salinity increases from north to south in the Bay of Bengal and decreases from north to south in the Arabian Sea (GALLAGHER, 1966). As RAMPAL (1966) has observed, this species as a stenohaline form is avoiding the area of high salinity (38‰) in the Mediterranean, the water mass with low salinity and high temperature in the northern Bay of Bengal and the water mass of high salinity and high temperature in the northern Arabian Sea, might possibly act as hydrological barrier for the distribution of *S. subula*. The unique subsurface O_2 minimum (0.5 ml l^{-1}) found north of 8° N might also be a major reason for the absence of this species in the northern part of the Indian Ocean.

In support of the relict theory of bipolarity, MEISENHEIMER (1905) traced the various stages in the migration of pteropods. He believed that the pteropods originally spread evenly from the Equator to the north and south without any gap. The next step was moving away from the warmest water on either side of the Equator. He quotes *S. subula* and *Cavolinia gibbosa* as examples of this migration from the Equator because they are rare in the equatorial zone and abundant in the subtropical zone. The gradual increase in the percentage occurrence of *S. subula* from equatorial to subtropical latitudes in the Indian Ocean supports this hypothesis, even though this species still occurs in the equatorial zone. As the Pacific and Atlantic provide 2 subtropical zones one on either side of the Equator, *S. subula* could easily have migrated from the warmer zone of the Equator to the cooler zone of the subtropical latitudes. This is almost evident from the paucity in the distribution of *S. subula* in the equatorial Pacific and Atlantic. In the Indian Ocean, for lack of a subtropical zone in the northern hemisphere, this species can migrate only towards the subtropical zone of the South Indian Ocean. This may account for the persistence of *S. subula* in the equatorial zone.

A similar phenomenon has been observed in the distribution of euphausiids in the Indian Ocean. Three species of euphausiids, *Euphausia brevis, E. mutica* and *E. recurva*, have centres of distribution in the subtropical latitudes of the North and South Pacific but are absent in the equatorial water mass. BRINTON (1962) has called this type of distribution biantitropical. BAKER (1965) says that *E. brevis* and probably *E. mutica* have a continuous distribution from the subtropics to the southern Bay of Bengal, while *E. recurva* has a northerly restricted distribution in the partially enclosed Indian Ocean.

From the present study it is difficult to explain the tropical submergence of *S. subula* in the northern part of the Indian Ocean as only 4 deep hauls (400 m to 880 m) were available. Tropical submergence is normally reported for a cold-water surface-living form inhabiting the deeper zone in the tropical latitudes (e. g. *Eukrohnia hamata*). Here the temperature forms the major factor of distribution. As *S. subula* is mainly a surface-living form, tolerating even the high temperature of the equatorial zone in the Indian Ocean, tropical submergence based on temperature would hardly apply to this species.

4.17

Species of the Genus Parasmittina Osburn (Bryozoa, Ascophora) from Indian Waters

N. R. Menon

Bryozoans of Indian waters have been dealt with in part by investigators on the basis of expedition collections. However, until recently there has been no comprehensive attempt to work out taxonomical and ecological aspects in detail. During investigations on the systematics and ecology of bryozoans of Indian waters, Menon (1967) collected 101 species of bryozoans from the west and east coasts of India. Menon and Nair (1967) listed 70 species of bryozoans hitherto unknown from Indian seas.

The present note records 9 species belonging to the genus *Parasmittina* Osburn, 1952, listed for the first time from Indian waters.

The detailed descriptions with figures, remarks and discussion of the species dealt with in this paper, has been published elsewhere (Menon, 1972).

1. Parasmittina signata (Waters), 1899

Usually found on gastropod shells and stones, this species enjoys a very wide distribution in the Indian Ocean and western Pacific Ocean.

2. Parasmittina elongata (Okada and Mawatari), 1936

Found growing as an encrustation on *Triphyllozoon tubulatum*. The material at hand shows structural differences from the figures and descriptions furnished by Okada and Mawatari. Rather discontinuously distributed, this species has since its recovery from Japanese waters been found only in the Bay of Bengal.

3. Parasmittina parsevalii (Audoin), 1826

This species was found encrusting a concrete slab dredged from a depth of 18 m off Cochin. The material from Indian waters shows some difference in avicular characteristics. This species is abundant in the Indo-Australian archipelago.

4. Parasmittina aviculata (Mawatari), 1952

Usually found encrusting calcareous polychaete tubes and gastropod shells. The present material was dredged from 58 m off Ponnani, SW coast of India. This species shows a close resemblance to *P. protecta*. Apart from the type locality, this species has been recorded only from the Arabian Sea.

5. Parasmittina egyptiaca (Waters), 1909

Found growing on gastropod shells at 50 m depth off Quilon, SW coast of India. Enjoys wide distribution.

6. Parasmittina tropica (Waters), 1909

Collected from a depth of 50 m off Quilon, SW coast of India. Considerable variations in specific characters occur in this typically tropical species. Main differences are centred around the adventitious avicular characteristics. Widely distributed in the Indo-Australian Archipelago.

7. Parasmittina california (Robertson), 1908

Previously found only on the Californian coast of America; the present record extends the distribution of this species to the Indian Ocean. It is very likely that this is a tropical and warm temperate species.

8. Parasmittina projecta (Okada and Mawatari), 1936

A single colony encrusting a gastropod shell was collected from a depth of 50 m off Quilon. Even through the characters of this material resemble those of *Smittina projecta* given by Okada and Mawatari (1936), certain striking differences have been noticed in the nature and disposition of the avicularia. Apart from the type locality, the Izu Peninsula in Japanese waters, this species has further been recorded only from the Arabian Sea.

4.18

Species of the Sub-Order Ctenostomata (Bryozoa) from Indian Waters

N. R. MENON

An extensive study of the taxonomy and ecology of marine and brackish water bryozoans of Indian waters has revealed that more than 100 species of bryozoans occur in the continental shelf region of the SW and SE coasts of India (MENON, 1967). Of these species 12 belong to the sub-order *Ctenostomata*. The majority of these were collected from wooden or glass panels used for the study of fouling bryozoans in Cochin waters or from the hulls of ships.

The species recorded are listed here with brief comments on occurrence and distribution. The detailed descriptions with figures, remarks and discussion of the different species dealt with in this paper will appear in Internationale Revue der gesamten Hydrobiologie, 1972.

1. Alcyonidium erectum SILEN, 1942

Several colonies were collected from appendages and carapace of *Portunus pelagicus*. This species was previously recorded from Japan; this is the first record from the Indian Ocean.

2. Alcyonidium polyoum HASSALI, 1841

Found epizoic on *Penaeus indicus* caught off Cochin, South-west coast of India. A cosmopolitan, this species shows considerable intraspecific differences in the nature of zoaria and number of tentacles.

3. Victorella pavida KENT, 1870

A common fouling bryozoan encountered in brackish waters of India. Cosmopolitan in distribution. Physiological races with conspicuous morphological differences are present in this species.

4. Nolella papuensis BUSK, 1886

Recorded as fouling organism from wooden and glass test panels immersed in Cochin Harbour, SW coast of India. Indo-Pacific in distribution.

5. Vesicularia papuensis BUSK, 1886

Collected from the hull of a ship. This is the first record of this species from Indian waters.

6. Amathia distans BUSK, 1886

Ten colonies were collected from the propeller of a boat dredged off Cochin from a depth of 18 m. A cosmopolitan, this ctenostome displays little intraspecific variation.

7. Amathia convoluta Lamouroux, 1816

Several colonies collected from Tuticorin, Bay of Bengal. Enjoys a very wide distribution.

8. Zoobotryon verticillatum Delle Chiaje, 1828

Four colonies collected from Madras Harbour, Bay of Bengal. This species exhibits few intraspecific differences. Circumtropical in distribution.

9. Bowerbankia gracilis Leidy, 1855

Three colonies found epizoic on calcareous polychaete tubes. Variations in length of the zooecia usually occur. Previously recorded from the Pacific; the present finding extends the distribution of this species to the Indian Ocean.

10. Triticella korenii Sars, 1874

Several colonies found epizoic on the thoracic appendages of a spider crab, caught off Cochin. First record of this species from the Indian Ocean.

11. Triticella pedicellate Alder, 1857

Several colonies collected from the walking legs of *Charybdis cuscuta*, caught off Cochin. Morphometrical variations occur between zooids of different colonies.

12. Aeverrillia setigera Hinks, 1887

Found as a fouler on glass panels exposed under water in Cochin harbour. Cosmopolitan in distribution.

4.19

Appendicularia from the
Indian Ocean, the Red Sea and the Persian Gulf

R. FENAUX

In the present study, I intend to show how our knowledge of the appendicularians living in the Indian Ocean, the Red Sea and the Persian Gulf developed.

There was much early sampling (Fig. 1) starting with Captain VON FREYMADL who took plankton from Zanzibar and the Seychelles Islands in 1893–95, and BRAUER who collected samples from the Seychelles Islands in 1895. In 1909, LOHMANN examined plankton from the west coast of Australia. He found only 5 species.

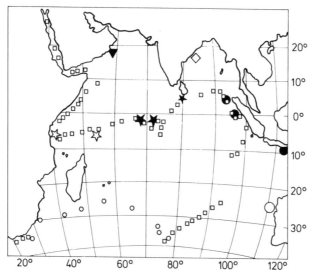

Fig. 1. Zooplankton samples from various cruises in the Indian Ocean: Samples from VON FREYMADL and BRAUER (open star), samples studied by LOHMANN (1931) (large open circle), Südpolar Expedition (small open circle), Tiefsee Expedition (open square), samples studies by SEWELL (1953) (filled triangle), samples studies by TOKIOKA (1955; 1956) (filled star and large filled circle) and samplés studies by GANAPATI and BHAVANARAYANA (1958) (rhomb)

More information on the other parts of the Indian Ocean had to await the publication of results obtained by the 2 main German expeditions (Fig. 1), the Tiefsee Expedition, which took place in 1898–1899, and the Südpolar Expedition 1901–1903. LOHMANN published systematic results from the former in 1914, but species distribution was not published until 1931. The complete results for the latter expedition were published by LOHMANN and BÜCKMANN in 1926. Very little work was done for the next 30 years.

The third cruise of the "Commandant Robert Giraud" in the Arabian Sea (Fig. 2) opens up the period of the IIOE. The studies which have been carried out in this period are not only based on the material from Indian Ocean Biological Centre (IOBC), but they were directly or indirectly stimulated by the IIOE.

The result are limited, as they have been obtained from incomplete material, but all the same they are interesting, as they were the first to concern the Oman Sea, i.e. between 10° N and the Persian Gulf. 23 species have been identified, 3 of them being new for the Indian Ocean: *Tectilaria fertilis, Megalocercus abyssorum* and *Fritillaria fagei*.

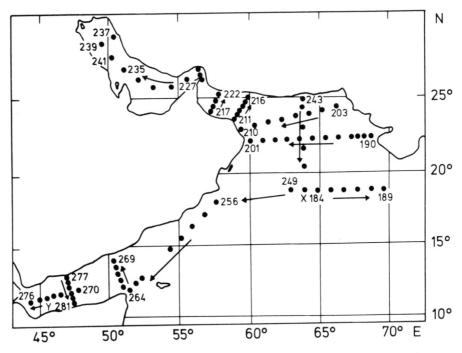

Fig. 2. Zooplankton samples from the third cruise of the "Commandant Robert Giraud"

On the whole there are 2 rich areas, the Gulf of Aden, and the Oman Sea, each containing 19 species, and two poor areas, the Gulf of Oman and the Persian Gulf with 12 and 6 species respectively. *Oikopleura longicauda* is the most abundant everywhere, followed by a small group stable in its composition but with a variable order in the different areas: *O. fusiformis, O. rufescens, O. cophocerca* and *Stegosoma magnum*. The only information concerning the appendicularians from the Persian Gulf comes from this cruise, the species collected are *O. longicauda, O. rufescens, St. magnum, F. formica, O. fusiformis* and *M. huxleyi. O. dioica* is absent in the Persian Gulf, despite the fact that it is a neritic species which should be found in this area. It is possible that it does not tolerate the high salinity occurring there, while it tolerates a big decrease in salinity.

Appendicularians were examined from 76 hauls made from June to August 1964 aboard the RV "Kistna" (Fig. 3) (FENAUX, 1969a). Of the 26 species determined, 10 were new for the Bay of Bengal and, among these, 2 were unknown in the Indian Ocean. The composition of the group formed by the most abundant and the most frequent species is characteristic of the fauna of the Indian Ocean. *O. longicauda* represents 50% of the total number of specimens collected, followed by *O. rufescens* 40%, and *M. huxleyi* 8%. The density of the species in the occidental zone decreases fairly regularly with latitude: 21 species in the south, then going on towards the north, 14, 11 and 2 species. In the area south of the Straits of Malacca only 5 species were found, but there were 18 where it

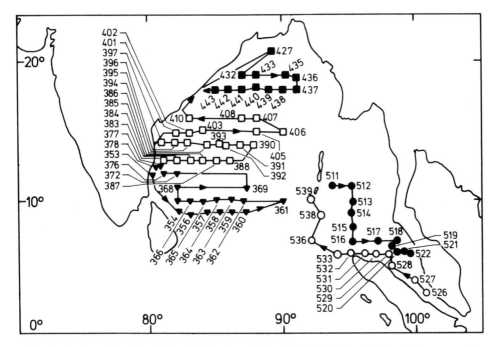

Fig. 3. Cruise track of the "Kistna" in the Bay of Bengal: No. 15 (triangle) No. 16 (open square) No. 17 (filled square) No. 18 (filled circle) and No. 20 (open circle)

opens into the Bay of Bengal. *O. longicauda* is the only species which is clearly more abundant in the north, most of the other species show a decreasing gradient from south to north. The appendicularians of Nosy-Bé (Madagascar) were collected in various areas over a period of 1 year (FENAUX, 1969b). 15 species were obtained in summer, 13 in autumn, 12 in winter and 11 in spring. All the species were previously known from the Indian Ocean. The most frequent are in decreasing order: *O. longicauda*, *M. huxleyi*, *O. fusiformis* and *O. rufescens*. The study of the seasonal variations showed that the frequency of *O. longicauda* is nearly 100% all the year round, while *M. huxleyi* is more frequent in summer and autumn, *O. fusiformis* in spring and *O. rufescens* in summer.

The most important part of the 1964 "Anton Bruun" cruise (Fig. 4) concerns the central part of the Indian Ocean, involving two parallel routes, one at 55° E, the other at 75° E, from 7° N to 42° S (FENAUX, 1971). *O. longicauda* is the most abundant, corresponding to 60% of the total number of the appendicularians, then come *O. cophocerca*, *O. rufescens*, *F. borealis*, *M. huxleyi*, *O. fusiformis* and *F. formica* with an abundance between 9 and 2%. No other species exceeds 2%.

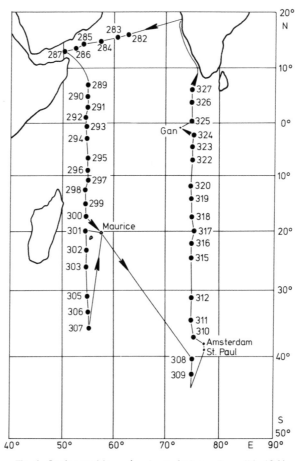

Fig. 4. Station positions of cruise 5 of "Anton Bruun" in 1964

A very important variation of the average number of appendicularians per sample as a function of latitude is given in Table 1. The increase is constant from south to north except between the Equator and 10° S, in other words, in a region where the Equatorial Countercurrent is usually noticeable.

A comparison between 2 corresponding areas between the Equator and latitude 20° in both hemispheres reveals that the southern area is poor: 79% of the appendicularians were collected from the north and 21% from the south. The variation of the number

Table 1. Variation of the average number of appendicularians from cruise 5 of "Anton Bruun"

Area	Number
South of 42° S	1
40° S to 30° S	7
30° S to 20° S	16
20° S to 10° S	132
10° S to Equator	106
Equator 10° N	485
10° N to 20° N	611

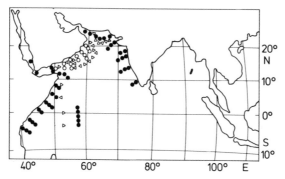

Fig. 5. Cruise tracks of the "Meteor" (filled circle) "Discovery" (open circle) "Anton Bruun" (triangle)

of species is different from the previous trend: there is a minimum of 1 in the south, but the maximum of 15 occurs between 10° and 20° S. Preferential locations are observed for some species. Thus it seems that *F. formica* and *F. pellucida* are more abundant in the east and *O. cophocerca* in the west.

As far as the Red Sea is concerned, 11 species have been found (FENAUX, 1970) and I am now studying the vertical and seasonal variations in the Gulf of Aqaba. The appendicularians were also studied in South African waters in 1964 and 1965; the results are reviewed by DE DECKER (1973).

BÜCKMANN (1972) deals for the major part with the appendicularians caught by the "Meteor", but includes material from the "Anton Bruun" and the "Discovery" cruises (Fig. 5). 30 species were found in all; of these 21 were already known in this area but *M. abyssorum* and *Folia gracilis* found by me were not encountered, and *F. arafoera*, *Tectillaria taeniogonia* and *Kowalevskia oceanica* were found for the first time in the Indian Ocean. The following species are the most abundant and the most frequent in decreasing order: *O. longicauda*, *M. huxleyi*, *O. rufescens*, *O. fusiformis*, *O. cophocerca*, *F. borealis*, and *F. pellucida*. But some species are of uneven distribution, e.g. *M. huxleyi* is abundant only off the Somali coast together with *O. intermedia* and the abundance of *F. tenella* and *F. venusta* is highest near the Kenya coast.

Each station is characterized by the combination of the 2 abundant species and there are 9 different dominating pairs. The more frequent are: *O. longicauda*, *O. rufescens*, at 37 stations; *O. longicauda*, *M. huxleyi*, at 30 stations and *O. longicauda*, *F. formica*, at 12 stations. Only 1 group does not include *O. longicauda* in the 2 most numerous species.

The area can be divided into some subareas which are characterized by the predominance of 1 or 2 species, or groups of species. It appears that the boundaries of the subareas coincide, in the main, with the boundaries of some water bodies represented in the "Summary of Oceanographic Conditions in the Indian Ocean" published by the U.S. Navy Hydrographic Office in 1960. The cruises of the "Discovery" and the "Anton Bruun" present one special interest. The first cruise was made during SW monsoon and the second 3 months later, between the monsoons but both along the Arabian coast. During the "Discovery" cruise 2 subareas were distinct: the western part characterized by the predominance of M. *huxleyi* and the eastern part by O. *longicauda*; during the "Anton Bruun" cruise, those differences disappeared.

Quantitatively there is no significant difference in subareas or distances from the shore and there is no relation between the quantity of appendicularians and the total plankton biomass or the phytoplankton from the upper layer. The size and state of maturity were recorded in representative samples for some species and considerations on geographical distribution with the maturity are given.

The early knowledge of this group was mainly based on systematic work. Subsequent studies gave information on geographical distribution. Finally, geographical distribution has been correlated with the distribution of water currents and water masses. The study of seasonal variations is now beginning for some areas.

I think we now know the major part of the species of the Indian Ocean and it seems they are the same ones to be found in all the temperate or tropical oceans, except for M. *huxleyi*. This species is an Indo-Pacific form and it would be interesting to know exactly what its status is in the Cape Town area, where the waters of the Indian and Atlantic Oceans converge.

There are many regions which were not so well known before the IIOE but which are better known at present, e.g. the Arabian Sea and the Bay of Bengal. Certain other regions, the hydrography of which is peculiar, such as the Agulhas Bank and the Somali coast, have also been investigated. Finally, interesting observations were made on the latitudinal variations in the central part of the Indian Ocean.

Thus it cannot be denied that here, as in many fields, the IIOE has been very benefical. However, for the appendicularians as for other fragile planktonic groups, the very bad state of preservation of many of the samples of the IOBC collection is to be regretted. Further disappointment arises from the fact that the number of cruises, their situations and the periods in which they took place, led one to hope that it would be possible to carry out a comprehensive study which would incorporate both space and time. The few collections which were or are in a state fit to be examined have given and will give only partial results, and they cannot be reconciled in space or time. Finally, mention should be made of the fact that the design of the standard net was for vertical hauls from 200 m to the surface, without intermediate closing; this precluded from the start the possibility of a study of bathymetric variations being carried out.

5. The Distribution and Ecology of Fish Larvae, Fish and Benthic Organisms

5.1

Kinds and Abundance of Fish Larvae in the Arabian Sea and the Persian Gulf

W. Nellen

During cruise I of the RV "Meteor" to the Arabian Sea and the Persian Gulf, fish larvae were caught routinely from December 1964 to April 1965 (Fig. 1 in Babenerd et al., 1973 this volume). Following the ichthyogeographical classification of Lagler, Bardach and Miller (1967), the zones fished for larvae were: the neritic zone (water mass over the shelf), the epipelagic zone (oceanic surface water down to 200 m), and the mesopelagic zone (water between 200 and 1 000 m). The larval stages of mesopelagic fish species are found mainly in the epipelagic zone, therefore faunistic elements of the third zone were probably over represented.

I. Material and Methods

1. Nets Used

The plankton nets used for these investigations were: 1. Heligoland larvae net (HLN), mouth opening 144 cm diameter, equivalent to 1.63 m², length of filtering net bag 2.2 m, 2. Ringtrawl net (RT), mouth opening 125 cm in diameter, equivalent to 1.23 m², length of net bag 4 m, and 3. Vertical Ringtrawl net (VRN), same size as the RT but with a net bag 6 m long. The VRN, like the HLN, was towed only vertically after all Heligoland larvae nets had been lost. The filtration efficiency was considered equal to that of the HLN. The RT was brought down obliquely at a ship's speed of 2 knots and was hauled in short horizontal steps; these tows were considered as oblique tows. Since the flow meters did not work well, the amount of water filtered was calculated very roughly according to ship's speed, time of haul, and size of net. All nets had a mesh aperture of 500 μ.

2. Station Work

Generally, one HLN and one RT sample or two HLN samples of different depths were made at each station. A total of 231 stations (Table 1) were covered with 227 HLN and 99 RT hauls. The standard HLN haul fished the upper 100 m of water; a second HLN haul at the same station was usually made from a depth of 200 m to the surface. With the RT, catches were done only down to 40–70 m. The samples were preserved in 4% formalin buffered with 100 g hexamethylene-tetramine to 1 l of 40% formalin. Off the

Table 1. Arrangement and number of fish-larvae net hauls in the investigation area of "Meteor" cruise during the IIOE

Area	Stations	Period	No. of stat. fished	No. of HLN hauls	No. of RT hauls
		1964			
southern part of Red Sea and inner part of Gulf of Aden	44 – 88	Nov. 30 – Dec. 14	8	16	5
Gulf of Aden profile	89 – 98	Dec. 16 – Dec. 18	7	6	7
north of Cape Guardafui and profile No. III	99 – 109	Dec. 19 – Dec. 23	10	7	9
profile No. IV	111 – 108	Dec. 24 – Dec. 27	7	7	4
profile No. V	123 – 131	Dec. 28 – Dec. 31	8	8	4
		1965			
profile No. VI	132 – 139	Jan. 1 – Jan. 4	8	9	3
profile No. VII	141 – 150	Jan. 5 – Jan. 10	10	10	4
profile No. VIII plus one shelf station	151 – 159	Jan. 11 – Jan. 15	9	9	3
profile No. IX	160 – 167	Jan. 22 – Jan. 24	7	9	3
profile No. X plus stations in the open Arabian Sea	168 – 181	Jan. 26 – Febr. 6	10	14	8
profile No. XI	182 – 190	Febr. 8 – Febr. 10	8	9	4
profile No. XII	193 – 202	Febr. 15 – Febr. 18	9	9	5
profile XIII	205 – 212	Febr. 20 – Febr. 26	8	7	4
profile No. XIV	213 – 221	Febr. 27 – Mar. 3	9	7	4
profile No. XV	222 – 230	Mar. 4 – Mar. 9	9	9	2
profile No. XVI	232 – 241	Mar. 11 – Mar. 13	8	11	–
NW profile into the Gulf of Oman	242 – 249	Mar. 19 – Mar. 24	8	15	–
Gulf of Oman	250 – 271	Mar. 24 – Mar. 31 ⎫	23	24	–
Gulf of Oman	379 – 368	Apr. 14 – Apr. 16 ⎬			
Persian Gulf	272 – 378	Mar. 31 – Apr. 14	65	41	30
			231	227	99

west coast of India and Pakistan, where ostracods were dominant in the plankton, it was necessary to add formalin to the plankton as soon as the catch came on deck, as the crustaceans severely damaged the delicate fish larvae by voracious feeding, even in the bucket.

3. Variations in the Catch According to Net and Kind of Tow

The number of species caught per haul was generally lower in the HLN samples than in the RT samples, and night catches were often more prolific than day catches. In areas where a considerable number of HLN and RT day and night samples were made, the mean difference between day and night is much more striking in the HLN than in the RT tows. While the HLN samples showed a mean ratio for number of species caught at night to number of species caught in daytime of 2.0, 2.5, and 3.8 in the three areas, southern Red Sea to Gulf of Aden, Cape Guardafui to Mombasa, and the open ocean between Mombasa and Cochin, the ratio for number of species caught at night to number of species caught by day was 1 for RT hauls. The HLN fished always somewhat deeper than the RT, so the less prolific day catches with the HLN were not likely to have occurred because most larvae stayed much deeper during the day. If this were so, the opposite effect should have resulted. However, many fish larvae species do show a near-surface distribution at night (HARTMANN, 1970; NELLEN and HEMPEL; 1970; NELLEN, 1972) and, as vertically towed nets whenever they do not follow a very straight vertical line tend to drag at the surface before lifting out of the water, the HLN may have filtered a higher volume of surface water compared to other depths. Such an effect may have increased the chance of catching more species at night.

During an oblique RT haul roughly 10 times more water was filtered than during a vertical HLN standard haul. Thus an RT haul probably integrates the number of fish

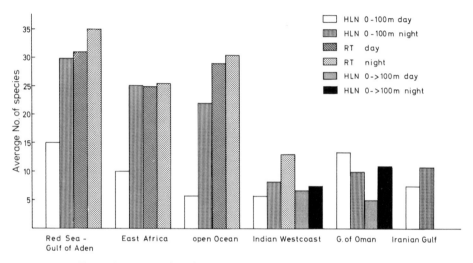

Fig. 1. Average number of species according to subarea and kind of haul

larvae species occurring in a certain area better than an HLN haul, and patchiness is thus more easily avoided with the RT than with the HLN.

There is no great difference in the number of species found in the RT hauls and the HLN night hauls (Fig. 1). Most fish larvae species caught were available in the water layer above 100 m depth.

Off the west coast of India most RT hauls were replaced by additional deep HLN hauls (usually 200 m). On average these hauls did not produce more species than the standard hauls. Most fish larvae would seem to have a rather shallow depth range. The differences in number of species caught by HLN during day and night were less accentuated in the eastern part of the area investigated (Fig. 1). This can probably be explained by fewer species and a greater abundance of specimens of these species.

These remarks concerning occurrence, distribution, and availability of species among fisch larvae must be understood only qualitatively and in a very general way. An analysis of catches from a single station may give quite another picture. Qualitative differences resulting from 3 kinds of tows at one station and within one night hour are shown in Fig. 2. No single sample included all 47 species found at this station. The RT which went down to only 70 m caught most species, namely 28, followed by the HLN tow from 200 to 0 m, which caught 27 species, only 20 species being caught by the HLN towed from 100 to 0 m. Besides the difference in the number of species, there is a difference

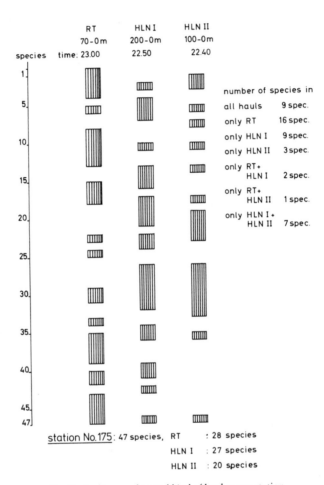

Fig. 2. Species number and kind of haul at one station

in species composition in the 3 hauls. Each net caught several species exclusively; in the RT those numbered 16, in the HLN 200−0 m 9, and in the HLN 100−0 m 3. Not more than 9 species from the total of 47 were found in all nets, and these 9 species did not even rank first in abundance in the samples. Only 5 of them appeared more than once among the 5 most abundant species in any of the 3 samples. The total number of larvae per m² sea surface was 10 in the RT, 35 in the HLN 100−0 m, and 39 in the HLN 200−0 m.

This example demonstrates the limit of reliability of a qualitative analysis of fish larvae distribution in a highly diverse tropical biotope. To get a relatively true idea of the amount and kind of fish larvae occurring in a certain area, the grid of stations probably must be quite dense, the net-opening must be wide to take at least the more common species by filtering a large amount of water within a short time, and the tow must cover the depth range within which the more important species are distributed.

The total of 326 samples contained about 55 000 specimens. Slightly more than 98% of these could be identified to family level. 107 different families were found in the material. Among these, 120 genera and about 65 species could be identified, several of the lower taxa representing juvenile or adult myctophids.

II. Results

1. Characteristics of Fish Larvae Distribution with Respect to Different Geographical Areas

The area investigated was divided into 7 subareas; these geographic differences reflect differences in the fish larvae fauna.

a) Subarea I: Southern Part of the Red Sea and Gulf of Aden

15 stations, 21 HLN standard hauls, 1 HLN>100−0 m hauls, 10 RT hauls.

This subarea can be expected to be influenced highly by the Red Sea and by its closeness to the shore. On the other hand the deep trench in the Gulf of Aden characterizes this area as partly oceanic.

The following families of fish larvae were caught on more than 65% of all stations on which samples were taken within this area.

Group	% of positive stations
Bregmacerotidae	67%
(eel leptocephali)	
Stomiatidae	
Synodidae	
Serranidae	73%
Carangidae	
Callionymidae	
Platycephalidae	
Apogonidae	
Labridae	80%
Gobiidae	
Gonostomidae	
Nomeidae	87%
Myctophidae	100%

This area offers a high variety of inshore and of oceanic forms as well. The frequent occurrence of larvae of the families Bregmacerotidae, Serranidae, Carangidae, Callionymidae, Platycephalidae, and Gobiidae demonstrates the near coastal character of these stations; Gonostomidae and Myctophidae are typical oceanic forms. The total number of probably not less than 85 species occurred in the samples from area I. Eleven + fiftyseven species were found per station (average 32.9). The diversity index d was calculated according to SIMPSON (1949). Because this value is influenced not only by the area but also by depth of haul, by time and by kind of net used (McGOWAN and FRAUENDORF, 1966) d is given according to type of gear and kind of haul:

	HLN, 100−0 m night	HLN, 100−0 m day	RT day and night
d	0.16 (n=13)	0.11 (n=8)	0.14 (n=10)

The low diversity indices were found in all kinds of samples; this indicates a high diversity and confirms the great variety in the fish larvae fauna of this area, as seen already at family level.

b) Subarea II: Cape Guardafui to Mombasa
59 stations, 56 HLN standard hauls, 1 HLN>100−0 m haul, 31 RT hauls.

Subarea II is mostly oceanic. The narrow shelf of the east coast of Africa contributed a large variety of scarce fish larvae that probably belong to coral fish. No less than 135 different species, probably more, were present in the fish larvae catches from area II. A wide range per station (from 1 to 102 species) was found (average 23.7). The most abundant oceanic forms outnumbered the other forms which occurred here, too. The families Nomeidae (75%), Gonostomidae (88%), and Myctophidae (96%) were so dominant that only these 3 appeared at more than 65% of all stations, but the large number of species, mainly in the families Myctophidae, Gonostomidae and in other families which were abundant, account for the fact that the diversity in this subarea was the highest of all:

	HLN, 100−0 m night	HLN, 100−0 m day	RT day and night
d	0.10 (n=22)	0.10 (n=33)	0.11 (n=31)

c) Subarea III: Open Ocean between East Africa and South India
16 stations, 15 HLN standard hauls, 5 HLN>100−0 m hauls, 11 RT hauls.

Subarea III is very similar to subarea II in that the oceanic character is typical for the stations covered here. The absence of many species found in subarea II is demonstrated by the range of number of species per station (only 3−61). The average number per station, however, is 25.4, thus a little higher than in subarea II. Most frequent again were the Gonostomidae and Myctophidae which occurred at 87 and 94% respectively of all stations in the open ocean between Africa and India. Labridae and Bothidae, which were slightly less common in subarea II, were found in 69% of the samples from the open ocean. Again the diversity for the fish larvae fauna was high.

	HLN, 100−0 m night	HLN, 100−0 m day	RT day and night
d	0.11 (n=8)	0.17 (n=7)	0.14 (n=11)

The ichtyogeographical situation changes rapidly as we approach the Indian side of the Arabian Sea. Here the stations were influenced more by the broad West Indian shelf and typical coastal characters are reflected in the composition of the fish larvae fauna.

d) Subarea IV: West Coast of India
51 stations, 29 HLN standard hauls, 24 HLN>100−0 m hauls, 16 RT hauls.

Looking just at the frequency of certain families, subarea IV still seems to be quite similar to subarea II and III, with Gonostomidae and Myctophidae very abundant and present at 89% and 91% respectively of all stations. Only the fact that Bregmacerotidae are more common here (found at 75% of all stations) distinguishes it from subareas II (60% Bregmacerotidae), and III (20% Bregmacerotidae). The typical difference from the subareas described before, however, is mainly in genera and species composition. Many species of myctophids and gonostomids (e.g. *Lampanyctus spec.* and *Cyclothone spec.*) were not found at all off the west coast of India. A total of not more than 65 species was found in subarea IV. The number of species ranged from 0−45 per station, with an average of only 9.3 species per station. The diversity was also low:

	HLN, 100−0 m night	HLN, 100−0 m day	HLN, >100−0 m day and night	RT day and night
d	0.38 (n=13)	0.33 (n=16)	0.38 (n=24)	0.35 (n=16)

e) Subarea V: Gulf of Oman
25 stations, 14 HLN standard hauls, 12 HLN >100−0 m hauls.

The number of species declined further in subarea V. Here an intensive mixing of water from the shallow Persian Gulf and from the Arabian Sea takes place, causing a turbulence that probably results in high nutrient values for this area. Large numbers of specimens and small numbers of species were typical of the stations in the Gulf of Oman. Only about 35 different species were caught altogether and the highest number per haul was 27, the lowest 3. On average, 10.4 species were present at each station. Most common were the families Myctophidae and Sudidae, occurring at 91% and 83% respectively of all stations. The family Myctophidae showed one species, *Benthosema pterota;* this and the high abundance of Sudidae larvae make the stations in the Gulf of Oman very similar to the stations off Karachi (Pakistan) included in subarea IV. The samples were not at all diverse. In subarea V very high values of d were quite common:

	HLN, 100−0 m night	HLN, 100−0 m day	HLN, >100−0 m day and night
d	0.74 (n=7)	0.54 (n=6)	0.84 (n=13)

The fish larvae fauna of the Persian Gulf no longer shows oceanic elements. The entire Gulf is a shelf area and such families as the myctophids and gonostomids are absent from the samples.

f) Subarea VI: Southern Persian Gulf
37 stations, 32 HLN standard hauls, 7 RT hauls.

The southern part of the Persian Gulf is characterized by fish larvae of the family Gobiidae and Apogonidae which were found at 84% and 65% respectively at all stations. No less than 47 different species were caught in this part of the Gulf and the number of species per station ranged from 0 to 26 (average 9.2). The samples were less diverse than the samples off tropical East Africa but more diverse than off India and in the Gulf of Oman.

	HLN, bottom−0 m night	HLN, bottom−0 m day	RT day and night
d	0.21 (n=22)	0.21 (n=10)	0.36 (n=7)

g) Subarea VII: Northern Persian Gulf
31 stations, 6 HLN standard hauls, 23 RT hauls.

In the northern Persian Gulf besides gobies, fishes of the family Clupeidae and Pomadasyidae were dominant. Pomadasyidae occurred at 91% of all stations, herring-like larvae at 80% and gobies at 69%. The differences in the samples which originated from further south may have been due to the sampling technique. For the very shallow stations in the northern Persian Gulf, vertical tows were not efficient, so the RT was mainly used; it was towed horizontally at a depth of about 3 m. The total number of species caught near the surface was 33, 2−22 at one station, average 11.3. The diversity was similar to that in the southern part of the Gulf:

	HLN, 100−0 m day	RT day and night
d	0.17 (n=5)	0.35 (n=23)

The short descriptions of the 7 subareas which were found to be different in respect of the fish larvae fauna include only the very common fish families which occurred at more than 65% of all stations in a subarea. For more detail, Fig. 3 gives a summary of the frequency with which larvae of all fish families were caught. Only 28 of the total of 107 families occurred at 50% or more of all stations in one or several of the subareas. By far the most common forms belonged to families Gonostomidae, Myctophidae, Labridae and Nomeidae and were found in mainly oceanic areas. The common neritic elements in nearshore and shelf zones were apogonids, carangids, and gobies. Bregmacerotidae larvae were found everywhere.

Fig. 4a−i shows the distribution of fish larvae of the more common families.

Fig. 3. Frequency of fish larvae types (family level) according to subarea. The lines show the percentage of stations in a subarea at which the fish larva type in question was caught

● Southern part of the Red Sea and Gulf of Aden	▪ open Ocean between Mombasa and Cochin	▲ Gulf of Oman
▴ Cape Guardafui - Mombasa	▫ Westcoast of Jndia	⊚ Southern Persian Gulf
		▪ Northern Persian Gulf

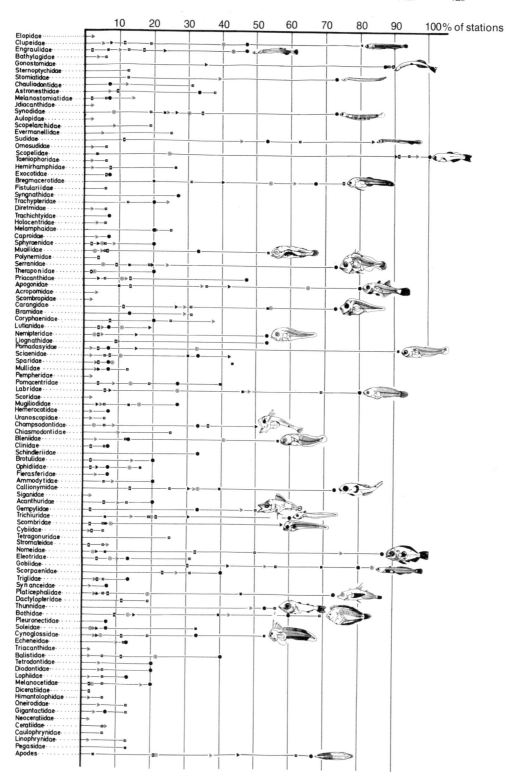

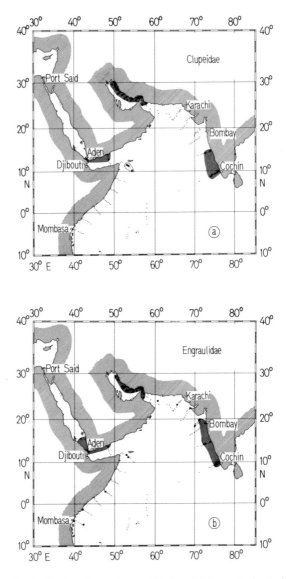

Fig. 4a–i. Distribution charts of several kinds of fish larvae in the Arabian Sea

2. Quantitative Aspects of Fish Larvae Distribution in the Arabian Sea

a) Concentrations of Fish Larvae in General

It is assumed that all HLN hauls fished the zone in which there were most fish larvae, whether the net was lowered to 100 m or 200 m depth. The following average concentrations per station was found:

I. Southern part of the Red Sea and Gulf of Aden: 75 larvae m^{-2} (22 samples), II. Cape Guardafui to Mombasa: 28 larvae m^{-2} (59 samples), III. Open Ocean between East Africa and South India: 18 larvae m^{-2} (20 samples), IV. West coast of India: 42 larvae m^{-2}

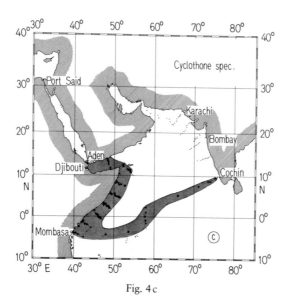

Fig. 4c

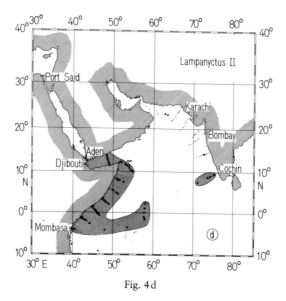

Fig. 4d

(53 samples), V. Gulf of Oman: 695 larvae m^{-2} (27 samples), VI. Southern Persian Gulf: 40 larvae m^{-2} (30 samples).

According to the forms of fish larvae found, subareas II and III were oceanic; these are the areas with the lowest numbers of fish larvae. The richest subareas were I and V, probably because these are areas of high productivity as a result of turbulent mixing of different water bodies (SIEDLER, 1968, PETER, 1967, RYTHER and MENZEL, 1955).

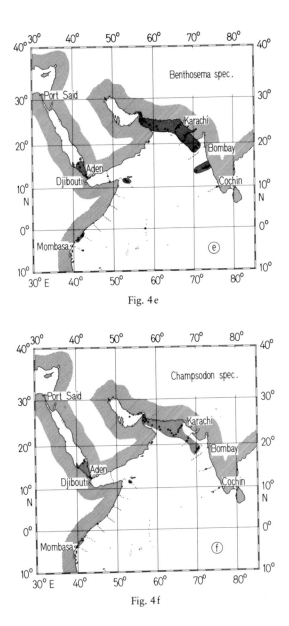

Fig. 4 e

Fig. 4 f

A relatively high concentration of fish larvae per m² was found also in the shallow Persian Gulf. A quantitative analysis of the material, however, can be given only for the southern part; further north, only surface tows with the RT net were done.

b) Larval Abundance of the More Common Groups

Myctophids were the most abundant (Table 2). Without doubt, this family includes also the greatest variation in species. At least 45 different species are represented in the

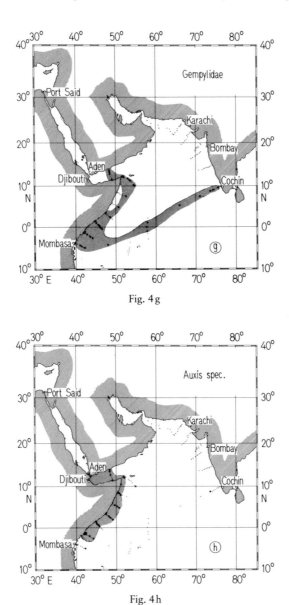

Fig. 4 g

Fig. 4 h

material, but in those areas where the concentration of myctophid larvae was most striking, i.e. in the Gulf of Oman and some stations between Bombay and Karachi, only a single species, *Benthosema pterota*, made up the bulk of the samples. No other fish

Table 2. Mean number of larvae m^{-2} for the more common fish families, only stations with positive hauls considered. (Number of stations with positive hauls in parenthesis; range = lowest and highest concentrations m^{-2} found in one subarea)

Subarea		I	II	III	IV	V	VI
No. of HLN stations		14	55	10	45	25	30
Clupeidae		6 (5)	2 (1)	0	5 (4)	3 (3)	15 (12)
	range	0.5 – 19.7	–	–	0.1 – 19.7	0.8 – 1.5	0.8 – 116.8
Engraulidae		5 (7)	2 (3)	0	5 (7)	15 (6)	5 (15)
	range	0.5 – 10.4	0.6 – 5.5	–	0.6 – 24.7	1.6 – 46.0	0.1 – 31.2
Gonostomidae		4 (8)	4 (37)	8 (8)	5 (35)	2 (10)	0
	range	0.6 – 31.0	0.1 – 34.7	0.6 – 27.0	0.1 – 39.2	0.8 – 3.5	–
Synodidae		7 (9)	3 (8)	0	1 (7)	3 (7)	6 (9)
	range	0.6 – 50.0	0.1 – 21.0	–	0.5 – 1.6	0.8 – 11.6	0.8 – 18.3
Sudidae		1 (7)	1 (14)	1 (2)	1 (8)	12 (24)	1 (2)
	range	0.6 – 4.6	0.5 – 4.0	0.6 – 1.3	0.6 – 4.3	0.8 – 60.3	0.8 – 1.4
Myctophidae		21 (14)	12 (53)	15 (9)	37 (41)	335 (25)	4 (6)
	range	0.6 – 237.0	0.6 – 79.0	0.6 – 58.3	0.6 – 528.0	2.1 – 1192.0	0.7 – 12.7
Bregmacerotidae		3 (8)	3 (31)	1 (3)	6 (32)	4 (9)	2 (21)
	range	0.6 – 15.5	0.1 – 41.5	0.6 – 1.8	0.6 – 35.0	0.8 – 13.8	0.8 – 5.2
Serranidae		2 (7)	1 (9)	0	3 (4)	5 (5)	3 (2)
	range	0.6 – 3.3	0.3 – 3.9	–	0.5 – 6.1	0.8 – 7.4	2.3 – 5.9
Apogonidae		5 (7)	1 (13)	0.6 (1)	3 (4)	6 (12)	3 (20)
	range	0.6 – 12.3	0.6 – 2.8	–	0.6 – 1.7	0.8 – 18.5	0.1 – 18.7
Carangidae		12 (8)	1 (8)	0	1 (3)	4 (7)	3 (14)
	range	0.6 – 54.2	0.5 – 3.1	–	0.6 – 1.5	0.8 – 16.3	0.8 – 14.8
Coryphaenidae		0.5 (2)	1 (11)	0	0.6 (2)	0	0
	range	0.5	0.5 – 1.8	–	0.1 – 0.9	–	–

Pomadasyidae	0	0	0	0	1 (4)	17 (11)
range	–	–	–	–	0.8–3.2	0.7–84.9
Sciaenidae	5 (3)	0.6 (1)	0.5 (1)	1.5 (2)	4 (12)	0.8 (1)
range	1.2–9.8	–	–	1.2–1.8	0.8–11.6	–
Labridae	2 (11)	2 (17)	3 (4)	1 (6)	1 (2)	3 (8)
range	0.5–3.1	0.5–10.4	0.6–12.0	0.1–2.5	0.8–1.6	0.8–5.9
Champsodontidae	1 (3)	0	0	1 (17)	4 (14)	0
range	0.6–4.3	–	–	0.6–3.1	0.8–11.3	–
Callionymidae	7 (6)	1 (15)	0	2 (8)	2 (7)	2 (9)
range	0.6–12.9	0.5–4.9	–	0.5–5.4	0.8–4.0	0.8–4.4
Gempylidae	4 (2)	1 (13)	0.5 (1)	0	0	0
range	2.2–5.5	0.5–3.1	–	–	–	–
Nomeidae	4 (8)	2 (32)	1 (6)	4 (13)	3 (16)	0
range	0.2–16.1	0.4–8.7	0.6–1.6	0.7–10.0	0.8–13.8	–
Gobiidae	12 (12)	5 (25)	0.5 (1)	4 (13)	4 (12)	8 (25)
range	0.5–44.1	0.5–61.8	–	0.6–35.5	0.8–16.9	0.7–29.1
Platycephalidae	3 (6)	2.5 (1)	0	0.6 (1)	0.8 (1)	1 (6)
range	0.5–3.7	–	–	–	–	0.7–1.3
Thunnidae (Auscis)	2 (5)	1 (13)	0.6 (1)	1.2 (1)	0	0
range	0.6–3.7	0.5–6.7	–	–	–	–
Katsuwonus pel.	0	1 (2)	1 (3)	0	0	0
range	–	0.1–1.2	0.6–1.8	–	–	–
Bothidae	3 (7)	1 (15)	0.6 (2)	1 (5)	1 (3)	0.8 (1)
range	0.6–8.5	0.6–2.5	0.5–0.6	0.6–3.0	0.8–0.9	–

larvae type was as abundant, and even the frequently occurring gonostomids rank far behind the myctophids in number per m². Lantern fish seem to be a very important link in the food chain in oceanic areas, comparable perhaps with herring-like fish and some gadids in the neritic and boreal zones respectively.

Larval concentrations were not very high for fish which may have commercial importance. Herring-like larvae were relatively common and abundant in the Persian Gulf, as were anchovy, which in addition appeared in considerable quantities on some stations in the Gulf of Oman as well. Carangids, probably *Decapterus* spec., seemed to have

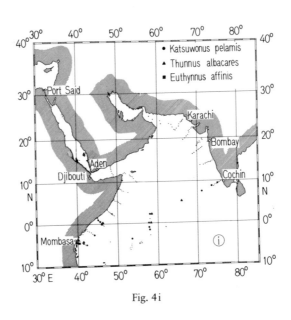

Fig. 4i

formed a spawning concentration in the southern Red Sea and the Gulf of Aden, as was also probable for nomeids, which could not be identified to the genera of species level, but which are supposed to be of some value for fisheries. Tuna larvae appeared more frequently in the Gulf of Aden and between Cape Guardafui and southern Somalia, but their concentration was not remarkably high at any station.

Species of other, non-commercial fish families of which larvae were found indicated either spawning communities with high larval concentrations in one or the other subarea, or scattered spawning activities. The first case, probably, is true for Synodidae in subarea I, II, V, and VI, for Sudidae in subarea V for Bregmacerotidae in subareas I, II, IV, and V, for Pomadasyidae in subarea VI and for Champsodontidae and Sciaenidae in subarea V. Apogonidae, Coryphaenidae, Labridae, Callionymidae, Gempylidae, Gobiidae, and Bothidae certainly were not rare in the samples but nowhere were high larval concentrations of these fishes found.

Tuna Fisheries and their Resources in the Indian Ocean

A. SUDA

Tuna fisheries, especially tuna longline fisheries, are well developed in the Indian Ocean. As shown in Table 1, the total amount of tunas and tuna-like fishes caught in the Ocean in 1968 amounts to 280 000 tons (FAO, 1969 b), accounting for about 12% of the total fish production from the Ocean.

155 000 tons are accounted for by longline fisheries of China (Taiwan), Japan and Korea operating over the wide offshore area. Their catch consists of large-sized tuna

Table 1. Annual amount of catches of tunas, bonitos and billfishes from the Indian Ocean by countries, 1964–1968. (FAO, 1969 b, Bull. Fish. Statistics, 1968)

	1964	1965	1966	1967	1968
Australia	0.1	0.1	0.1	0.1	0.1
Ceylon	22.7	25.6	30.0	42.8	56.5
China (Taiwan)	7.1	4.9	3.6	12.0	34.2
India	16.3	12.9	13.2	13.6	16.7
Japan	76.5	84.3	81.5	108.9	107.9
Korea	0.1	0.8	0.8	3.7	11.6
Malaysia	5.4	6.8	8.3	7.2	7.7
Maldives	12.0	17.6	21.4	24.1	22.7
Pakistan	9.6	10.1	12.2	11.0	11.2
Reunion	0.1	0.1	0.1	0.2	0.3
Southern Yemen	3.6	2.5	1.5	1.3	1.6
USSR	1.2	2.4	6.2	8.4	5.3
Indian Ocean Total	155.0	168.0	180.0	234.0	279.0

species such as albacore, bigeye, yellowfin and southern bluefin and billfishes. Species caught by coastal countries surrounding the Ocean include, in addition to large-sized species, small-sized tuna such as skipjack, little tuna and frigate mackerel. Catch of these species by coastal countries was estimated at around 125 000 tons in 1968.

In the present paper the author presents maps of the distribution of tuna, and he tries to describe their contribution to the fishery and the relationship between the locality of catch and environmental conditions, mainly by employing the longline fishing data.

I. Distribution of Albacore, Bigeye, Yellowfin and Southern Bluefin

1. Distribution at Fishable Age

Fig. 1 (a−h) demonstrates the occurrence of longline-caught large tunas in the second and fourth quarters of the year, shown by depicting the maximum average longline hooking-rate over the period between 1966 and 1968. Here, the longline hooking-rate is the average number of fish caught per 100 longline hooks. The major concentration of each species reveals a peculiar pattern as will be described below.

a) Yellowfin (Fig. 1 a and b)

This species generally occurs over the low latitudinal areas north of 10° S. The distribution also expands southward along the African coast especially during the first

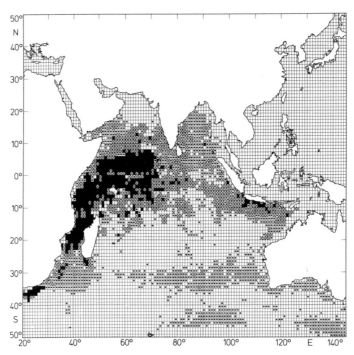

Fig. 1. Distribution of longline hooking-rates of 4 tuna species for 2 quarters of the years 1966 to 1968, expressed as maximum average hooking-rate for each 1° square. (Filled circle < 1.0; cross 1.0–3.0; black square > 3.0) a Distribution of longline hooking-rate of yellowfin tuna in the second quarter of the years 1966–1968

half of the year, and the Australian coast during the second half of the year. Over the offshore area south of 10° S the occurrence is sporadic.

b) Albacore (Fig. 1 c and d)

Albacore occupies the intermediate latitudinal area between 10° S and 35° S and its sphere of occurrence hardly overlaps that of yellowfin.

c) Bigeye (Fig. 1 e and f)

The species occurs in 2 separate areas. The northern concentration is in the waters of low latitudes as in the case of the yellowfin.

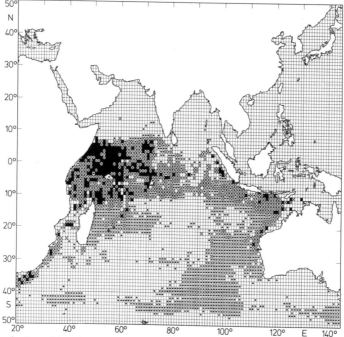

Fig. 1 b. Distribution of longline hooking-rate of yellowfin tuna in the fourth quarter of the years 1966 – 1968

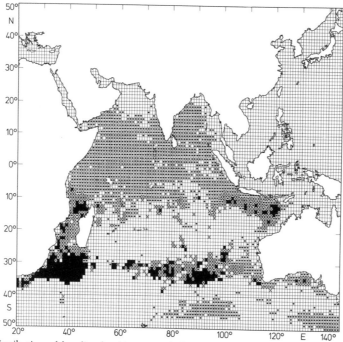

Fig. 1 c. Distribution of longline hooking-rate of albacore tuna in the second quarter of the years 1966 – 1968

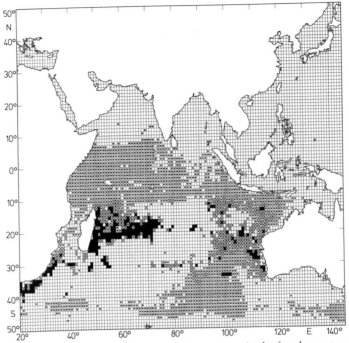

Fig. 1d. Distribution of longline hooking-rate of albacore tuna in the fourth quarter of the years
1966 — 1968

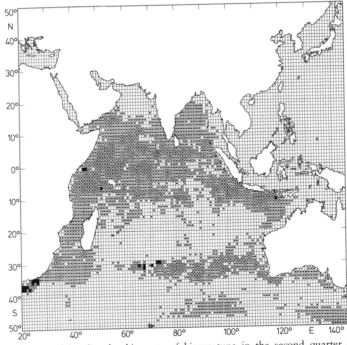

Fig. 1e. Distribution of longline hooking-rate of bigeye tuna in the second quarter of the years
1966 — 1968

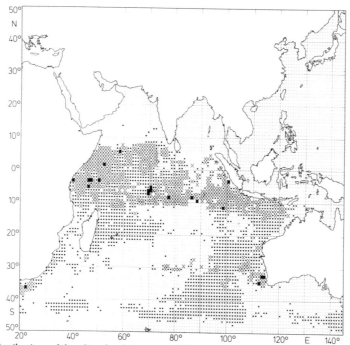

Fig. 1 f. Distribution of longline hooking-rate of bigeye tuna in the fourth quarter of the years 1966–1968

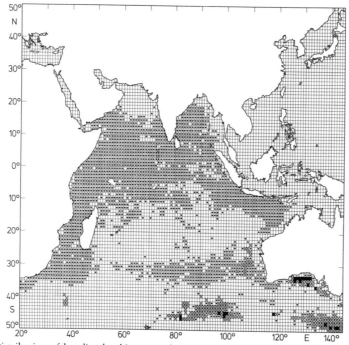

Fig. 1 g. Distribution of longline hooking-rate of southern bluefin tuna in the second quarter of the years 1966–1968

The other concentration is located along $30° - 35°$ S in the southernmost part of the albacore distribution. The northern group comprises mature individuals and the southern one immature individuals (Sakamoto, 1967).

d) Southern Bluefin (Fig. 1 g and h)

Southern bluefin is distributed in the zonal waters in an east-west direction in the Sub-Antarctic area with the exceptional northward expansion along the west coast of

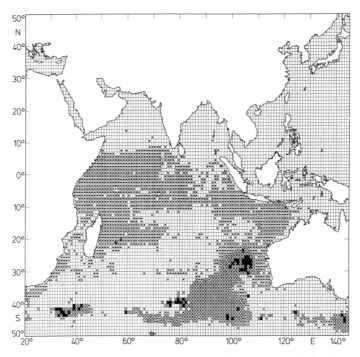

Fig. 1 h. Distribution of longline hooking-rate of southern bluefin tuna in the fourth quarter of the years 1966 — 1968

Australia during the fourth and first quarters of the year. Another concentration occurs along the southern coast of Australia.

2. Distribution at Larval Stage

The distribution of the larvae of 4 large tuna species is given by Ueyanagi (1969). Their distribution can be summarized as follows:

a) Yellowfin

Yellowfin larvae appear to occur over the relatively low latitudinal area north of $10°$ S.

b) Bigeye

Larval bigeye also seems to spread over the low latitudes north of $10°$ S.

c) Albacore

Albacore at the larval stage is distributed in a different manner from yellowfin and bigeye. The occurrence is observed in the waters between 10°S and 25°S.

d) Southern Bluefin

The distribution of larvae of this species is restricted to a very small area between 10°S and 20°S off the NW coast of Australia. Although similar hydrographic conditions are to be found in other areas, such as off the west coasts of South Africa and South America, surveys did not show spawning there. It seems, therefore, that the area off NW Australia is the only spawning area of the southern bluefin.

In general, it is suggested that the spawning grounds of large-sized tunas are restricted to the lower latitudinal waters, the area north of the southern boundary of the South Equatorial Current. In addition, each species shows a specific pattern of larval distribution, yellowfin and bigeye tending to spawn in the lowest latitudinal areas, whereas albacore and southern bluefin remain subtropical species, also with respect to the distribution of their larvae. The limited area in the eastern part of the South Equatorial Current is the spawning ground for southern bluefin.

II. Distribution of Smaller Tunas (Skipjack, Little Tuna and Frigate Mackerel)

1. Distribution at Fishable Age

Commercial fisheries for small tunas are dispersed over the Indian Ocean area and little information on these species is available in the present study. As to skipjack, the

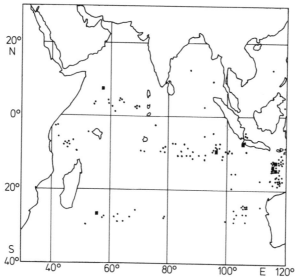

Fig. 2. Occurrence of juvenile skipjack tuna from stomach contents of longline caught billfishes from the Indian Ocean (MORI, unpublished)

longline hooking-rate in various parts of the Ocean suggests a wide distribution of this species over the tropical and sub-tropical waters (KASAHARA, 1968). Also the occurrence of juvenile sklipjack from the stomach contents of longline-caught billfishes supports the same nature of distribution (Fig. 2, MORI, unpublished).

2. Distribution at Larval Stage

The occurrence at larval stage is demonstrated for skipjack by UEYANAGI (1969), and for little tuna and frigate mackerel by YABE, YABUTA and UEYANAGI (1963). The distribution of their abundance shows 2 types, with skipjack spawning over a wide oceanic area, while larvae of the little tuna and frigate mackerel are mainly found in coastal waters. The habitats of the latter 2 species probably do not extend so far offshore during their life cycle.

III. Contribution of Tunas to the Fisheries in the Indian Ocean

The annual catches of the 4 large-sized tunas are given in Table 2. The average catch for these 4 species in the Indian Ocean in 1968 per 1 000 km² is 1.78 tons. The corresponding values for the Pacific and the Atlantic Ocean are 2.16 and 1.59 tons

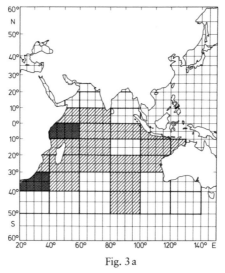

Fig. 3 a

Fig. 3 a—e. Average annual catch for the years 1966—1968 in tons per 1 000 longline hooks for different species and areas (10° latitude by 20° longitude). a) Average annual catch combined for yellowfin, albacore bigeye and southern bluefin. (Hatched area 1.0—1.5 times the average annual catch in the Indian Ocean, cross-hatched area > 1.5 times the average.) Average annual catch of yellowfin b), albacore c), bigeye d), and southern bluefin e). Symbols for b—e: hatched area 1.0—2.0 times the average annual catch in the Indian Ocean, cross-hatched area > 2.0 times the average

respectively (Table 3). The amount of all tunas and tuna-like fishes combined is 3.72 tons, which is comparable with 5.25 tons and 3.78 tons for the Pacific and the Atlantic Oceans, respectively. For comparison, total yields of marine fisheries for the 3 major

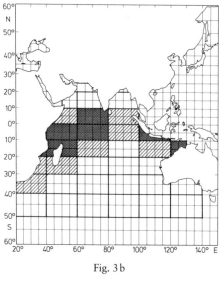

Fig. 3 b

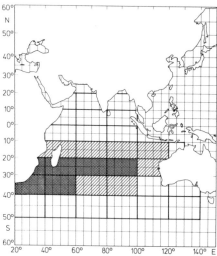

Fig. 3 c

Table 2. Annual catch of the 4 species of large sized tunas from the Indian Ocean by China (Taiwan), Japan, Korea and USSR (FAO 1969b, IOFC: TM/70/Information Paper 5)

	1960	1961	1962	1963	1964	1965	1966	1967	1968
Southern Bluefin	46.6	42.5	23.7	23.3	22.0	21.7	13.4	27.9	30.4
Yellowfin	35.7	32.3	45.1	30.1	20.1	23.1	28.9	32.3	56.2
Albacore	12.9	16.8	22.8	15.7	15.5	14.7	14.2	21.0	16.7
Bigeye	10.6	12.2	19.5	16.8	15.2	16.9	18.0	24.7	30.3
Four species combined	105.8	103.8	111.1	85.9	72.8	76.4	74.5	105.9	133.6

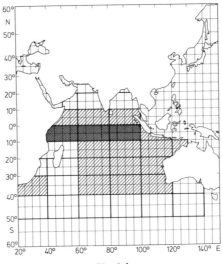

Fig. 3 d

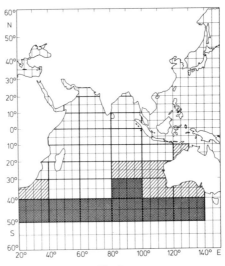

Fig. 3 e

Table 3. Comparison of marine catches of the 3 major oceans in 1968

Ocean	Area (10⁶ km²)	Amount of total catch (10³ tons)			Metric tons per 10³ km²		
		A	B	C	A	B	C
Indian	74.917	133.6	279	2200	1.78	3.72	29.37
Pacific	179.679	388.4	944	31300	2.16	5.25	174.20
Atlantic	106.463	169.7	403	23100	1.59	3.78	216.98

A: Four large-sized tuna species combined
B: Tunas and tunalike fishes combined
C: Whole marine fishes combined

oceans are calculated as follows: 29, 174, and 217 tons per 1 000 km² for the Indian, the Pacific and the Atlantic Oceans respectively. These statistics suggest that tuna stocks in the Indian Ocean are fairly highly utilized, though other fisheries are still under-developed.

Fig. 3 (a–e) gives average amounts of catch in weight of tuna species and 4 large-sized tuna species combined, per 1 000 longline hooks, by unit area (10 latitudinal by 20 longitudinal degrees) and on a yearly basis. The values employed here indicate the efficiency of each species in unit fishing effort. For the 4 large-sized species combined (Fig. 3a), the areas of high productivity in the longline fishery are widely dispersed over the entire Ocean, though more frequently observed in the western part of the Ocean.

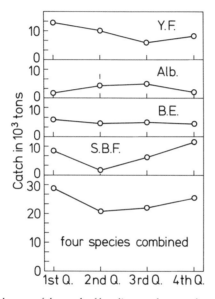

Fig. 4. Seasonal changes of the catch of longline caught tunas from the Indian Ocean

The average catch per 1 000 hooks over the whole Ocean is 580 kg. Of course, the geographical distribution of productivity of individual tuna species is quite different among species, reflecting the difference in distributional pattern by species. The average amounts of species caught per 1 000 hooks over the whole Ocean are 193 kg, 138 kg, 140 kg and 117 kg for yellowfin, bigeye, southern bluefin and albacore, respectively. In terms of weight, yellowfin account for the largest contribution to the longline catch.

These values indicate that the biomass of yellowfin is the largest and that of albacore is the smallest among those of the 4 large-sized tuna species exploited by longline gear in the Ocean.

Seasonal changes in the average amount of catch per 1 000 longline hooks of the species over the whole Ocean are demonstrated in Fig. 4. The catch per 1 000 hooks for the 4 large-sized tuna species combined is largest in the first quarter of the year. It decreases somewhat in the second and third quarters. However, this value is comparatively stable throughout the whole year, as each species has its peak at a different season and consequently compensates for the others. The seasonal change in the amount of catch per 1 000 hooks for individual species is remarkable, even in the case of yellowfin which inhabit the tropical zone with its comparatively small seasonal change in oceanographic conditions. This species peaks in the first quarter in the western part of the tropical waters and in the third quarter in the eastern part of the Ocean.

Concerning the skipjack, though insufficient information is available, the more frequent occurrences of larval fish from larvae net sampling and of juvenile fish from examination of the stomach contents of billfishes, as compared to those of the 4 large-sized tuna species, suggest a larger potential yield of this species than of large-sized tunas.

IV. Discussion of the Relationship between Distribution of Catches of Tunas and Environmental Conditions

In the Indian Ocean, as mentioned in the previous chapter, remarkable seasonal changes in longline catches of species are observed even in the lower latitudes. The amplitude of seasonal fluctuations seems larger than in other oceans. The changes are probably connected with changes in environmental conditions.

However, detailed examination of this relationship has not yet been carried out. In the present paper, the distribution of catch is related to the surface current system, the pattern of permanent thermocline and the upwelling.

1. Surface Current System, Water Type and Distribution of Tunas

NAKAMURA, YABUTA and MIMURA (1955) and MIMURA and NAKAMURA (1959) discussed this relationship. They suggested that different species occur in the different current systems.

a) In the South Equatorial Current area, albacore is abundant but yellowfin is not.

b) A remarkable concentration of yellowfin occurs during the northern hemisphere summer, in the Equatorial Countercurrent area and in the zone with variable currents between the South Equatorial Current and the SE monsoon drift. Albacore is absent in these areas.

c) Over the NE and SW monsoon current areas, which are other habitats of yellowfin, albacore seldom occurs.

On the basis of recent data (Fig. 1 a−h), the general relationship between species distribution and ocean current systems, and/or water type, is summarized as follows: The relationship between species distribution and ocean current system, and/or water type, is more clearly observed with a species which occurs in the sub-tropical or sub-Antarctic area.

a) Southern Bluefin

The longline fishing occurs in the west-wind drift area, where individuals are caught before maturing. When they mature, they move northward to the area off the NW coast of Australia where they are influenced in some way by the west-wind drift. Very young fish are found in the coastal waters off S and SE Australia. It was revealed by ROCHFORD (1958) and ROBINS (1958) that the concentration of young fish in the coastal area is related to the sub-Antarctic water. Thus the feature of the occurrence of this species is closely linked with the sub-Antarctic water (SHINGU, 1970).

b) Albacore

The sub-tropical gyre and its neighbouring waters are the territory of albacore. The northern half of the gyre, that is the South Equatorial Current area, forms its spawning ground. The southern part of the gyre, which is the area of the eastward current, is a habitat of young albacore.

c) Yellowfin

The concentration of yellowfin is observed over a wide area north of $10°$ S including the North Equatorial Current area (NE monsoon drift during the northern hemisphere winter period), the Equatorial Countercurrent area (during the northern hemisphere winter period), the SW monsoon drift area and the northernmost part of the South Equatorial Current area. Consequently, it is suggested that the occurrence of the species coincides with the Indian Equatorial Water (SVERDRUP, JOHNSON and FLEMING, 1942). The seasonal expansion of the distribution along both the African and Australian coasts is perhaps to be interpreted as a seasonal expansion of the influence of the Indian Equatorial Waters towards higher latitudes.

d) Bigeye

Distribution of this species is somewhat complicated because the species occurs in 2 separate waters, one in the area north of the northern boundary of the South Equatorial Current and the other in the area of the subtropical gyre. The immature group of this species occurs in the southern half of the sub-tropical gyre together with immature albacore, and the mature fish in the equatorial water along with yellowfin. However, as will be discussed in the next section, over the area north of the northern boundary of the South Equatorial Current, the species is supposed to inhabit a deeper layer than yellowfin and a vertical separation between the 2 species is indicated.

Thus, these 4 large-sized tuna species share their own domains independently. It is notable that the way of sharing is, more or less, correlated with the surface current system and or water type. Also, it is pointed out that the stage of sexual development is another factor of differentiation of distribution.

2. Permanent Thermocline and Efficiency of Fishing for Bigeye by Longline Gear

SUDA, KUME and SHIOHAMA (1969) discussed, mainly on the basis of information from longline fishing in the Pacific Ocean, that the formation of the longline ground of bigeye is likely to be related to the depth of the permanent thermocline over the area where the tropical surface layer is well developed. In such a case, where the thermocline occurs at about 100 m below the surface, a high hooking-rate of bigeye is experienced. The following is an interpretation of the good coincidence between effective catch by longline and thermocline depth of 100 m:

a) longline-caught bigeye do not scatter in the tropical surface layer but occur in the thermocline itself, or just below it;

b) when the thermocline is situated around a depth of 100 m and coincides with the depth of hooks, the longline gear works well in catching bigeye.

In the Indian Ocean, the information available on the depth of the thermocline is not sufficient for the present study. The results of past research, for instance bathythermograph data compiled by the U.S. National Oceanographic Data Center (1966), indicate that the average depth of the thermocline over the equatorial waters is around 100 m, accompanying ridges and troughs in a complex way. Such an indication helps to explain the effective catch of bigeye in the equatorial waters of the Ocean north of 10° S. As is suggested in the foregoing section, bigeye seems to be a deep-layer swimmer. WATANABE (1961), depending on the data obtained mainly from the Pacific Ocean, observed the appearance of scratches made on the smoked glass of a depth recorder set on a hookline of longline gear when fish are caught, and examined the depth of formation of such scratches. He suggested that bigeye was hooked, on average, at $80 - 100$ m while yellowfin was hooked in a significantly shallower layer. (Table 4).

Table 4. Depth of occurrence of the scratch on the smoked glass of a depth recorder set on a hookline of longline gear, which is supposedly caused when a fish is hooked. (After WATANABE, 1961)

Date	Locality	Species	Depth range of the scratch in m
May 12, 1960	6° 28′ S, 120° 21′ W	Bigeye	$80 - 82 - 87$
do.	do.	do.	$58 - 98 - 112$
May 13, 1960	5° 51′ S, 120° 14′ W	Yellowfin	$0 - 32$
May 25, 1960	4° 50′ N, 119° 05′ W	Yellowfin?	$0 - 30$
May 26, 1960	5° 01′ N, 118° 59′ W	Yellowfin?	$0 - 30$
May 28, 1960	4° 33′ N, 118° 47′ W	Yellowfin	$0 - 44$
May 29, 1960	4° 10′ N, 118° 51′ W	do.	$0 - 26$
do.	do.	do.	$0 - 40$
June 2, 1960	5° 44′ N, 122° 49′ W	Bigeye	$70 - 90 - 96$
June 3, 1960	5° 41′ N, 122° 51′ W	Yellowfin?	$0 - 33$
do.	do.	Yellowfin	$0 - 32$
June 5, 1960	5° 49′ N, 125° 51′ W	Yellowfin?	$0 - 45$
June 18, 1960	4° 14′ N, 136° 11′ W	Yellowfin	$0 - 20$
June 16, 1960	4° 33′ N, 137° 08′ W	do.	$0 - 16$
Oct. 7, 1960	6° 44′ S, 58° 23′ E	Yellowfin?	$12 - 30 - 66$
Oct. 13, 1960	7° 31′ S, 48° 41′ E	Yellowfin?	$0 - 40$
Oct. 8, 1960	7° 50′ S, 48° 49′ E	Yellowfin?	$0 - 28$
Oct. 19, 1960	7° 23′ S, 47° 46′ E	Yellowfin	$0 - 30 - 63$
Oct. 22, 1960	3° 28′ S, 48° 23′ E	do.	$0 - 14$
Oct. 23, 1960	3° 26′ S, 49° 08′ E	do.	$0 - 22$
Nov. 3, 1960	3° 13′ S, 45° 22′ E	Yellowfin?	$0 - 44$
Nov. 12, 1960	2° 08′ S, 48° 04′ E	Yellowfin	$0 - 50$
Nov. 14, 1960	5° 47′ S, 47° 05′ E	do.	$0 - 36$
Nov. 19, 1960	6° 07′ S, 47° 49′ E	Yellowfin?	$0 - 58$
Nov. 29, 1960	6° 20′ S, 47° 13′ E	Yellowfin?	$0 - 62$

Therefore, it is supposed that bigeye inhabits greater depths than yellowfin. Thus, though both species demonstrate similar patterns of geographical distribution, their habitats appear to be separated vertically.

3. Upwelling and Concentration of Tunas

Occurrence of upwelling is reported from certain areas of the eastern (WYRTKI, 1961, 1962; ROCHFORD, 1962) and western parts (WOOSTER, SCHAEFER and ROBINSON, 1967; CUSHING, 1969) of the Ocean. However, only few studies have been made of the relationship between upwelling and concentration of tunas. Here, a remarkable upwelling in the Arabian Sea is considered as an example. As shown in Fig. 5 a and b, longline data do not necessarily cover the whole area of upwelling. Still, remarkable features are suggested regarding seasonal changes in the distribution of hooking-rates of yellowfin and bigeye in the area:

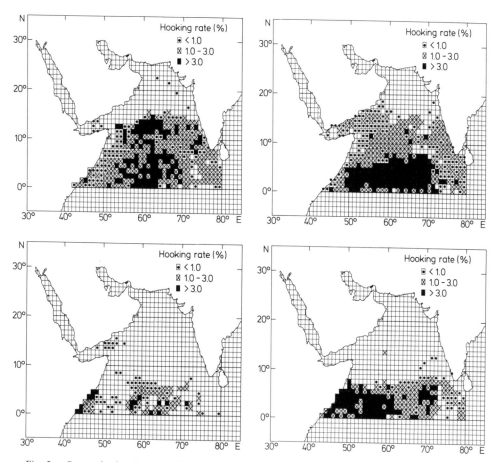

Fig. 5 a. Quarterly distribution of hooking-rate of yellowfin tuna in the Arabian Sea, 1966–1968

a) The coastal area of Somalia and SE Arabia, where the upwelling is located, is characterized by poor longline catches of the tunas, at least in the second and third quarters of the year, when the upwelling is more intense.

b) Concentration of the tunas takes place in the area away from the Somalian coast during the first and second quarters of the year. In the fourth quarter of the year, it tends to approach the coast.

c) Northward expansion of fish concentrations of high density appears in the first and second quarters of the year, and is especially remarkable in the first quarter,

contrary to the general expectation that the center of distribution should shift southward during the northern hemisphere winter period. In the third and fourth quarters
of the year, the northern extreme of concentration of the fishes moves to the south
and a poor area of tunas seems to prevail along the western coast of India. During

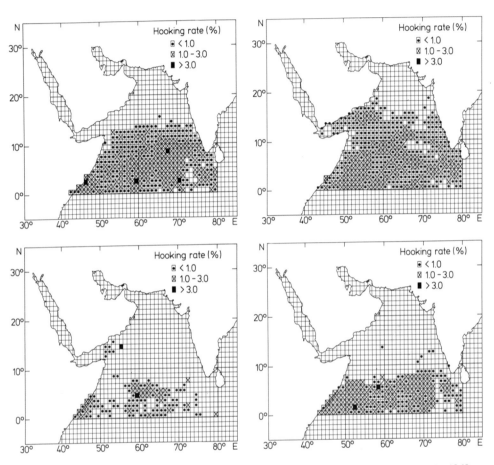

Fig. 5b. Quarterly distribution of hooking-rate of bigeye tuna in the Arabian Sea, 1966–1968

the third quarter of the year, upwelling is reported along the Malabar Coast (CUSHING,
1969) and the above-mentioned southward spread of the area of poor productivity of
tunas seems to be attributable to this upwelling.

Thus, as far as the longline data from the Arabian Sea are concerned, rather poor
catches of yellowfin and bigeye in the upwelling zone are indicated.

On the other hand, the hooking-rate of the longline fishery in the waters south of the
Great and Small Sunda Islands, where the occurrence of upwelling is suggested, does not

indicate in any quarter of the year such poor productivity of tunas as was observed in the Arabian Sea. MIMURA and NAKAMURA (1959) reported a fairly high hooking-rate of bigeye in the area during the northern hemisphere summer when upwelling occurs, as is pointed out by WYRTKI (1962) and ROCHFORD (1962).

It is the author's opinion that the linkage between upwelling and the occurrence of tunas is not to be explained in a simple way but in a complicated one, which is connected with, perhaps, fishing methods, the ecological condition of the fish, and other environmental conditions apart from upwelling.

4. Tentative Considerations on the Factors Determining Distribution and Abundance of Tunas

In the foregoing discussion, it was indicated that yellowfin is the most predominant among the 4 large-sized tuna species. Less abundant are southern bluefin, bigeye and albacore, respectively. The occurrence of the 4 tuna species clearly differs in its geographical distribution. The subantarctic water is the territory of the southern bluefin. The subtropical gyre is the habitat of albacore. The distribution of yellowfin coincides with that of the Indian equatorial water. Bigeye live together with albacore in the sub-tropical gyre when they are immature, and with yellowfin in the Indian equatorial water when they are mature.

It seems that the best explanation for the manner of distribution of tunas is, as suggested by NAKAMURA (1954), that each species inhabits its own area of a certain ocean current or water type. In Fig. 6, it is clear that boundaries between distributions of species are almost the same as those which exist between ocean currents, water types, or ocean current and water type. This appears to control the distribution of tunas more efficiently than the primary productivity of the Ocean. For instance, in spite of the indication of low primary productivity, albacore occurs exclusively in the subtropical gyre.

This is in contrast to the common anticipation that there must be a good coincidence of high primary productivity with high concentrations of tunas. Even a negative correlation is sometimes observed, as already demonstrated in the Arabian Sea where upwelling brings high primary productivity.

However, the following consideration leads to some ideas about the relationship between primary productivity and the abundance of tunas. It is observed that the Indian equatorial water supports the yellowfin stock which appears to be the largest biomass among the 4 large-sized tuna species in the Indian Ocean. On the other hand, the subtropi-cal gyre maintains the smallest species stock, that of albacore. The biomass of southern bluefin, which is the second in size among the 4 species, is maintained in the subantarctic waters. Such a combination of size of species biomass and current system or water type as a domain suggests that a relationship between primary productivity and abundance of tunas should be interpreted less through the geographical or superficial correspondence of the relationship than through the comparison between the size of biomass and the accumulated productivity in the habitat by species. It is noted by McGILL (1966), KETCHUM (1969) and CUSHING (1969) that upwellings are observed in the Arabian Sea and the Bay of Bengal and along the southern coast of the Great and Small Sunda Islands and that the low latitudinal area north of 10° S is more enriched than the area of the sub-tropical gyre. In the subantarctic area, primary productivity is higher than that in the subtropical gyre. The difference of stock size among populations of yellowfin, albacore and southern bluefin is understood as a reflection of the difference in primary productivity among their domains. In practice, the relation between primary productivity and abundance of tunas must be rather an obscure one because of time lags between the peak seasons of productivity on different trophic levels; at the same time, a spatial dispersion

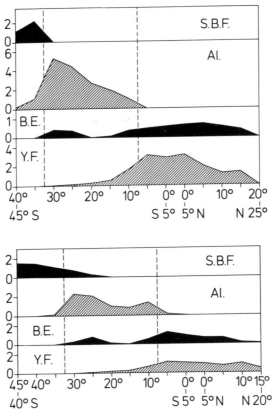

Fig. 6. Latitudinal changes in hooking-rates of the 4 large-sized tuna species in areas of south-north direction on the whole year basis, a: between 55° and 60° E, b: between 90° and 95° E. Southern bluefin: S.B.F., albacore: Al., bigeye: B.E., yellowfin: Y.F.

of the production is expected on higher levels. Therefore, the relation between primary productivity and the abundance of tunas is probably an indirect one.

The manner of distribution of bigeye is much more complicated. Immature bigeye occur along the southern boundary of the sub-tropical gyre. The mature group occurs along the bottom of tropical surface water. Thus, the occurrence of this species is characterized by its concentration along the boundary of a current system or a water type. As already suggested, the domain of this species is neither the enriched Indian equatorial water nor the fertilized subantarctic water. The manner of the distribution of the species might be interpreted as an example of "Edge effect".

V. Discussion on the Prospects of Tuna Fisheries in the Indian Ocean

The stocks of large-sized tunas are considered to be more or less fully exploited and substantial increases in catch may not be realized by increased effort (SHOMURA et al., 1967; FAO 1968, 1969; KIKAWA et al., 1969). The observed relationships between catch and effort indicate that the maximum sustainable yield for individual species may not be far from the following estimates (FAO, 1969a): yellowfin 30−35, albacore 20−25, bigeye 22−28, and southern bluefin 35−40 thousand tons. Analyses of catch-effort relationships and the size composition of commercial catches, together with the calculation of yield per recruitment, suggest that the recent depletion of resources of the 4 large-sized tuna species has been caused by increased fishing rather than by a decrease in recruitment. It is the author's opinion that the present activities of the fisheries seem to be around the level at which the maximum sustainable yield could be realized. Therefore, fixing the activites of fisheries at around the level of recent years appears to be the first step necessary for rational management.

Resources of the small-sized species are still under-utilized. However, we do not have a useful means of examining more effective ways to exploit these resources because of the lack of biological and environmental information. Among the small-sized species, little tuna and frigate mackerel are coastal species and may be of possible concern to local fisheries but not to fisheries which operate on a large scale in the open ocean.

5.3

Zoogeography of the Fishes of the Indian Ocean

D. M. COHEN

As a prelude to considering the present state of knowledge on the distribution of Indian Ocean fishes and in order to interject some perspective, I propose to briefly discuss a series of questions with which zoogeographers concern themselves and to discuss two different approaches to zoogeography.

I. Zoogeographic Questions

A. Where does an animal or group of animals live? For fishes, this topic might appropriately be subtitled geography and taxonomy, for until recently the study of fish distribution has been pursued almost exclusively by systematists. Describing the *where* of an animal requires information on the *what* of an animal. Ideally, knowledge of a regional fauna should progress in the following sequence.

a) Species descriptions and range extensions
b) Regional checklists and keys based on a)
c) Supraregional group revisions
d) Regional checklists and keys based on c)

The scene then is set for the zoogeographer to delimit patterns of distribution and to analyze them in the light of information from disciplines other than taxonomy. Unfortunately, for purposes of this Symposium, even the first category is imprecisely known for most tropical fishes.

B. Why does an animal or group of animals live where it does and not elsewhere? This question leads to a consideration of habitats, niches isolating mechanisms, and competition, and the zoogeographer must use concepts drawn from evolution and ecology. These data often are considered implicitly by fish zoogeographers, but for most kinds of fishes much pertinent information is accumulated under the term natural history and has yet to be suitably organized or quantified for use in zoogeography.

C. Whence and how did animals—or their ancestors arrive? Although there is no doubt that some species or groups of species have evolved *in situ*, it is equally obvious that some have arrived from elsewhere. Here again the zoogeographer must look to ecology with an eye to answering problems of dispersal, and to taxonomy (and when possible palaeontology) as a guide to phylogeny. Needless to say, information on the past history of the land and of the sea is invaluable.

II. Approaches to Zoogeography

Although combinations of the above 3 general topics are inherent in virtually all studies of animal distribution, zoogeographers tend to come in 2 fairly distinct varieties –

historical and ecological. Both have common ground in the questions posed above. The raw data for both approaches is the same, but the objectives are very different.

Historical zoogeography traditionally has described distribution patterns of phyletic groups (i.e. species, genus, family or other taxonomic category) with the objective of applying these data to understanding phylogeny. Examples may be found in the taxonomic revisions cited later in this paper. In the historical-phyletic approach the taxa analyzed may live in different habitats, have different ecological requirements and varying modes of dispersal. The unifying feature is phylogeny, which is rigidly formalized through the hierarchy of taxonomic classification. Ecological information, when considered at all, is not accorded similar treatment, in some instances because it is simply unavailable, in others because there is no adequate method of coping with it within the analytical scheme. Considerable emphasis is placed on looking to the past to explain present distributions. Although some attempt is made to use data accruing from the methods of historical zoogeography for predictive purposes, this is a subsidiary objective.

Ecological zoogeography is concerned with environmental parameters and distributions, both of individual species and of ecological assemblages of species. One of the earliest uses of the ecological method in fish zoogeography was that of MURRAY and HJORT (1912), who stressed the importance of changes in relative abundance of species taken by bottom trawl in different biogeographic regions of the North Atlantic shelf and slope. The geographical distribution of broadly defined complexes that include species with commercial value has been discussed by RASS (1959, 1965). More recently, formal approaches to the problem of characterizing faunas have been given by FAGER and LONGHURST (1968) for demersal fishes in the Gulf of Guinea, DAY and PEARCY (1968) for demersal fishes off the coast of Oregon, and EBELING et al., (1970) for deep pelagic animals off Southern California. In this ecological approach, numerous taxa may be considered, but all are generally members of the same community. The unifying feature is habitat, which is rigidly selected by the sampling program. Taxonomic information is necessary but of secondary importance. Distributions are described chiefly in terms of existing environmental parameters, their origins are rarely questioned. High predictive values has been predicated (LONGHURST, 1969) and is perhaps the chief contribution that zoogeography can make to the rational exploitation of marine resources.

Although reasons for studying plant and animal distribution are diverse, the approaches have common ground in the data necessary to adequately answer their questions, and it seems obvious that early emergence of what MACARTHUR and WILSON (1967) call a "truly comprehensive theory of biogeography" will be of advantage to all.

The approach taken in the following discussion of Indian Ocean fish has been dictated by the limited amount of accurate taxonomic data in revisional studies, which can serve as sources for describing distribution patterns. Ecological information varies from virtually non-existent for some kinds of shore fishes to fairly adequate for some oceanic species. I have attempted to compare species or genera that are found in roughly similar habitats, although the groupings are very broad indeed. Various authors (for example PARIN and BEKLEMISHEV, 1966) have proposed models, for purposes of fish zoogeography, that describe spatial and temporal variation in the location of a species. These kinds of data are important in explaining distribution, but except for some commercially important species, there is little such information on the Indian Ocean fauna.

Temperature is generally acknowledged as the single most important determinant of fish distribution. The 20° surface isotherm in winter generally coincides with the limits of distribution of reef building corals, and for marine organisms dwelling close to shore is accepted as the approximate boundary between tropical and temperate regions. EKMAN (1953) and others have divided the shallow water tropical marine faunas of the world into 4 sections: eastern Pacific, western Atlantic, eastern Atlantic and, largest of all, Indo-Pacific. It is the last of these with which we are here chiefly concerned, and I can do no better than to quote from MYERS (1941). "By far the richest of the 4 tropical shore fish faunas is the Indo-Pacific, and it contains practically all the families and a considerable number of the genera that make up the fauna of the other 3, in addition to many families and genera not found elsewhere ..."

"The geographical boundaries of the Indo-Pacific shore fish fauna are, in general, the area from Natal to the head of the Red Sea and the coasts and islands eastward to the

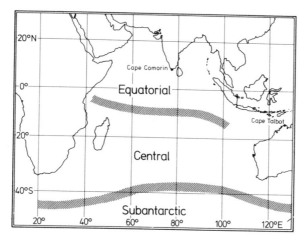

Fig. 1. The Indian Ocean. The longitude of Cape Comorin 77° 33′ E separates the western from the eastern Indian Ocean. Cape Talpot about 127° E on the coast of western Australia is taken as the demarcation between the eastern Indian Ocean and the western Pacific. Hatched areas indicate the approximate boundaries between the main water masses. (From EBELING, 1962)

Tuamotos and Hawaii, north to Kiushiu and Chekiang, and south to the Great Barrier Reef and New Caledonia ..."

"The homogeneity of the Indo-Pacific fauna is at once apparent from the fact that great numbers of shore species exist from one end to the other of it, the records of capture running from the Red Sea and Delagoa Bay to Honolulu, Tahiti, and Okinawa ..."

"... Within the main region itself, there are doubtless fairly distinctive subregions that could be defined even on the basis of available data, but our painful lack of knowledge of distributional data makes such definition difficult."

MYERS goes on to describe the paucity of collections and criticizes the poor quality of extant taxonomic work. But now museums and storehouses are bulging with collections from the IIOE and related activities; taxonomists are hard at work, and critical taxonomic revisions are beginning to appear. Data from some of them and from earlier work are examined below.

Fig. 1 shows the geographical scheme used in the following discussion and tables.

The western Indian Ocean is taken to include the Persian Gulf and the Red Sea, unless otherwise indicated. The boundary between the western and the eastern Indian Ocean is the longitude of Cape Comorin at the southern tip of India. Western Pacific includes the Indo-Australian Archipelago, the Great Barrier Reef, the China Sea, the Philippines and Japan. The dividing line between the eastern Indian Ocean and the western Pacific on the north coasts of Western Australia is taken as Cape Talbot.

Unequal sampling is a possible source of error, as the coral reef areas (and perhaps other habitats as well) of the western Indian Ocean probably have been better collected than those of the eastern Indian Ocean.

III. Distributions of Fishes Living in Various Habitats

1. Tropical Shore

The Indian Ocean may contain between 3 000 and 4 000 species of tropical shore fishes. Although many of these are named, very few have been accorded taxonomic attention sufficient to allow their use in zoogeography. I have examined the distributional data on 91 species in 6 taxonomic groups and find 2 reasonably coherent distribution patterns.

Genus *Ecsenius*, family Blenniidae, is a group of 18 species found on coral reefs or along rocky shores around the world in the tropics. Adults average 4 to 8 cm in length and are predominantly sedentary. Of the 10 Indian Ocean species (Table 1; data from

Table 1. Genus *Ecsenius* (Family Blenniidae) in the Indian Ocean

	Red Sea	W. Indian	E. Indian	W. Pacific	Cent. Pacific
aroni	×				
gravieri	×				
frontalis	×				
nalolo	×	×			
pulcher		×			
oculus			×	×	
yaeyamaensis			×	×	×
midas	×	×	×		×
lineatus		×		×	
bicolor		×	×	×	×

Springer, 1971) 3 are restricted to the Red Sea and Gulf of Aden; 2 species are restricted to the western Indian Ocean; 2 eastern Indian Ocean species live also in the Pacific; 3 species are found from the western Indian Ocean to the Pacific.

Family Gobiesocidae, the clingfishes, contains about 110 species found around the world in tropical and temperate regions. Adults average 5 to 6 cm in length and are usually attached to a substrate by means of a ventral sucking disc. Of the 11 tropical species known from the Indian Ocean (Table 2; data from Briggs, 1969 and other Briggs papers cited therein; Briggs and Link, 1963; Smith, 1964, 1965, 2 are found only in the Red Sea; 5 species are restricted to the western Indian Ocean; 1 is found only

Table 2. Family Gobiesocidae in the tropical Indian Ocean

	Red Sea	W. Indian	E. Indian	W. Pacific
L. lineatus	×			
erythraeus	×			
smithi		×		
coccinotaenia		×		
ctenion		×		
caritus		×		
lusheri		×		
sandaracatus			×	
D. lineatus		×		×
briggsi		×		×
bolini		×		×

in the eastern Indian Ocean; 3 species are apparently widespread as they have been taken in the western Indian Ocean and in the western Pacific.

Family Cirrhitidae, the hawkfishes, is a circumtropical group of 34 species found mostly in rocky or coral reef areas. Adults average approximately 12 cm in length but may reach 50 cm and are benthic and generally maintain contact with a substrate. Twelve species have been reported from the Indian Ocean (Table 3; data from RANDALL, 1963).

Table 3. Family Cirrhitidae in the tropical Indian Ocean

	Red Sea	W. Indian	E. Indian	W. Pacific	Cent. Pacific
calliurus	×				
punctatus		×			
guichenoti		×			
indicus			×		
bleekeri			×		
hemistictus			×		×
pinnulatus	×	×			×
forsteri	×	×	×	×	×
oxycephalus	×	×	×	×	×
typus		×		×	
arcatus		×		×	×
fasciatus		×		×	×

A single species is endemic to the Red Sea; 2 species are restricted to the western Indian Ocean; of the 3 eastern Indian Ocean species, 1 is found also in the Pacific; 6 species range from the western Indian Ocean to the Pacific.

Genus Acanthurus, the surgeonfishes of the family Acanthuridae, are circumtropical with about 35 species. Adults average 30 cm and are herbivores in reef and other shallow areas. A pelagic larval stage, the acronurus, has been taken at considerable distances from land. A total of 19 species is known from the Indian Ocean (Table 4; data from RANDALL, 1956; 1960). A single species is endemic to the Red Sea; 3 species are restricted to the

Table 4. Genus *Acanthurus* (Family Acanthuridae) in the Indian Ocean

	Red Sea	W. Indian	E. Indian	W. Pacific	Cent. Pacific
sohal	×				
polyzona		×			
tennenti		×			
melanosternon		×			
pyroferus			×	×	×
glaucopareius			×	×	×
bleekeri	×	×	×	×	×
xanthopterus	×	×	×	×	×
nigrofuscus	×	×	×	×	×
gahhm	×	×	×	×	×
leucosternon		×	×	×	
bariene		×		×	
triostegus		×	×	×	×
lineatus		×	×	×	×
mata		×	×	×	×
guttatus		×		×	×
dussumieri		×		×	×
thompsoni		×		×	×
nigroris		×		×	×

western Indian Ocean; 2 species are found in the eastern Indian Ocean and Pacific but not to the west; 13 species are widespread, living from the western Indian Ocean to the Pacific.

Although 52 species seem ridiculously few on which to base conclusions, a consistent pattern seems to emerge. It may be summarized as follows: Red Sea endemics, 13%; western Indian Ocean (in some instances Red Sea as well but not including Red Sea endemics) only, 22%; eastern Indian Ocean only, 6%; eastern Indian Ocean to the western or central Pacific, 15%; widespread, occurring from the Red Sea or western Indian Ocean to the western or central Pacific, 48%. Particularly notable is the fact that all species common to the eastern and western Indian Ocean are also found in the Pacific. The distribution in the Indian Ocean of the shorefish family Serranidae, the sea basses, has been discussed by POSTEL, FOURMANOIR and GUÉZÉ (1963), and although most of their analyses are not comparable with the system followed in the present paper, it is significant that these authors found 44% of 64 Indian Ocean serranids to be widespread in occurrence, with distributions ranging from the western Indian Ocean through the Indo-Australian Archipelago.

The genus is a more subjective taxonomic category and represents a greater degree of information pooling but, here too, the same pattern emerges. The 23 genera of salariine blennies are circumtropical with 16 living in the Indian Ocean (Table 5; data from SMITH-VANIZ and SPRINGER, 1971). Only 1 genus is endemic to the Red Sea; 1 genus is restricted to the western Indian Ocean; 2 genera are found in the western and eastern Indian Oceans but not in the Pacific; none live only in the eastern Indian Ocean; 2 genera occur in the eastern Indian Ocean and Pacific; 9 genera are widespread, living from the western Indian Ocean to the Pacific, and represent 62% of the total. Here again, about half the taxa are widespread and small degrees of endemism are found in the Red Sea and the western Indian Ocean.

Three other groups of shorefishes show a very different pattern. The acanthurid subfamily Nasinae has 16 species throughout the Indo-Pacific. Nasines average about 50 cm in length and tend to be larger fishes than are the species of *Acanthurus,* and they live in deeper waters in channels, between coral banks and at the reef margins. Thirteen species are found in the Indian Ocean (SMITH, 1966); 1 is a Red Sea endemic; 2 live only in the western Indian Ocean and 10 are found from the western Indian Ocean to the

Table 5. Genera of Tribe *Salariini* (Family Blenniidae) in the Indian Ocean

	Red Sea	W. Indian	E. Indian	W. Pacific	Cent. Pacific
Alloblennius	×				
Pereulixia		×			
Hirculops	×	×	×		
Antennablennius	×	×	×		
Prealticus			×	×	×
Andamia			×		×
Mimoblennius	×		×	×	
Alticus	×	×	×	×	×
Atrosalarias	×	×	×	×	×
Cirripectes	×	×	×	×	×
Ecsenius	×	×	×	×	×
Istiblennius	×	×	×	×	×
Salarias	×	×	×	×	×
Glyptoparus		×	×	×	×
Stanulus		×	×	×	×
Entomacrodus		×	×	×	×

Pacific. The circumtropical blenny genus *Entomacrodus* has 22 species, 7 of which live in the Indian Ocean; all but 1 are found in the Pacific as well (SPRINGER, 1967). The shallow-water anglerfishes of the family Antennariidae are sedentary species averaging about 10 cm in lenth. They number about 55 species, of which 20 have been found in the tropical Indian Ocean; 2 are known only from the eastern Indian Ocean; another eastern Indian Ocean species lives also in the Pacific; 17 species are widespread, ranging from the western Indian Ocean to the Pacific (SCHULTZ, 1957, 1964).

The preceding 3 groups contain 39 Indian Ocean species of which 85% are widespread in distribution, being found from the western Indian Ocean to the Pacific. There is little endemism in the Red Sea or in the eastern and the western Indian Ocean. Only a single species is found in the eastern and western Indian Oceans and is not found in the Pacific as well.

2. Tropical Continental Shelf

Data suitable for the analysis of distribution in continental shelf fishes are sparse. I have used 2 groups, both of which include some shallow-water fishes but appear to have most of their species distributed at depths of 30 to 400 meters.

Superfamily Triacanthoidea consists of 26 species of tropical plectognath fishes found in the Indo-Pacific and western Atlantic (Table 6; data from TYLER, 1968, 1970).

Table 6. Superfamily Triacanthoidea in the Indian Ocean

	W. Indian	E. Indian	W. Pacific
omen	×		
fraserbrunneri	×	×	
centriscoides		×	×
japonicus		×	×
nieuhofi		×	×
weberi		×	×
angustifrons		×	×
oxycephalus		×	×
platycheilus	×	×	×
ethiops	×	×	×
navigatoris	×	×	×
biaculeatus	×	×	×
strigilifer	×	×	×
retrospinus	×		×

They average about 11 to 12 cm in length and probably live on or near the bottom as adults; some are known to have pelagic larvae. Fourteen species live in the Indian Ocean, of which 1 is a western Indian Ocean endemic; 1 is found in the western and eastern Indian Ocean; 6 live in the eastern Indian Ocean and the Pacific; and 6 are widespread, having been taken from the western Indian Ocean to the western Pacific.

Genus *Parapercis*, family Mugiloididae contains 32 Indo-Pacific tropical and temperate species, of which 14 are known from the tropical Indian Ocean (Table 7; data

Table 7. Genus *Parapercis* (Family Mugiloididae) in the tropical Indian Ocean

	Red Sea	W. Indian	E. Indian	W. Pacific	Cent. Pacific
simulata	×	×			
somaliensis		×			
bivitatta		×			
trispilota		×			
emeryana			×	×	
tetracantha			×	×	
hexophthalma	×	×	×	×	
polyophthalma	×	×		×	
nebulosa		×	×	×	
xanthozoa		×	×	×	
alboguttata		×	×	×	
cephalopunctata		×	×	×	
schaundslandi		×			×
pulchella		×		×	

from SCHULTZ, 1968). Four species are found only in the western Indian Ocean; 2 species are found in the eastern Indian Ocean and Pacific and 8 species occur from the western Indian Ocean to the Pacific.

These 2 shelf groups seem to agree with the first category of shore fishes in that about half of the Indian Ocean species are widespread. For shore and shelf fishes combined, only 29% of the species considered were restricted to part or all of the Indian Ocean and not found also in the Pacific.

3. Continental Slope and Abyssal

The slope and abyssal fauna may be lower in number of species than the shorefish fauna by an entire order of magnitude. Revisionary studies are correspondingly fewer. I present data on the species of the Ophidioidei (Table 8; data from ALCOCK, 1899; NORMAN, 1939; and DE BEAUFORT, 1951, modified with information in my own

Table 8. Order Ophidioidei, benthic or benthopelagic species on the continental slope and abyssal plain of the Indian Ocean

	W. Indian	E. Indian	W. Pacific	Cent. Pacific
affinis	×			
rivers-andersoni	×			
bruuni	×			
squamiceps	×			
brunswigi	×			
longipes	×			
melampeplus	×			
analis	×			
trichiurus	×			
guentheri	×			
D. nigripinnis	×			
Cataetyx sp.	×			
Hoplobrotula sp.	×			
Mixonus sp.	×			
Genus sp.	×			
vaillianti	×	×		
simum	×	×		
fragilis	×	×		
M. nigripinnis	×	×		
pterotus	×	×		
squamipinne	×	×		
melanocephalus		×		
Diplacanthopoma sp.		×		
maculata		×		
hextii		×		
muraenolepis		×	×	
Enchelybrotula sp.		×	×	
Barathrodemus sp.		×	×	
glutinosus	×	×	×	
nigricaudis	×	×	×	
conjugator	×	×	×	
steatiticus	×	×	×	
multifilis	×	×	×	
diaphanus	×	×	×	
argenteum	×	×	×	
macropus	×		×	
longimana	×		×	
brunnea	×		×	
raniceps	×		×	
robustus	×		×	
bartschi	×		×	
armatus	×	×	×	×
niger	×	×	×	×

manuscripts and notes; and from NIELSEN, 1969). This order contains fishes from a wide diversity of habitats, but the present discussion is limited to the 43 Indian Ocean species which as adults live on or close to the bottom at depths from about 250 to 4 800 m. Particularly notable is the high degree of endemism in the Indian Ocean, with 58% of the species found there only. There are also distinct separations within the Indian Ocean: western Indian Ocean, 35%; eastern Indian Ocean, 9%, common to both, 14%; eastern Indian Ocean and to the east, 7%; and widespread species, 35%. Slope and abyssal fishes seem to have more restricted distributions than do shore or shelf fishes.

There are no deepwater ophidioids known from the Red Sea, and MARSHALL and BOURNE (1964) note that the deep-sea benthic fish fauna in general is very small, consisting of but 6 species. This they attribute to the 150 m sill which serves as a barrier to the ingress of species from the open sea, and to the warmer water at comparable depths.

4. Tropical Epipelagic

The epipelagic fish fauna, which is small and relatively well studied, has been the subject of a scholarly treatise by PARIN (1968), who stressed the diversity of the fauna and classified its ecological origins. He distinguished between littoral and oceanic species, plankton and nekton, permanently epipelagic species and those that are temporarily so, and finally between species that are only accidental visitors from the shore or deeper water, as distinguished from obligatory visitors. I have analyzed the distributions of 2 groups of fishes that as adults are found chiefly, though not entirely, in the upper pelagic of the littoral.

Family Belonidae, the needlefishes, is circumtropical and temperate with about 30 species. Needlefishes may average a meter in length and are active swimmers. Their eggs have sticky filaments and attach to floating objects. The tropical Indian Ocean contains 11 species and subspecies (Table 9; data from PARIN, 1967; and CRESSEY and

Table 9. Family Belonidae in the Indian Ocean

	Atlantic	Red Sea	W. Indian	E. Indian	W. Pacific	Cent. Pacific
platura		×				
choram		×	×			
urvilli				×	×	
gavialoides				×	×	
incisa				×	×	×
strongylura			×	×	×	
platyura			×	×	×	×
leiura			×	×	×	×
melanotus		×	×	×	×	×
hians	×	×	×	×	×	×
crocodilus	×	×	×	×	×	×

COLLETTE, 1970), of which 2 are restricted to the Red Sea-Persian Gulf; 3 are found in the eastern Indian Ocean and Pacific and 6 species are widespread, having been taken from the western Indian Ocean to the Pacific. Of the widespread species, 1 is estuarine, basically continental and is absent from offshore oceanic islands; 1, which PARIN (1967) calls pseudoceanic, is characteristically found around islands; another pseudoceanic species is often found far out at sea. PARIN (1968) also mentions 2 other widely distributed species the young of which are found at sea among drifting algae.

Genus *Sardinella,* Family Clupeidae has 15 Indo-Pacific species, of which 12 have been reported from the Indian Ocean (CHAN, 1965); 11 of these are widespread and range into the Pacific; 1 is found in the eastern and western Indian Ocean but not in the Pacific. Although in general *Sardinella* adults are less oceanic than needlefish adults, the belonids have a lower proportion of widespread species.

Among the permanent truly oceanic epipelagic fishes PARIN (1968) lists examples of the larger carcharinid sharks, flying fishes, sauries, tunas, marlins, bramids, stromateoids, and ocean sunfishes. Most of the species are widely distributed throughout the tropics and the zoogeographer is less concerned with presence or absence and more with local centers of abundance, which are often separated in time and space and represent feeding grounds and breeding areas. This topic will most certainly be covered in greater detail by other authors and I will not pursue it here at greater length.

5. Deep-water Pelagic

The deep-water pelagic fishes of the Indian Ocean number about 300 species (based on midwater trawling catches during cruises 3 and 6 or the RV "Anton Bruun" during the IIOE), many of which appear to be widely distributed. EBELING (1962) and others have proposed that an important guide to delimiting the distribution patterns of the deep midwater fauna is the concept of water masses as defined by the relationship between temperature and salinity. He has surveyed the distribution of 135 species of bathypelagic fishes throughout the world and finds that species living in the Indian central and Indian equatorial water masses (combined) have a 45% overlap with the fauna of the South Atlantic central water and a 75% overlap with the Indonesian fauna. He further states, "The central water masses of the South Atlantic, Indian Ocean and western South Pacific resemble each other in the physico-chemical and biological properties and, perhaps, should be considered for our purpose as one. All 3 are broadly interconnected, even around the tip of Africa, and have almost a common bathypelagic fish fauna." It seems reasonable to conclude from the above that the boundaries between the 3 major Indian Ocean water masses: equatorial, central and subantarctic (Fig. 1), function as zoogeographic boundaries. The distribution of several groups is examined in light of this idea.

Melamphaids are the only deep-water Indian Ocean fishes for which temperature-salinity data have been published. For several other groups data is available for areal and in some instances probable depth distribution, so that a rough attempt can be made to assign species to water mass.

Family **Melarnphaidae** is a group of about 35 species of bathypelagic fishes which average approximately 7 cm in length. Although small, they are apparently actively swimming predators. Most of the species are widespread in occurrence and some are found in all 3 oceans. Three recently revised genera, *Melamphaes* (EBELING, 1962), *Sio* (MOSS, 1962) and *Scopelogadus* (EBELING and WEED, 1963) have 11 species or subspecies in the Indian Ocean, none of which is endemic. Six species appear to have their centers of abundance in the equatorial water mass; 3 appear to be characteristic of the central water mass; 1 might be considered to transcend the boundary, and 1 species lives south of the central water mass in subantarctic water.

Stomiatoids are predatory bathypelagic fishes averaging about 20 cm in length. Two species of *Chauliodus* are found in the Indian Ocean; 1, which is worldwide, lives in the central water mass and in equatorial water as well, but only to about 10° N, where it is replaced by a second species which is endemic to the Arabian Sea and Bay of Bengal. GIBBS and HURWITZ (1967) find the distribution of the second species correlated with an oxygen poor layer, high productivity at relatively shallow depths and the influence of warm, high-salinity water from Red Sea and Persian Gulf. A somewhat similar situation has been reported by GOODYEAR and GIBBS (1969) for 2 species of *Astronesthes*. Both live in the equatorial water mass of the Indian Ocean; however, 1 which is found in the south part lives also in the Pacific; the other, an endemic, is distributed in the Arabian Sea and Bay of Bengal. The authors suggest that oxygen is a determining factor. The genus *Stomias* has 4 Indian Ocean species, all of which are found in other oceans. Two species are typically taken in equatorial and 1 in central water; another is characteristic of the region of the subtropical convergence. A unique convergence stomiatoid fauna has been suggested by GIBBS (1969), which is similar in concept to the postulated ecotone fauna inhabiting the boundary between north central and subarctic water in the North Pacific (BEKLEMISHEV and PARIN, 1960).

For deep-water pelagic fishes the boundaries of temperature-salinity defined water masses appear to function as boundaries for some but not all species.

Family Myctophidae, the lanternfishes, is the largest family of oceanic fishes with 300 to 500 species found around the world. Apparently most species perform diel vertical migrations which may place a population in one water mass at night and in a different one during the day. I have examined the areal distribution of 50 species, most of which are not restricted to the Indian Ocean, based on data from taxonomic papers by BEKKER (1964) and NAFPAKTITIS and NAFPAKTITIS (1969) on part of the Indian Ocean fauna. Eighteen species appear to live in the region of the equatorial water mass; 8 are found in equatorial and central water areas; 6 are in the central water area; 11 live in the central and subantarctic regions; 5 are restricted to the subantarctic; and 2 are latitudinally widespread, living from the Arabian Sea to the subantarctic. Approximately 42% of the species of lanternfishes probably transcend water mass boundaries. Whatever the reason, however, latitude does demark myctophid ranges in the Indian Ocean.

6. Temperate Shore

The temperate-water shore fauna of South Africa and southwest Australia are quite distinct from their northern tropical neighbors and probably from each other as well, although some common genera are present. In general, the cool-water Indian Ocean fishes of South Africa are part of a fauna that extends north along the Atlantic coast of Africa to southern Angola. The western Australian cool-water fishes are part of a fauna that ranges along the south coast of Australia to Tasmania and New Zealand. The South African fauna is fairly well known; the Australian one is so poorly studied and described that few precise comparisons are possible.

Several groups of shorefishes can be mentioned. Of the temperate Indian Ocean gobie-socids, 4 species in as many genera are known from South Africa; 2 species in 2 genera are cool-water Australian; no species but 1 genus is common to both regions (BRIGGS, 1955). A similar pattern is present in the 6 species of shallow-water viviparous ophidioids

(COHEN, 1966); 4, in 3 genera are South African; 2, in 2 genera, are Australian; neither the same species nor genera are found in both areas.

The small tidepool fishes of the family Clinidae are particularly abundant in South Africa and their distribution has been studied by PENRITH (1970) who found 28 species. None of these is conspecific or congeneric with the handful of species recorded from western Australia (MILWARD, 1967).

IV. Conclusions

The data given above for Indian Ocean shore and benthic deep-sea fishes generally confirm statements by MYERS; there is a large element of the fauna that is widespread in the Indo-Pacific. Furthermore, the Indian Ocean itself does not appear to be a natural zoogeographic unit, as there are very few species found both in the western and eastern parts that do not live in the Pacific. There are, however, some distinct areas of endemism, certainly the Red Sea and the western Indian Ocean. Regarding the latter, although I have presented no documentation, it seems probable that the Arabian Sea and the south-western part of the Indian Ocean are local centers. The eastern Indian Ocean fauna probably is best considered as part of the fauna of the western Pacific, as there are few species in the eastern Indian Ocean that are not shared.

It is generally accepted that the Indo-Australian region has the greatest number of shallow water species, and with this I agree. Furthermore, it has been postulated that the number of species decreases in a gradient to the west (see for example TALBOT, 1970). However, the limited data that I have compiled above does not substantiate such a decrease. For the groups covered we find 91 species in the eastern Indian Ocean and 91 in the western Indian Ocean. True, there are only 30 in the Red Sea, but special reasons may exist to explain this situation.

For pelagic fishes, more widespread species seem to be the rule, although exceptions do exist. At least some of the deep-water species are distributed roughly according to water mass distribution.

Few reliable data exist on which to assess distributional patterns of temperate water shore fishes, but there seem to be few, if any, widely distributed species.

There are no well-documented quantitative studies on the characterization and distribution of species complexes, although RASS (1965) has given preliminary qualitative data on assemblages of commercially useful fishes, and HIDA and PEREYRA (1966) have discussed trawl catches at the family level. Although regional guides for identification are available, thorough and well-documented world-wide taxonomic revisions are much needed for such commercially important groups as the clupeoids, flatfishes, sciaenids, lutjanids, lethrinids, sparids and serranids, to name but a few. Until adequate classifications are available, it will be difficult to properly characterize species complexes or study their distribution.

Fish Ecology of the Red Sea and Persian Gulf*

H. Steinitz

Among the important factors of Red Sea and Persian Gulf ecology are the following:

A. The Red Sea is a deep basin with warm surface-to-bottom water; it has an extremely shallow sill at the narrow southern entrance allowing very little exchange of water and creating, therefore, a largely separate water body; its geographical position and extension cause in a northward direction a declining temperature and an ascending salinity gradient in the surface water.

B. The Persian Gulf is a shallow basin with no sill separating it from the open ocean; it has high temperature maxima and high salinities, but no prominent gradients have been observed.

Neither sea has been thoroughly explored biologically, and certainly not with regard to fishes, but the Persian Gulf even less than the Red Sea. Consequently, it is difficult to compare the ecological characterization of their respective fish faunas. Nonetheless, it can be said that the Persian Gulf is probably considerably poorer in fish species than the Red Rea. What is certain is that bathypelagic and abyssal species are (largely or completely) absent and endemic littoral species, if they exist at all, are much less numerous than in the Red Sea. The Red Sea, on the other hand, has bathypelagic as well as abyssal fish which are, however, adapted to warm-water conditions.

Among the littoral fishes (the largest eco-group of fishes in the Indian Ocean), the coral fishes play a central role. The endemics of the Red Sea are found among these. The coral fishes seem to be poorly represented in the Persian Gulf.

From the point of view of productivity, the Red Sea falls into 2 parts with the dividing line between the richer south and the poorer north at about 20° N. Phytoplankton and associated flora, the basic links of food chains, are more amply developed in the south. The higher yield of fishes corresponds with old and new records of observations. There are more sharks, more turtles, more sea birds and more porpoises in the southern areas of the Red Sea than in its north.

The Red Sea seems to promote speciation tendencies in numerous invertebrate groups and fish. But much more data than we have at present, and a critical evaluation of these data, are required to conform this conclusion. One of the urgent problems of future research is to explain how the interplay of environmental parameters accelerates intrinsic speciation tendencies. Temperature (possibly combined with salinity) may be one of the chief factors influencing the fauna in the Red Sea. The temperature gradient of the littoral waters, which ascends along the coast line of the Red Sea, turns these waters into an ideal natural laboratory; it could be studied extensively to supplement the field

---

* Abstract of the paper delivered by the late Prof. H. Steinitz at the Kiel Symposium.

data with controlled laboratory experiments. It is worth mentioning in this connection that there are indications of a south-to-north trend in the Red Sea in the variation of certain morphological characters of fishes, and that it has been claimed for certain invertebrates that the percentage of endemic species increases in a northward direction.

5.5

Some Patterns of the Distribution of Bottom Fauna in the Indian Ocean

A. A. Neyman, M. N. Sokolova, N. G. Vinogradova, and F. A. Pasternak

The information available on the composition and distribution of bottom fauna prior to the organization of the IIOE was very inadequate, especially with regard to the deep-water regions of the open ocean. Therefore, investigations of the patterns of qualitative and quantitative distribution of bottom fauna were included in the plan of Soviet oceanological research in the Indian Ocean and carried out using the standard methods adopted on the research ships of the Soviet Union.

I. The Quantitative Distribution of Bottom Fauna

Systematic studies of the patterns of quantitative benthos distribution were started on board the "Vityaz" 1959 to 1960 and as a result of 4 cruises much material has accumulated, collected at stations fairly evenly covering the northern part of the ocean. The stations occupied in its southern part are not so numerous but here a very complicated picture of distribution can hardly be expected. Finally, the ships of the Institute of Marine Fisheries and Oceanography, working mainly in the regions of the continental shelf, have also begun investigations on the patterns of benthos distribution. Practically no investigations in this field have been conducted by other expeditions.

Although our knowledge of the quantitative distribution of bottom invertebrates in the ocean is far from adequate, we may safely assert that it is most closely related to food supply. The basic food producer in the ocean is phytoplankton and to a far lesser extent, coastal macrophytes. A distinct zonality is observed in the quantitative distribution of phytoplankton: generally its abundance increases sharply in a meridional direction from the near-polar to the boreal regions. Further on, in the tropical zone, the amount decreases again, reaching here its minimum value. An increase in the abundance of plankton algae, sometimes quite a significant one, is observed in the equatorial zone. This picture has its mirror image in the Southern Hemisphere. Near shore this scheme is somewhat obscured by the fact that here the ascent of subsurface water rich in nutrients prevails over sinking. The vertical food chains are those through which the food produced on the surface is conveyed to the bottom-dwelling consumers. On the floor of the ocean the general patterns of quantitative life distribution are the same as in the upper layers.

In temperate zones, and especially near the coasts, benthos is far richer than in the tropics and the open parts of the ocean. Geographical zonality is also related to the intensity of coastal run-off. But irrespective of its intensity, the amount of organic matter brought into the ocean from land is not comparable with the quantities produced by phytoplankton activity. The effect of river discharge on the abundance of benthos is felt only in the immediate proximity of the mouths of great rivers.

The quantitative abundance of bottom fauna in the Indian Ocean which extends over the tropical and southern temperate zones is generally determined by the same regularities that govern the development of benthic life in all oceans (Fig. 1).

In the northern part of the Indian Ocean the highest biomass of benthos is found, as was to be expected, in the near-shore regions of continents and islands bordering the ocean. However, it is only at single stations that the biomass of benthos reaches values of several hundred g m^{-2}, which are quite common on the continental shelf of temperate latitudes. But even within the shelf main areas of the northern part of the ocean, the Arabian Sea and the Bay of Bengal, are not equivalent in regard to their benthic productivity. The

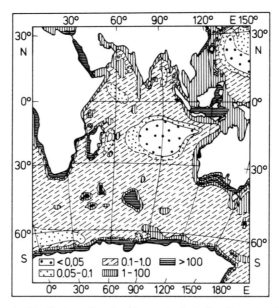

Fig. 1. Distribution of benthos biomass in the Indian Ocean (g m^{-2})

Arabian Sea is characterized by a richer bottom fauna (SOKOLOVA and PASTERNAK, 1962), and on its northern coasts we discovered a biomass exceeding 500 gm^{-2}, the maximum value recorded for the Indian Ocean. However, the average benthos biomass in this part of the coast does not exceed 35 g m^{-2}. Southward, along the coasts of the Arabian peninsula and Africa down to the Strait of Mozambique, it decreases gradually (on the average from 15 − 20 to 3 − 5 g m^{-2}). A decrease in the biomass of bottom fauna from 25 − 30 to 5 g m^{-2} is also observed along the western coasts of India. The abundance of bottom life in the southern parts of the Arabian Sea is due to an inflow of equatorial waters of low salinity causing a strongly expressed stratification of water masses (ELIZAROV, 1968). In the parts of the shelf under consideration the bottom fauna is richest at a depth of 25 − 75 m and extremely poor at 80 − 150 m due to an inflow at this depth of subsurface water with a low O$_2$ content.

In accordance with the general productivity of the northern part of the ocean, the bottom fauna on the shelf of the Bay of Bengal and the Andaman Sea was found to be much poorer than that of the Arabian Sea, its biomass varying between some fractions of a gram to 10 g m^{-2}, although in the immediate proximity of the mouth of the Ganges a value of 42.8 g m^{-2} was recorded (SOKOLOVA and PASTERNAK, 1962). A similar increase in the development of bottom life was observed at the mouth of the Irrawaddy River. In all other coastal regions of the tropical zone of the Indian Ocean the biomass of bottom invertebrates is generally fairly low, seldom attaining 10 g m^{-2}. Local bursts of bottom fauna development are observed around certain parts of the Andaman Sea and the Malay Archipelago, along the western coasts of Java and Sumatra, in the region of intensive upwelling. A low benthos biomass is characteristic of the NW part of the Australian shelf (2.6—8 g m^{-2}). To the south, according to the general scheme of the development of life in the ocean, the productivity of bottom fauna increases again. On the shelf of western Australia its biomass averages 15 g m^{-2} and on the shelf of the Great Australian Bight 16 g m^{-2}. The insignificant increase in biomass observed along the western coast of Australia may be explained by the fact that here the shore is washed by subtropical waters of low productivity (NEYMAN, 1965).

In the western part of the Great Australian Bight a cyclonic winter circulation results in a local increase of productivity: here the benthos biomass reaches an average of 22 g m^{-2}.

In the tropical, as in the southern temperate part of the ocean, the biomass of benthos decreases with increasing depth. However, in the tropical zone the process is not as sharply expressed as in the boreal zone because the abundant inflow of organic matter from the neritic region overrides the effect of increasing depth beyond the upper 1000 m. Therefore at all depths greater than 1000 m the biomass of benthos is expressed by values of the same order, ranging between 2.75 and 1.76 g m^{-2} (BELYAEV and VINOGRADOVA, 1961).

In the northern part of the ocean a high biomass of benthos is characteristic not only of the coastal regions but also of the whole Arabian Sea. Here at a considerable distance from the shore and at a depth of more than 3000 m the biomass reaches 1.92 g m^{-2} and more, a value quite unusual for the open waters of the tropical zone. The analysis of dynamic charts shows that the circulation of the Arabian Sea is represented by non-stationary eddies, producing intensive turbulent exchange and replenishment of the surface water with biogenic substances. The extreme richness of plankton in the Arabian Sea is favored by an intensive ascent of subsurface water along its western coasts during the period of winter monsoons. Another characteristic feature of the Arabian Sea is the presence of a thick O_2 minimum layer extending from the layer of density discontinuity to a depth of 1000—1250 m. In the upper part of this layer (down to 600 m) free H_2S was discovered. A quantitative minimum of plankton was recorded in the whole thickness of the layer of the O_2 minimum, but at a depth of 1500 m the biomass of zooplankton abruptly increases again. The deep-sea plankton of the Arabian Sea is even richer relative to the surface plankton than is usually observed in the ocean (VINOGRADOV, 1962). The explanation of this phenomenon suggested by VINOGRADOV is fully applicable to the extreme abundance of the benthos: the intermediate waters are poor in plankton and oxygen, and active consumption and oxidation of the precipitated organic matter proceed slowly, so that large amounts of nutrients are conveyed to the deep-water layers and the ocean floor. The presence of an O_2-minimum layer and of H_2S also has a direct effect on the distribution of bottom organisms. Thus a minimum biomass is characteristic of some areas of the Murray Ridge. In separate regions, directly washed by water containing up to 0.1 mg H_2S l^{-1}, the bottom fauna is extremely impoverished e.g. 0.01 g m^{-2}, or may be entirely absent. It is only below the H_2S layer that the biomass of bottom invertebrates begins to increase again ($0.22-0.44$ g m^{-2}).

It is possible that the existence in the eastern part of the Arabian Sea of a constant circulation with water sinking at its centre, may lead to the creation of a halistatic area, where an impoverishment in food resources down to the bottom may easily be assumed. At any rate the benthos biomass in this region is reduced to 0.3 g m^{-2}.

At the same time the general productivity of the bottom population of the Arabian Sea is still very high, and its wealth presents a phenomenon which is quite extraordinary for the tropical zone. Judging from several bottom samples taken with grabs, high indices of biomass are characteristic also of the great depths near the NW coasts of Africa (up to 1 g m^{-2}). This is the area worked by the German expedition on the "Meteor" which, among other research work, carried out investigations on the quantitative distribution of meiofauna. The data obtained show a high density of the colonies of these bottom organisms (up to 170 000 ind. m^{-2}). Unfortunately, no quantitative determinations were made of the biomass of meiofauna (Thiel, 1966). The abundance of life in the whole water column of the region under consideration may be explained by an intensive ascent of deep waters, brought about by the monsoon current spreading out northwards and southwards like a broad fan.

The quantitative distribution of benthos presents quite another picture in the Bay of Bengal, the floor of which is an accumulative plain with little relief. Owing to the lowered salinity of the surface layer, the sharp stratification of water within the Bay, and the sinking of the layer of density discontinuity to a depth of 100 m, the phytoplankton is extremely poor, as is the zooplankton. These factors are also responsible for the feeble development of bottom life in the Bay of Bengal. The benthos biomass in the open part of the Bay is very evenly distributed and varies between 0.11 and 0.45 g m^{-2}. At one of the stations in its central part the bottom fauna was found to be as low as 0.06 g m^{-2}, and still lower (0.04 g m^{-2}) in the western part. Analogous values of benthos biomass are characteristic of the central regions of the Andaman Sea (Sokolova and Pasternak, 1962, 1964).

A very low benthos biomass (less than 0.2 g m^{-2}) was recorded in the open deepwater part of the Indian Ocean situated within the tropical zone.

In the more productive western half of the ocean the bottom fauna is more abundant than in its eastern half. Here, as a rule the biomass of benthos is never less than 0.1 g m^{-2} (a lower biomass was recorded only in the SW part of the Mascarene Basin and in an area lying to the north of the Equator between longitudes 55° and 70° E). The benthos of the eastern half of the Ocean is extremely poor. Here an area of minimum development of bottom life between latitudes 5° and 30° S closely coincides with a subtropical circulation of waters of extremely low productivity. The biomass of benthos in this area does not exceed 0.05 g m^{-2}, with an average of 0.04 g m^{-2}.

Southwards, beyond the tropical zone, the biomass of bottom fauna increases again reaching no less than $0.2-0.4$ g m^{-2} to the south of latitude 30° S.

Most important in the biomass of bottom fauna are polychaetes, especially at great depths (50%); in shallow-water areas crustaceans are almost as important as polychaetes (25%), with a predominance of decapods and amphipods (21%), followed by the epifauna (15%). At great depths the proportion of crustaceans is reduced to 10% with a predominance of Tanaidacea and Isopoda. Sponges become more important, while molluscs play an insignificant part at all depths.

II. Trophic Structure

The bottom population of the ocean may be divided into three groups according to their food habits: detritus-feeders (feeding on detritus from bottom sediments), seston-feeders (feeding on particulate matter suspended in the bottom water layer) and carnivores (feeding on living or dead bodies). Thus the basic food of bottom animals consists of detritus, and the source of detritus is the organic matter produced in the surface layer of the ocean, which reaches the sea floor after undergoing considerable transformation.

In all the more or less productive regions of the ocean feeding conditions at all depths are favorable for the existence of all 3 trophic groups of bottom invertebrates.

Conversely, in the least productive regions, usually remote from the shore and lying within tropical latitudes, feeding conditions are most adverse. Here in the impoverished benthic communities detritus-feeding invertebrates are either absent or insignificant.

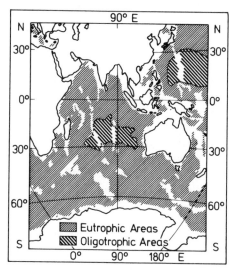

Fig. 2. Eutrophic and oligotrophic areas of the Indian Ocean

Regions with unfavorable feeding conditions, usually confined to the spaces of deep-sea basins, are defined as oligotrophic, and all the other regions as eutrophic.

Eutrophic conditions are created in coastal areas where rising water masses prevail over downward water movements. This, however, does not exclude the possibility that unfavorable feeding conditions may arise for some reason or other, even on the shelf, when the effect is comparable to that observed in oligotrophic regions. Such places were discovered in the Indian Ocean, on the shelf of western India (at depths of 75 – 150 m), in shallow-water areas in the eastern parts of the Bay of Bengal and the Andaman Sea, and in the eastern part of the shelf of the Great Australian Bight (NEYMAN, 1968, 1970). In these, the bottom fauna was represented almost entirely by seston-feeding invertebrates with insignificant biomass. In the rest of the nearshore shallow-water areas the feeding conditions are eutrophic and the bottom fauna is represented by all 3 trophic groups.

A distinct zonality is observed in their distribution, determined by the relief of the sea floor and the type of sedimentation. In the immediate proximity of the shore, in the region of transit of suspended matter, seston-feeding epifauna invertebrates usually predominate. Further out, with the gradual decrease of water movement and increasing precipitation of suspended matter, seston-feeders give way to detritophages sorting out detritus from the surface of the sediments, and then to detritophages swallowing detritus together with the mud.

As in all other oceans, eutrophic conditions may arise along all the periphery of the Indian Ocean even at depths below 3000 m (Fig. 2). Consequently, the eutrophic region encompasses the Arabian Sea with the adjacent Somali Basin, the Mascarene and Mozambique Basins, the Bay of Bengal with the adjacent parts of the Central Indian and Coco Basins, the deep-sea Java Trench, the greater of the rift zone, the southern part of the Crozet Basin and, finally, both the Antarctic Basins. The sediments of the vast eutrophic area of the Indian Ocean are represented by foraminiferan and radiolarian oozes in the north, and diatom oozes in the south. The content of organic C in the sediments varies in different parts of the region but is generally no less than 0.3% (by weight), Eh is characterized by negative or low positive values, and the oxygenated layer is either absent or of insignificant thickness (BEZRUKOV, 1964; LISITZIN, 1960). Both seston-feeding and detritus-feeding invertebrates are widely distributed in the macrobenthos of the eutrophic region. As in shallow-water areas, their spatial distribution is determined by the food supply, bottom relief and local rate of sedimentation. A detailed study of the distribution of trophic groups was carried out in particular in the Bay of Bengal (SOKOLOVA and PASTERNAK, 1964), and it was possible to demonstrate a clear-cut succession of zones of predominant development of a certain type of feeding, with increasing depth and under the effect of changing macrorelief and feeding conditions. A predominance of seston-feeders in the lower part of the shelf is succeeded by a predominance of sorting detritophages on the slope and indiscriminate detritophages in the depths of the central part of the bay.

Unlike the Pacific and the Atlantic Oceans, the Indian Ocean, owing to its position in the tropical belt and in the southern temperate zone, has only one oligotrophic area. This region occupies the southern parts of the Central Indian Basin, the Australian Basin and the northern half of the Crozet Basin and coincides with the boundaries of a southern subtropical gyre characterized by waters of extremely low productivity. This part of the ocean is more than 3 800 — 4 000 m deep. The sediments in the northern part of the oligotrophic region (down to latitudes 15–17° S) are represented by radio-literally paved with them. The content of organic C in the sediments of the oligotrophic oozes. Ferro manganese concretions are widespread here and in places the sea floor is larian oozes and in the southern part by deep-sea red clays and carbonate-foraminiferan area is 0.3% or less, while En reaches high positive values. In the sediments of the northern half of the region, minimum concentrations of humic acids were recorded, a fact which is directly related to the low content of organic C (BORDOVSKY, 1964).

The macrobenthos of the oligotrophic region is characterized by a general quantitative and qualitative impoverishment of bottom fauna; prevalent here are sestonophagous invertebrates which feed on particulate matter from the bottom water layer, e.g. sponges, cirripedes and polychaetes of the Serpulidae family. Detritus feeders which swallow detritus together with the mud, such as holothurians, irregular sea-urchins or sea-stars are entirely absent. In the trawl catches, the ratio by weight of seston-feeding to detritus-feeding invertebrates is expressed in values lower than unity, irrespective of the mesorelief.

The passage from eutrophic to oligotrophic conditions proceeds gradually with the decrease of organic matter precipitated on the sea floor and the slowing down of the rate of sedimentation. Under transitional trophic conditions the unevenness in the distribution of trophic groups increases as compared with eutrophic regions, notwithstanding the similarity of the mesorelief.

III. Some Remarks on the Biogeography of Bottom Invertebrates in the Indian Ocean

There have been no recent detailed studies of the distribution of zoogeographical complexes in the coastal shallow-water areas of the Indian Ocean. The results of faunistic investigations carried out in 1966 on board the "Academician Knipovitch" merely added some details to the widely known scheme of EKMAN (1935) and revealed that within the Indo-West-Pacific area the zoogeographical boundary lies on the shelf of western India, located at about the latitude of Nova Goa. This boundary coincides with the northern limit of the penetration of equatorial waters onto the shelf of western India (ELIZAROV, 1968). Here the ranges of a number of species of bivalve and gastropod molluscs living in the shallow-water areas of the western and eastern parts of the Indian Ocean, come together. Further on, beyond the shelf of India, this limit seems to run along the Laccadive Islands. In any case, the penaeids of the western Indian Ocean and some other invertebrates do not spread northward and westward of this limit (STAROBOGATOV, in print). According to this author, endemic species must exist among the penaeids inhabiting the whole extent of the shelf between Nova Goa and the Straits of Malacca. As regards the zoogeographical zonation of the abyssal region, the analysis of the geographical distribution of some hundred species of invertebrates living in depths of more than 2 000 m has shown that the deep-sea fauna of the Indian Ocean is less self-contained than that of the Pacific and the Atlantic Oceans. It is not integral, and species common to the northern and southern parts of the ocean are not numerous. The dissociation of the fauna increases with increasing depth of habitat. An important part is played in the deep-sea benthos of the nothern half of the Indian Ocean by species common to the Pacific (nearly 50%); in the southern part of the Indian Ocean antarctic forms predominate (nearly 80%), and among the broadly eurybathic forms are those common to the Atlantic (VINOGRADOVA, 1962).

VINOGRADOVA assigns the northern part of the Indian Ocean, as a sub-region, to the Pacific-North-Indian deep-sea region and its southern part, as an Indian province, to the Antarctic-Indo-Pacific sub-region of the Antarctic deep-sea region.

6. Transfer of Organic Matter in Different Trophic Levels
6.1

Production in the Indian Ocean and the Transfer from the Primary to the Secondary Level

D. H. CUSHING

During the Indian Ocean Expedition many measurements of primary production were made with the ^{14}C technique and many hauls with nets from about 200 m were taken. One of the objects of the expeditions was to estimate primary and secondary production and the transfer coefficients, and to obtain a measure of tertiary production.

I. Methods

The measurements of primary production in the Indian Ocean (Fig. 1c) have been summarized by KABANOVA (1968) as charts of productivity in the northern summer (period of the SW monsoon) and in the northern winter (period of the NE monsoon). The results are given here as average values for each 5° square of latitude and longitude and are corrected by 1.45 (STEEMANN NIELSEN, 1964; GOLDMAN, 1968), as gC m^{-2} day^{-1} in

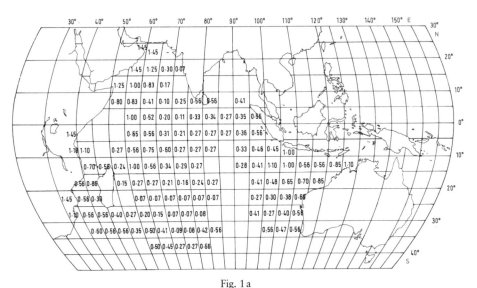

Fig. 1 a

Fig. 1. Primary productivity in the Indian Ocean (KABANOVA, 1968) in gC m^{-2} day^{-1}. a) in the SW monsoon; b) in the NE monsoon; c) the distribution of stations for primary productivity during the IIOE (KABANOVA, 1968); the symbols indicate the different ships

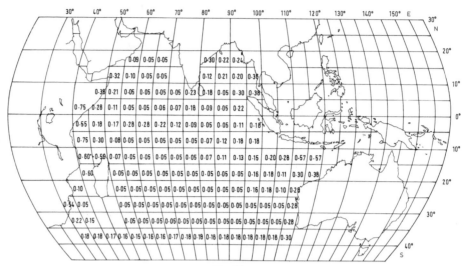

Fig. 1b

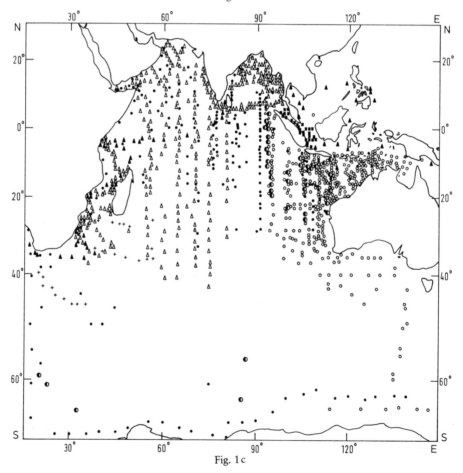

Fig. 1c

each monsoon (Figs. 1a, b). The average values are raised by 180 to give gC m^{-2} 180 day^{-1} in each monsoon (Figs. 2a, b see also map on the inside of the back cover).

Estimates of zooplankton biomass, sampled with the 1 m net, or the Juday net (see TRANTER, 1963, for a comparison of nets; BARNES and TRANTER, 1965, show that the Juday net catches 1.6 x the quantity caught by the Indian Ocean standard net, but

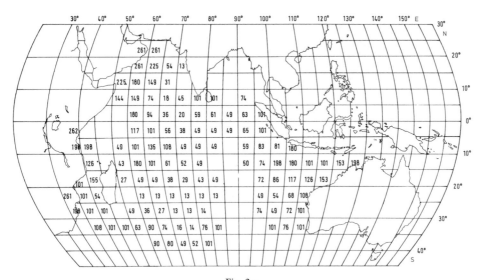

Fig. 2a

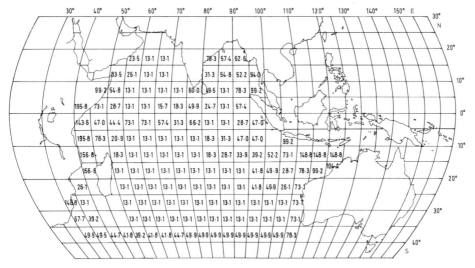

Fig. 2b

Fig. 2. Primary productivity in the Indian Ocean in gC m^{-2} 180 day^{-1}. a) in the SW monsoon; b) in the NE monsoon

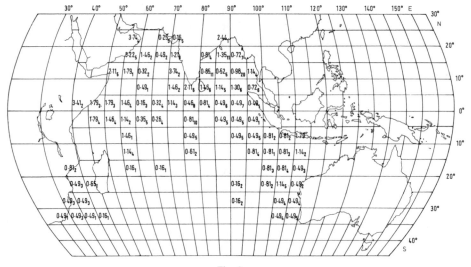

Fig. 3 a

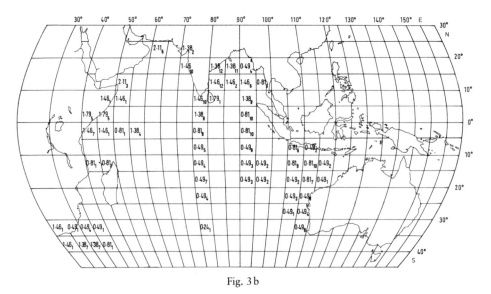

Fig. 3 b

Fig. 3. Secondary stock in the Indian Ocean (IOBC 1968 a, b) in gC m^{-2}. a) in the SW monsoon;
b) in the NE monsoon

is much more variable) and the Indian Ocean net, were taken from IOBC (1968 a, b);
the night samples from the top 200 m of the ocean were used to obtain average stock
estimates in 5° squares by the two monsoon periods. Quantities in ml m^{-2} were converted
to gC m^{-2} with the factor 0.065 (CUSHING, 1971 a) (Figs. 3 a, b). From the World Atlas
of Sea Surface Temperatures (U.S. Navy Hydrographic Office, 1944), monthly averages

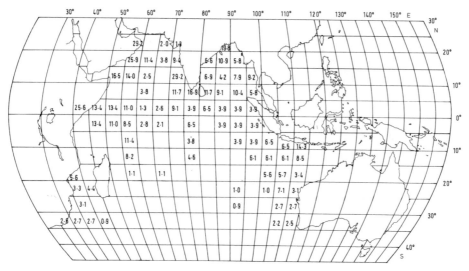

Fig. 4a

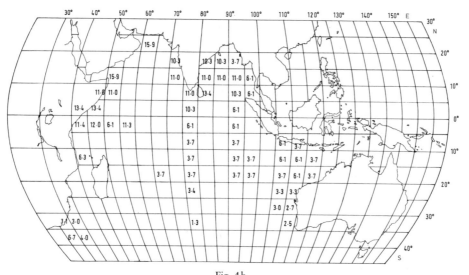

Fig. 4b

Fig. 4. Secondary production in the Indian Ocean in gC m^{-2} 180 day^{-1}. a) in the SW monsoon;
b) in the NE monsoon

were calculated for each 5° square. MARSHALL and ORR (1955) give the duration of copepodid stages at 10° C and at 15° C, together with the relative duration of all stages during one generation. A relationship between the duration of a generation and temperature was established: $D = 71.72 \ t^{-1.22}$, where t is temperature in ° C and D is duration of the copepodid generations in days. Then stock in gC m^{-2} is raised by

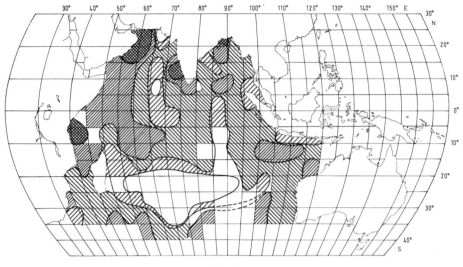

Fig. 5a

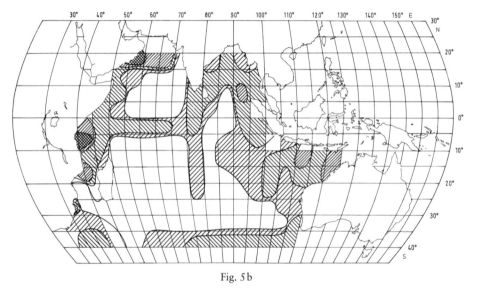

Fig. 5b

Fig. 5. Tertiary production in the Indian Ocean in tons wet weight $\cdot 10^5$. a) in the SW monsoon; b) in the NE monsoon

☐ <5   ▨ 5-10   ▧ 10-20   ▨ 20-40   ▨ >40   tons wet weight $\cdot 10^5$

$180 \cdot n^{-1}$, where n is the number of generations at the appropriate average temperature in the 5° square. So it was possible to obtain estimates of gC m^{-2} 180 day^{-1} of secondary production for each 5° square for each monsoon (Figs. 4a, b).

From the estimates of primary and secondary production in gC m^{-2} 180 day^{-1} estimates of gC m^{-2} 180 day^{-1} tertiary production were obtained by taking 1% of primary production and 10% of secondary production and using a mean of the two values. The carbon was raised to wet weight of fish, using the factor 7.47 (VINOGRADOV, 1953), and the quantities were raised to the 5° square by the area factor 6.774 · 10⁵; for those squares cut by a coastline, a further area factor was incorporated. Figs. 5a and b shows the distribution of tertiary production by half-yearly periods in each monsoon.

ROTHSCHILD and YONG (1970) have assembled data on stock density and effort by 10° squares in the Indian Ocean for yellowfin, *Thunnus albacares*, (BONNATERRE); bigeye, *Thunnus obesus* (LOWE); southern bluefin, *Thunnus thynnus* (LINNAEUS); and albacore,

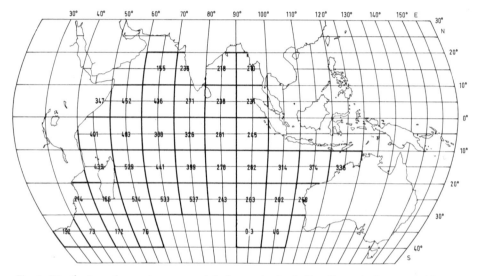

Fig. 6. Distribution of tuna in an unexploited state in the Indian Ocean in kg wet weight per 100 hooks per night. (After ROTHSCHILD and YONG, 1970)

Thunnus alalunga (BONNATERRE). For each square, they fitted a curve of catch per effort on effort using a fourth-order polynomial. The fitted value of stock density in n per 100 hooks has been taken at least effort to give some estimate of stock density before fishing started. Mean sizes of albacore are given in YOSHIDA and OTSU (1962), of yellowfin in MIMURA et al. (1963a), of bigeye in MIMURA et al. (1963b) and of southern bluefin in ROBINS (1963). So the total weight of the tuna species was obtained in kg per 100 hooks per night (Fig. 6).

II. Results

1. Primary Production

CUSHING (1971a, b) has distinguished four categories of primary production: a) > 1.0 gC m⁻² day⁻¹ in the major upwelling systems; b) $0.3-1.0$ gC m⁻² day⁻¹ in lesser systems; c) < 0.3 gC m⁻² day⁻¹ in some minor upwellings; d) < 0.1 gC m⁻² day⁻¹

in the open ocean. During the SW monsoon, it will be seen that a fair proportion of the Arabian Sea is highly productive. Between 55 and 65° E, the rich area extends south to 15° C. The coast of East Africa from Zanzibar to the South African border, including the Mozambique Channel, is quite rich. Production is quite high off Ceylon and there is an extensive area of high production in the eastern tropical ocean with a high peak off Java, where there is an upwelling system. The poorest area is in the centre of the southern subtropical anticyclone. The richest areas are in the Arabian upwelling, the Mozambique Channel and in the eastern tropical oceans. A rough distribution of productivity during the SW monsoon by area is given in Table 1.

Table 1. Productivity in the Indian Ocean during the SW monsoon

Area	$gC\ m^{-2}\ day^{-1}$	No. of squares
Arabian upwelling	1.16	8
Arabian Sea	0.76	16
Javan upwelling	0.85	3
East tropical ocean	0.70	16
Equatorial region	0.40	18
East Africa and Mozambique Channel	0.83	13

The average productivity for the whole ocean is 0.50 gC m^{-2} day^{-1}, which is surprisingly high. It is a pity that the Bay of Bengal was inadequately sampled during the SW monsoon, because upwelling probably occurs there off the Orissa coast of India and east of the Andaman Islands.

Fig. 1b shows the productivity in gC m^{-2} day^{-1} in the Indian Ocean during the period of the NE monsoon. It is immediately obvious that the productivity is considerably less. Indeed the average for the NE monsoon is 0.15 gC m^{-2} day^{-1}, which is less than one-third of the value in the SW monsoon. The productive areas are less well pronounced; the equatorial region, the East African coast, the Bay of Bengal and the eastern tropical ocean are regions of relatively high production (Table 2).

Table 2. Productivity in the Indian Ocean during the NE monsoon

Area	$gC\ m^{-2}\ day^{-1}$	No. of squares
Arabian upwelling	0.23	6
Arabian Sea	0.12	14
Javan upwelling	0.28	1
East tropical ocean	0.26	12
Equatorial region	0.15	16
East Africa and Mozambique Channel	0.42	10
Bay of Bengal	0.21	14

Compared with the SW monsoon period, most regions are reduced by a factor of three, as expected from the comparison of the averages. In the Arabian Sea, there is a reduction of five times, as there is in the Arabian upwelling.

2. Secondary Production

In Fig. 3a is given the distribution of secondary stock as gC m^{-2} during the SW monsoon and in Fig. 3b that during the NE monsoon. The subscripts refer to the number of hauls made in each square. Some hauls made during the period of the NE monsoon were not used because, when compared with the primary production, they yielded transfer coefficients (see below) greater than 40%. Some horizontal hauls were made during the expedition and it is possible that they have been included. Whatever the true reason for the aberrant transfer coefficients, it has led to a shortage of observations in the Arabian Sea during the NE monsoon period.

Secondary production as $gC \ m^{-2} \ 180 \ day^{-1}$ is illustrated in Figs. 4a and b. There are not enough observations for the detailed analysis by region which was made for the distributions of primary production. However, secondary production appears to be highest off the coasts of southern Arabia, Somalia, the Malabar coast of India, off Ceylon and the northern part of the Bay of Bengal, as might be expected from the distribution of upwellings. Direct comparison with primary production can be made with the use of the charts of $gC \ m^{-2} \ 180 \ day^{-1}$ at both trophic levels (Fig. 2 in primary production and Fig. 4 in secondary production). The average secondary production during the SW monsoon is $7.3 \ gC \ m^{-2} \ 180 \ day^{-1}$ that during the NE monsoon is $7.0 \ gC \ m^{-2} \ 180 \ day^{-1}$. The difference is very much less than might have been expected from the very marked difference in primary production between the two monsoons. The sampling in the NE monsoon is poor in the central part of the ocean as compared with that in the SW monsoon, so perhaps a better sampling of secondary production during the NE monsoon would yield a lower average.

The estimate of secondary production depends upon the duration of copepodid generations, the mortality rates are unknown. It is assumed that copepods are the dominant herbivores, or that the generation time of other herbivores can be described by the same rule. VINOGRADOV and VORONINA (1962) described a cruise of the "Vityaz" in the northern and equatorial part of the Indian Ocean. They show that the maximum abundance of herbivorous copepods is found in the South Equatorial Current and in the eastern tropical ocean; the ship did not go into the Arabian Sea proper or the Bay of Bengal. Hence it is likely that copepds are the dominant herbivores, supported by euphausids in some regions, as in the other oceans.

3. Tertiary Production

The figures of tertiary production are taken, by squares, from those of primary and secondary production. Because more samples were taken of the primary production, the charts in Figs. 5a and b are based more on the production of algae. During the period of the SW monsoon (Fig. 5a), there are four high points, off the coast of Arabia, off Zanzibar, and off the Malabar coast of India and in the northernmost part of the Bay of Bengal. Here the tertiary production is greater than $40 \cdot 10^5$ tons wet weight per 5° square per 180 days. But the most remarkable feature of the chart is the extensive area of tertiary production, between Arabia and Madagascar, of $20 - 40 \cdot 10^5$ tons wet weight per 5° square per 180 days; there are other patches at the same level in the Bay of Bengal and in the eastern tropical ocean. Further, there is a fairly heavy level of production all over the northern and equatorial parts of the ocean. Only in the centre of the southern sub-tropical anticyclone is there a really low production, $< 5 \cdot 10^5$ tons wet weight per 5° square 180 day^{-1}.

During the NE monsoon, the areas of low production are very much more extensive. However, there is still a high patch off southern Arabia and east Africa, with a relatively high band in the equatorial region. The Bay of Bengal and the eastern tropical ocean again appear to be relatively rich, but not as rich as during the period of the SW monsoon.

In the NE monsoon, the total production throughout the ocean is about $1.3 \cdot 10^8$ tons wet weight and during the SW monsoon $2.0 \cdot 10^8$ tons wet weight. So the total annual tertiary production is $3.3 \cdot 10^8$ tons wet weight. By far the greater proportion of this quantity lies in the open ocean and is part of the oceanic ecosystem, most of which is inaccessible to exploitation by fishermen. However, in the upwelling areas another form of ecosystem is found. Off southern Arabia, for example, there might be an annual production of $4 - 5 \cdot 10^6$ tons.

4. Tuna Production

The tuna stock before exploitation is given as kg per 100 hooks night^{-1}, by 10° squares, throughout the ocean in Fig. 6. The main point is that more tuna are found in the western half of the ocean and that most are found to the east and SE of Madagascar. From the distribution of tertiary production, the higher densities in the equatorial region might be expected, taking into account the possibility that the classification of data by squares may be a little coarse. However, the productive area east and SE of Madagascar is unexpected and there is little production there at the primary, secondary and tertiary levels. The catches by weight in that area were predominantly of yellowfin tuna; the explanation of the concentration remains obscure.

Attempts were made to transform the total weight of tuna stock into production units in gC m^{-2}. Those needing estimates of the catchability of the hooks and the migration speeds failed through lack of information.

5. Transfer Coefficients

Ecological efficiency is defined as the ratio of yield in one trophic level to that in the one below (Slobodkin, 1961). If yield is a constant fraction of production, then the ratio in production is an estimate of ecological efficiency. This ratio I have called a transfer coefficient, to distinguish it from the stricter term ecological efficiency. The transfer coefficient was calculated as the ratio of gC m^{-2} 180 day^{-1} in secondary production to that in primary production; the values range from about 2% to about 34%.

In Fig. 7 the transfer coefficients are plotted against the primary production as gC m^{-2} 180 day^{-1} in both monsoons. The open circles show the points for the SW monsoon and the triangles those for the NE monsoon. The black circles are averages for intervals on the abscissa and a curve has been fitted by eye to the average points. The mean transfer coefficient for the whole ocean for both monsoons is very close to 10%, which is near the value found by Slobodkin in his experimental *Daphnia* populations. The highest transfer coefficient obtained with chickens is about 40%. For animals which have to search for food, perhaps survive for periods of time on less than a maximum ration, and which have to devote perhaps 15% of body weight or more to reproduction, the transfer coefficient must be considerably less than 40%. If half of any increment to adult body weight must be devoted to reproduction and if half must be devoted to energy spent on searching, then the 40% is reduced to 10%. But as Steele (1965) has pointed out, if much of the biomass is composed of non-reproducing juveniles a higher transfer coefficient is sometimes possible, up to 25%. In this case the secondary production comprises a number of generations. The simplest way of looking at the problem is to consider the gonad weight as a proportion of the body weight. From generation to generation the first gonad has to create so much excess material in order to produce a second gonad one generation later. For *Calanus finmarchicus*, the ratio of gonad to body weight is 0.15 (from data given in MARSHALL and ORR, 1952) and this tends to increase for smaller copepods. Perhaps the highest transfer coefficients of just over 20% represent a mean ratio of gonad to body weight.

The fact that the observed mean value of 10% is close to that expected implies either that the primary and secondary productions are well estimated or that they are both biased in the same way. Therefore, if the primary production is considered to be correct, so is the secondary production. If true secondary production were 50% greater than the estimate given, the mean transfer coefficient would be 15%.

The most important point about Fig. 7 is the decline in transfer coefficient from just over 20% in areas of low production to about 5% in the areas of high production,

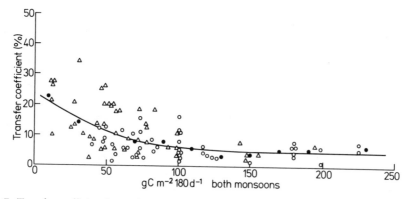

Fig. 7. Transfer coefficient from primary to secondary production as function of primary production. Open circles SW monsoon; triangles NE monsoon; filled circles averages for both monsoons for intervals of primary production

which is a difference of 4 times. In the section on primary production it was suggested that the productivity of the major upwelling areas was greater than 1 gC m^{-2} day^{-1} and that in the centres of the deep oceans it was less than 0.1 gC m^{-2} day^{-1} (about 0.05 gC m^{-2} day^{-1}). But in secondary production, this difference of 10 to 20 times will be reduced to one of 2.5−5.0 times; to put it another way, the secondary production in upwelling areas should be about 0.05 gC m^{-2} day^{-1} and that in the centre of the ocean 0.01−0.02 gC m^{-2} day^{-1}. So some variation in quantity in a spatial sense is damped in the transfer from primary to secondary production. Whether the same sort of process occurs in the transfer to tertiary production is unknown.

A most interesting point about Fig. 7 is the decrease in transfer coefficient with increasing primary production. There is a contrast between the quasi steady-state cycle of the deep subtropical ocean and the discontinuous one characteristic of the upwelling areas. The latter is essentially that of temperate waters, with a delay period between the development of the algal reproductive rate and that of full grazing capacity. It is possible that algae are destroyed in excess of the needs of the herbivores and so there is an excess of particulate matter in the water and even diatomaceous ooze on the sea bed. So the animals which need hardly swim from algal cell to algal cell generate the basic inefficiency of the system; even the vertical migration of the herbivores is likely to be less in the somewhat more turbid waters of the upwelling areas. In the quasi steady-state cycle in the deep ocean, the delay period is probably very short indeed, if it exists at all, and from the low amplitude of the predator-prey oscillation one would expect efficient transfer. Indeed with searching, vertical migration and the need to reproduce, the transfer coefficient can be as high as $20-25\%$. Of the various constraints to efficiency, it is possible that the reproductive load is the heaviest. But the details of the mechanism may be in the feeding — that the particulate material is small (because the ocean is clear) and that organic material is transferred downwards in depth by vertical migration and predation (VINOGRADOV, 1953).

III. Discussion

In biological oceanography, a study of production is the study of a whole ecosystem in terms   of the flow of energy, material or numbers through it. In fisheries biology it is the study of the same ecosystem in terms of the output of edible fish. In this paper it is considered that most of the edible fish occur (except tuna-like fishes) in the upwelling areas or along the coastal reefs. The estimates of tertiary producers are of fish in the main and some use could be made of them.

Fish populations, however, depend upon the production of herbivores directly, in that recruitment may be partly determined during the larval stages in the plankton. Hence greater variability in recruitment might be expected in the upwelling areas than in the open ocean — that is, if recruitment depends upon the match or mismatch of larval production to that of their food in time. As most of the fish in upwelling areas are sardine-like and hence not able to stabilize their numbers very well (CUSHING, 1971 a), the variability of recruitment to the fish stocks may be high. It remains, however, that commercial fisheries are found in areas which are productive and with inefficient transfer, because the fish concentrate. Elsewhere, where transfer is efficient, fish do not concentrate and can only be caught with gear like pelagic long-lines.

6.2

Seasonal Studies of a Pelagic Ecosystem (Meridian 110° E)

D. J. TRANTER

The Indian Ocean is a seasonal ocean (RAMAGE, 1969; WYRTKI, 1973). When the International Indian Ocean Expedition began, Australia was better equipped to make continuous observations in the eastern segment of the ocean than to study the entire ocean in any one aspect. Plans were laid for a series of "seasonal biological cruises".

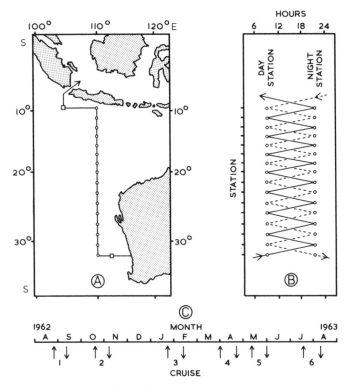

Fig. 1. The study area and sampling strategy

It was hoped that these would be useful, not only in their own right, but also as a frame of reference for biogeography.

In view of the zonal nature of the ocean, a south-north section was chosen for the study — meridian 110° E. This lay sufficiently close to the coast for logistic purposes, yet far enough west to penetrate the anti-cyclonic Indian Ocean gyre. The section extended far enough north to cross the South Equatorial Current (WYRTKI, 1962; HAMON, 1965), and far enough south to enter the northern fringe of the West Wind Drift. The concept of a parallel section farther west was rejected in favour of greater frequency of observations on a single section line.

Fig. 1 shows the study area and the sampling strategy. Stations were at regular intervals in space (90 miles) and time (12 hours). Each of the 16 stations was worked twice per cruise – on the way north and on the way south, once by night and once by day. The interval between consecutive observations at the same station varied from $1-2$ weeks in the northern part, to $3-4$ weeks in the southern part. This interval was regular from cruise to cruise. The interval between cruises varied from $6-12$ weeks. Six cruises were made in all.

The first results were introduced by ROCHFORD in Volume 20 of the Australian Journal of Marine and Freshwater Research (ROCHFORD, 1969; NEWELL, 1969; HUMPHREY and KERR, 1969; JITTS, 1969; TRANTER and KERR, 1969; LEGAND, 1969). A brief note on the phytoplankton from 2 of the 6 cruises was published by DESROSIERES (1965). Various components of the midwater trawl collections were the subject of special studies (ROGER, 1966; LEGAND, 1967; LEGAND and RIVATON, 1967, 1969; MICHEL, 1968; CASTLE, 1969; REPELIN, 1970; GUEREDRAT, 1971) and these results have recently been brought together in a review (LEGAND et al., 1971).

The present paper deals with the ecosystem as a whole, with particular emphasis on the cycles of change at each trophic level – their seasonal amplitudes and phase relationships. An attempt is made to distinguish changes due to ecological succession from changes due to horizontal translation.

I. Material and Methods

The study is based principally on data and results already published. The data, together with the field and laboratory methods used, appear in a series of Oceanographic Cruise Reports (CSIRO Aust., 1965 a–d; 1966 a, b) and are available also from World Data Centres. The information on zooplankton taxa and copepod species is not yet published; it is available in the data store of the CSIRO Division of Fisheries and Oceanography, Cronulla, Australia. Other data from the literature were used to calculate seasonal amplitudes for various waters.

In investigating the various interactions in this ecosystem, extensive use was made of correlation and regression analysis, the strengths and weaknesses of which (CASSIE, 1961; MARGALEF, 1968) are recognized. In interpreting the biological significance of correlations that are significant statistically, frequent reference was made to the distribution patterns of each variable as a function of latitude and time (Fig. $4-10$, 15).

II. Physical Environment

The epipelagic habitat in the eastern Indian Ocean is a lens of warm water bounded below by a permanent thermal discontinuity (ROCHFORD, 1962, 1969). This lens, like that in the Sargasso Sea (MENZEL and RYTHER, 1960), is deepest in the subtropics ($200-300$ m). Towards lower latitudes the layer shallows ($50-100$ m). As a result of this convexity, a rich supply of nutrients lies immediately beneath the tropical euphotic layer, and far beneath the euphotic layer of the subtropics (Fig. 2 and WYRTKI, 1973,

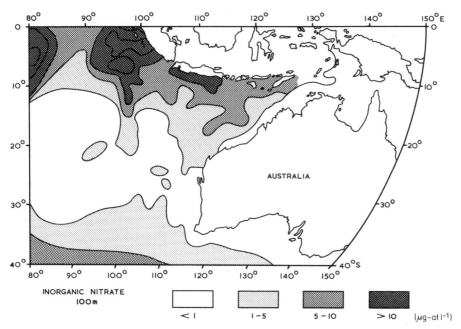

Fig. 2. Inorganic nitrate (100 m) in the eastern Indian Ocean. (Based on WYRTKI, 1971)

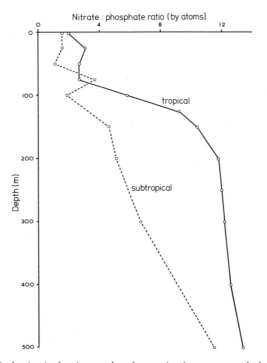

Fig. 3. Reduction in the nitrate : phosphate ratio of water, towards the surface

Fig. 2 this volume). The nitrate: phosphate ratio of the water is not constant but shows a gradual decline towards the surface (Fig. 3), reflecting biological differences in the history of these two major nutrients through the food web (GRILL and RICHARDS, 1964; BEERS, 1966; THOMAS, 1966). The boundary between the tropical and subtropical zones lies near latitude 18° S. (ROCHFORD, 1962, 1969). South of this, a strong shallow thermocline (25 – 75 m) develops in late summer, dividing the mixed layer into an upper and a lower stratum.

The subtropical area is essentially the eastern part of a large anti-cyclonic gyre, as in the Pacific and Atlantic, lying between the zonally oriented equatorial waters and the subantarctic cyclones (REID, 1962; WYRTKI, 1973, this volume). Within such anti-cyclonic gyres, surface waters converge and sink. To the north and to the south, surface waters diverge and upwelling tends to occur.

The tropical zone is dominated by the SE monsoon winds (= SE trades) for a large part of the year (May to November). These reinforce the South Equatorial Current which flows strongly across the section line north of about 15° S. (HAMON, 1965). During the SE monsoon season (southern winter) the stream lies further to the north and flows at maximum strength. In the opposite season, corresponding to the southern summer, the stream lies further to the south and its flow is weaker.

III. Standing Stocks

The general level (concentration) of various biological properties and their variations with depth, latitude, and time have been described by ROCHFORD (1969), JITTS (1969), HUMPHREY and KERR (1969), NEWELL (1969), TRANTER and KERR (1969), and LEGAND (1969). The distribution of these properties, in relation to latitude and time, is shown in Figs. 4 – 10. These distributions are based on column averages. Primary productivity is

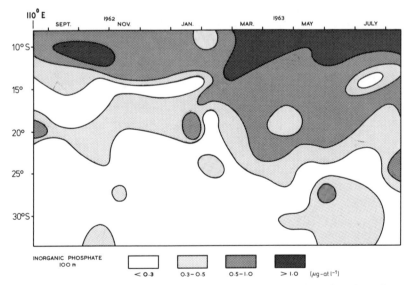

Fig. 4. Inorganic phosphate distribution (100 m) with respect to latitude and month. (After ROCHFORD, 1969)

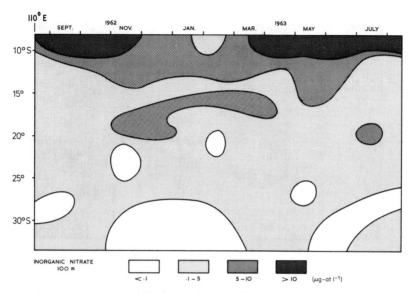

Fig. 5. Inorganic nitrate distribution (100 m) with respect to latitude and month. (After ROCHFORD, 1969)

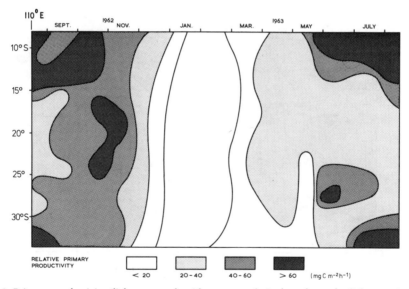

Fig. 6. Primary productivity (light-saturated) with respect to latitude and month. Column values to 150 m. (After JITTS, 1969)

based on values obtained by the light-bath technique; these are fairly well correlated with simulated *in situ* values (Fig. 11). There was a general trend towards higher values in the tropics, particularly during the SE monsoon season. It was evident that primary productivity, chlorophyll *a*, and seston (particulate carbon) each reached their seasonal minimum during the period of the late summer thermocline.

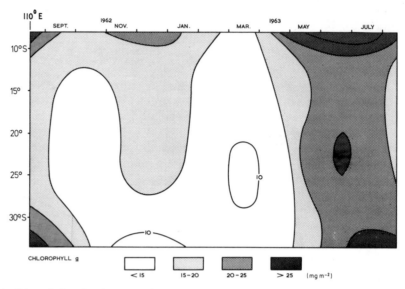

Fig. 7. Chlorophyll *a* distribution with respect to latitude and month. Column values to 150 m. (After HUMPHREY and KERR, 1969)

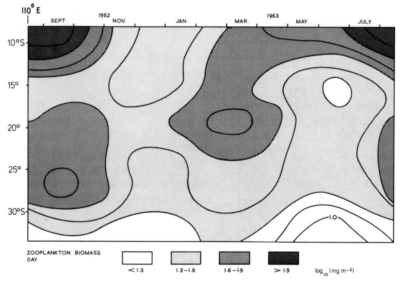

Fig. 8. Day zooplankton biomass with respect to latitude and month. Column values to 200 m. (After TRANTER and KERR, 1969)

Surface nutrients were generally low, even in areas where upwelling had previously been recorded (WYRTKI, 1962). Chlorophyll *a* was concentrated well beneath the surface, usually at about 75 m. The depth of the photosynthetic layer, as indicated by light-

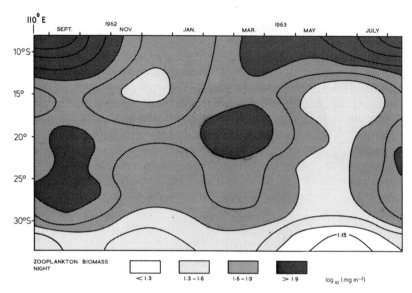

Fig. 9. Night zooplankton biomass with respect to latitude and month. Column values to 200 m.
(After TRANTER and KERR, 1969)

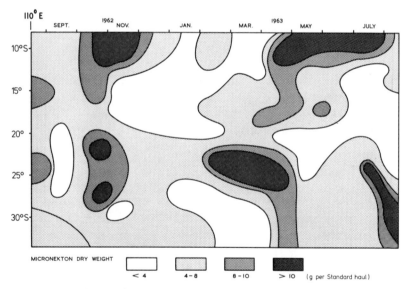

Fig. 10. Micronekton dry weight with respect to latitude and month. Oblique hauls to 200 m;
per standard haul of 10 000 m. (After LEGAND, 1969)

saturated carbon fixation, averaged 85 m, ranging from 60 m at its shallowest (January –
February) to 130 m at its deepest (October).

Table 1 gives mean levels for each standing stock, cruise by cruise. Separate values

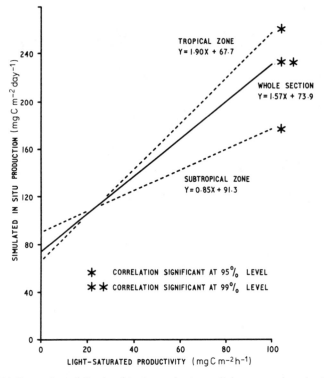

Fig. 11. Regressions of simulated *in situ* production on light-saturated productivity.
(Data from JITTS, 1969)

are given for tropical and subtropical zones. No attempt is made in this review to place
these levels in a geographic context. The emphasis is on seasonal variation and the interaction of one trophic level with another.

In Table 2, the levels of these biological properties are compared in terms of their
carbon equivalents. The mean seasonal carbon equivalent at each trophic level is expressed

Table 1. Mean levels for various biological properties along meridian 110° E. During six cruises in
1962−63. (/, day value/night value)

Biological Property	Cruise					
	Jan−Feb 1963	Mar−Apr 1963	May−Jun 1963	Jul−Aug 1963	Aug−Sep 1962	Oct−Nov 1962
(a) *Tropical Zone* (North of 18° S.)						
Zooplankton Biomass (mg m^{-3})	31/87	47/71	42/63	63/109	84/113	50/46
Total MWT Catch (g dry weight per 10 000 m column)	9.66	15.98	16.28	12.90	21.10	23.38
MWT Zooplankton	2.00	4.80	2.30	2.12	7.85	5.62
MWT Macroplankton	2.80	3.65	5.78	5.90	6.10	9.37
MWT Micronekton	4.56	7.25	7.93	4.43	6.52	7.97

Table 1 (continued)

Primary Productivity ($mgC\ m^{-2}\ h^{-1}$)	3	26	41	58	53	60
Chlorophyll a ($mg\ m^{-2}$)	18/18	13/12	26/27	20/18	20/22	14/14
Chlorophyll c ($mg\ m^{-2}$)	48/39	33/27	40/45	54/48	61/67	42/43
Inorganic Nitrate (μg-at l^{-1})	6.02	6.02	7.53	5.13	6.55	5.33
Inorganic Phosphate (μg-at l^{-1})	0.65	0.60	0.62	0.56	0.62	0.75

(b) *Subtropical Zone*
(South of 18° S.)

Zooplankton Biomass	41/51	44/53	21/35	28/58	46/72	43/76
Total MWT Catch	10.07	12.86	8.21	11.51	13.62	16.76
MWT Zooplankton	1.97	2.04	1.64	1.94	3.27	4.93
MWT Macroplankton	2.74	2.54	2.36	2.91	4.51	3.39
MWT Micronekton	4.76	7.99	3.93	6.21	4.73	7.97
Primary Productivity	4	26	32	40	44	53
Chlorophyll a	15/13	11/12	23/25	20/21	21/21	13/13
Chlorophyll c	39/38	27/26	47/61	58/57	61/71	37/33
Inorganic Nitrate	1.08	1.03	1.58	1.41	0.93	0.78
Inorganic Phosphate	0.28	0.28	0.34	0.30	0.29	0.32

Table 2. Standing stock and turnover of C at various trophic levels, with respect to phytoplankton carbon

Biological Property	Carbon Equivalent	Percentage of Phytoplankton Standing Stock						Annual Mean
		J−F 1963	M−A 1963	M−J 1963	J−A 1963	A−S 1962	O−N 1962	
(a) *Tropical Zone*								
Total Particulate Carbon	Direct Measure	260	430	246	289	−	−	306
Phytoplankton	($mg\ m^{-2}$ Chlorophyll a) $\times 50$	100	100	100	100	100	100	100
Zooplankton	($mg\ m^{-2}$ Wet Weight) $\times .03$	58	71	28	73	62	39	55
Micronekton	($mg\ m^{-2}$ Dry Weight) $\times .50$	2.5	6.0	2.9	2.5	3.0	5.7	3.8
Carbon Fixation:	Direct Measure							
Simulated *in situ* (per day)		11	13	13	34	10	10	15
Artificial light (per hour)		0.3	4.3	3.0	6.4	4.8	8.6	4.6
(b) *Subtropical Zone*								
Total Particulate Carbon	As above	455	347	272	269	−	−	336
Phytoplankton	As above	100	100	100	100	100	100	100
Zooplankton	As above	47	53	17	33	41	70	43
Micronekton	As above	3.7	6.7	1.6	3.0	2.3	6.1	3.9
Carbon Fixation	As above							
Simulated *in situ* (per day)		14	15	10	15	11	12	13
Artificial light (per hour)		0.6	4.3	2.6	3.8	4.2	8.2	3.9

as a percentage of the standing stock of phytoplankton carbon. The validity of the comparison depends upon the conversion factors used. The carbon equivalent for micronekton is derived from VINOGRADOV (1953) who found little variation from one fish to another. The carbon equivalent for zooplankton was determined directly on representative samples from each cruise, by NEWELL. The carbon equivalent for chlorophyll *a* lies within the range of values usually recommended (HAGMEIER, 1961; RYTHER and MENZEL, 1965; EPPLEY, 1968; ZEITZSCHEL, 1970). To have used a higher value for the (oligotrophic) subtropical zone and a lower value for the (more eutrophic) tropical zone, in line with EPPLEY's recommendations, would have accentuated the existing difference between the 2 zones, but may nevertheless have been justified.

The Table shows that there was from 2 to 3 times as much detrital carbon in the water as living phytoplankton carbon. Zooplankton carbon ranged from 17 to 73% of phytoplankton carbon, the ratio generally being higher in the tropics (mean, 55%) than in the subtropics (mean, 43%). Micronekton carbon ranged from 1.6 to 6.7% of phytoplankton carbon. The daily primary production measured by the simulated *in situ* technique ranged from 10 to 34% of the phytoplankton standing stock in the tropics (turnover, 3 − 10 days), and from 10 to 15% in the subtropics (turnover, 6 − 10 days). These are surprising values, particularly the low level of detrital carbon and high level of zooplankton carbon, relative to phytoplankton carbon; in the Sargasso Sea, for example, zooplankton carbon is only 15% of phytoplankton carbon (BEERS, 1966). The significance of these ratios in relation to energy transfer is dealt with in the discussion.

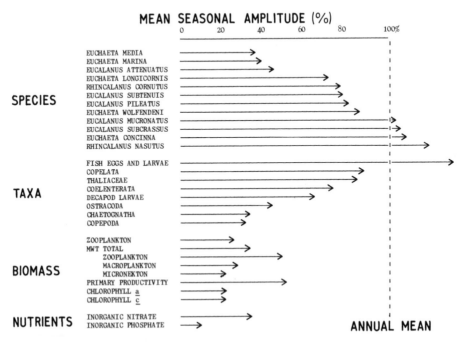

Fig. 12. Mean seasonal amplitude of species, taxa, biological stocks, and nutrients in the eastern Indian Ocean

IV. Seasonal Amplitudes

Some idea of the seasonal variation in biological properties in the study area can be obtained from Figs. 4–10. Seasonal variation is usually expressed in terms of the annual range. This is satisfactory for properties that vary in a regular way, but less satisfactory for those that have large, non-seasonal components of variability. To compare one biological property with another and one part of an ocean with another, a better measure of seasonal amplitude is required. I have chosen the standard deviation of

Table 3. Seasonal variation[+] in various biological properties during 1962–63, in the tropical and subtropical zones of the study section. (Column values; +, coefficient of variation of cruise means)

| Variable | Seasonal Variation (%)[+] | | | |
| | Tropical | | Subtropical | |
	Day	Night	Day	Night
Zooplankton Species:				
Euchaeta media	45		31	
Euchaeta marina	40		44	
Eucalanus attenuatus	41		58	
Euchaeta longicornis	59		55	
Rhincalanus cornutus	56		105	
Eucalanus subtenuis	126		37	
Eucalanus pileatus	82		57	
Euchaeta wolfendeni	102		70	
Eucalanus mucronatus	104		98	
Eucalanus subcrassus	94		115	
Euchaeta concinna	109		–	
Rhincalanus nasutus	104		140	
Zooplankton Taxon:				
Fish eggs and larvae	176	30	175	132
Copelata	97	72	106	97
Thaliaceae	71	131	87	79
Coelenterata	62	52	103	99
Decapod larvae	71	49	51	41
Ostracoda	68	44	35	43
Chaetognatha	47	49	29	36
Copepoda	74	32	19	24
Zooplankton Biomass	35	32	27	26
Midwater trawl total	–	31	–	24
Midwater trawl zooplankton	–	58	–	48
Midwater trawl macroplankton	–	41	–	26
Midwater trawl micronekton	–	25	–	29
Primary productivity	55	–	52	–
Chlorophyll a	26	30	29	32
Chlorophyll c	22	29	29	37
Column phosphate	10	–	8	–
Column nitrate	14	–	27	–

monthly (or quarterly) means. For the purpose of comparison, the value is expressed as a percentage of the annual mean (coefficient of variation).

Using this index of seasonal amplitude, various biological properties are compared in Fig. 12. Particular species and taxa were chosen to encompass the diversity in trophic habit and origins that makes up the zooplankton community: for example, Copelata and Thaliacea are algal grazers, Chaetognatha and Coelenterata are predatory, and

Table 4. Seasonal variation[+] in biological properties in other areas of the world ocean. (+, coefficient of variation of monthly or quarterly means; P, phytoplankton; Z, zooplankton). Data according to various sources from the literature

| Area | Numerical abundance | | | | | | Biomass | | Productivity | Pigments | Nutrients | |
	Species P	Species Z	Taxon P	Taxon Z	Total P	Total Z	Zooplankton	Micronekton	Productivity	Pigments	Phosphate	Nitrate
(a) Oceanic												
Sub-arctic												
Stn "P" (N. Pacific)							85		60	26		11
Stn "B" (Labrador Sea)	228				111	219						
Stn "M" (Norwegian Sea)	246				165							
Antarctic	110					93	41					
Sub-antarctic							71			87		
Sub-tropical												
Sargasso Sea	148		81 − 316	27			87		87	49		
Gulf Stream				26								
Tropical												
Eastern Pacific							14	41	31	19		
(b) Coastal												
Temperate												
Long Is. Sound					142	80	66			46	51	112
Str. Georgia (BC)	177						123		88	51	34	39
Plymouth				75		62				86	39	
Irish Sea	106	167					83					
Sub-tropical												
Sydney (Aust.)				33		140	104			48		30
Tropical												
Singapore				56	130	56				80	59	
Cochin (S. India)			188	107	187				57	73		

Copepoda and Ostracoda have diverse feeding habits (Raymont, 1963); Eucalanid copepods are largely herbivores and Euchaetid copepods are carnivores; fish eggs and larvae and most of the decapod larvae are drawn from non-planktonic stock.

Fig. 12 shows that there is a general trend towards increasing seasonal amplitude, from nutrients and biomass to plankton numbers. The variation is greater at the species level (copepod species: 40 − 120%) than at the taxon level (total Copepoda: 40%). Within the various taxa, fish eggs and larvae showed the greatest seasonal amplitude (120%)

followed by Copelata and Thaliacea, two herbivorous groups (80%). For zooplankton biomass, micronekton dry weight, and phytoplankton (chlorophyll *a*), the variation was much the same (25%) but higher for (light-saturated) primary productivity. The seasonal amplitude of nitrate was 4 times that of phosphate.

Table 3 shows seasonal amplitudes separately for tropical and subtropical zones, by day and night. In general, there was a greater day-night difference in seasonal amplitude for the tropics than for the subtropics, particularly in the case of fish eggs and larvae and Copepoda (day > night) and Thaliaceae (night > day). In some cases there was a marked zonal difference in seasonal amplitude, for example for the copepod species *Rhincalanus nasutus* (greater in subtropics) and *Eucalanus subtenuis* (greater in tropics). Elsewhere, differences were slight.

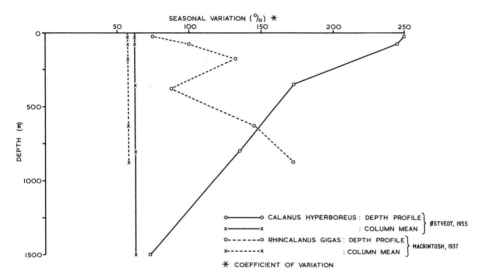

Fig. 13. Seasonal variation of zooplankton at high latitudes as a function of depth.
(After Ostvedt, 1955, and Mackintosh, 1937)

It is not the present purpose to explain these various differences in biological terms. It is to establish the magnitude of seasonal variation in this part of the ocean so that it may be compared in this respect with other better-known regions of the world ocean.

Table 4 gives seasonal amplitudes for other areas, calculated from data in the literature. These are separated into coastal and oceanic regimes. Comparison with Table 3 and Fig. 12 shows that seasonal amplitudes in the eastern Indian Ocean are low, but nonetheless significant. For example, variation is less than in the Sargasso Sea (Menzel and Ryther, 1960) but greater than in the eastern Pacific (Blackburn et al., 1970).

A point of interest which emerged from these comparisons is that the high amplitudes often recorded from high latitude epipelagic areas do not necessarily reflect the situation in the water column as a whole (Fig. 13). In fact, the seasonal amplitude for the total water column is well within the range of amplitudes characteristic of the tropical and subtropical eastern Indian Ocean. The large seasonal amplitudes for particular strata are caused by vertical migrations from one stratum to another.

V. Trophic Relationships

1. Evidence of Trophic Succession

If the seasonal variation observed in nearly every biological property is the result of a seasonal cycle of plankton production, then the variations in these properties ought to be inter-related.

In its simplest form, the plankton cycle is conceived to be a "food chain" with algae as the first link, algal herbivores (zooplankton) as the second, primary carnivores (zooplankton) as the third, secondary carnivores (micronekton) as the fourth, pelagic squid as the fifth, and predatory nekton as the sixth. Each trophic level is considered, ideally, to draw on the energy resources of the level immediately below. So, matter is conveyed along the food chain leaving depletion in its wake. Each standing stock increases in succession, reaches a maximum, and then declines. The problem is to distinguish changes such as these from those of horizontal translation.

Where peaks at adjacent trophic levels are close in phase, their values will be well-correlated (STEEMANN NIELSEN, 1957; CUSHING, 1958). Where the time lag is considerable, there will be high negative correlations—for example when grazing or predation pressure is increasing or declining. With such a model of plankton production in mind, I have sought to determine whether or not there is evidence of trophic succession in our study area during the year of study.

It has often been proposed that time lags are short in warm waters (e.g. CUSHING, 1958). Therefore, in the analysis that follows of data from meridian 110° E, correlations based on concurrent pairs of values are considered first of all.

Table 5 shows correlation values between various components of the zooplankton catch, representing holoplankton, meroplankton, and each major trophic type. The table shows that these diverse components are well correlated; they vary in a similar way. Of a total of 112 correlations, no less than 102 were significant at the 95% level, of which not more than 5—6 could be due to chance. Most of these (86) were significant also at the 99% level. Of the 26 correlations that were not significant at this level, more than half were for the tropical zone by night; of the 10 that were not significant even at the 95% level, 5 involved the rather unique component fish eggs and larvae, 2 involved decapod larvae, 2 Chaetognatha, and 1 Copepoda. The various components of the midwater trawl catch are similarly well-correlated, particularly in the subtropical zone (Table 6 b).

It is clear, then, that the time lag between the seasonal cycles of the various zooplankton components is very short. Consequently it is not possible to locate evidence of trophic succession. It is necessary to extend the search more widely.

Table 6 shows the correlations between zooplankton (as a whole) and other biological properties, viz. phytoplankton (chlorophyll a), productivity (light-saturated), phosphate, and nitrate. The values on which the correlations are based are column means, 200 m in the case of zooplankton and nutrients, and 150 m in the case of chlorophyll a and productivity. The nutrients column was taken to 200 m rather than to the bottom of the mixed layer, because the N/P profile showed a progressive increase from the surface to round about this depth (Fig. 3).

In calculating correlation coefficients, values for zooplankton (species, taxa, and biomass) and for the various midwater trawl components were transformed by logs.

No transformation was made for other variables because it was found in general that they were normally distributed. Fig. 14, for example, demonstrates the difference between the cumulative frequency distributions for chlorophyll a and for zooplankton biomass.

Table 6 shows that there are fewer significant correlations between zooplankton and other variables than between zooplankton and the various components of the mid-

Table 5. Correlation between representative zooplankton taxa, in tropical and subtropical zones, by day and night. (** significant at 99% level; * significant at 95% level; N.S. not significant)

Taxa		Tropical zone		Subtropical zone	
		Day	Night	Day	Night
x	y	(n = 33)	(n = 35)	(n = 57)	(n = 54)
Copelata	Thaliaceae	**	**	**	**
	Copepoda	**	N.S.	**	**
	Ostracoda	**	**	**	**
	Coelenterata	**	**	**	**
	Chaetognatha	**	*	**	**
	Decapod larvae	**	N.S.	*	**
	Fish eggs and larvae	**	N.S.	**	**
Thaliaceae	Copepoda	**	**	**	**
	Ostracoda	**	*	**	**
	Coelenterata	**	**	**	**
	Chaetognatha	**	**	**	**
	Decapod larvae	**	**	**	**
	Fish eggs and larvae	**	N.S.	**	**
Copepoda	Ostracoda	**	*	**	**
	Coelenterata	**	**	**	**
	Chaetognatha	**	N.S.	**	**
	Decapod larvae	**	**	*	**
	Fish eggs and larvae	**	N.S.	**	**
Ostracoda	Coelenterata	**	**	**	**
	Chaetognatha	**	**	*	**
	Decapod larvae	**	N.S.	**	*
	Fish eggs and larvae	*	**	**	*
Coelenterata	Chaetognatha	**	N.S.	**	**
	Decapod larvae	**	*	*	**
	Fish eggs and larvae	**	*	**	**
Chaetognatha	Decapod larvae	**	**	*	**
	Fish eggs and larvae	*	N.S.	**	**
Decapod Larvae	Fish eggs and larvae	*	N.S.	*	**

water trawl catch. However, in the tropical zone, but only in the tropical zone, zooplankton is well correlated with productivity (99% significance), phosphate (99% significance), and nitrate (95% significance); this may be surprising, since productivity is not well correlated either with nutrients or phytoplankton. In the subtropical zone, and only in the subtropical zone, phytoplankton is positively correlated with productivity and negatively correlated with midwater trawl (MWT) macroplankton and plankton.

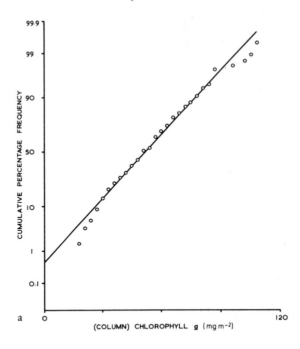

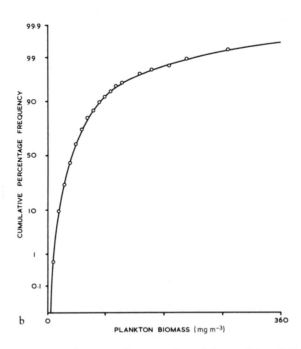

Fig. 14. Cumulative percentage frequencies for untransformed data. a Chlorophyll *a*; b Zooplankton
biomass

Is is clear, even from this preliminary analysis, that there are basic biological differences between the tropical and subtropical zones. However, the correlations that were obtained, based as they are on concurrent pairs of values, are not easy to interpret. in terms of cause and effect. Some allowance needs to be made for natural time lags between one cycle and another. Serial correlations are required. In calculating these, we have been limited by the sampling frequency.

Table 6 a. Correlation matrices for various biological properties by day and night in the tropical zone (** significant at 99% level; * significant at 95% level; N.S. not significant)

	Zooplankton	Chlorophyll a	Productivity	Phosphate	Nitrate	
Zooplankton						Day Tropical (n = 33 − 36)
Chlorophyll a	0.26					
Productivity	0.54**	0.23				
Phosphate	0.48**	0.23	0.26			
Nitrate	0.40*	0.46**	0.16	0.49**		

	Zooplankton	Chlorophyll a	MWT Plankton	MWT Macroplankton	MWT Micronekton	
Zooplankton						Night Tropical (n = 35)
Chlorphyll a	0.33					
MWT Plankton	0.36*	0.29				
MWT Macroplankton	0.24	0.24	0.36*			
MWT Micronekton	0.14	−0.15	0.29	0.57**		

Three trophic levels were chosen for the first approach viz, phytoplankton, zooplankton, and micronekton. Although zooplankton is not an homogeneous entity, at least there is no overlap with the other trophic levels that have been selected. Observations at each position (station) were associated with others on the same occasion (normal correlations) and also with observations prior and subsequent (serial correlations). This was done for 2 time intervals: that between consecutive cruises (N, N+1), and that between consecutive legs of the same cruise (n, n+1). The results are shown in Table 7.

The table shows that, for the data as a whole, these 3 biological characteristics varied with space and time in a fashion consistent with the concept of trophic succession. There were high correlations between the phytoplankton of one cruise (P_N) and the zooplankton

Table 6b. Correlation matrices for various biological properties by day and night in the subtropical zone (** significant at 99% level; * significant at 95% level; N.S. not significant)

Day sub-tropical (n = 57−60)

	Zooplankton	Chlorophyll *a*	Productivity	Phosphate	Nitrate
Zooplankton					
Chlorophyll *a*	−0.15				
Productivity	0.08	0.44**			
Phosphate	0.10	0.11	0.05		
Nitrate	0.05	0.14	−0.12	0.66**	

Night sub-tropical (n = 51−53)

	Zooplankton	Chlorophyll *a*	MWT Plankton	MWT Macroplankton	MWT Micronekton
Zooplankton					
Chlorophyll *a*	−0.21				
MWT Plankton	0.46**	−0.41**			
MWT Macroplankton	0.41**	−0.33*	0.46**		
MWT Micronekton	0.27*	−0.25	0.46**	0.21	

of the next (Z_{N+1}); and between the zooplankton of one cruise (Z_N) and the micronekton of the next (M_{N+1}). However, there were also many variations, and some exceptions to this general trend. It is from these that further insight may be sought about causal relationships.

2. Zooplankton and Phytoplankton

a) Subtropical Zone, March−August

Here, zooplankton and phytoplankton are fluctuating out of phase with one another, the time lag being of the order of the interval between cruises (in this case, 6−8 weeks). The result is that concurrent observations (Z:P) are negatively correlated and those separated in time by 6−8 weeks (P_N:Z_{N+1}, Z_N:P_{N+1}) are positively correlated. Serial correlations with an interval between the correlated observations of only 3−4 weeks (P_n:Z_{n+1}, Z_n:P_{n+1}) are of the same order as those with zero time displacement. This shows that the time lag between the phytoplankton and zooplankton cycles corresponds more closely to the interval between cruises than to the interval between consecutive legs of the same cruise. The resultant pattern suggests a classical predator-prey interaction in which zooplankton is the predator and phytoplankton the prey. It is possible, of course,

Table 7. Normal correlations (concurrent values) and serial correlations (consecutive values) between phytoplankton (P) +, zooplankton (Z), and micronekton (M). (N = cruise; n = leg; +, chlorophyll a; ** significant at 99% level; * significant at 95% level; N.S. not significant)

Zone	Period	Zooplankton:Phytoplankton					Zooplankton:Micronekton				
		$Z_N:P_{N+1}$	$Z_n:P_{n+1}$	$Z:P$	$Z_{n+1}:P_n$	$Z_{N+1}:P_N$	$Z_{N+1}:M_N$	$Z_{n+1}:M_n$	$Z:M$	$Z_n:M_{n+1}$	$Z_N:M_{N+1}$
Tropical: (North of 18° S.)	August–February (N=6–12 weeks)	+.27 N.S.	−.13 N.S.	+.12 N.S.	+.60**	−.24 N.S.	−.12 N.S.	−.07 N.S.	+.03 N.S.	+.52 N.S.	+.72**
	March–August (N=6–8 weeks)	+.46*	+.04 N.S.	+.28 N.S.	+.22 N.S.	+.37 N.S.	+.44 N.S.	+.61 N.S.	+.42*	+.87**	+.44 N.S.
	Whole Year	+.31*	−.03 N.S.	+.20 N.S.	+.35*	+.08 N.S.	+.21 N.S.	+.33 N.S.	+.27 N.S.	+.67**	+.59**
Subtropical: (South of 18° S.)	August–February	−.05 N.S.	+.15 N.S.	+.03 N.S.	−.16 N.S.	+.25 N.S.	−.12 N.S.	−.18 N.S.	+.44*	+.12 N.S.	+.08 N.S.
	March–August	+.35*	−.42*	−.33*	−.24 N.S.	+.49**	−.22 N.S.	+.63*	+.15 N.S.	+.04 N.S.	+.42 N.S.
	Whole Year	−.06 N.S.	−.16 N.S.	−.16 N.S.	−.21 N.S.	+.34**	−.18 N.S.	+.22 N.S.	+.31*	+.04 N.S.	+.28 N.S.
Whole Section August–February		+.13 N.S.	+.06 N.S.	+.09 N.S.	+.16 N.S.	+.05 N.S.	−.10 N.S.	−.11 N.S.	+.31 N.S.	+.31 N.S.	+.34*
Whole Section March–August		+.37**	−.21 N.S.	−.04 N.S.	+.01 N.S.	+.43**	+.17 N.S.	+.62**	+.34*	+.40 N.S.	+.51**
Whole Section Whole Year		+.12 N.S.	−.07 N.S.	+.02 N.S.	+.07 N.S.	+.24**	+.03 N.S.	+.29 N.S.	+.33**	+.34*	+.45**
Time Displacement (weeks)		6–12	1–4		1–4	6–12	6–12	1–4	0	1–4	6–12

that translation (water mass movement) may be involved. This question is discussed in detail at a later stage.

For the remainder of the year (August—February), correlations in the subtropical zone were not very well developed.

b) Tropical Zone, August— February

Here, the phytoplankton and zooplankton cycles were more in phase. The response by zooplankton (Z_{n+1}) to changes in the standing stock of phytoplankton (P_n) was much swifter than in the subtropical zone. The time lag coincided fairly closely with the interval between consecutive legs of the same cruise, which in this part of the section was less than 2 weeks. Zooplankton and phytoplankton were not negatively correlated as in the subtropical zone during the alternate season. This indicated that the food supply (primary production) was keeping pace with the grazing rate.

c) Tropical Zone, March—August

There is no clear pattern here as in the cases described above. The only correlation that approached significance was that between the zooplankton of one cruise (Z_N) and the phytoplankton of the next $(P_N + 1)$. Such a situation could arise if the zooplankton were recycling nutrients later used in phytoplankton production. This possibility arises again in connection with other results and is there discussed at greater length.

3. Zooplankton and Nutrients

a) Tropical Zone

We have already seen that concurrent phytoplankton and zooplankton values are not well correlated in the tropical zone; there is a time lag of $1-2$ weeks between phytoplankton fluctuations and the consequent zooplankton response. The high correlations between zooplankton on the one hand, and phosphate, nitrate, and productivity on the other are therefore most intriguing. These correlations were compared with corresponding serial correlations (Table 8). This table shows that correlations between zooplankton and productivity, phytoplankton and productivity, and phytoplankton and nitrate are reduced by time intervals (either positive or negative) as short as $1-2$ weeks; the introduction of a time lag does not materially increase the value of the correlation.

These results indicate that the relationship between zooplankton and nutrients is a direct and fairly immediate one. They suggest that, in the tropical zone at least, zooplankton plays a mayor role in the recycling and regeneration of nutrients. The fact that the N/P ratio declines towards the surface (Fig. 3) suggests that the recycling of phosphate may be faster than that of nitrate. The fact that phytoplankton is well correlated with nitrate (0.46), but not with phosphate (0.23), (Table 6 a), is probably connected with this N/P differential; it seems likely that both phytoplankton and N/P fluctuate in unison under heavy grazing pressure, the one as a direct result of grazing, the other as a result of the more rapid rate of phosphate recycling associated with zooplankton excretion.

b) Subtropical Zone

Apart from the correlation between phosphate and nitrate which is a general feature of most oceanic systems, the only variables that are well correlated by day are phyto-

Table 8. Normal correlations (concurrent values) and serial correlations (consecutive values) between zooplankton (Z), phytoplankton (P) +, productivity p, and inorganic nitrate (I.N.). (n = leg; t = time; +, chlorophyll a; ** significant at 99% level; * significant at 95% level; N. S. not significant)

Zone	Zooplankton : Productivity			Phytoplankton+ : Productivity			Phytoplankton : Nitrate		
	$Z_n:p_{n+1}$	$Z:p$	$Z_{n+1}:p_n$	$P_n:p_{n+1}$	$P:p$	$P_{n+1}:p_n$	$P_n:I.N._{n+1}$	$P:I.N.$	$P_{n+1}:I.N._n$
Tropical ($t_{n+1}-t_n = 1-2$ weeks)	+.17	+.54**	+.06	+.09	+.23	+.13	+.46	+.46**	+.47*
Subtropical ($t_{n+1}-t_n = 3-4$ weeks)	−.16	+.08	+.11	+.25	+.44**	+.21	+.32	+.14	−.06
Both ($t_{n+1}-t_n = 1-4$ weeks)	0	−	+.12	+.04	−	+.18	+.19	−	+.28

plankton and productivity (Table 6 b). This is the natural consequence of the functional relation between the two in the absence of rapid recycling induced by over-grazing. As we have already seen (Table 7), the general trend in this zone is for zooplankton and phytoplankton to fluctuate out of phase with each other; as a consequence, phytoplankton and productivity values separated in time by 3 – 4 weeks (Table 8) show a weaker (serial) correlation than do concurrent pairs of values.

4. Zooplankton Hervivores and Zooplankton Carnivores

Table 9 is a correlation matrix for 12 copepod species (Appendix, species with *), 7 herbivores *(Eucalanus* and *Rhincalanus)* and 5 carnivores *(Euchaeta).* Their inter-relationships are shown both for the tropical and the subtropical zone. The correlations in each zone are arranged in geometric blocks of different trophic significance. These are herbivores: herbivores (H:H); herbivores:carnivores (H:C); and carnivores:carnivores (C:C).

The correlations involving species 5 and 8 reveal less about their trophic associations than their geographic distribution. Species 5 *(Eucalanus subtenuis)* is correlated with many others in the subtropics and none at all in the tropics. Species 8 *(Euchaeta concinna)*

Table 9. Correlation matrix for 7 species of copepod herbivores *(Eucalanidae)* and 5 species of copepod carnivores *(Euchaetidae)* in the tropical and subtropical zones of the study section. (Only those correlations that were significant at the 95% level or higher are represented, for species see Appendix)

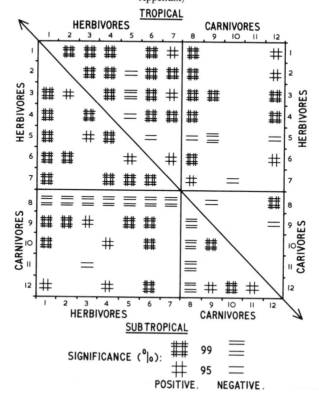

is correlated with several others in the tropics and none at all in the subtropics. This suggests that the former is a subtropical and the latter a tropical species. Other species are more uniformly distributed throughout both zones.

Of the remaining correlations (110), more than half (61) are positive, providing further evidence of the general response to what must surely be a common determining influence. The block with the highest proportion (100%) of significant correlations occurred in the tropical zone (H:H) as did the block with the lowest proportion (10%) of significant correlations (C:C). The remaining blocks were ranked as follows:

H:H, Subtropics (approx. 66%)
C:C, Subtropics (approx. 66%)
H:C, Subtropics (approx. 40%)
H:C, Tropics (approx. 40%)

Two of the negative correlations were in the block C:C (Tropics) and one each in H:C (Tropics) and H:C (Subtropics).

The results show that, in the tropics, the seasonal cycles of copepod herbivores are more generally in phase, and the seasonal cycles of copepod carnivores less generally in phase, than in the subtropics. The phase relationship between herbivores and carnivores is generally much the same from one zone to the other.

5. Zooplankton and Benthos

Along the coasts of western Australia and southern Indonesia are benthic populations whose larvae drift into the open ocean where, for the duration of their larval life, they coexist with the epipelagic plankton community. Prominent among these are the larvae of stomatopods (mantis shrimps) and panulirid lobsters. These were taken along the 110° E. section during the study period, particularly by the midwater trawl.

The distribution and abundance of stomatopod larvae from the midwater trawl collections formed the subject of a special study by MICHEL (1968). His material was made up of two main groups, concentrated to the north and to the south of the tropical-subtropical boundary. MICHEL believes that these 2 stocks came from the shores of southern Indonesia and the shores of western Australia respectively. The populations of west Australian origin begin their life cycle in the southern summer (January–February), as indicated by the frequency of early larval stages, and leave the plankton in the spring and early summer of the following year. Indonesian populations have a continuous breeding season.

The west Australian species of rock lobster are separated into tropical and sub-tropical components, the southern species *(Panulirus longipes cygnus)* forming the basis of a lucrative fishery (BOWEN and CHITTLEBOROUGH, 1966) from which about 11 million individuals are taken each year. The larvae (phyllosoma) of *P. longipes* are concentrated south of 18° S., while those of tropical species, for example *P. penicillatus,* are concentrated to the north of this boundary (CHITTLEBOROUGH and THOMAS, 1969).

The life cycle of *P. longipes* is similar to that of the stomatopods studied by MICHEL. The early phyllosoma leave the coast during the summer months and return as late-stage phyllosoma in the spring and early summer of the following year, making an approximate larval life of 10 – 12 months.

These long-lived meroplankton organisms are important in two main respects. They are an integral part of the pelagic ecosystem; and they are an indicator of seasonal oceanic drift. It is this drift that distributes the products of the food web throughout the pelagic biotope.

6. Zooplankton and Micronekton

One would, perhaps, expect that the time lag between the zooplankton and micro-nekton cycles would be much greater than between the zooplankton and phytoplankton cycles, since life span generally increases progressively along the food chain. However on our study section, concurrent micronekton and zooplankton values were frequently well correlated (Table 7). This is a matter of considerable interest. Four patterns of interaction can be distinguished, corresponding to each zone and season.

a) Tropical Zone, August—February

Here there is a progressive trend towards closer correlations between zooplankton and micronekton with greater (positive) phase shift. The serial correlation (Z_N: M_{N+1}) is closest with a time displacement of $6-12$ weeks corresponding to the interval between consecutive cruises. Such a correlation could be based, in this case, on a direct life-history response (spawning and larval development) by micronekton populations to fluctuations in the supply of zooplankton food; in any event the aggregation is a transient phenomenon (Fig. 10).

b) Tropical Zone, March—August

The time lag here is shorter than in the opposing season. Values separated in time by only $1-2$ weeks (Z_n : M_{n+1}), corresponding to the interval between consecutive legs of the same cruise, are serially correlated. The correlation is very close (0.87); even concurrent values are well correlated (0.42). Such a swift response by the micronekton population in terms of spawning and larval development is most unlikely. This is probably a translation effect—that is, the result of micronekton populations drifting through the area of observation. This thesis is later discussed in more detail in relation to micronekton life histories.

c) Subtropical Zone, March—August

During this period, the only correlation that approached significance was that between micronekton on the first leg of a cruise and zooplankton on the return leg (M_n: Z_{n+1}), the (negative) time displacement being $3-4$ weeks. This is probably fortui-tous. On the other hand, such a situation could arise as a result of a spawning migration timed to anticipate a regular, cyclical zooplankton maximum.

7. Micronekton and Nekton

LEGAND has made a detailed study of the distribution, abundance, and life histories of 23 species of mesopelagic fish taken by the midwater trawl (LEGAND, 1967; LEGAND and RIVATON, 1967, 1969; LEGAND et al., 1971). These species are polarized into tropical and subtropical components, some species having separate populations in each zone. The boundary between the 2 zones lies between 15 and 18° S. The subtropical component is concentrated between 24 and 26° S.

A conspicuous feature of the distribution of these fish is their tendency to drift long distances from one latitude to another in synchrony with their breeding habits. A conspicuous example is the myctophid *Scopelopsis multipunctatus*. The adults spawn in the subtropics in mid-winter, and the young develop gonads in the tropics about 9 months later (May). *Gonostoma? rhodadenia*, on the other hand, spawns in the tropic zone.

It is a fairly general characteristic that, whatever the distributional focus of the species, the displacement from south to north takes place between October and March, and the displacement towards the south between April and September. This raises the question whether there is some mass transport of water with such a pattern.

No observations were made at higher trophic levels than micronekton during the present study. However there is information about pelagic schools of southern bluefin tuna *(Thunnus thynnus maccoyii)* and sperm whales *(Physeter catodon)* in the general study area. Sperm whales feed principally on squid (CHITTLEBOROUGH, personal communication). Tuna feed on squid and smaller carnivores (ROBINS, 1963), though not necessarily the same components taken with the midwater trawl (KING and IVERSON, 1962).

The southern bluefin tuna is a cool-water species living mainly in the West Wind Drift (SHINGU, 1967). The species makes a remarkable northward migration into warm water to spawn in the waters south of Indonesia. On their way to and from their spawning grounds, the populations aggregate in two particular areas that have come to be known as the "Oka" and "Oki" fishing grounds (MIMURA and WARASHINA, 1962). The first lies to the north of 20° S. and extends from our study section towards the east. The second lies to the south fo 20° S. and extends from our study section to the west. Sperm whale records spanning nearly 200 years (TOWNSEND, 1935) show that these are the same areas where that species also aggregates. The first area lies within our tropical zone, the second within our subtropical zone.

Of the 2 tuna fishing grounds, the richer are the subtropical grounds, the principal fishing seasons being September — October (northward migration) and January — February (return migration) (KIKAWA, 1964; WARASHINA and HISADA, 1970). The annual catch on the subtropical grounds in 1960 — 61 (immediately before our study period) was 40 000 tons. Taken over an area 10 degrees square, this is equivalent to approximately 4×10^{-3} g C m^{-2} year^{-1}. This is an order of magnitude greater than would be expected on the basis of the endemic primary production assuming a 6-stage food chain with transfer coefficients of 10^{-1} per link.

These seasonal concentrations of sperm whales and tuna bear such a striking similarity to the seasonal distribution of micronekton (Fig. 10), that one can safely conclude they are all part of the same pelagic food chain. In general the nekton concentration occurs immediately before the micronekton maximum. It is important to remember that there is a connecting link for which we have no observations, viz. pelagic squid.

VI. Species Diversity

Species diversity is an important parameter of the ecosystem (MACARTHUR, 1965; MARGALEF, 1968). It is a measure of ecological structure. Systems with high diversity have more trophic pathways through which energy may flow (MACARTHUR, 1955). There is a food web rather than a food chain. MARGALEF (1968) believes that diversity is also an index of maturity, the mature ecosystem producing less entropy than the immature. Such views are not universal (SLOBODKIN, 1969); nevertheless they hold great attraction for planktologists who work with systems which show a rapid and measurable response to environmental change.

The most useful measure of diversity is the Shannon-Wiener information function H (MACARTHUR, 1965):

$$H = - \sum_{i=1}^{N} p_i \log_e p_i$$

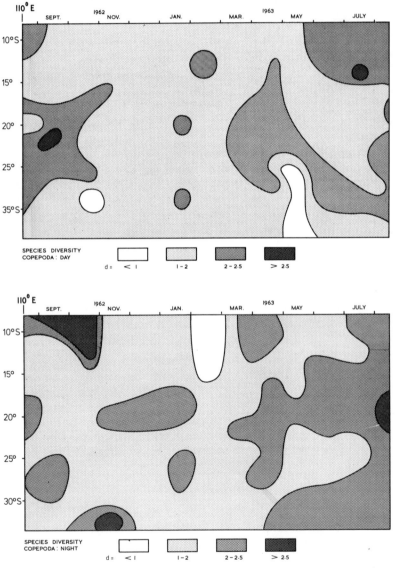

Fig. 15. Species diversity of selected copepods with respect to latitude and month. a Day; b Night

where N is the number of species in the count and p_i is the proportion of the total number of individuals, in the i th species. Units are measured in bits or nits depending on whether logs are taken to the base 2 or the base e. $\log_e N$ measures the diversity of N equally common species.

I have taken 46 species of copepods (Appendix) as a basis for comparisons of species diversity between zones and seasons (Figs. 15 a, b). These belong to the families Eucalanidae (herbivores) and Euchaetidae, Sapphirinidae, and Copiliidae (carnivores).

The figure shows that diversities were usually high and sometimes approached the upper limits usually found in nature (MARGALEF, 1968). They were generally higher in winter than in summer, with a zonal maximum between the tropics and subtropics. In spring, night diversities were occasionally high at the extreme north and south of the

Table 10. Correlation between species diversity of selected copepods (H_T), copepod concentration (C), zooplankton biomass (Z), chlorophyll *a* (P), productivity (p), and species diversity of copepods taken by midwater trawl (H_G)

Zone	Period	H_T: C	H_T: Z	H_T: P	H_T: p	H_T: H_G
Tropical	Aug. 62 – Feb. 63	+.22	−.11	+.13	−	−
	Mar. 63 – Aug. 63	+.22	+.16	−.04	−	−
	Whole Year	+.17	0	+.02	+.25	+.30
Subtropical	Aug. 62 – Feb. 63	+.39**	+.34*	+.20	−	−
	Mar. 63 – Aug. 63	+.29*	+.41**	−.05	−	−
	Whole Year	+.32**	+.37**	+.05	+.11	−.03
Whole Section	Aug. – Feb.	+.23	+.06	+.13	−	−
Whole Section	Mar. – Aug.	+.27**	+.34**	−.04	−	−
Whole Section	Whole Year	+.24**	+.19	+.03	+.15	+.20

Significance (%):   ** 99   * 95

section. There were rare instances of low species diversity: one in summer in the region of the South Equatorial Current and one in autumn in the southern part of the study area. The first was the result of conspicuous dominance by the carnivore *Euchaeta russelli* which reached absolute concentrations approaching 200 m^{-3}; the second was the result of dominance by the herbivore *Eucalanus subtenuis*. These are instances of transient instabilities, a trend that was soon reversed in favour of more complex ecosystems.

Diversity was correlated neither with phytoplankton (chlorophyll *a*) nor with productivity, at least so far as concurrent values were concerned (Table 10). This applied to zone and season as well as to the data as a whole. On the other hand, diversity was highly correlated with both copepod numbers and zooplankton biomass – but only in the subtropical zone.

These results differ in several significant respects from those of GUEREDRAT (1971) who used a somewhat different group of copepods (from the midwater trawl). In general his group included a larger proportion of deepwater forms. Nevertheless, since "the diversity of the ecosystem is reflected with little distortion at several levels" (MARGALEF, 1968), the present differences are somewhat surprising and need to be further investigated.

VII. Discussion

In this study, interest is centred on the dynamics and stability of the pelagic eco-system — the forces which induce fluctuations within the system, and the stabilizing forces which keep those fluctuations within certain bounds. At the species level, fluctuations arise as a result of environmental variations in available energy, time-lag phenomena, and variations in age at death (MACARTHUR, 1955). Similar influences determine stability at the community (food web) level.

Biological communites are usually much more stable in low latitudes than in high latitudes (DUNBAR, 1960; MACARTHUR, 1965; PIANKA, 1966). This general principle is held to apply also to pelagic ecosystems (STEEMANN NIELSEN, 1957; CUSHING, 1958), the two best known instances being the Sargasso Sea (MENZEL and RYTHER, 1960; 1961) and the eastern tropical Pacific (BLACKBURN, 1966; BLACKBURN et al., 1970). Pelagic ecosystems in the tropical and subtropical Indian Ocean might therefore be expected to be equally stable. On the other hand, the monsoons of the Indian Ocean area represent a unique source of instability whose impact on the pelagic ecosystem has never yet been gauged.

The pelagic ecosystem has many co-ordinates: 3 in space and 2 in time. The time co-ordinates are succession and translation. Depth, translation, and the rapidity of succession (especially in warm waters) make the system one of unparalleled complexity. The form it takes at any point in space (e.g. an oceanographic station) varies from time to time, like cloud formations in the sky, representing the instantaneous balance between gain and loss (MARGALEF, 1968).

In view of such complexity, the ecosystem is better considered as a process rather than as a structure, in analogy with laboratory chemostats (MALEK and FENCL, 1966). It is one consequence of such continuous flow systems that too fast a rate of flow or too slow a rate of reproduction leads to "washout" of the system relative to a fixed point of observation. Time-series changes in estuarine plankton populations have been considered in such a way (KETCHUM, 1954; BARLOW, 1955; TRANTER and ABRAHAM, 1971).

As a corollary of this, populations disappear from such an ecosystem in reverse order to their reproductive rate at the point of observation. As a result, trophic sequences separate in space like pigments on a chromatographic column. VINOGRADOV, VORONINA and SUKHANOVA (1961) for example, found the spatial maxima of algae, herbivores, primary carnivores, and secondary carnivores in the Indian Ocean to be displaced at successive distances from the source of nutrient enrichment whence the food chain had its orgin, each trophic level in turn developing to a peak at the site of maximal net recruitment. Similar conclusions have been reached more recently by TIMONIN (1969).

It follows, therefore, that from any one oceanographic station, the trophic sequence can be traced a limited distance through the food web; where observations span a wider area, as in the present study, the sequence can be followed farther. In the discussion which follows, I have assumed that succession can be traced as far as the second trophic level (herbivores); beyond this point in the food web, the observed changes are more likely to be the consequence of translation, a product of food webs generated farther upstream. If such an assumption is true, even approximately, then nutrient enrichment, primary production, grazing, excretion (by grazers), and remineralization may profitably be examined from the window represented by the study section, for cause and effect relationships.

1. Components of Instability

a) Fluctuations in Energy Input

The seasonal amplitude (coefficient of variation) in primary productivity is of the order of 50% of the annual mean in both the tropical and subtropical regions of the eastern Indian Ocean (Table 3), a fluctuation that is not so small compared with other regions of the world ocean. For example, it is nearly as great as that at station "P" in the Canadian Subarctic and it is much more than in the eastern tropical Pacific (Table 4).

Such instabilities in energy input are a latent source of instability throughout the food web (Ryther and Menzel, 1965) and, no doubt, a large component of the seasonal amplitude in zooplankton biomass (48%) has its origin here. On the other hand, the seasonal amplitude in micronekton (dry weight) is only 20% of the annual mean, a level that is much lower than that of the primary energy source, and much lower than that in the eastern tropical Pacific (Table 4). An explanation for this anomaly will later be sought.

b) Time Lags

Blackburn et al. (1970) found the seasonal cycles of phytoplankton and zooplankton in the eastern tropical Pacific to be low in amplitude and close in phase. Our results for the tropical part of the eastern Indian Ocean are somewhat similar. However, the seasonal cycle of micronekton showed such close coincidence with the plankton cycles at times that there is doubt whether they belong to the same trophic sequence. This represents a second anomaly.

The best known study of seasonal changes in a subtropical pelagic ecosystem is that of Menzel and Ryther (1960) in the Sargasso Sea. Their system was typically in a steady state, plankton values being fairly low, except in the spring, and the cycles close in phase. Our results for the subtropical eastern Indian Ocean show similar low amplitudes but, in contrast with the Sargasso Sea, cycles of phytoplankton and zooplankton are distinctly out of phase for a large part of the year. This represents a third anomaly which requires an explanation.

In other respects, these eastern Indian Ocean pelagic ecosystems, like those in the eastern tropical Pacific and subtropical Sargasso Sea, follow the general pattern of seasonal variation so well described by Cushing (1958).

2. Horizontal Translation

Each of the anomalies noted above may be explained in terms of horizontal movement of waters and the consequent translation of those populations that are unable, by their own powers of locomotion, to move independently. The changes observed on our section line take on more meaning if they are regarded as a combination of ecological succession and translation. For example, horizontal translation introduces a time lag to the subtropical ecosystem where, previously, there may have been a steady state as in the Sargasso Sea. Towards the origin of the food web, translation introduces instability; but towards the periphery of the food web, translation introduces an element of stability, as evidenced by the relatively low seasonal amplitude of micronekton and the phase coincidence of the micronekton and plankton cycles.

It is of considerable importance to examine in closer detail the nature of this horizontal translation, first from a biological, then from a physical point of view.

The mesopelagic fish populations studied by LEGAND (1967) are a valuable source of information about horizontal translation. Although these fish (principally myctophids and stomiatids) are powerful migrants from one stratum to another, their capacity for horizontal migration is limited, except by way of the prevailing currents. Consequently as a result of their low reproductive rate (relative to lower trophic levels), their appearance at fixed observation points in space (stations) is discontinuous, the duration of their presence being determined by the length of the breeding season of the parent stock located further upstream (LEGAND, 1967; LEGAND and RIVATON, 1969). Populations of the myctophid *Scopelopsis multipunctatus*, for example, appear in sequence along the study section, at consecutive stages of developmental maturity (LEGAND, 1967; LEGAND et al., 1971).

These micronekton populations are the main food of oceanic squid (NESIS, 1970) which, in turn, are the principal diet of such predatory nekton as sperm whales and southern bluefin tuna. These large predators are the nomads of the pelagic ecosystem, maintaining their presence at fixed points in space not by their rapid reproduction as at low trophic levels, but by their powers of independent movement.

Other components of the pelagic ecosystem whose history is dictated by the forces of translation rather than succession are the long-lived larvae of eels (leptocephala), rock lobsters (phyllosoma), and mantis shrimps whose distribution in the eastern Indian Ocean have been the subject of special studies by CASTLE (1969), CHITTLEBOROUGH and THOMAS (1969), and MICHEL (1968). Whereas eels spawn in the open ocean, rock lobsters spawn only near the coast; their larvae are taken first out to sea and then brought back again some 12 months later. The latter are unique in 3 respects: reproduction of the species is located at a site peripheral to the pelagic ecosystem of which they form a part; a proportion of the pelagic larvae must eventually return for the species to survive; and the duration of larval life is of the order of 12 months. The larvae may be regarded as upstream "additives" to the ecosystem whose presence or absence at any observation point downstream is a function of the continuity or discontinuity of the breeding season of the coastal stocks from which they arise.

The physical requirements for viable recruitment to rock lobster populations are so unique that spawning of the adults and the subsequent larval drift must surely be synchronized with seasonal changes in the water movements. Some form of closed physical system must exist — either a two-way translation with a seasonal frequency, or a closed gyre with an orbital period of approximately 12 months. It is of considerable practical and theoretical importance to determine the nature of this physical mechanism. This is relevant not only to rock lobster recruitment but also to the presence of sub-tropical concentrations of micronekton and nekton, and to the stability anomalies already noted.

ROCHFORD (1969) has shown that there are seasonal intrusions of low-salinity water within the subtropical region in autumn and winter, and seasonal intrusions of high-salinity water within the tropical zone in spring and summer. These results, and those of NEYMAN, FILJUSHKIN and SCHERBININ(1966) on the prevailing currents, suggest a seasonal interaction between the waters of the tropical and subtropical zones. MICHEL (1968), GUEREDRAT (1971), and LEGAND et al. (1971) accept this as the physical mechanism responsible for the characteristic distribution of the midwater trawl components which they studied.

Further information is available in the Oceanographic Atlas of the Indian Ocean (WYRTKI,

1971) concerning this tropical-subtropical interaction. Centred at a depth of about 100 m there is a weakly developed "west Australian gyre", bounded by the South Equatorial Current in the north, meridian 100° E. in the west, the West Wind Drift in the South, and the coast of western Australia (between Cape Leeuwin and Northwest Cape) in the east. This regional gyre separates from the southern flank of the South Equatorial Current in early autumn and turns south and east across the study section (110° E.) carrying tropical water well into the subtropical zone. The southward drift continues into late autumn and early winter, and is gradually replaced in spring and summer by drift from the south central Indian Ocean towards the east and north across our study section.

This pattern of oceanic drift provides a continuous corridor, over the space of one year, for organisms to drift in a full anti-clockwise circle. Whether or not they do so depends on whether, when, and for how long they join the roundabout. For example, early phyllosoma might move directly out to sea in summer because they are confined to the immediate surface stratum (CHITTLEBOROUGH and THOMAS, 1969).

I believe that the West Australian gyre explains the otherwise anomalous subtropical concentrations of micronekton (Fig. 10) near which sperm whales and southern bluefin tuna aggregate on their northward migrations (TOWNSEND, 1935; MIMURA and WARASHINA, 1962). I suggest that these concentrations are derived principally from plankton production of tropical origin, perhaps as a result of nutrient enrichment at the Java Dome (CUSHING, 1969). I would also propose that the gyre is responsible in part for the observed instabilities and anomalies earlier in the food web; these are the result, in part, of the seasonal impact of monsoon generated water movements upon a subtropical system which might otherwise have maintained a steady state.

3. Components of Stability

The variety of ways by which the primary source of energy can filter through the food web is a measure of the stability of the system (MACARTHUR, 1955). Species diversity is a measure of the variety of energy users; recycling mechanisms provide avenues of re-use.

a) Species Diversity

Little can be said at present about species diversity as a whole because the available data include certain groups of copepods only; later studies will deal with diversity in a wider context. However, both the patterns of diversity that I obtained (Figs. 15a and b) and those of GUEREDRAT (1971) show that diversity is generally high throughout the study area, particularly where tropical and subtropical waters mix.

No doubt this increase is due, in part, to the union of two slightly different faunas. However, more than this would seem to be involved. It is curious that species diversity in the copepods that I examined is a function of zooplankton biomass in the subtropics, but not in the tropics (Table 10). If the subtropics are as poor as nutrient concentrations would suggest (Fig. 2, and WYRTKI, 1973 Fig. 2 this volume), then the subtropical habitat may have reached the species saturation limit, there being a limit to the similarity of species with limited resources (MACARTHUR, 1965). It would follow that species diversity would increase where subtropical waters are enriched by tropical intrusions.

I would think that such a response would lead to composite stability at least equal to that of either interacting system. If so, then instabilities resulting from the interaction of 2 trophic sequences that are out of phase would gradually dissipate, rather than gain momentum, in the subsequent history of the hybrid food web. This could be part of the reason why seasonal amplitude at the micronekton level is particularly low.

b) Recycling Mechanisms

Where processes are rapid and time lags are short, as in warm-water pelagic ecosystems (CUSHING, 1958), there are many avenues for re-use of energy and nutrients. The present study throws some light on 2 such mechanisms in particular — recycling of nutrients, and recycling of detritus.

Evidence has accumulated over the last 10 years or so that zooplankton excretion plays a major role in nutrient regeneration. HARRIS (1959) calculated that zooplankton excretion of nitrogen compounds (particularly ammonia) accounted for 77% of the average daily phytoplankton demand for this element during the spring bloom and over 40% of the demand throughout the year. CONOVER, MARSHALL and ORR (1959) showed that *Calanus* in captivity excreted large amounts of inorganic phosphorus in soluble form, and drew attention to earlier observations by GARDINER (1937) that zooplankton kept in seawater for 3 hours increased the dissolved phosphate content of the water by 300 – 600%. The significance of these various results was emphasized by KETCHUM (1963).

Independently, REID (1962) made the surprising discovery that zooplankton volumes were highly correlated with inorganic phosphate, even in quite small tongues of water; he concluded that "any reasonable allowance of time lag for growth renders this close agreement baffling". It is now becoming clear that, whatever indirect relationships might exist, this particular correlation is largely the result of a direct cause and effect relationship between zooplankton and nutrients by way of zooplankton excretion and remineralization of nutrients (CUSHING, 1969). If zooplankton excretion is an important avenue of nutrient regeneration in cool waters, how much more likely is it to play a crucial role in the productivity of warm waters!

The present results provide evidence of this. Perhaps for the first time in a field situation, measures of chlorophyll and productivity are available, which demonstrate that zooplankton is the cause, and nutrients the effect, and not the reverse. The fact that the zooplankton-nutrients correlation was significant in the tropics and not the subtropics is of interest. Perhaps zooplankton played a greater role in nutrient mineralization in the tropics because here there was more continuous nutrient enrichment through the shallow density discontinuity leading to more continuous algal production. In the subtropics where the algal supply was less continuous (as evidenced by the fact that zooplankton and phytoplankton were often out of phase), grazing may have resulted in less immediate waste, hence less nutrient release in excretion. If this were the case, the consequent time lag due to the slower remineralization of particulate matter would tend to perpetuate the phase difference between phytoplankton and zooplankton.

Let us now look at the second avenue of recycling, i.e. the re-use of detritus.

Total particulate carbon in the study area is low by comparison with other seas HAGMEIER, 1964b; NEWELL, 1969; ZEITZSCHEL, 1970; FINENKO and ZAIKA, 1969). The detrital component of this carbon averaged barely twice the living phytoplankton carbon (Table 2); the average ratio is 5 (PARSONS, 1963) and in some upwelling areas it is as high as 10 (RYTHER and MENZEW, 1965; ZEITZSCHEW, 1970). NEYMAN et al. (1973, this volume) has indicated that detritus is the staple diet of the open ocean bottom fauna.

It can be shown, as follows, that part of this detritus is used by zooplankton because their rations in the form of living algal biomass are inadequate: from VINOGRADOV (1968) we learn that the total zooplankton content of the water column is, on the average, 2.5 times as much as in the upper 200 m in tropical eutrophic areas of the Indian Ocean, and it is 4.3 times as much in subtropical oligotrophic areas. Applying these ratios to our data, we find that the zooplankton content of the total water column is 137% of the phytoplankton in the tropics, and 185% of the phytoplankton in the subtropics. If the zooplankton require daily rations equivalent to $^1/_{20}$ their body carbon (MENZEL and RYTHER, 1961; MULLIN and BROOKS, 1970), then they would use each day in the tropics about 46% of the primary algal production and, in the subtropics, about 71%. Since, at any one time, barely 30% or so of algal production is present as living algae, the dead component, viz. detritus, must serve to supplement the rations of the zooplankton.

It is clear, that zooplankton recycle part of the daily algal production before it is remineralized by decomposition. These avenues of re-use accelerate the flow of energy through the ecosystem and add to its stability. There may be many other mechanisms of recycling, particularly in warm waters.

4. Total Dynamics of the Ecosystem

The results indicate that elements of both translation and ecological succession are responsible for the changes observed in the study area, the main interacting forces being:

a) Enrichment of tropical surface waters in winter by dynamic uplift associated with the South Equatorial Current.

b) Impoverishment of subtropical surface waters in late summer by thermal stratification.

c) Meridional transport of tropical waters towards the south in autumn and winter, and subtropical waters towards the north in spring and summer.

d) Heavy algal grazing and rapid nutrient recycling.

These changes constitute an annual cycle which may conveniently be considered to begin in late summer (March) when chlorophyll is at a minimum along the entire section (Fig. 7; Table 1). The stratification and impoverishment of subtropical waters which drift towards the north (ROCHFORD, 1969) combine with heavy grazing by both zooplankton (Figs. 8, 9; Table 7) and macroplankton (Table 6) to establish a seasonal catastrophe throughout the area. The zooplankton starve and are preyed upon by micronekton; by June, as predation continues (Fig. 10), they are much reduced in abundance (Figs. 8, 9).

In winter (June – August) the subtropical thermocline breaks down and regenerated nutrients lying between the seasonal thermocline and the "permanent thermal discontinuity" (ROCHFORD, 1969) become available for plant production. These are used immediately, leaving little evidence of enrichment (ROCHFORD, 1969). Meanwhile in the tropics the South Equatorial Stream gains strength, and the dynamic uplift associated with the current (WYRTKI, 1962; ROCHFORD, 1969) enriches the euphotic zone with nutrients which here also, are immediately utilized in algal production (Figs. 6, 7). There is a rapid response by tropical herbivores to this increased food supply, and a slower response by the subtropical population (Figs. 8, 9) which has been exposed to greater starvation (Fig. 7) and predation (Fig. 10). By September these populations have reached a maximum throughout the section and are beginning to overgraze (Fig. 7). In the tropics, their excretion leads to rapid remineralization of nutrients, the remineralization of phosphate being more rapid than that of nitrate. In the subtropics, there is greater assimilation, and as a consequence remineralization is less immediate.

During this season, species reach the southern limit of their meridional drift, the distance of their journey being determined by the duration of their life. The longer-lived micronekton become concentrated in the subtropics where the southerly drift comes to rest. Here they are exploited by pelagic schools of sperm whales and southern bluefin tuna which, in turn, are harvested by Man. Those late-stage larvae of rock lobsters and mantis shrimps that lie on the coastal fringes of this return drift are repatriated and recruited to the adult stocks.

The next part of the annual cycle may be considered to begin at this point. With the changing of the seasons, high-salinity subtropical water from the main South Indian Ocean gyre begins to drift north and east across the study area carrying with it, perhaps, the early larvae of stomatopod and rock lobster populations which habitually spawn in the summer months (Michel, 1968; Chittleborough and Thomas, 1969).

As a result of the previous heavy grazing and excretion, primary production continues well into November (Fig. 5). The resultant detritus decomposes and remineralizes and, as grazing pressures weakens (Figs. 8, 9), there is further algal production. This is rapidly grazed down in the subtropics by the surviving zooplankton herbivores, which now face starvation as stratification reduces primary production to the seasonal minimum (Fig. 6), and as predators drift northward through the area taking heavy toll. Those predators with the longest life cycle penetrate deep into the tropical area (Legand et al., 1971) where they find surviving populations of certain plankton carnivores (e.g. *Euchaeta russelli*) on which to feed. The continuity of plankton production associated with the South Equatorial Current throughout the winter provides forage for those macroplankton and micronekton which develop fast enough to exploit such food reserves (Table 2; Fig. 10).

Appendix*

Species of copepods used in calculating indices of diversity, species with * have been used in Table 9.

Eucalanidae
* *Eucalanus subtenuis*
* *E. attenuatus*
  E. crassus
  E. dentatus
  E. elongatus
  E. hyalinus
* *E. mucronatus*
* *E. pileatus*
* *E. subcrassus*
* *Rhincalanus cornutus*
* *R. nasutus*
Euchaetidae
  Euchaeta acuta
* *E. concinna*
* *E. longicornis*
* *E. marina*
* *E. media*
  E. russelli
  E. spinosa
  E. tenuis
* *E. wolfendeni*
Copiliidae
  Copilia mirabilis
  C. hendorfii

C. lata
C. longistylus
C. mediterranea
C. quadrata
C. vitrea
Sapphirinidae
  Sapphirina gemma
  S. angusta
  S. auronitens
  S. darwinii
  S. gastrica
  S. nigromaculata
  S. intestinata
  S. lactens
  S. maculosa
  S. metallina
  S. stellata
  S. opalina
  S. ovatolanceolata
  S. sali
  S. scarlata
  S. bicuspidata
  S. sinuicauda
  S. salpae
  S. vorax

References

ALCOCK, A.: A descriptive catalogue of the Indian deep-sea fishes in the Indian Museum, 211 pp. Calcutta: Indian Museum 1899.

ALDER, J.: Catalogue of the zoophytes of Northumberland and Durham. Trans. Tyneside Field Club, 93–162 (1857).

ALVARIÑO, A.: Two new chaetognaths from the Pacific. Pac. Sci. 15, 67–77 (1961).

ALVARIÑO, A.: The Chaetognatha of the Monsoon Expedition in the Indian Ocean. Pac. Sci. 28, 336–348 (1964).

ALVARIÑO, A.: Chaetognaths. Oceanogr. Mar. Biol. Ann. Rev. 3, 115–194 (1965).

ALVARIÑO, A.: The Chaetognatha of the Naga Expedition (1959–1961) in the South China Sea and the Gulf of Thailand. I. Systematics. Naga Rep. Univ. Calif. Scripps Inst. Oceanogr. 4, 1–197 (1967).

ARAVINDAKSHAN, P. N.: Preliminary report on the geographical distribution of the species of Carinariidae and Pterotracheidae (Heteropoda, Mollusca) from the International Indian Ocean Expedition. Bull. Natl. Inst. Sci. India 38, 575–585 (1969).

ARUGA, Y., ICHIMURA, S.: Characteristics of photosynthesis of phytoplankton and primary production in the Kuroshio. Bull. Misaki Mar. Biol. Inst. Kyoto Univ. 12, 3–20 (1968).

AUDOUIN, J. V.: Explication sommaire des planches de polypes de l'Égypte et de la Syrie. In: Description de l'Égypte. Hist. Nat. 1, 225–244 (1826).

BABENERD, B., BOJE, R., KREY, J., MONTECINO, V.: Microbiomass and detritus in the Arabian Sea during the winter monsoon 1964/65. In: The biology of the Indian Ocean, 233–237 (ZEITZSCHEL, B. Ed.) Berlin–Heidelberg–New York: Springer 1973.

BAILEY, R. S.: The pelagic distribution of sea-birds in the western Indian Ocean. Ibis 110, 493–519 (1968).

BAKER, A. C. DE: The latitudinal distribution of Euphausia species in the surface waters of the Indian Ocean. Discovery Rep. 33, 309–334 (1965).

BALECH, E.: Tintinnoinea y Dinoflagellata del Pacifico. Rev. Mus. Argent. Cienc. nat. "Bernardino Rivadavia", Inst. Nac. Invest. Cienc. Nat. (Zool.) 7, 3–253 (1962).

BANG, N. D.: Major eddies and frontal structures in the Agulhas Current retroflexion area in March 1969. Oceanogr. S. Afr. S.A.N.C.O.R., Durban, B 2, 16 pp. 1970.

BANSE, K.: On upwelling and bottom trawling off the southwest coast of India. J. Mar. Biol. Assoc. India 1, 33–49 (1959).

BANSE, K.: Bemerkungen zu meereskundlichen Beobachtungen vor der Ostküste von Indien. Kieler Meeresforsch. 16, 214–220 (1960).

BANSE, K.: Further observations on the upwelling off the west coast of India and its biological effects. Abst. II Int. Ocean. Congress, 18, Moscow (1966).

BANSE, K.: Hydrography of the Arabian Sea shelf of India and Pakistan and effects on demersal fishes. Deep-Sea Res. 15, 45–79 (1968).

BARLOW, J. P.: Physical and biological processes determining the distribution of zooplankton in a tidal estuary. Biol. Bull. Mar. Biol. Lab. Woods Hole 109, 211–225 (1955).

BARNARD, K. H.: Amphipoda. Sci. Rep. John Murray Exped. 4, 131–201 (1937).

BARNES, H.: Apparatus and methods of oceanography. 341 pp. London: Allen & Unwin 1959.

BARNES, H., TRANTER, D. J.: A statistical examination of the catches, numbers and biomass taken by three commonly used plankton nets. Aust. J. Mar. Freshwat. Res. 16, 293–306 (1965).

BEERS, J. R.: Studies on the chemical composition of the major zooplankton groups in the Sargasso Sea off Bermuda. Limnol. Oceanogr. 11, 520–528 (1966).

BEKKER, V. E.: Slendertailed luminescent anchovies (genera, Loweina, Tarletonbeania, Gonichthys and Centrobranchus) of the Pacific and Indian Oceans. Systematics and distribution. Tr. Inst. Okeanol. Akad. Nauk SSSR 73, 11–75 (1964).

BEKLEMISHEV, K. V., PARIN, N. V.: The biogeographical boundaries of the pelagic zone of the northern half of the Pacific Ocean during the winter of 1958/59. Tr. Inst. Okeanol. Akad. Nauk SSSR **41**, 257–265 (1960).

BELJAEV, G. M., VINOGRADOVA, N. G.: Quantitative distribution of bottom fauna in the northern half of the Indian Ocean. Dokl. Akad. Nauk SSSR **138**, 1191–1194 (1961).

BENNETT, E. B.: Turbulent diffusion, advection and water structure in the North Indian Ocean. Ph. D. Dissertation, Univ. of Hawaii 1970.

BERDUGO, V.: Preliminary report on the calanoid copepods of the Gulf of Eilat (in preparation).

BEZRUKOV, P. L.: Research in the Indian Ocean by the Survey Vessel "Vitiaz" on its thirty-third voyage. Okeanologiia **1**, 745–753 (1961).

BEZRUKOV, P. L.: Sedimentation in the central and northern parts of the Indian Ocean. International Geological Congress. XXII. Session. Rep. Sov. Geol. 41–52 (1964).

BIECHELER, B.: Observation de la capture et de la digestion des proies chez un Péridinéen vert. C. R. Séances Soc. Biol., Paris **122**, 1173–1175 (1936).

BIERI, R.: The distribution of the planktonic Chaetognatha in the Pacific and their relationship to the water masses. Limnol. Oceanogr. **4**, 1–28 (1959).

BILLARD, A.: Hydroides récoltés par M. Ch. Gravier dans le Golfe de Tadjoura. Bull. Mus. Natl. Hist. Nat. **10**, 480–485 (1904).

BILLARD, A.: Cambridge Expedition to the Suez Canal. IV. Trans. Linn. Soc. Lond. (Zool.) **22**, 85–104 (1926).

BLACKBURN, M.: Relationship between standing crops at three successive trophic levels in the eastern Pacific Ocean. Pac. Sci. **20**, 36–58 (1966).

BLACKBURN, M., LAURS, R. M., OWEN, R. W., ZEITZSCHEL, B.: Seasonal and areal changes in standing stocks of phytoplankton, zooplankton and micronekton in the eastern tropical Pacific. Mar. Biol. **7**, 14–31 (1970).

BOBZIN, E.: Vergleichende Betrachtung des Klimas und der kalten Auftriebströmungen an der süd-westafrikanischen und südarabischen Küste. Dtsch. Übersee Met. Beob. **23**, 1–18 (1922).

BODEN, B. P.: The euphausiid crustaceans of southern African waters. Trans. R. Soc. S. Afr. **34**, 181–243 (1954).

BOGOROV, V. G., VINOGRADOV, M. E.: Some features of plankton biomass distribution in the surface water in the Indian Ocean during the winter of 1959/60. Okeanol. Issled. **4**, 72–75 (1961).

BÖHM, A.: Peridineen aus dem persischen Golf und dem Golf von Oman. Arch. Protistenkd. **74**, 188–197 (1931).

BÖHM, A.: Zum Variationsproblem der Peridineen. Oesterr. Bot. Z. **84**, 271–281 (1935).

BORDOVSKI, O. K.: On the characteristics of the organic matter in the bottom sediments of the Pacific and Indian Oceans. Environment and processes of petroleum formation. 100–129. Moscow: Nauka 1964.

BOTTERO, J. S.: An analysis of upwelling off the southeast Arabian Coast during the summer monsoon. M. Sc. Thesis, Oregon State University 1969.

BOWEN, B. K., CHITTLEBOROUGH, R. G.: Preliminary assessment of stocks of the western Australian crayfish, *Panulirus cygnus* George. Aust. J. Mar. Freshwat. Res. **17**, 93–121 (1966).

BOWMAN, T. E.: A new copepod of the genus *Calanus* from the northeastern Pacific with notes on *Calanus tenuicornis* Dana. Pac. Sci. **9**, 413–422 (1955).

BOWMAN, T. E.: The pelagic amphipod genus *Parathemisto* (Hyperiidae) in the North Pacific and adjacent Arctic Ocean. Bull. U.S. Natl. Mus. **112**, 343–392 (1960).

BRANDHORST, W.: Thermocline topography, zooplankton standing crop, and mechanisms of fertilization in the eastern tropical Pacific. J. Cons. Int. Explor. Mer **24**, 16–31 (1958).

BRIGGS, J. C.: A monograph of the clingfishes (Order *Xenopterygii*). Stanford Ichtyol. Bull. **6**, 1–224 (1955).

BRIGGS, J. C.: A new species of *Lepadichtys* (Gobiesocidae) from the Seychelles, Indian Ocean. Copeia **1969**, 464–466 (1969).

BRIGGS, J. C., LINK, G.: New clingfishes of the genus *Lepadichtys* from the northern Indian Ocean and Red Sea (Pisces, Gobiesocidae). Senckenb. Biol. Frankfurt. **44**, 101–105 (1963).

BRINTON, E.: The distribution of Pacific euphausiids. Bull. Scripps Inst. Oceanogr. **8**, 51–270 (1962).

BRINTON, E.: Barriers between the tropical Pacific and Indian Ocean euphausiid species (zooplankton, Crustacea). Proc. Int. Congr. Zool. **1**, 204 (1963).

BRINTON, E., WATANAPRIDA, C.: Distribution and abundance of the Naga euphausiid crustaceans.

In: Ecology of the Gulf of Thailand and the South China Sea, a report on the results of the Naga expedition, 1959–61. Scripps Inst. Oceanogr. Ref. No. 63–6, 70–74 (1963).

BRODSKIY, K. A.: The taxonomy of marine plankton organisms and oceanography. Oceanology 5 (4), 1–12 (1965).

BRUJEWICZ, S. W., BOGOYAVLENSKY, A. N., IVANENKOV, V. N., SAPOZHINKOV, V. V., CHERNYAKOVA, A. M., GUSAROVA, A. N., KONNOV, V. A.: Chemical structures of waters of the Indian and Pacific Oceans and the Antarctic region. Abstr. II Int. Ocean. Congress, 66–68, Moscow (1966).

BÜCKMANN, A.: Die Appendicularien von den Fahrten der "Meteor", der "Anton Bruun" und der "Discovery" aus dem arabischen Meer im Rahmen der IIOE. "Meteor" Forschungsergeb. D (10), 1–45 (1972).

BURFIELD, S. T.: Chaetognatha. Great Barrier Reef Exped. Sci. Rep. 5, 459–473 (1950).

BURFIELD, S. T., HARVEY, E. J. W.: The Chaetognatha of the Sealark Expedition. Trans. Linn. Soc. Lond. (Zool.) 19, 93–119 (1926).

BUSK, G.: Report on the Polyzoa collected by H. M. S. "Challenger" during the years 1873–76. II. The Cyclostomata, Ctenostomata and Pedicellana 17, 1–47 (1886).

CASSIE, R. M.: The correlation coefficient as an index of ecological affinities in plankton populations. Mem. Ist. Ital. Idrobiol. 13, 151–177 (1961).

CASTLE, P. H. J.: Species structure and seasonal distribution of Leptocephali in the eastern Indian Ocean (110° E) Cah. ORSTOM (Oceanogr.) 7, 53–88 (1969).

CHAN, W. L.: A systematic revision of the Indo-Pacific clupeid fishes of the genus Sardinella (Family Clupeidae) Jap. J. Ichthyol. 12, 104–118, 13, 1–39 (1965).

CHATERJI, G. C., KARUNAKARAN, C., SIDDIQUE, H. N.: Exploration of minerals on the continental margin of India. An appraisal of the existing data. Bull. Natl. Inst. Sci. India 38, 552–562 (1968).

CHERIYAN, P. V.: Hydrographical studies in and around the Cochin Harbour. Bull. Mar. Biol. Oceanogr. Univ. Kerala 3, 9–17 (1967).

CHITTLEBOROUGH, R. G., THOMAS, L. R.: Larval ecology of the western Australia marine crayfish, with notes upon other panulirid larvae from the eastern Indian Ocean. Aust. J. Mar. Freshwat. Res. 20, 199–223 (1969).

CHUN, C.: Aus den Tiefen des Weltmeeres, 549 pp. Jena: Fischer 1900.

CLARKE, G. L.: Diurnal migration of plankton in the Gulf of Maine and its correlation with changes in submarine irradiation. Biol. Bull. 65, 402–436 (1933).

CLARKE, G. L., KELLY, M. G.: Variation in transparency and in bioluminescence on longitudinal transects in the western Indian Ocean. Bull. Inst. Oceanogr. Monaco. 64 (1319), 1–20 (1964).

CLARKE, G. L., EWING, G., LORENZEN, C.: Remote measurement of ocean color as an index of biological productivity. In: Proc. Symp. Remote Sens. Environ. 6 (1970).

CLEVE, P. T.: Plankton of the South African Seas. I. Copepoda. Mar. Invest. S. Afr. 3, 177–210 (1904).

COHEN, D. M.: A new tribe and a new species of ophidioid fish. Proc. Biol. Soc. Wash. 79, 183–204 (1966).

CONOVER, R. J., MARSHALL, S. M., ORR, A. P.: Feeding and excretion of Calanus finmarchicus with reference to the possible role of the zooplankton in the mineralization of organic matter (unpublished Manuscript 59–32). Woods Hole Oceanogr. Inst. 1–12 (1959).

CREITZ, G. I., RICHARDS, F. A.: The estimation and characterization of plankton populations by pigment analysis. III. A note on the use of Millipore membran filters in estimation of plankton pigments. J. Mar. Res. 14, 211–216 (1955).

CRESSEY, R., COLLETTE, B.: Copepods and needlefishes: a study on host parasite relationships. Fish. Bull. U.S. Fish. Wildl. Serv. 68, 347–431 (1970).

Cruise Report, Zulun I: UNESCO Oceanographic Traning Course for Regional Countries of the Indian Ocean held in Pakistan (24 October to 5 December 1964) 83 pp.

CSIRO Aust.: Oceanographical observations in the Indian Ocean in 1963. H.M.A.S. "Gascoyne", Cruise G 1/63. Oceanogr. Cruise Rep. CSIRO Aust. 21 (1965 a).

CSIRO Aust.: Oceanographical observations in the Indian Ocean in 1963. H.M.A. S. "Diamantina", Cruise Dm 1/63. Oceanogr. Cruise Rep. CSIRO Aust. 23 (1965 b).

CSIRO Aust.: Oceanographical observations in the Indian Ocean in 1963. H.M.A.S. "Diamantina", Cruise Dm 2/63. Oceanogr. Cruise Rep. CSIRO Aust. 24 (1965 c).

CSIRO Aust.: Oceanographical observations in the Indian Ocean in 1963. H.M.A.S. "Diamantina", Cruise Dm 3/63. Oceanogr. Cruise Rep. CSIRO Aust. 25 (1965 d).

CSIRO Aust.: Oceanographical observations in the Indian Ocean in 1962. H.M.A.S. "Gascoyne", Cruise G 4/62. Oceanogr. Cruise Rep. CSIRO Aust. 17 (1966 a).

CSIRO Aust.: Oceanographical observations in the Indian Ocean in 1962. H.M.A.S. "Diamantina", Cruise Dm 4/62. Oceanogr. Cruise Rep. CSIRO Aust. 20 (1966 b).

CURRIE, R. I.: The Indian Ocean standard net. Deep-Sea Res. 10, 27–32 (1963).

CUSHING, D. H.: The vertical migration of planktonic Crustacea. Biol. Rev. 26, 158–192 (1951).

CUSHING, D. H.: The seasonal variation in oceanic production as a problem in population dynamics. J. Cons. Int. Explor. Mer 24, 455–464 (1958).

CUSHING, D. H.: Upwelling and fish production. FAO Fish. Tech. Pap. 84, 40 pp. FAO Rome (1969).

CUSHING, D. H.: Upwelling and fish production. Adv. Mar. Biol. 1971 a.

CUSHING, D. H.: The dependence of recruitment on parent stock in different groups of fishes. J. Cons. Int. Explor. Mer (1971 b) (in press).

CUSHING, D. H., HUMPHREY, G. F., BANSE, K., LAEVASTU, T.: Report of the committee on terms and equivalents. Rapp. P.-V. Réun. Cons. Int. Explor. Mer 144, 15–16 (1958).

DAHL, F.: Über die horizontale und vertikale Verbreitung der Copepoden im Ozean. Verh. Dtsch. Zool. Ges. 4, 61–80 (1894).

DALES, R. P.: The distribution of some heteropod molluscs off the Pacific Coast of North America. Proc. Zool. Soc. Lond. 122, 1007–1015 (1952).

DARLINGTON, P. J.: Biogeography of the southern end of the world. 236 pp. Cambridge, Harvard University Press 1965.

DAVY, E. G.: The cyclones of January, February and March 1970 in the SW Indian Ocean. Mar. Obs. 41, 33–36 (1971).

DAY, D. S., PEARCY, W.: Species associations of benthic fishes on the continental shelf and slope off Oregon. J. Fish. Res. Board Can. 25, 2665–2675 (1968).

DE BEAUFORD, L. F.: The fishes of the Indo-Australian Archipelago. IX. 484 pp. Leiden: E. J. Brill 1951.

DE DECKER, A.: Zur Ökologie und Verbreitung der Copepoden aus dem Meeresplankton Südafrikas. Biol. Jaarb. Dodonaea Gent 30, 86–122 (1962).

DE DECKER, A.: Agulhas Bank plankton. In: The biology of the Indian Ocean 189–219 (ZEITZSCHEL, B. Ed.). Berlin–Heidelberg–New York: Springer 1973.

DELALO, E. P.: Distribution of zooplankton biomass in the Red Sea and the Gulf of Aden in winter 1961/62. Okeanol. Issled. 15, 131–139 (1966).

DELLE CHIAJE, S.: Memoire sull storia e notomia degli Animali senza vertebre del Regno di Napoli 3 (1828).

DELLA CROCE, N., ANGELINO, M. I.: *Penilia avirostris* Dana nelle acque del Banco Agulhas. Boll. Mus. Ist. Biol. Univ. Genova 36, 1–14 (1969).

DERENBACH, J.: Erweiterung und Entwicklung einiger summarisch-chemischer und zytologischer Methoden zur Untersuchung des Planktons in seinem natürlichen Lebensraum. Diss. Kiel 92 pp. 1969.

DESROSIERES, R.: Observations sur le phytoplancton superficiel de l'Océan Indien oriental. Cah. ORSTOM (Océanogr.) 3, 31–37 (1965).

Deutsches Hydrographisches Institut: Monatskarten für den Indischen Ozean. Publ. 2422, Hamburg 1960.

DICK, R. I.: *Hyperiidea* (Crustacea: Amphipoda). Keys to South African genera and species and a distribution list. Ann. S. Afr. Mus. 57, 25–86 (1970).

DIETRICH, G.: The unique situation in the environment of the Indian Ocean. In: The biology of the Indian Ocean, 1–6 (ZEITZSCHEL, B. Ed.). Berlin–Heidelberg–New York: Springer 1973.

DIETRICH, G., DÜING, W., GRASSHOFF, K., KOSKE, P. H.: Physikalische und chemische Daten nach Beobachtungen des Forschungsschiffes "Meteor" im Indischen Ozean 1964/65. Meteor-Forschungsergeb. A (2) 145 pp. 1966.

DIETRICH, G., KRAUSE, G., SEIBOLD, E., VOLLBRECHT, K.: Reisebericht der Indischen Ozean Expedition mit dem Forschungsschiff "Meteor" 1964/1965. Meteor-Forschungsergeb. A (1) 1–52 (1966).

DIETRICH, G., ULRICH, J.: Atlas zur Ozeanographie. 76 pp. Mannheim: Bibliographisches Institut 1968.

DOGIEL, V.: Beiträge zur Kenntnis der Peridineen. Mitt. Zool. Stn. Neapel 18, 1–45 + 2 pl. (1906).

DONCASTER, L.: Chaetognatha, with a note on the variation and distribution of the group. Fauna Geogr. Maldive-Laccadive Archip. 1, 209–218 (1903).

DUGDALE, R. C., GOERING, J. J., RYTHER, J. H.: High nitrogen fixation rates in the Sargasso Sea and the Arabian Sea. Limnol. Oceanogr. **9**, 507–510 (1964).

DUGDALE, R. C., GOERING, J. J.: Uptake of new and regenerated forms of nitrogen in primary productivity. Limnol. Oceanogr. **12**, 196–206 (1967).

DÜING, W.: Die Vertikalzirkulation in den küstennahen Gewässern des Arabischen Meeres während der Zeit des Nordostmonsuns. Meteor-Forschungsergeb. **A** (3) 67–83 (1967).

DÜING, W.: The monsoon regime of the currents in the Indian Ocean. Int. Indian Ocean Exped., Oceanogr. Monogr. **1**, 68 pp. Honolulu: East-West Center-Press 1970.

DÜING, W., KOSKE, P. H.: Hydrographische Beobachtungen im Arabischen Meer während der Zeit des Nordostmonsuns 1964/65. Meteor-Forschungsergeb. **A** (3) 1–43 (1967).

DUNBAR, M. J.: The evolution of stability in marine environments. Natural selection at the level of ecosystem. Am. Nat. **94**, 129–136 (1960).

DUNCAN, C. P.: The Agulhas current. Ph. D. Dissertation, Univ. of Hawaii 1970.

DUNTLEY, S. Q.: Underwater visibility. In: The Sea **1**, 452–455 (HILL, M. N. Ed.). New York: John Wiley and Sons (Interscience) 1962.

EBELING, A. W.: Melamphaidae I. Systematics and zoogeography of the species in the bathypelagic fish genus *Melamphaes* Günther. Dana Rep. **58**, 1–164 (1962).

EBELING, A. W., IBARA, R. M., LAVENBERG, R. J., ROHLF, F. J.: Ecological groups of deep-sea animals off southern California. Bull. Los Ang. Cty. Mus. Nat. Hist. **6**, 1–43 (1970).

EBELING, A. W., WEED, W. H.: Melamphaidae III. Systematics and distribution of the species in the bathypelagic fish genus *Scopelogadus* Vaillant. Dana Rep. **60** (1963).

EBELING, A. W.: Zoogeography of tropical deep-sea animals. Stud. Trop. Oceanogr. **5**, 593–613 (1967).

EKMAN, S.: Tiergeographie des Meeres. Leipzig: Akad. Verlagsges. 1935.

EKMAN, S.: Zoogeography of the sea. 417 pp. London: Sidgwick and Jackson 1953.

ELIZAROV, A. A.: Preliminary results of oceanographic investigations of the western coast of India. Tr. Vses. Nauchno-Issled. Inst. Morsk. Rybn. Khoz. Okeanogr. **64**, 94–101 (1968).

EL-SAYED, S. Z.: On the productivity of the southern Ocean (Atlantic and Pacific Sectors). In: Antarctic Ecology **1**, 119–135 (HOLDGATE, M. W. Ed.). London–New York: Academic Press 1970.

EL-SAYED, S. Z.: "Eltanin"-Cruise 46, Antarct. J. U.S.**7** (1971).

EMERY, K. O.: Sediments and water of Persian Gulf. Bull. Am. Assoc. Pet. Geol. **40**, 2354–2383 (1956).

EPPLEY, R. W.: An incubation method for estimating the carbon content of phytoplankton in natural plankton samples. Limnol. Oceanogr. **13**, 574–582 (1968).

FAGER, E. W., LONGHURST, A.: Recurrent group analysis of species assemblages of demersal fish in the Gulf of Guinea. J. Fish. Res. Board Can. **25**, 1405–1421 (1968).

FAO: Report of a meeting of a group of experts on tuna stock assessment. FAO Fish. Rep. **61**, 1–45 (1968).

FAO: Report of the IOFC Working Party on stock assessment in relation to immediate problems of management in the Indian Ocean. FAO Fish. Rep. **82**, 1–25 (1969).

FAO: Catches and landings, 1968. Yearbook of fishery statistics. **26**, 315 pp. 1969.

FENAUX, R.: Sur quelques appendiculaires d'Israel. Bull. Sea Fish. Res. Stn. Isr. **29**, 3–7 (1960).

FENAUX, R.: Les appendiculaires de la troisième campagne du "Commandant Robert Giraud" en Mer d'Arabie. Bull. Inst. Oceanogr. Monaco **62** (1302), 1–14 (1964).

FENAUX, R.: Les appendiculaires de la Mer Rouge (note faunistique). Bull. Mus. Natl. Hist. Nat. (2e Sér.) Paris **38**, 784–785 (1966).

FENAUX, R.: Les appendiculaires du Golfe Bengale. Expédition Internationale de l'Océan Indien. (Chroisière du "Kistna" juin-août 1964) Mar. Biol. **2**, 252–264 (1969 a).

FENAUX, R.: Les appendiculaires de Madagascar (Region de Nosy-Bé) Variations saisonnières. Cah. ORSTOM (Océanogr.) **7**, 29–37 (1969 b).

FENAUX, R.: Répartition verticale des Tuniciers pélagiques au large d'Eilat (Golfe d'Aqaba). A. Appendiculaires. Bull. Soc. R. Sci. Liège, **39**, 200–205 (1970).

FENAUX, R.: Les appendiculaires de la partie centrale de l'Océan Indien. Expédition Internationale de l'Océan Indien (Croisière n° 5 de l'"Anton Bruun", février, mars, avril, 1964). Symposium on Indian Ocean. Cochin, 1971 (in press).

FINENKO, Z. Z., ZAIKA, V. Y.: Suspended organic matter in the waters of the Arabian Sea. Oceanology **9**, 504–509 (1969).

FLEMINGER, A.: New calanoid copepods of *Pontella* Dana and *Labidocera* Lubbock with notes on the distribution of the genera in the Gulf of Mexico. Tulane Stud. Zool. **5**, 19–34 (1957).

FLEMINGER, A., HULSEMANN, K.: Systematics and distribution of the species of the genus *Pontellina* Dana (Copepoda, Calanoida). Fishery Bull. (in press).

FOGG, G. E.: Discussional remark on primary production. In: Antarctic Ecology, I p. 186 (HOLDGATE, M. W., Ed.). London–New York: Academic Press 1970.

FOXTON, P.: A mass fish mortality on the Somali Coast. Deep-Sea Res. **12**, 17–19 (1965).

FRAGA, F.: Distribution of particulate and dissolved nitrogen in the western Indian Ocean. Deep-Sea Res. **13**, 413–425 (1966).

FRASER, J. H.: The role of ctenophores and salps in zooplankton production and standing crop. Rapp. P.-V. Réun. Cons. Int. Explor. Mer **153**, 121–123 (1962).

FRONTIER, S.: Zooplancton récolté en Mer d'Arabie, Golfe Persique et Golfe d'Aden. I. Données générales. Répartition quantitative. Cah. ORSTOM (Océanogr.) **3**, 17–30 (1963 a).

FRONTIER, S.: Zooplancton récolté en Mer d'Arabie, Golfe Persique et Golfé d'Aden. II. Ptéropodes–systematique et répartition. Cah. ORSTOM (Océanogr.) **6**, 233–254 (1963 b).

FROST, B. W., FLEMINGER, A.: A revision of the genus *Clausocalanus* (Copepoda, Calanoida) with remarks on distributional patterns in diagnostic characters. Bull. Scripps Inst. Oceanogr. **12**, 1–235 (1968).

FROST, B. W.: Distribution of the oceanic, epipelagic copepod genus *Clausocalanus* with an analysis of sympatry of North Pacific species. Ph. D. Dissertation., Univ. California, San Diego 319 pp. 1969.

FURNESTIN, M. L.: Chaetognathes récoltés en Méditerranée par le "Président Théodore Tissier" aux mois de juin et julliet 1950. Trav. Stn Aquicult. Pêche Castiglione (Nouv. Sér) **4**, 277–317 (1952).

FURNESTIN, M. L.: Contribution à l'étude morphologique, biologique et systématique de *Sagitta serrato dentata* Krohn des eaux atlantiques du Maroc. Bull. Inst. Océanogr. Monaco **50**, (1025), 1–39 (1953).

FURNESTIN, M. L.: Quelques échantillons de zooplancton du Golfe d'Eilat (Aqaba). Bull. Sea Fish. Res. Stn. Isr. **16**, 6–14 (1958).

FURNESTIN, M. L., BALANÇA, J.: Chaetognathes de la Mer Rouge (Archipel. Dahlac). Bull. Sea Fish. Res. Stn. Isr. **52**, 3–20 (1968).

FURNESTIN, M. L., CODACCIONI, J. C.: Chaetognathes du nord-ouest de l'Océan Indien (Golfe d'Aden–Mer d'Arabie–Golfe d'Oman–Golfe Persique) Cah. ORSTOM (Océanogr.) **6**, 143–171 (1968).

GALLAGHER, J. F.: The variability of water masses in the Indian Ocean. Data Center, Gen. Ser. Publ. G–11, 1–74 (1966).

GANAPATI, P. N., BHAVANARAYANA, P. V.: Pelagic tunicates as indicators of water movements off Waltair coast. Curr. Sci. **27**, 57–58 (1958).

GARDINER, A. C.: Phosphate production by planktonic animals. J. Cons. Int. Explor. Mer **14**, 144–146 (1937).

GARG, J. N., MURTY, C. B., JAYARAMAN, R.: Vertical distribution of oxygen in the Bay of Bengal and the Andaman Sea during February–March 1963. Bull. Natl. Inst. Sci. India **38**, 40–48 (1968).

GARP STUDY GROUP: Report on the first session of the Study Group on tropical disturbances, Madison 1968.

GEORGE, J.: A preliminary report on the distribution and abundance of planktonic ostracods in the Indian Ocean. Symposium on Indian Ocean. Bull. Natl. Inst. Sci. India **38**, 641–649 (1969).

GIBBS, R.: *Photonectes munificus,* a new species of melanostomiatid fish from the South Pacific subtropical convergence, with remarks on the convergence fauna. Contrib. Los Ang. Cty. Mus. Nat. Hist. **149**, 1–6 (1968).

GIBBS, R.: Taxonomy, sexual dimorphism, vertical distribution and evolutionary zoogeography of the bathypelagic fish genus *Stomias* (Stomiatidae). Smithson. Contrib. Zool. **31**, 1–25 (1969).

GIBBS, R., HURWITZ, B.: Systematics and zoogeography of the stomatoid fishes, *Chauliodus pammelas* and *C. sloani,* of the Indian Ocean. Copeia **1967**, 798–805 (1967).

GIESBRECHT, W.: Systematik und Faunistik der pelagischen Copepoden des Golfes von Neapel. Fauna und Flora des Golfes von Neapel. **19**, 1–831 (1892).

GODEAUX, J.: Tuniciers pélagiques du Golfe d'Eilat. Bull. Sea Fish. Res. Stn. Isr. **29**, 9–15 (1960).

GOLDBERG, E. D., WALKER, T. J., WHISENAND, A.: Phosphate utilization by diatoms. Biol. Bull. **101**, 274–284 (1951).

GOLDMANN, C. R.: The use of absolute activity for eliminating serious errors in the measurement of primary productivity with C^{14}. J. Cons. Int. Explor. Mer **32**, 172–179 (1968).

GOODYEAR, R., GIBBS, R.: Systematics and zoogeography of stomatoid fishes of the *Astronestes cyaneus* species group (Astronesthidae), with descriptions of three new species. Arch. Fischereiwiss. **20**, 107–131 (1969).

GOPALAKRISHNAN, K., BRINTON, E.: Preliminary observations on the distribution of Euphausiacea from the International Indian Ocean Expedition. Bull. Natl. Inst. Sci. India **38**, 594–612 (1969).

GORDEYEV, E. J.: Quantitative distribution of suspended material in the surface waters of the northern part of the Indian Ocean. Okeanologiia **64**, 202–213 (1964).

GRAHAM, H. W.: An oceanographic consideration of the dinoflagellate genus *Ceratium*. Ecol. Monogr. **11**, 99–116 (1941).

GRAHAM, H. W.: Studies on the morphology, taxonomy and ecology of the *Peridiniales*. Publ. Carnegie Inst. Wash. **542**, 129 pp. 1942.

GRAHAM, J.: Secchi disc observations and extinction coefficients in the central and eastern North Pacific Ocean. Limnol. Oceanogr. **11**, 184–190 (1966).

GRICE, G. D., HULSEMANN, K.: Bathypelagic calanoid copepods of the western Indian Ocean. Proc. U.S. Natl. Mus. **122**, 1–67 (1967).

GRILL, E. V., RICHARDS, F. A.: Nutrient regeneration from phytoplankton decomposing in seawater. J. Mar. Res. **22**, 51–69 (1964).

GUEREDRAT, J. A.: Distribution de quatre espèces de copepodes bathypélagiques dans l'ouest du Pacifique équatorial et tropical sud. Deep-Sea Res. **16**, 361–375 (1969).

GUEREDRAT, J. A.: Variations saisonnières de la diversité spécifique des copepods de l'Océan Indien le long du 110° E. Symp.: Indian Ocean and adjacent seas. Cochin, India (1971) (in press).

HAAKE, F. W.: Zur Tiefenverteilung von Milioliden (Foraminiferen) im Persischen Golf. Palaeontol. Z. **44**, 196–200 (1970).

HAGMEIER, E.: Plankton-Äquivalente. Kieler Meeresforsch. **17**, 32–47 (1961).

HAGMEIER, E.: Zum Gehalt an Seston und Plankton im tropischen Atlantik. Helgoländer Wiss. Meeresunters. **11**, 270–286 (1964a).

HAGMEIER, E.: Zum Gehalt an Seston und Plankton im Indischen Ozean zwischen Australien und Indonesien. Kieler Meeresforsch. **20**, 12–17 (1964b).

HALIM, Y.: Dinoflagellates of the south-east Caribbean Sea (East-Venezuela). Int. Rev. Gesamt. Hydrobiol. **52**, 701–755 (1967).

HALIM, Y.: Plankton of the Red Sea. Oceanogr. Mar. Biol. Ann. Rev. **7**, 231–275 (1969).

HAMON, B. V.: Geostrophic currents in the south-eastern Indian Ocean. Aust. J. Mar. Freshwat. Res. **16**, 255–271 (1965).

HAMON, M.: Chaetognathes recueillis dans la Baie de Nhatrang-Cauda (Vietnam). Bull. Mus. Natl. Hist. Nat. Paris **28**, 466–473 (1956).

HANDA, N., TOMINAGA, H.: A detailed analysis of carbohydrates in marine particulate matter. Mar. Biol. **2**, 228–235 (1969).

HANDA, N., YANAGI, K.: Particulate organic matter of the chlorophyll *a* maximum layer in the ocean. Bull. Plankt. Soc. Jap. **17**, 42–49 (1970).

HANSEN, H. J.: The Schizopoda of the Siboga Expedition. Siboga Exped. **37**, 1–123 (1910).

HANSEN, H. J.: The genera and species of the order Euphausiacea, with account of remarkable variation. Bull. Inst. Océanogr. Monaco **210**, 1–54 (1911).

HANSEN, H. J.: The euphausiacean crustaceans of the Albatross Expedition to the Philippines. Proc. U.S. Natl. Mus. **49**, 635–654 (1916).

HANSEN, V. K.: The Indian Ocean Biological Center: The center for sorting plankton samples of the International Indian Ocean Expedition. Deep-Sea Res. **13**, 229–234 (1966).

HARRIS, E.: The nitrogen cycle in Long Island Sound. Bull. Bingham Oceanogr. Collect. **17**, 31–65 (1959).

HART, T. J., CURRIE, R. I.: The Benguela Current. "Discovery" Rep. **31**, 123–298 (1960).

HARTMANN, J.: Verteilung und Nahrung des Ichthyoneuston im subtropischen Nordostatlantik. Meteor-Forschungsergeb. **D** (8) 1–60 (1970).

HARTMANN, M., LANGE, H., SEIBOLD, E., WALGER, E.: Oberflächensedimente im Persischen Golf und Golf von Oman. I. Geologisch-hydrologischer Rahmen und erste sedimentologische Ergebnisse. Meteor-Forschungsergeb. **C** (4) 1–76 (1971).

HASLE, G. R.: A quantitative study of phytoplankton from the equatorial Pacific. Deep-Sea Res. **6**, 38–59 (1959).

HASLE, G. R.: An analysis of the phytoplankton of the southern Pacific Ocean. Hvalrådets Skr. **52**, 168 pp. 1969.

HASSAL, A. H.: Supplement to a catalogue of Irish zoophytes. Ann. Mag. Nat. Hist. **7**, 363–373 (1841).

HEINRICH, A. K.: The surface plankton of the Central Pacific. Tr. Inst. Okeanol. Akad. Nauk SSSR **41**, 42–47 (1960).

HEINRICH, A. K.: On the surface plankton of the North-East Pacific. Tr. Inst. Okeanol. Akad. Nauk SSSR **65**, 77–94 (1964).

HEINRICH, A. K.: The ranges of neuston copepods in the Pacific Ocean. Zool. Zh. **48**, 1456–1466 (1969).

HENTSCHEL, E.: Allgemeine Biologie des Südatlantischen Ozeans. Wiss. Ergeb. Dtsch. Atl. Exped. "Meteor" 1925–27, **11**, 343 pp. (1936).

HEYDORN, A. E. F.: The Chaetognatha off the west coast of the Union of South Africa. Invest. Rep. Div. Fish. South Afr. **36**, 1–56 (1959).

HIDA, T., PEREYRA, W.: Results of bottom trawling in Indian Seas by RV "Anton Bruun" in 1963. Proc. Indo-Pac. Fish. Counc. **11**, 156–171 (1966).

HINCKS, T.: On the Polyzoa and Hydroida of the Mergui Archipelago Collected for the Trustees of the Indian Museum, Calcutta. J. Linn. Soc. Lond. (Zool.) **21**, 121–136 (1887).

HOLMES, R. W.: The Secchi disc in turbid coastal waters. Limnol. Oceanogr. **15**, 688–694 (1970).

HOLM-HANSEN, O., LORENZEN, C. J., HOLMES, R. W., STRICKLAND, J. D. H.: Fluorometric determination of chlorophyll. J. Cons. Int. Explor. Mer **30**, 3–15 (1965).

HOUBOLT, J. J. H. C.: Surface sediments of the Persian Gulf near the Qatar Peninsula. Diss. Univ. Utrecht, 113 pp. 1957.

HUMPHREY, G. F.: The concentration of plankton pigments in Australian waters. CSIRO Aust. Rep. Div. Fish. Oceanogr. **9**, 27 pp. 1960.

HUMPHREY, G. F.: The concentration of chlorophylls *a* and *c* in the south-east Indian Ocean. Aust. J. Mar. Freshwat. Res. **17**, 135–145 (1966).

HUMPHREY, G. F., KERR, J. D.: Seasonal variations in the Indian Ocean along 110° E. III. Chlorophylls *a* and *c*. Aust. J. Mar. Freshwat. Res. **20**, 55–64 (1969).

HYMAN, L. H.: The Invertebrates. **5**, 71 pp. New York: McGraw-Hill 1959.

ICHIMURA, S., FUKUSHIMA, H.: On the chlorophyll content in surface water of the Indian and the Antarctic Oceans. Bot. Mag., Tokyo **76**, 395–399 (1963).

ILLIG, G.: Die Schizopoden der Deutschen Tiefsee-Expedition. Rep. Valdivia Exped. **22**, 397–625 (1930).

IOBC: Maps on total zooplankton biomass in the Arabian Sea and the Bay of Bengal. In: International Indian Ocean Expedition Plankton Atlas **1** (1) (Panikkar, N. K., Ed.), NIO, CSIR New Delhi (1968 a).

IOBC: Maps on total zooplankton biomass in the Indian Ocean. In: International Indian Ocean Expedition Plankton Atlas **1** (2) (Panikkar, N. K., Ed.), NIO, CSIR New Delhi (1968 b).

IOBC (Indian Ocean Biological Centre): Handbook to the International Zooplankton Collections. **1**, station list. 129 pp. IOBC Natl. Inst. Oceanogr., CSIR, Cochin, India 1969.

IOBC: Distribution of Copepoda and decapod larvae in the Indian Ocean. In: International Indian Ocean Expedition Plankton Atlas **2** (1) (Panikkar, N. K., Ed.) NIO, CSIR New Delhi (1970 a).

IOBC: Distribution of fish eggs and larvae in the Indian Ocean. In: International Indian Ocean Expedition Plankton Atlas **2** (2) (PANIKKAR, N. K., Ed.) NIO, CSIR New Delhi (1970 b).

IVANENKOV, V. N., GUBIN, F. T.: Water masses and hydrochemistry of the western and southern parts of the Indian Ocean. Tr. Morsk. Gidrofiz. Inst. Akad. Nauk. SSSR **22**, 33–115 (1960).

IVANENKOV, V. N., ROZANOV, A. G.: Hydrogen sulfide contamination of intermediate layers of water in the Arabian Sea and the Bay of Bengal. Okeanologiia **1**, 443–449 (1961).

JAYARAMAN, R.: Upwelling along the east coast of India. Curr. Sci. **34**, 121–122 (1965).

JAYARAMAN, R., SESHAPPA, G.: Phosphorus cycle in the sea with particular reference to tropical inshore waters. Proc. Indian Acad. Sci. **46**, 110–125 (1957).

JERLOV, N. G.: Optical studies of ocean water. Rep. Swed. Deep Sea Exped. **3**, 1–59 (1951).

JERLOV, N. G.: The equatorial currents in the Indian Ocean. Rep. Swed. Deep Sea Exped. **3**, 115–125 (1953).

JERLOV, N. G.: Optical Oceanography. Oceanogr. Mar. Biol. Ann. Rev. **1**, 89–114 (1963).

JERLOV, N. G.: Optical classification of ocean waters. In: Physical aspects of light in the sea. 45–49 (TYLER, J. E. Ed.) Honolulu: Univ. Hawaii Press 1964.

JERLOV, N. G.: Factors influencing the colour of the oceans. In: Studies in Oceanography. 260–264 (YOSHIDA, K., Ed.) Seattle: Univ. Washington press 1965.

JERLOV, N. G.: Optical Oceanography. 194 pp. Amsterdam: Elsevier Publishing Co. 1968.

JITTS, H. R.: Seasonal variations in the Indian Ocean along 110° E. IV. Primary Production. Aust. J. Mar. Freshwat. Res. **20**, 65–76 (1969).

JOHN, C. C.: Sagitta of the Madras Coast. Bull. Madras. Gov. Mus., New Ser. (Nat. Hist.) **3**, 1–10 (1933).

JOHN, D. D.: The southern species of the genus Euphausia. "Discovery" Rep. **14**, 193–324 (1936).

JOHNSON, D. H.: The role of the tropics in the global circulation. In: The Global Circulation of the Atmosphere. 113–136 (CORBY, G. A., Ed.) London: Royal Meteorological Society 1970.

JONES, E. C.: Evidence of isolation between populations of *Candacia pachydactyla* (Dana)– (Copepoda, Calanoida) in the Atlantic and Indo-Pacific Oceans. Symp. Ser. Mar. Biol. Assoc. India, 406–410 (1966a).

JONES, E. C.: The general distribution of species of the calanoid copepod family *Candaciidae* in the Indian Ocean with new records. Symp. Ser. Mar. Biol. Assoc. India, 399–405 (1966b).

JONES, N. S.: Cumacea of the Benguela Current. "Discovery" Rep. **27**, 279–292 (1955).

JONES, N. S.: Cumacea from the west coast of Africa. Atlantidae Rep. **4**, 183–212 (1956).

KABANOVA, J. G.: Primary production and nutrient salt content in the waters of the Indian Ocean. Okeanologiia **4**, 72–75 (1961).

KABANOVA, J. G.: Primary production and nutrient salt content in the Indian Ocean waters in October–April 1960/61. Tr. Inst. Okeanol. Akad. Nauk. SSSR **64**, 85–93 (1964).

KABANOVA, J. G.: Primary production of the northern part of the Indian Ocean. Oceanology **8**, 214–225 (1968).

KARSTEN, G.: Das Indische Phytoplankton. Wiss. Ergeb. Dtsch. Tiefsee Exped. "Valdivia" **2**, 221–348 (1907).

KASAHARA, K.: Present and future prospect of skipjack fisheries. Bull. Jap. Soc. Fish. Oceanogr. 127–132 (1964).

KÄSLER, R.: Die Verbreitung der Dinophysiales im Südatlantischen Ozean. Wiss. Ergeb. Dtsch. Atl. Exped. "Meteor" 1925–27. **12**, 165–237 (1938).

KEMP, S., HARDY, A. C., MACKINTOSH, N. A.: Discovery investigations, objects, equipment and methods. "Discovery" Rep. **1**, 141–232 (1929).

KENT, S.: On a new Polyzoon, *Victorella pavida* from the Victoria Docks. Q. J. Microsc. Sci. **10**, 34 (1870).

KETCHUM, B. H.: Relation between circulation and planktonic populations in estuaries. Ecology **35**, 191–200 (1954).

KETCHUM, B. H.: Regeneration of nutrients by zooplankton. In: Biological, chemical and radiochemical studies of marine plankton. Unpublished Manuscript WHOI Ref. 62–4 (1963).

KETCHUM, B. H.: Productivity of marine communities. In: The encyclopedia of marine resources. 553–559. (RIRTH, F. E., Ed.) New York: Van Nostrand Reinhold Company 1969.

KHMELEVA, N. N.: Role of radiolarians in the estimation of the primary production in the Red Sea and the Gulf of Aden. Dokl. Akad. Nauk. SSSR **172**, 1430–1433 (1967).

KIKAWA, S.: A study on Indomaguro *(Thunnus thynnus maccoyii?)* in the area south of 20° S. lat. from the examination of ovary weight and maturity. Rep. Nankai Reg. Fish. Res. Lab. **20**, 37–57 (1964).

KIKAWA, S., KOTO, T., SHINGU, C., NISHIGAWA, Y.: Status of tuna fisheries in the Indian Ocean as of 1968. Bull. Far Seas Fish. Res. Lab. **2**, 1–28 (1969).

KIMOR, B.: The Suez Canal as a link and a barrier in the migration of planktonic organisms. Proc. Joint Oceanogr. Assembly (Tokyo 1970) 480 (1971).

KING, J. E., IVERSON, R. T. B.: Midwater trawling for forage organisms in the Central Pacific, 1951–1956. Fish. Bull. U.S. Fish Wildl. Serv. **210**, 271–321 (1962).

KOBLENTZ-MISHKE, O. J., VOLKOVINSKY, V. V., KABANOVA, J. G.: Plankton primary production of the world ocean. In: Scientific exploration of the South Pacific, 183–193. (WOOSTER, W. S., Ed.) Washington: National Academy of Sciences 1970.

KOFOID, C. A., SKOGSBERG, T.: The Dinoflagellata: the Dinophysoidae. Mem. Mus. Comp. Zool. Harv. **51**, 1–766, 31 pls. (1928).

KOFOID, C. A., SWEZY, O.: The free-living unarmored Dinoflagellata. Mem. Univ. Calif. **5**, 1–562, 12 pls. (1921).

KOMAROVSKY, B.: The occurrence of *Evadne tergestina* Claus in the summer plankton of the Gulf of Eilat (Aqaba). Bull. Sea Fish. Res. Stn. Isr. **16**, 1–2 (1958).

KORRINGA, P.: Oyster culture in South Africa. Invest. Rep. Div. Fish. South Afr. **20**, 83 pp. 1956.

KOSKE, P. H.: Hydrographische Verhältnisse im Persischen Golf auf Grund von Beobachtungen von F. S. "Meteor" im Frühjahr 1965. Meteor-Forschungsergeb. **A** (11) 58–73 (1972).

KREY, J.: Eine neue Methode zur quantitativen Bestimmung des Planktons. Kieler Meeresforsch. **7**, 58–75 (1950).

KREY, J.: Der Detritus im Meere. J. Cons. Int. Explor. Mer **26**, 263–280 (1961).

KREY, J.: Die mittlere Tiefenverteilung von Seston, Mikrobiomasse und Detritus im nördlichen Nord-atlantik. Kieler Meeresforsch. **20**, 18–29 (1964).

KREY, J.: Primary production in the Indian Ocean. In: The biology of the Indian Ocean. 115–126 (ZEITZSCHEL, B. Ed.) Berlin–Heidelberg–New York: Springer 1973.

KREY, J., BANSE, K., HAGMEIER, E.: Über die Bestimmung von Eiweiß im Plankton mittels der Biuretreaktion. Kieler Meeresforsch. **13**, 35–40 (1957).

KREY, J., BOJE, R., GILLBRICHT, M., LENZ, J.: Planktological-Chemical data of the "Meteor"-Expedition to the Indian Ocean 1964/65. Meteor-Forschungsergeb. **D** (9), 120 pp. 1971.

KUHL, W.: Chaetognatha. Bronn's Klassen. Ord. Tierreich, **4**, 1–266 (1938).

KUMARI, P. S.: Phosphorus fractions in Porto Novo waters (11° 29′ N, 79° 49′ E) during 1965/66. Bull. Natl. Inst. Sci. India **38**, 87–92 (1968).

KUSJMINA, A. I.: Summer phytoplankton of Tonkin Bay and adjoining waters. Abst. Symp. Indian Ocean and adjacent seas, Cochin. Mar. Biol. Assoc. India, 29–30 (1971).

LAFOND, E. C.: Oceanographic studies in the Bay of Bengal. Proc. Indian Acad. Sci. **B** (46), 1–46 (1957).

LAFOND, E. C.: Indian Ocean. McGraw-Hill Yearbook of Science and Technology, 213–216 (1965).

LAFOND, E. C., LAFOND, K. G.: Studies of oceanic circulation in the Bay of Bengal. Bull. Natl. Inst Sci. India **38**, 164–183 (1968).

LAGLER, K. F., BARDACH, J. E., MILLER, R.: Ichthyology, study of fishes. 545 pp. London–New York: Wiley 1967.

LAMOUROUX, J. V. F.: Historie des polypiers coralligènes flexibles, vulgairement nommés zoophytes. **84**, 559 pp. 1816.

LANG, B. T.: The taxonomic problem of *Eucalanus elongatus* Dana. Annls Fac. Sci. Saigon, 93–102 (1967).

LEESE, J. A., BOOTH, A. L., GODSHALL, F. A.: Archiving and climatological applications of meteorological satellite data. ESSA Techn. Rep. NESC 53 (1970).

LEGAND, M.: Cycles biologiques des poissons mésopélagiques dans l'Est de l'Océan Indien. Première Note: *Scopelopsis multipunctatus* Brauer, *Gonostoma* sp., *Notolynchnus valdiviae* Brauer. Cah. ORSTOM (Océanogr.) **5**, 47–71 (1967).

LEGAND, M.: Seasonal variations in the Indian Ocean along 110° E. VI. Macroplankton and micronekton biomass. Aust. J. Mar. Freshwat. Res. **20**, 85–103 (1969).

LEGAND, M., BOURRET, P., GUEREDRAT, J. A., MICHEL, A., REPELIN, R., ROGER, C.: Aspects écologi-ques du plancton et du micronecton dans l'est de l'Océan Indien. Abst. Symp. Indian Ocean and adjacent seas, Cochin. Mar. Biol. Assoc. India, 51–52 (1971).

LEGAND, M., RIVATON, J.: Cycles biologiques des poissons mésopélagiques dans l'est de l'Océan Indien. Deuxième note: Distribution moyenne des principales espèces de l'ichthyofaune. Cah. ORSTOM (Océanogr.) **5**, 73–98 (1967).

LEGAND, M., RIVATON, J.: Cycles biologiques des poissons mésopélagiques dans l'est de l'Océan Indien. Troisième note: Action prédatrice des poissons micronectoniques. Cah. ORSTOM (Océanogr.) **7**, 29–45 (1969).

LÉGER, G.: Les populations phytoplanctoniques au point P = 42° 47′ N, G = 7° 29′ E Greenwich. Bovée laboratoire du COMEXO/CNEXO A. Généralités et premier séjour (21–27 février 1964) Bull. Inst. Océanogr. Monaco 69 (1412) 1–42 (1971).

LEVEAU, M., SZEKIELDA, K. H.: Situation hydrologique et distribution du zooplancton dans le NW de la Mer d'Arabie. 2nd European Symp. on Marine Biology. Sarsia **34**, 285–298 (1968).

LISITZIN, A. P.: Sedimentation in the southern parts of the Indian Ocean. International Geological Congress. XXI Session. Reports of Soviet Geologists, 86–103 (1960a).

LISITZIN, A. P.: Distribution and composition of the suspended matter in the Indian Ocean waters. Okeanol. Issled. 2, 71–85 (1960b).

LOHMANN, H.: Copelata und Thaliacea, in: Die Fauna Südwest-Australiens 2, 143–149 (1909).

LOHMANN, H.: Die Appendicularien der "Valdivia"-Expedition. Verh. Dtsch. Zool. Ges. 157–192 (1914).

LOHMANN, H.: Die Appendicularien der Deutschen Tiefsee-Expedition. Wiss. Ergeb. Dtsch. Tiefsee Exped. "Valdivia", 21, 158 pp. 1931.

LOHMANN, H., BÜCKMANN, A.: Die Appendicularien der Deutschen Südpolar-Expedition 1901–1903. Dtsch. Südpol Exped. 18, 63–231 (1926).

LONGHURST, A.: Species assemblages in tropical demersal fisheries. FAO Fish. Rep. 51, 147–168 (1969).

LORENZEN, C. L.: Vertical distribution of chlorophyll and phaeopigments: Baja California. Deep-Sea Res. 14, 735–746 (1967).

LUTZE, G. F., GRABERT, B., SEIBOLD, E.: Lebendbeobachtungen an Großforaminiferen (Heterostegina) aus dem Persischen Golf. Meteor-Forschungsergeb. C (6) 21–40 (1971).

MACARTHUR, R.: Fluctuations of animal populations and a measure of community stability. Ecology 36, 533–536 (1955).

MACARTHUR, R.: Patterns of species diversity. Biol. Rev. 40, 510–533 (1965).

MACARTHUR, R., WILSON, E.: The theory of island biogeography. 203 pp. Princeton (1967).

MACKINTOSH, N. A.: The seasonal circulation of the Antarctic macroplankton. "Discovery" Rep. 16, 365–412 (1937).

MALEK, I., FENCL, Z.: Theoretical and methodological basis of continuous culture of micro-organisms. 665 pp. New York: Academic Press 1966.

MARGALEF, R.: Perspectives in ecological theory. 111 pp. Univ. Chicago Press 1968.

MARKTANNER-TURNERETSCHER, G.: Die Hydroiden des K. K. Naturhistorischen Hofmuseums. Ann. Naturhist. Hofmus. 5, 195–286 (1890).

MARSHALL, N. B., BOURNE, D.: A photographic survey of benthic fishes in the Red Sea and Gulf of Aden, with observations on their population density. Bull. Mus. Comp. Zool. Harv. 132, 223–244, pls. 1–4 (1964).

MARSHALL, S. M., ORR, A. P.: On the biology of Calanus finmarchicus. VII. Factors affecting egg production. J. Mar. Biol. Ass. U. K. 30, 527–548 (1952).

MARSHALL, S. M., ORR, A. P.: The biology of a marine copepod Calanus finmarchicus (Gunnerus). 188 pp. Edinburgh: Oliver and Boyd 1955.

MAUCHLINE, J., FISHER, L. R.: The biology of euphausiids. In: Adv. Mar. Biol. 7, 454 pp. (RUSSEL, F. S., YONGE, M., Eds.). London–New York: Academic Press 1969.

MAWATARI, S.: Bryozoa of KII Peninsula. Publ. Seto Mar. Biol. Lab. 2, 261–288 (1952).

MAXIMOVA, M. P.: Nutrients in the troposphere and subtroposphere of the Indian Ocean and their relation to productivity. Proc. Joint Oceanogr. Assembly (Tokyo 1970) 490–494 (1971).

MCCLAIN, E. P., BAKER, D. R.: Experimental large-scale snow and ice mapping with composite minimum brightness charts. ESSA Techn. Mem. NESCTM 12, 19 pp. Washington: Dept. of Commerce 1969.

MCEVEN, G. F., JOHNSON, M. W., FOLSON, T. R.: A statistical analysis of the performance of the Folson plankton sample splitter, based upon test observations. Arch. Meteorol. Geophys. Bioklimatol. A (7) 502–527 (1954).

MCGILL, D. A.: The distribution of phosphorus and oxygen in the Atlantic Ocean, as observed during the IGY, 1957–58. Prog. Oceanogr. 2, 127–211 (1963).

MCGILL, D. A.: Chemical and biological observations in the western Indian Ocean during the southwest monsoon, 1963. Abst., II Int. Ocean. Congress. 248–249 Moscow (1966).

MCGILL, D. A.: Fertility of the ocean. In: The encyclopedia of oceanography, 268–272. (FAIRBRIDGE, R. W., Ed.) New York: Reinhold Publishing Corporation 1966.

MCGILL, D. A., LAWSON, T. J.: The distribution of chlorophyll in the western Indian Ocean during the northeast monsoon period. Woods Hole Oceanographic Inst. Ref. 66–12, 69 pp. (unpublished manuscript) (1966).

MCGOWAN, J. A.: The systematics, distribution and abundance of Euthecosomata of the North Pacific. Ph. D. Dissertation, Univ. California San Diego, 197 pp. 1960.

McGOWAN, J. A., FRAUNDORF, V. J.: The relationship between size of net used and estimates of zooplankton diversity. Limnol. Oceanogr. **11**, 456–469 (1966).

MEIRA, C.: Contribucao para o estudo dos eufausiaceos do arquipelagio do Cabo Verde. Notas Cent. Biol. Aquat. Trp., Lisb. **19**, 27 pp. 1970.

MEISENHEIMER, J.: Pteropoda. Wiss. Ergeb. Dtsch. Tiefsee Exped. "Valdivia" 1898–1899, **9**, 1–314 (1905).

MENON, M. A. S.: Observations on the distribution of the plankton of Trivandrum Coast. Proc. Indian Acad. Sci. B **22**, 31–62 (1945).

MENON, N. R.: Studies on the Polyzoa of the south-west coast of India. 548 pp. Ph. D. Thesis, University of Kerala (1967).

MENON, N. R.: Species of the genus *Parasmittina* (Bryozoa, Ascophora) from Indian waters. Mar. Biol. **14**, 72–84 (1972).

MENON, N. R., NAIR, N. B.: The ectoproctous bryozoans of the Indian waters. J. Mar. Biol. Assoc. India **9**, 430–433 (1967).

MENZEL, D. W.: Particulate organic carbon in the deep sea. Deep-Sea Res. **14**, 229–238 (1967).

MENZEL, D. W., RYTHER, J. H.: The annual cycle of primary production in the Sargasso Sea off Bermuda. Deep-Sea Res. **6**, 351–367 (1960).

MENZEL, D. W., RYTHER, J. H.: Annual variations in primary production of the Sargossa Sea off Bermuda. Deep-Sea Res. **7**, 282–288 (1961).

MICHAEL, E. L.: Classification and vertical distribution of Chaetognatha of the San Diego region. Univ. Calif. Publ. Zool. **8**, 21–186 (1911).

MICHAEL, E. L.: Report on the Chaetognatha collected by the United States Steamer Albatross during the Philippine Expedition 1907–1910. Bull. U.S. Natl. Mus. **100**, 1 235–277 (1919).

MICHEL, A.: Dérive des larves de stomatopodes de l'est de l'Océan Indien. Cah. ORSTOM (Océanogr.) **6**, 13–41 (1968).

MILLARD, N. A. H.: Hydrozoa from the coasts of Natal and Portuguese East Africa. Part I. Calyptoblastea. Ann. S. Afr. Mus. **44**, 165–226 (1958).

MILLARD, N. A. H.: Hydroids from the south-west Indian Ocean. Ann. S. Afr. Mus. **50**, 169–194 (1967).

MILLARD, N. A. H.: South African hydroids from the Dr. Th. Mortensen's Java–South African Expedition, 1929–1930. Vidensk. Medd. Dan. Naturhist. Foren. Kbh. **131**, 251–288 (1968).

MILWARD, N.: The Clinidae of Western Australia. (Teleostei, Blennioidea.) J. R. Soc. West. Aust. **50**, 1–9 (1967).

MIMURA, K., NAKAMURA, H.: Tuna fishing ground in the Indian Ocean and its adjacent waters. In: Average year's condition on tuna longline fisheries, 1958-Edition, 354–414. (Nankai Regional Fish. Res. Lab., Tokyo Ed.) Federation of Japan Tuna Fishermen's Cooperative Associations 1959.

MIMURA, K., Staff of the Nankai Regional Fish. Res. Lab., Kochi, Japan: Synopsis of the biology data on yellowfin tuna *Neothunnus macropterus* Temminck and Schlegel 1842 (Indian Ocean). In: Proc. of the world scientific meeting on the biology of tunas and related species, 319–349 (Rosa, H. Jr. Ed.) FAO Fish. Rep. **6** (2) (1963a).

MIMURA, K., Staff of the Nankai Regional Fish. Res. Lab., Kochi, Japan: Synopsis of the biology of bigeye tuna *Parathunnus mebachi* Kishinouye 1923 (Indian Ocean). In: Proc. of the world scientific meeting on the biology of tunas and related species, 350–379 (Rosa, H. Jr. Ed.) FAO Fish. Rep. **6** (2) (1963b).

MIMURA, K., WARASHINA, I.: Studies on Indomaguro *(Thunnus maccoyii?)*. Rep. Nankai Reg. Fish. Res. Lab. **16**, 135–154 (1962).

MIYAKE, Y.: The geochemical balance of nutrient matters of the oceans. Abst. II Int. Oceanogr. Congress 256, Moscow (1966).

MOISEEV, P.: Living resources of the World Ocean. Moscow, 330 pp. 1969.

MOJUMDER, P.: Observations on the hydrological conditions of the surface waters off Waltair (Bay of Bengal) during 1964–66. J. Mar. Biol. Assoc. India **9**, 164–172 (1968).

MOKIEVSKAYA, V. V.: Some hydrochemical features of the northern part of the Indian Ocean. Okeanol. Issled. **4**, 50–61 (1961).

MOORE, H. B.: The zooplankton of the upper waters of the Bermuda area of the North Atlantic. Bull. Bingham Oceanogr. Collect. **12**, 1–97 (1949).

MORCOS, S. A.: Physical and chemical oceanography of the Red Sea. Oceanogr. Mar. Biol. Ann. Rev. **8**, 73–202 (1970).

MORI, T.: The pelagic Copepoda from the neighbouring waters of Japan, Yokendo, Tokyo. 150 pp. 1937.

MORI, T.: The occurence of juvenile skipjack in the stomach contents of longline billfishes from the Indo-Pacific area (unpublished).

MOSS, S.: Melamphaidae II. A new melamphaid genus, *Sio*, with a redescription of *Sio nordenskjöldii* (Lönnberg). Dana-Rep. **56**, 1–10 (1962).

MOSTERT, S. A.: Distribution of inorganic phosphate and dissolved oxygen in the southwest Indian Ocean. Invest. Rep. **54**, 23 pp. Cape Town, Rep. of S. Africa. Department of Commerce and Industries, Division of Sea Fisheries 1966.

MULLIN, M. M.: Size fractionation of particulate organic carbon in the surface waters of the western Indian Ocean: Addendum. Limnol. Oceanogr. **10**, 610–611 (1965).

MULLIN, M. M.: Distribution, morphometry and seasonal biology of the planktonic copepods, *Calanus tenuicornis* and *C. lighti,* in the Pacific Ocean. Pac. Sci. **23**, 438–446 (1969).

MULLIN, M. M., BROOKS, E. R.: Growth and metabolism of two planktonic, marine copepods as influenced by temperature and type of food. In: Marine food chains, 74–95. (STEELE, J. H., Ed.). Edinburgh: Oliver and Boyd 1970.

MURPHY, G. I.: Effect of water clarity on albacore catches. Limnol. Oceanogr. **4**, 86–93 (1959).

MURRAY, J., HJORT, J.: The depths of the ocean. 821 pp. maps 1–4, pls 1–9. London: Macmillan 1912.

MURTY, P. S. N., REDDY, C. V. G.: Distribution of phosphorus in the marine sediments off the east coast of India. Bull. Natl. Inst. Sci. India **38**, 405–410 (1968).

MURTY, P. S. N., REDDY, C. V. G., VARADACHARI, V. V. R.: Distribution of total phosphorus in the shelf sediments of the west coast of India. Proc. Natl. Inst. Sci. India **34 B**, 134–141 (1968).

MURTY, C. S., VARADACHARI, V. V. R.: Upwelling along the east coast of India. Bull. Natl. Inst. Sci. India **38**, 80–86 (1968).

MYERS, G. S.: The fish fauna of the Pacific Ocean, with especial reference to zoogeographical regions and distribution as they effect the international aspects of fisheries. Proc. Pac. Sci. Congr. **3**, 201–210 (1941).

NAFPAKTITIS, B., NAFPAKTITIS, M.: Lanternfishes (Family Myctophidae) collected during cruises 3 and 6 of the RV Anton Bruun in the Indian Ocean. Bull. Los Ang. Cty. Mus. Nat. Hist. **5**, 1–79 (1969).

NAIR, V. R.: A preliminary report on the biomass of chaetognaths in the Indian Ocean comparing the southwest and northeast monsoon periods. Proc. Symp. Indian Ocean, Bull. Natl. Inst. Sci. India **38**, 747–752 (1969).

NAKAMURA, H.: Ocean current and tuna fishing grounds. Suisan Kagaku **14**, 9–17 (1954).

NAKAMURA, H., YABUTA, Y., MIMURA, K.: Longline tuna fishing ground in the Indian Ocean. Proc. Indo-Pac. Fish. Counc. 1955, Sec. II, 1–19 (1955).

NAVAS, D.: *Halistaura bruuni* sp. nov. (Leptomedusae, Mitrocomidae) with notes on its distribution and ecology. Mar. Biol. **2**, 307–310 (1969).

NAVAS, D.: New records of Hydromedusae from the Indian Ocean. Contrções Inst. Oceanogr. Univ. S. Paulo (Sér. Oceanogr. biol) **22**, 1–33 (1971).

NEL, E. A.: The microplankton of the south-west Indian Ocean. Invest. Rep. Div. Fish., South Afr. **62**, 106 pp, + suppl. tables 6–8 (1968).

NELLEN, W.: Horizontale und vertikale Verteilung der Planktonproduktion im Golf von Guinea und in angrenzenden Meeresgebieten während der Monate Februar bis Mai 1964. Kieler Meeresforsch. **23**, 48–67 (1967).

NELLEN, W.: Der Einfluß der Großen Meteor Bank auf Plankton und Neuston. Meteor-Forschungsergebn. D (13) 1972 (in press).

NELLEN, W., HEMPEL, G.: Beobachtungen am Ichthyoneuston der Nordsee. Ber. Dtsch. Wiss. Komm. Meeresforsch. **21**, 311–348 (1970).

NEMOTO, T.: Food of baleen whales with reference to whale movements. Sci. Rep. Whales Res. Inst., Tokyo **14**, 149–290 (1959).

NEPGEN, C. S. DE V.: Euphausiids of the west coast of South Africa. Invest. Rep. Div. Fish. South Afr. **28**, 1–30. (1957).

NESIS, K. N.: The biology of the giant squid of Peru and Chile, *Dosidicus gigas*. Oceanology 10, 108–118 (1970).

NEWELL, B. S.: Seasonal variations in the Indian Ocean along 110° E. II. Particulate carbon. Aust. J. Mar. Freshwat. Res. 20, 51–54 (1969).

NEWELL, B. S., KERR, J. D.: Suspended organic matter in the southeastern Indian Ocean. Aust. J. Mar. Freshwat. Res. 19, 129–138 (1968).

NEYMAN, A. A.: Some data of the quantitive distribution of the benthos in the shelf coastal area of Australia. Okeanologiia 5, 142–146 (1965).

NEYMAN, A. A.: Characteristics of bottom population on the shelf of western and southern Australia. Tr. Vses. Nauchno-Issled. Inst. Morsk. Rybn. Khoz. Okeanogr. 64, 204–209 (1968).

NEYMAN, A. A.: Quantitative distribution of bottom fauna over the shelf in the Great Australian Bay and off New Zealand. Okeanologiia 10, 517–520 (1970).

NEYMAN, V. G., FILJUSHKIN, B. N., SCHERBININ, A. D.: The structure and the circulation of waters in the eastern part of the Indian Ocean during the summer monsoon. Oceanol. Res. 15, 5–22 (1966).

NEYMAN, A. A., SOKOLOVA, M. N., VINOGRADOVA, N. G., PASTERNAK, F. A.: Some patterns of the distribution of bottom fauna in the Indian Ocean. In: The biology of the Indian Ocean, 467–473 (ZEITZSCHEL, B. Ed.) Berlin–Heidelberg–New York: Springer 1973.

NIELSEN, J.: Systematics and biology of the Aphyonidae (Pisces, Ophidioidea). Galathea Rep. 10, 1–89, pl. 1–4 (1969).

NORMAN, J. R.: Fishes. John Murray Exped. 1933–34 Sci. Rep. 7, 1–116 (1939).

NORRIS, D. R.: Possible phagotrophic feeding in *Ceratium lunula* Schimper. Limnol. Oceanogr. 14, 448–449 (1969).

NORRIS, R. E.: Unarmoured marine dinoflagellates. Endeavour 25, 124–128 (1966).

NORRIS, R. E.: Algal consortisms in marine plankton. In: Proc. Semin. Sea, Salt and Plants, 178–189 + 1 pl. (KRISHNAMURTHY, V., Ed.) (1967).

OKADA, Y., MAWATARI, S.: Bryozoa fauna collected by the "Misago" during the zoological survey around Izu Peninsula II. Sci. Rep. Tokyo Bunrika Daigaku 2, 127–147 (1936).

OKUTANI, T.: On pterotrachean fauna in Japanese waters. Bull. Tokai Reg. Fish. Res. Lab. 16, 15–21 (1957).

OLIVEIRA, L. P. H. DE: Estudos sobre o micropláncton capturado durante a viagem do navio hidrográfico Lahmeyer nas baías de Ilha Grande e Sepetiba. Mem. Inst. Oswaldo Cruz 44, 441–488 (1947).

OREN, O. H.: A note on the hydrography of the Gulf of Eilat. Bull. Sea Fish. Res. Stn. Isr. 30, 1–14 (1962).

ORREN, M. J.: Hydrological observations in the south west Indian Ocean. Invest. Rep. Div. Fish. South Afr. 45, 61 pp. 1963.

OSBURN, R. C.: Bryozoa of the Pacific coast of America. II. Cheilostomata-Ascophora. Rep. Allan Hancock Pac. Exped. 14, 271–611 (1952).

ØSTVEDT, O. J.: Zooplankton investigations from Weather Ship M in the Norwegian Sea, 1948–49. Hvalradets Skr. 40, 1–93 (1955).

OWEN, R. W., ZEITZSCHEL, B.: Phytoplankton production: seasonal change in the oceanic eastern tropical Pacific. Mar. Biol. 7, 32–36 (1970).

PALDI, R.: The Persian (Arabian) Gulf and Gulf of Oman. An annotated bibliography for the years 1859–1965. FAO Fish. Circ. Rome 117, 1–15 (1968).

PANIKKAR, N. K.: Fishery resources of the Indian Ocean. Bull. Natl. Inst. Sci. India 38, 811–832 (1969).

PANIKKAR, N. K., JAYARAMAN, R.: Biological and oceanographic differences between Arabian Sea and Bay of Bengal. Proc. Indian Acad. Sci. L 14 (B), 231–240. (1966).

PARIN, N.: Review of marine belonids of the western Pacific and Indian Oceans. Tr. Inst. Okeanol. Akad. Nauk SSSR 84, 3–83 (1967).

PARIN, N.: Ichthyofauna of the epipelagic zone. Tr. Inst. Okeanol. Akad. Nauk SSSR 186 pp. (1968). English translation: U.S. Department Commerce TT 69–59020.

PARIN, N., BEKLEMISHEV, K.: Significance of long term changes in the circulation of the Pacific waters for the distribution of pelagic animals. Gidrobiol. Zh., Kiew 1 (1966).

PARSONS, T. R.: Suspended organic matter in the sea. Prog. Oceanogr. 1, 203–239 (1963).

PATHANSALI, D.: Some observations on the distribution of Chaetognatha west of Penang Island. Publ. Seto Mar. Biol. Lab. **15**, 391–397 (1968).

PAVLOV, V. M.: Optical properties of the main water masses in the northern part of the Indian Ocean. Okeanol. Issled, **4**, 44–49 (1961).

PEERY, K. (Ed.): Results of the Persian Gulf – Arabian Sea oceanographic surveys 1960–61. U.S. Naval Oceanogr. Off. Techn. Rep., **176**, 239 pp. Washington (1965).

PENRITH, M. L.: The distribution of the fishes of the family Clinidae in southern Africa. Ann. S. Afr. Mus. **55**, 135–150 (1970).

PETER, K. J.: Preliminary report on the density of fish eggs and larvae of the Indian Ocean. Bull. Natl. Inst. Sci. India **38**, 854–863 (1967).

PETERS, N.: Die Bevölkerung des Südatlantischen Ozeans mit Ceratien. Wiss. Ergeb. Dtsch. Atl. Exped. "Meteor" 1925–27, **12**, 1–69 (1932).

PIANKA, E. R.: Latitudinal gradients in species diversity. Am. Nat. **100**, 33–46 (1966).

PIERCE, E. L.: The Chaetognatha over the continental shelf of North Carolina with attention to their relation to the hydrography of the area. J. Mar. Res. **12**, 75–92 (1953).

PONOMAREVA, L. A.: On the studies of Euphausiacea of the Arabian Sea and the Bay of Bengal. Tr. Inst. Okeanol. Akad. Nauk SSSR **64**, 265–270 (1964).

PONOMAREVA, L. A.: Euphausiids of the Red Sea collected in summer 1966 by R. V. Academician S. Vavilov. Mar. Biol. **1**, 263–265 (1968).

PONOMAREVA, L. A.: Investigations on some tropical euphausiid species of the Indian Ocean. Mar. Biol. **3**, 81–86 (1969).

POOLE, H. H., ATKINS, W. R. G.: Photo-electric measurements of submarine illumination throughout the year. J. Mar. Biol. Assoc. U.K. **15**, 455–483 (1929).

POSTEL, E., FOURMANOIR, P., GUEZE, P.: Serranidés de La Réunion. Mem. Inst. Fr. Afr. Noire. **68**, 349–384 (1963).

PRASAD, R. R.: Preliminary observations on the temperature gradients and light penetration in the upper 200 feet of water in the Bay of Bengal. Proc. Indian Acad. Sci. (A) **36**, 61–69 (1952).

PRASAD, R. R.: A bibliography of plankton in the Indian Ocean. Indian Nat. Com. Ocean. Res. **3**, 1–86 (1964).

PRASAD, R. R.: Recent advances in the study of production in the Indian Ocean. Abst. II Int. Oceanogr. Congr. 293, Moscow (1966).

PRASAD, R. R.: Zooplankton biomass in the Arabian Sea and the Bay of Bengal with a discussion on the fisheries of the region. Proc. Natl. Inst. Sci. India **35**, 399–437 (1969).

PRASAD, R. R., BANERJI, S. K., NAIR, P. V. R.: A quantitative assessment of the potential fishery resources of the Indian Ocean and adjoining seas. Indian J. Anim. Sci. **40**, 73–98 (1970).

PRUTER, A. T.: Trawling results of R. V. Anton Bruun in the Bay of Bengal and Arabian Sea. Commer. Fish. Res. **26**, 27–35 (1964).

PUFF, A.: Das kalte Auftriebwasser an der Ostseite des nordatlantischen – und der Westseite des nordindischen Ozeans. Dissertation, Universität Marburg, 99 pp. 1890.

QASIM, S. Z.: Some problems related to the food chain in a tropical estuary. In: Marine food chains, 45–51 (STEELE, J. H. Ed.) Edinburgh: Oliver & Boyd 1970.

QASIM, S. Z.: Environmental control of commercially exploitable marine resources. J. Sci. Indus. Res. 30, 11–16 (1971).

QASIM, S. Z.: Productivity of backwaters and estuaries. In: The biology of the Indian Ocean, 143–154 (ZEITZSCHEL, B. Ed.) Berlin–Heidelberg–New York: Springer 1973.

QASIM, S. Z., REDDY, C. V. G.: The estimation of plant pigment of Cochin Backwater during the monsoon months. Bull. Mar. Sci. Gulf Caribb. **17**, 95–110 (1967).

QASIM, S. Z., BHATTATHIRI, P. M. A., ABIDI, S. A. H.: Solar radiation and its penetration in a tropical estuary. J. Exp. Mar. Biol. Ecol. **2**, 87–103 (1968).

QASIM, S. Z., WELLERSHAUS, S., BHATTATHIRI, P. M. A., ABIDI, S. A. H.: Organic production in a tropical estuary. Proc. Indian Acad. Sci. **69**, 51–94 (1969).

QASIM, S. Z., GOPINATHAN, C. K.: Tidal cycle and the environmental features of Cochin Backwater (a tropical estuary). Proc. Indian Acad. Sci. **69**, 336–348 (1969).

QASIM, S. Z., BHATTATHIRI, P. M. A., DEVASSY, V. P.: The influence of salinity on the rate of photosynthesis and abundance of some tropical phytoplankton. Mar. Biol. **12**, 200–206 (1972a).

QASIM, S. Z., BHATTATHIRI, P. M. A., DEVASSY, V. P.: Growth-kinetics and nutrient requirements of two tropical marine phytoplankton. J. Mar. Res. (1972b) (in press).

QASIM, S. Z., SANKARANARAYANAN, V. N.: Organic detritus of a tropical estuary. Mar. Biol. 15, 193–199 (1972).

RABSCH, U.: Zur Verteilung von Sauerstoff und von Nährstoffen im Persischen Golf auf Grund von Beobachtungen v. F. S. „Meteor" im Frühjahr 1965. Meteor-Forschungsergeb. A (11), 74–88 (1972).

RAKESTRAW, W.: Some observations on silicate and oxygen in the Indian Ocean. In: Recent research in fields of hydrosphere, atmosphere and nuclear geochemistry (Sugawara Festival Volume – Tokyo) 243–255 (1964).

RAMAGE, C. S.: Indian Ocean surface meteorology. Oceanogr. Mar. Biol. Ann. Rev. 7, 11–30 (1969).

RAMAGE, C. S., MILLER, F. R., JEFFERIES, C.: Meteorological Atlas of the International Indian Ocean Expedition I. The surface climate of 1963 and 1964. National Science Foundation. U.S. Government Printing Office. Wash. D. C. 13 pp. 144 charts. 1972.

RAMAM, K. V. S., MURTHY, K. V. S.: Transparency measurements along some typical sections off Malabar and Coromandel coasts. Bull. Natl. Inst. Sci. India 38, 277–283 (1968).

RAMAM, K. V. S., KURUP, C. K. B., MURTHY, K. V. S.: Water masses of the Arabian Sea in the upper 500 meters. Bull. Natl. Inst. Sci. India 38, 240–253 (1968).

RAMAMIRTHAM, C. P., JAYARAMAN, R.: Some aspects of the hydrographical conditions of the back-waters around Willington Island (Cochin). J. Mar. Biol. Assoc. India 5, 170–177 (1963).

RAMPAL, J.: Pêches planctoniques, superficielles et profondes en Méditerranée occidentale. VI Ptero-podes. Rev. Trav. Inst. Pêches Marit. 30, 375–383 (1966).

RANDALL, J.: A revision of the surgeon fish genus Acanthurus. Pac. Sci. 10, 159–235 (1956).

RANDALL, J.: A new species of Acanthurus from the Caroline Islands, with notes on the systematics of other Indo-Pacific surgeon fishes. Pac. Sci. 14, 267–279 (1960).

RANDALL, J.: Review of hawkfishes (Cirrhitidae). Proc. U.S. Natl. Mus. 114, 389–451 pls. 1–15 (1963).

RAO, T. S. S.: Studies on the penetration of light in the Bay of Bengal. I. Transparency of the waters on the east coast of India and its significance. Proc. Natl. Inst. Sci. India (B). 23, 165–190 (1957).

RAO, T. S. S.: Zooplankton studies in the Indian Ocean. In: The biology of the Indian Ocean, 243–255 (ZEITZSCHEL, B. Ed.) Berlin–Heidelberg–New York: Springer 1973.

RAO, T. S., GANAPATI, P. N.: Studies on Chaetognatha in the Indian Sea III. Systematics and distribution in the waters off Visakhapatnam. Andhra Univ. Mem. Oceanogr. 2, 147–163 (1958).

RAO, S. V. S.: Preliminary observations on the total phosphorus content of the inshore waters of the Malabar coast off Calicut. Proc. Indian Acad. Sci. 45, 77–85 (1957).

RAO, L. V. JAYARAMAN, R.: Upwelling in the Minicoy region of the Arabian Sea. Curr. Sci. 35, 378–380 (1966).

RAO, L. V., JAYARAMAN, R.: Vertical distribution of temperature, salinity and density in the upper 500 meters of the north equatorial Indian Ocean during the north east Monsoon period. Bull. Natl. Inst. Sci. India 38, 123–147 (1968).

RAO, L. V., JAYARAMAN, R.: Hydrographical features of the southern and central Bay of Bengal during the transition period between winter and summer. Bull. Natl. Inst. Sci. India 38, 184–205 (1968).

RAO, V. C., RAO, T. S. S.: Distribution of total phosphorus in the Bay of Bengal. Bull. Natl. Inst. Sci. India 38, 93–102 (1968).

RASS, T.: Biogeographical fishery complexes of the Atlantic and Pacific Oceans and their comparison. J. Cons. Int. Explor. Mer 24, 243–254 (1959).

RASS, T.: Commercial ichthyofauna and fisheries resources of the Indian Ocean. Tr. Inst. Okeanol. Akad. Nauk SSSR 80, 3–31 (1965).

RAYMONT, J. E. G.: Plankton and productivity in the oceans. 660 pp. London: Pergamon Press 1963.

REDDY, C. V. G., SANKARANARAYANAN, V. N.: Distribution of phosphates and silicates in the central western North Indian Ocean in relation to some hydrographical factors. Bull. Natl. Inst. Sci. India 38, 103–122 (1968a).

REDDY, C. V. G., SANKARANARAYANAN, V. N.: Distribution of nutrients in the shelf water of the Arabian Sea along the west coast of India. Bull. Natl. Inst. Sci. India 38, 206–220 (1968b).

REDDY, C. V. G., MURTHY, P. S. N., SANKARANARAYANAN, V. N.: An incidence of very high phosphate concentrations in the waters around the Andaman Islands. Curr. Sci. 37, 17–19 (1968).

REEVE, M. R.: Observations on the biology of a chaetognath. In: Some contemporary studies in marine science. 613–630 (BARNES, H. Ed.) London: George Allen and Unwin Ltd. 1966.

REID, J. L.: On circulation, phosphate, phosphorus content and zooplankton volumes in the upper part of the Pacific Ocean. Limnol. Oceanogr. 7, 287–306 (1962).

REID, J. L., NOWLIN, W. D., Jr.: Transport of water through the Drake Passage. Deep-Sea Res. 18, 51–64 (1971).

REPELIN, R.: Phronimidae du Bassin Indo-Australian (Amphipodes, Hyperides). Cycle genital et répartition saisonnière. Relations quantitatives et ecologiques. Cah. ORSTOM (Océanogr.) 8, 65–110 (1970).

RICHARDS, F. A., THOMPSON, T. G.: The estimation and characterization of plankton populations by pigment analysis. II A spectrophotometric method for estimation of plankton pigments. J. Mar. Res. 11, 156–172 (1952).

ROBERTSON, A.: The incrusting cheilostomatous Bryozoa of the west coast of North America. Univ. Calif. Publ. Zool. 4, 253–344 (1908).

ROBINS, J. P.: F. R. V. "Marelda". Comm. Sci. Industr. Res. Org. Rep. 22, 1–15 (1958).

ROBINS, J. P.: Synopsis of biological data on bluefin tuna Thunnus thynnus maccoyii (Castelnau) 1872. In: Proc. of the world scientific meeting on the biology of tunas and related species, 562–587 (ROSA, H. Jr. Ed.) FAO Fish. Rep. 6, (2), (1963).

ROCHFORD, D. J.: Characteristics and flow path of the intermediate depth waters of the southwest Indian Ocean. J. Mar. Res. 17, 483–504 (1958).

ROCHFORD, D. J.: Hydrology of the Indian Ocean. II. The surface waters of the southeast Indian Ocean and Arafura Sea in the spring and summer. Aust. J. Mar. Freshwat. Res. 13, 226–251 (1962).

ROCHFORD, D. J.: Some features of organic phosphorus distribution in the southeast Indian and southwest Pacific Oceans. Aust. J. Mar. Freshwat. Res. 14, 119–138 (1963).

ROCHFORD, D. J.: Seasonal variations in the Indian Ocean along 110° E. 1. Hydrological structure of the upper 500 m. Austr. J. Mar. Freshwat. Res. 20, 1–50 (1969).

ROGER, C.: Étude sur quelques espèces d'Euphausiacés de l'est de l'Océan Indien (100° E). Cah. OSTROM (Océanogr.) 4, 73–103 (1966).

ROTHSCHILD, B. J., YONG, M. Y. Y.: Materials for study of changes in apparent abundance of tunas in the Indian Ocean, 1952–65. Data Rep. U. S. Fish Wildl. Serv. 49, 349 pp. 1970.

Royal Society: International Indian Ocean Expedition RRS "Discovery", Cruise 1. South East Arabian Upwelling Region. Cruise Report. 24 pp. London: Royal Society 1963.

Royal Society: International Indian Ocean Expeditions RRS "Discovery", Cruise 3 Report. Oceanographic work in the western Indian Ocean 1964. 55 pp. London: Royal Society 1965.

ROZANOV, A. G.: Distribution of phosphate and silicate in the waters of the northern part of the Indian Ocean. Tr. Inst. Okeanol. Akad. Nauk SSSR 64, 102–114 (1964).

ROZANOV, A. G., BYKOVA, V. S.: Distribution of nitrate and nitrite in the waters of the northern part of the Indian Ocean. Tr. Inst. Okeanol. Akad. Nauk SSSR 64, 94–101 (1964).

RUSSELL, F. S., YONGE, C. M.: The Seas. 376 pp. London: Frederick Warne & Co. Ltd. 1963.

RYTHER, J. H., MENZEL, D. W.: On production, composition and distribution of organic matter in the western Arabian Sea. Deep-Sea Res. 12, 199–209 (1965).

RYTHER, J. H., HALL, J. R., PEASE, A. K., BAKUN, A., JONES, M. M.: Primary production in relation to the chemistry and hydrography of the western Indian Ocean. Limnol. Oceanogr. 11, 371–380 (1966).

SADLER, J. C.: Average cloudiness in the tropics from satellite observations. Int. Indian Ocean Exped. Meteorol. Monogr. Dep. Geophys. Univ. Hawaii 2 (1968).

SAIJO, Y.: Summary report on photosynthetics and chlorophyll in the eastern Indian Ocean observed by Japanese ships during IIOE. Inf. Bull. Planktol. Jap. 12, 72–78 (1965).

SAIJO, Y.: Matière organique en suspension dans les eaux profondes. 8e Symposion sur la mer profonde. Mer. Tokyo 7, 56–62 (1969).

SAIJO, Y.: The formation of the chlorophyll maximum in the Indian Ocean. In: The biology of the Indian Ocean, 171–173 (ZEITZSCHEL, B. Ed.) Berlin–Heidelberg–New York: Springer 1973.

SAIJO, Y., IIZUKA, S., ASAOKA, O.: Chlorophyll maximum in Kuroshio and adjacent area. Mar. Biol. 4, 190–196 (1969).

SAKAMOTO, H.: Regional change in the age composition of bigeye caught by longline gear in the Indian Ocean. Rep. Nankai Reg. Fish. Res. Lab. 25, 59–66 (1967).

SANKARANARAYANAN, V. N., REDDY, C. V.: Nutrients of the northwest Bay of Bengal. Bull. Natl. Inst. Sci. India 38, 148–163 (1968).

SANKARANARAYANAN, V. N., QASIM, S. Z.: Nutrients of the Cochin Backwater in relation to environmental characteristics. Mar. Biol. **2**, 236–247 (1969).

SARASWATHY, M.: Distribution of Gaussia (Copepoda-Metridiidae) in the upper 200 m in the Indian Ocean. In: The biology of the Indian Ocean. 335–338 (ZEITZSCHEL, B. Ed.) Berlin–Heidelberg–New York: Springer 1973.

SARMA, D. V. R., GANAPATI, P. N.: Hydrography of the Kakinada Bay. Bull. Natl. Inst. Sci. India **38**, 49–79 (1968).

SARNTHEIN, M.: Sedimentologische Merkmale für die Untergrenze der Wellenwirkung im Persischen Golf. Geol. Rundschau **59**, 649–666 (1970).

SARNTHEIN, M.: Pteropods and Heteropods in surface sediments of the Persian Gulf. The biology of the Indian Ocean. Kiel 1970. Unpubl. Abst.

SARNTHEIN, M.: Oberflächensedimente im Persischen Golf und Golf von Oman. II Quantitative Komponenten-Analyse der Grobfraktion. "Meteor"-Forschungsergeb. C (5) 1–113 (1971).

SARS, G. O.: Om en hidtil lidet kjent mankelig slaegtstype of Polyzoa. Forh. Videnskapsselsk. Kristiania 386–400 (1874).

SARS, G. O.: Preliminary notices on the Schizopoda of H. M. S. Challenger Expedition. Forh. Videnskapsselsk. Kristiana **7**, 1–43 (1883).

SARS, G. O.: Copépodes particulièrement bathypélagiques provenant des campagnes scientifiques du Prince Albert Ier de Monaco. Res. Camp. Sci. Monaco **69**, 408 pp. 127 pls. (1924–1925).

SCHILLER, J.: Dinoflagellatae (Peridineae). In: Kryptogamen-Flora **10**, 1–617 (RABENHORST, L. Ed.) Leipzig: Akademische Verlagsges. 1933.

SCHMAUS, P. H.: Die Rhincalanus-Arten, ihre Systematik, Entwicklung und Verbreitung. Zool. Anz. **48**, 305–319; 356–368 (1917).

SCHMAUS, P. H., LEHNHOFER, K.: Copepoda IV: Rhincalanus Dana 1852 der Deutschen Tiefsee-Expedition. Systematik und Verbreitung der Gattung. Wiss. Ergeb. Dtsch. Tiefsee Exped. "Valdivia" **23**, 355–400 (1927).

SCHMIDT, H.-E.: Distribution of Hydromedusae in the Indian Ocean. In: The biology of the Indian Ocean, 283–287 (ZEITSCHEL, B. Ed.) Berlin–Heidelberg–New York: Springer 1973.

SCHMIDT, H.-E.: Some new records of hydroids from the Gulf of Aqaba with zoogeographical remarks on the Red Sea area. Proc. Mar. Biol. Assoc. India (in press).

SCHMIDT, H.-E.: Hydromedusae from the eastern Mediterranean Sea. Bull. Sea Fish, Res. Stn. Isr. (in press).

SCHULTZ, L. P.: The frogfishes of the family Antennariidae. Proc. U.S. Natl. Mus. **107**, 47–105, 14 pls. (1957).

SCHULTZ, L. P.: Three new species of frogfishes from the Indian and Pacific Oceans with notes on other species (family Antennariidae). Proc. U.S. Natl. Mus. **116**, 171–182 (1964).

SCHULTZ, L. P.: Four new fishes of the genus Parapercis with notes on other species from the Indo-Pacific area (family Mugiloididae). Proc. U. S. Natl. Mus. **124**, 1–16, pls. 1–3 (1968).

SEARS, M.: Notes on siphonophores II. A revision of the Abylinae. Bull. Mus. Comp. Zool. Harv. **109**, 1–110 (1953).

SEBASTIAN, M. J.: Euphausiacea from Indian Seas: systematics and general considerations. Symp. Ser. Mar. Biol. Assoc. India **1**, 233–254 (1966).

SEIBOLD, E.: Nebenmeere im humiden und ariden Klimabereich. Geol. Rundschau **60**, 73–105 Stuttgart (1970).

SEIBOLD, E., VOLLBRECHT, K.: Die Bodengestalt des Persischen Golfs. "Meteor"-Forschungsergeb. C (2), 29–56 Berlin–Stuttgart (1969).

SEROVA, V. V.: Some mineralogical features of suspended matter from the Indian Ocean. Okeanologiia **9**, 462–474 (1969).

SERYI, V. V., KHIMITSA, V. A.: The hydrology and chemistry of the Gulf of Aden and the Arabian Sea. Okeanologiia **6**, 994–1003 (1963).

SEWELL, R. B. S.: The free-swimming planktonic Copepoda. Systematic account. Sci. Rep. John Murray Exped. **8**, 1–303 (1947).

SEWELL, R. B. S.: The free swimming planktonic Copepoda. Geographical distribution. Sci. Rep. John Murray Exped. **8**, 317–592 (1948).

SEWELL, R. B. S.: The pelagic Tunicata. Sci. Rep. John Murray Exped. **10**, 1–90 (1953).

SHAH, N. M.: Observations on the hydrographical conditions in the port of Cochin area. Symposium on underwater acoustics and oceanography held by Indian Naval Physical Laboratory, Cochin (1961).

SHANNON, L. V.: Hydrology of the south and west Coasts of South Africa. Invest. Rep. Div. Fish. South Afr. **58**, 1–22 (1966).

SHARMA, G. S.: Thermocline as an indicator of upwelling. J. Mar. Biol. Assoc. India **8**, 8–19 (1966).

SHARMA, G. S.: Seasonal variation of some hydrographic properties of the shelf waters off the west coast of India. Bull. Natl. Inst. Sci. India **38**, 263–276 (1968).

SHERMAN, K.: Pontellid copepod distribution in relation to surface water types in the central North Pacific. Limnol. Oceanogr. **8**, 214–227 (1963).

SHERMAN, K.: Pontellid copepod occurence in the central South Pacific. Limnol. Oceanogr. **9**, 476–484 (1964).

SHIH, C. T.: The systematics and biology of the family Phronimidae (Crustacea, Amphipoda). Dana Rep, **74**, 1–100 (1969).

SHINGU, C.: Distribution and migration of the southern bluefin tuna. Rep. Nankai Fish. Res. Lab. **25**, 19–35 (1967).

SHINGU, C.: Studies relevant to distribution and migration of the southern bluefin tuna. Bull. Far Seas Fish. Res. Lab. **3**, 57–113 (1970).

SHOMURA, R. S., MENASVETA, D., SUDA, A., TALBOT, T.: The present status of fisheries and assessment of potential resources of the Indian Ocean and adjacent seas. FAO Fish. Rep. **54**, 1–32 (1967).

SIDDIQUE, H. N., CHAUDHURY, A. N.: The distribution of phosphates in some samples of the shelf sediments of the west coast of India. Bull. Natl. Inst. Sci. India **38**, 483–490 (1968).

SIEDLER, G.: Schichtung und Bewegungsvorgänge am Südausgang des Roten Meeres. "Meteor"-Forschungsergeb. **A** (4) 1–76 (1968).

SIEGFRIED, W. R.: The Hyperiidea (Amphipoda) off the west coast of southern Africa. Invest. Rep. Div. Fish. South Afr. **48**, 1–12 (1963).

SILAS, E. G., MATHEW, K. J.: *Stylocheiron indicus,* a new euphausiid (Crustacea, Euphausiacea) from Indian seas. Curr. Sci. **36**, 169–172 (1967).

SILAS, E. G., SRINIVASAN, M.: A new species of Eukrohnia from the Indian Seas with notes on three other species of Chaetognatha. J. Mar. Biol. Assoc. India **10**, 1–33 (1969).

SILEN, L.: Carnosa and Stolonifera (Bryozoa) collected by Prof. Sixten Bock's expedition to Japan and the Bonin Islands. Ark. Zool. **34**, 1–33 (1942).

SIMPSON, E. H.: Measurement of diversity. Nature **163**, 688 (1949).

SLOBODKIN, L. B.: Growth and regulation of animal populations. 184 pp. New York: Holt, Rinehart and Winston 1961.

SLOBODKIN, L. B.: Pathfinding in ecology. Rev. Sci. **164** (3881) 817 (1969).

SMITH, J. L. B.: The clingfishes of the western Indian Ocean and the Red Sea. Ichthyol. Bull. J. L. B. Smith Inst. Ichthyol. Rhodes Univ. **30**, 581–596, pls. 92–97 (1964).

SMITH, J. L. B.: A new clingfish from southern Mozambique. Ann. Mag. Nat. Hist. **13**, 641–644, pl. 14 (1965).

SMITH, J. L. B.: Fishes of the subfamily Nasinae with a synopsis of the Prionurinae. Ichthyol. Bull. J. L. B. Smith Inst. Ichthyol. Rhodes Univ. **32**, 635–682, pls. 103–104 (1966).

SMITH, R. L.: Upwelling. Oceanogr. Mar. Biol. Ann. Rev. **6**, 11–46 (1968).

SMITH, W. L., RAO, P. K., KOFFLER, R., CURTIS, W. R.: The determination of sea surface temperatures from satellite High Resolution Infrared Window Radiation measurements. Mon. Weather Rev., Wash. D.C. **98**, 604–611 (1970).

SMITH-VANITZ, W., SPRINGER, V. G.: Synopsis of the tribe Salariini, with description of five new genera and three new species (Pisces, Blenniidae). Smithson. Contr. Zool. 73 (1971).

SNYDER, H. G., FLEMINGER, A.: A catalogue of zooplankton samples in the marine invertebrate collections of Scripps Institution of Oceanography. SIO Ref. 65–14 A, 1–140 (1965).

SOKOLOVA, M. N., PASTERNAK, F. A.: Quantitative distribution of bottom fauna in the northern parts of Arabian Sea and Bay of Bengal. Dokl. Akad. Nauk SSSR **144**, 645–648 (1962).

SOKOLOVA, M. N., PASTERNAK, F. A.: Quantitative distribution and trophic zonation of the bottom fauna in the Bay of Bengal and Andaman Sea. Tr. Inst. Okeanol. Akad. Nauk SSSR **64**, 271–296 (1964).

SOURNIA, A.: Variations saisonnières et nycthémérales du phytoplancton marine et de la production primaire dans une baie tropicale, à Nosy-Bé (Madagascar). Int. Rev. Gesamt. Hydrobiol. **53**, 1–76 (1968).

SPRINGER, V. G.: Revision of the circumtropical shorefish genus Entomacrodus (Blenniidae, Salariinae). Proc. U. S. Natl. Mus. **122**, 1–150, pls. 1–30 (1967).

SPRINGER, V. G.: Revision of the fish genus Ecsenius (Blennidae, Blenniiae, Salariini). Smithson. Contr. Zool. **72**, 1–64 (1971).

STECHOW, E.: Zur Kenntnis der Hydroidenfauna des Mittelmeeres, Amerikas und anderer Gebiete. Zool. Jahrb. Syst. Oekol. Geogr. Tiere **47**, 29–270 (1924).

STEELE, J. H.: Some problems in the study of marine resources. Spec. Publ. Int. Comm. Northwest Atl. Fish **6**, 463–476 (1965).

STEEMANN NIELSEN, E.: Untersuchungen über die Verbreitung, Biologie und Variation der Ceratien im südlichen Stillen Ocean. Dana Rep. **4**, 67 pp. (1934).

STEEMANN NIELSEN, E.: Die Ceratien des Indischen Ozeans und der ostasiatischen Gewässer. Dana Rep. **17**, 33 pp. (1939).

STEEMANN NIELSEN, E.: The use of radioactive carbon (^{14}C) for measuring organic production in the sea. J. Cons. Int. Explor. Mer. **18**, 117–140 (1952).

STEEMANN NIELSEN, E.: The balance between phytoplankton and zooplankton in the sea. J. Con. Int. Explor. Mer. **23**, 178–188 (1957).

STEEMANN NIELSEN, E.: On the determination of the activity in ^{14}C- ampoules. ICES CM 1964/105, Plankton Committee, 2 pp. 1964.

STEEMANN NIELSEN, E., AABYE JENSEN, E.: Primary organic production – the autotrophic production of organic matter in the oceans. Galathea Rep. **1**, 49–136 (1957).

STEEMANN NIELSEN, E., HANSEN, V. K.: Measurements with the carbon-14 technique of the respiration rates in natural populations of phytoplankton. Deep-Sea Res. **5**, 222–233 (1959).

STEEMANN NIELSEN, E., JØRGENSEN, E. G.: The adaptation of plankton algae. 1. General part. Physiol. Plant. **21**, 401–413 (1968 a).

STEEMANN NIELSEN, E., JØRGENSEN, E. G.: The adaptation of plankton algae. 3. With special consideration of the importance in nature. Physiol. Plant. **21**, 647–654 (1968 b).

STEINITZ, H.: A tentative list of immigrants via the Suez Canal. Isr. J. Zool. **16**, 166–169 (1967).

STEINITZ, H.: Remarks on the Suez Canal as pathway and as habitat. Rapp. P.-V. Réun. Comm. Int. Explor. Sci. Mer Méditerr. **19**, 139–141 (1968).

STONE, J. H.: The Chaetognatha community of the Agulhas Current: Its structure and related properties. Ecol. Monogr. **39**, 433–463 (1969).

STOSCH, H. A. VON: Zum Problem der sexuellen Fortpflanzung in der Peridineengattung *Ceratium*. Helgoländer Wiss. Meeresunters. **10**, 140–152 (1964).

STRICKLAND, J. D. H.: Solar radiation penetrating the ocean. A review of requirements, data and methods of measurements with particular reference to photosynthetic productivity. J. Fish. Res. Board Can. **15**, 453–493 (1958).

STRICKLAND, J. D. H.: Measuring the production of marine phytoplankton. Bull. Fish. Res. Board Can. **122**, 1–172 (1960).

STRICKLAND, J. D. H., PARSONS, T. R.: A manual of seawater analysis. Bull. Fish. Res. Board Can. **125**, 2nd Ed. 203 pp. 1965.

STRICKLAND, J. D. H., PARSONS, T. R.: A practical handbook of seawater analysis. Bull. Fish. Res. Board Can. **167**, 311 pp. 1968.

STRONG, A. E., RUFF, I. S.: Utilising satellite–observed solar reflections from the sea surface as an indicator of surface wind speeds. In: Proc. Symp. Remote Sens. Environ. **1**, 181–185 (1970).

STUBBINGS, H. C.: Pteropoda. Sci. Rep. John Murray Exped. 1933–34. **5**, 15–33 (1938).

SUBRAHMANYAN, R.: Phytoplankton organisms of the Arabian Sea off the west coast of India. J. Indian Bot. Soc. **37**, 435–447 (1958).

SUBRAHMANYAN, R.: Observations on the effect of the monsoons in the production of phytoplankton. J. Indian Bot. Soc. **39**, 78–89 (1960).

SUBRAHMANYAN, R.: The Dinophyceae of the Indian Seas. Mem. 2. Mar. Biol. Assoc. India. 129 pp. Mandapam Camp, India (1968).

SUBRAHMANYAN, R., SARMA, A. H. V.: Studies on the phytoplankton of the west coast of India. III: Seasonal variation of the phytoplankters and environmental factors. Indian J. Fish. **7**, 307–336 (1960).

SUBRAHMANYAN, R., SARMA, A. H. V.: Studies on the phytoplankton of the west coast of India. IV: Magnitude of the standing crop for 1955–62 with observations on nanoplankton and its significance to fisheries. J. Mar. Biol. Assoc. India **7**, 406–419 (1965).

Suda, A., Kume, S., Shiohama, T.: An indicative note on a role of permanent thermocline as a factor controlling the longline fishing ground for bigeye tuna. Bull. Far Seas Fish. Res. Lab. 1, 99–114 (1969).

Sukhanova, I. N.: On the tropical phytoplankton of the Indian Ocean. Dokl. Akad. Nauk SSSR 142, 1162–1164 (1962a).

Sukhanova, I. N.: On the specific composition and distribution of the phytoplankton in the northern Indian Ocean. Tr. Inst. Okeanol. Akad. Nauk SSSR 58, 27–39 (1962b).

Sukhanova, I. N.: The phytoplankton of the north-eastern part of the Indian Ocean in the season of the south-western monsoon. Tr. Inst. Okeanol. Akad. Nauk SSSR 65, 24–31 (1964).

Sukhanova, I. N.: Some data on the phytoplankton of the Red Sea and the western Gulf of Aden. Oceanology 9, 243–247 (1969).

Sukhanova, I. N.: Distribution of phytoplankton in the Indian Ocean (unpublished manuscript).

Sverdrup, H. V., Johnson, M. W., Fleming, R. H.: The Oceans, their Physics, Chemistry and General Biology. 1087 pp. New York: Prentice Hall Inc. 1942.

Swallow, J. C., Bruce, J. G.: Current measurements off the Somali Coast during the southwest monsoon of 1964. Deep-Sea Res. 13, 861–888 (1966).

Swift, E., Taylor, W. R.: Bioluminescence and chloroplast movement in the dinoflagellate *Pyrocystis lunula*. J. Phycol. 3, 77–81 (1967).

Szekielda, K.-H.: The development of upwelling along the Somali Coast as detected with the Nimbus 2 and Nimbus 3 satellites. Goddard Space Flight Center, Greenbelt X-651-70-419, 52 pp. 1970a.

Szekielda, K. H.: The effect of cyclonic and anticyclonic watermovements on the distribution of organic matter. Goddard Space Flight Center, Greenbelt. X-622-70-40 (1970b).

Szekielda, K. H., Salomonson, V. V., Allison, L. J.: Seasonal sea surface temperature variations in the Persian Gulf as recorded by Nimbus 2 HRIR. Preprint. Greenbelt, Maryland: Goddard Space Flight Center 1970.

Taft, B. A., Knauss, J. A.: The equatorial undercurrent of the Indian Ocean as observed by the Lusiad expedition. Bull. Scripps Inst. Oceanogr. 9, 1–163 (1967).

Talbot, F. H.: The South East Asian area as a centre of marine speciation: an ecological analysis of causes. Rep. Aust. Akad. Sci. 12, 43–50 (1970).

Tattersall, W. M.: On the Mysidacea and Euphausiacea collected in the Indian Ocean during 1905. Trans. Linn. Soc. Lond. (Zool.) 15, 119–136 (1912).

Tattersall, W. M.: The Euphausiacea and Mysidacea of the John Murray Expedition to the Indian Ocean. Sci. Rep. John Murray Exped. 5, 203–246 (1939).

Taylor, F. J. R.: *Brachydinium*, a new genus of the Dinococcales from the Indian Ocean. J. S. Afr. Bot. 29, 75–77, 1 pl. (1963).

Taylor, F. J. R.: A study of the phytoplankton of the south western Indian Ocean. Ph. D. Thesis, Univ. Cape Town, 494 pp. (MS 1964).

Taylor, F. J. R.: Phytoplankton of the south western Indian Ocean. Nova Hedwegia 12, 433–476, 9 pls. (1967, dated 1966).

Taylor, F. J. R.: Application of the scanning electron microscope to the study of tropical microplankton. Proc. Symp. Indian Ocean and Adjacent Seas, Cochin, 1971 (1972a) (in press).

Taylor, F. J. R.: Unpublished observations on thecate stages in the dinoflagellate form genus *Pyrocystis* by the late C. A. Kofoid and Josephine Michener. Phycologia (1972b) (in press).

Taylor, F. J. R., Cattell, S. A.: *Discroerisma psilonereiella* gen. et sp. n., a new dinoflagellate from British Columbia coastal waters. Protistologica 5, 169–172 (1969).

Technical Report: Z-I-1967: The results of oceanographic cruise Z-I-1967 in the northeastern sector of the Arabian Sea on P.N.S. Zulfiquar. Univ. Karachi Publ. (Mar. Biol.) 1, 57 pp. 1968.

Thiel, H.: Quantitative Untersuchungen über die Meiofauna des Tiefseebodens. Veröff. Inst. Meeresforsch. Bremerh. (Sonderb.) 2, 131–147 (1966).

Thomas, W. H.: Surface nitrogenous nutrients and phytoplankton in the northeastern tropical Pacific Ocean. Limnol. Oceanogr. 11, 393–400 (1966).

Thompson, H.: Pelagic Tunicates of Australia. CSIRO Australia, Melbourne 196 pp., 75 pl. (1948).

Thomson, J. M.: The Chaetognatha of south-eastern Australia. Rep. Div. Fish. Oceanogr. CSIRO, Aust. 14, 1–43 (1947).

Thomson, J. M.: Some Chaetognatha from western Australia. J. R. Soc. West. Aust. 31, 17–18 (1948).

THORSON, G.: Bottom Communities. In: Treatises on marine ecology and paleoecology, 1 (ecology), 17, p. 501. (HEDGEPETH, J. W., Ed.). 129 pp. New York: The Geological Society of America 1957.

TIMONIN, A. G.: The structure of pelagic associations. The quantitative relationship between different trophic groups of plankton in frontal zones of the tropical ocean. Oceanology 9, 686–694 (1969).

TOKIOKA, T.: Systematic studies of the plankton organisms occurring in Iwayama Bay Palao. III. Chaetognaths from the bay and adjacent waters. Contrib. Seto Mar. Biol. Lab. Palao Trop. Biol. Stn. Stud. 2, 527–548 (1942).

TOKIOKA, T.: Pelagic tunicates and chaetognaths collected during the cruises to the New Yamato Bank in the Sea of Japan. Publ. Seto Mar. Biol. Lab. 2, 1–25 (1951).

TOKIOKA, T.: Chaetognaths of the Indo-Pacific. Annot. Zool. Jap. 25, 307–316 (1952).

TOKIOKA, T.: A small collection of chaetognaths and pelagic tunicates from the north eastern part of the Indian Ocean. Publ. Seto Mar. Biol. Lab. 5, 75–78 (1955).

TOKIOKA, T.: On chaetognaths and appendicularians collected in the central part of the Indian Ocean. Publ. Seto Mar. Biol. Lab. 5, 197–200 (1956).

TOKIOKA, T.: A glimpse upon chaetognaths and pelagic tunicates collected in the lagoon water near Noumea, New Caledonia. Publ. Seto Mar. Biol. Lab. 8, 51–53 (1960).

TOKIOKA, T.: The outline of investigations made on chaetognaths of the Indian Ocean. Inf. Bull. Planktol. Jap. 8, 5–11 (1962).

TOKIOKA, T.: Supplementary notes on the systematics of Chaetognatha. Publ. Seto Mar. Biol. Lab. 13, 231–242 (1965).

TOKIOKA, T., PATHANSALI, D.: Spadella cephaloptera forma angulata raised to the rank of species. Publ. Seto Mar. Biol. Lab. 12, 145–148 (1964).

TORELLI, B.: Eufausiacei del Mar Rosso. Mem. R. Com. Talassogr. Ital. 208, 1–17 (1934).

TOTTON, A. K., BERGMANN, H. E.: A synopsis of the Siphonophora. 1–230. British Museum (Nat. Hist.) London 1965.

TOWNSEND, C. H.: The distribution of certain whales as shown by the log book records of American whale ships. Zoologica, 19, 1–50 (1935).

TRANTER, D. J.: Zooplankton abundance in Australian waters. Aust. J. Mar. Freshwat. Res. 13, 106–142 (1962).

TRANTER, D. J.: Comparison of zooplankton biomass determinations by Indian Ocean standard net, Juday net and Clarke Bumpus sampler. Nature, Lond. 198, 1179–1180 (1963).

TRANTER, D. J.: Seasonal studies of a pelagic ecosystem (Meridian 110° E). In: The biology of the Indian Ocean, 487–520 (ZEITZSCHEL, B. Ed.). Berlin–Heidelberg–New York: Springer 1973.

TRANTER, D. J., ABRAHAM, S.: Coexistence of species of Acartiidae (Copepoda) in the Cochin Backwater, a monsoonal estuarine lagoon. Mar. Biol. 11, 222–241 (1971).

TRANTER, D. J., GEORGE, J.: Nocturnal abundance of zooplankton at Kavaratti and Kalpeni, two atolls in the Laccadive Archipelago. (Presented at the Symposium on Corals and Coral Reefs, Mandapam, 1969) (in press).

TRANTER, D. J., KERR, J. D.: Seasonal variations in the Indian Ocean along 110° E.V. Zooplankton biomass. Aust. J. Mar. Freshwat. Res. 20, 77–84 (1969).

TREVALLION, A.: An investigation of detritus in Southampton water. J. Mar. Biol. Assoc. U.K. 47, 523–532 (1967).

TSURUTA, A.: Distribution of plankton and its characteristics in oceanic fishing grounds, with special reference to their relation to fishery. J. Shimonoseki Univ. Fish. 12, 1–214 (1963).

TYLER, J. E.: The Secchi disc. Limnol. Oceanogr. 13, 1–6 (1968).

TYLER, J.: A monograph on plectognath fishes of the superfamily Triacanthoidea. Monogr. Acad. Nat. Sci. Phila. 16, 1–364 (1968).

TYLER, J.: New records of triacanthoid plectognath fishes. Not. Natl. Acad. Nat. Sci. Phila., 435, 1–7 (1970).

UEYANAGI, S.: Observation on the distribution of tuna larvae in the Indo-Pacific Ocean with emphasis on the delineation of spawning areas of albacore, Thunnus alalunga. Bull. Far Seas Fish. Res. Lab. 2, 177–256 (1969).

UNESCO: Zooplankton sampling. Monographs on oceanographic methodology. 2, 1–176 (1968).

U.S. National Oceanographic Data Center: Atlas of bathythermographic data, Indian Ocean. Publ. G-6 (1966).

U.S. National Oceanographic Data Center: Inventory of archived data. Catalog series. Publication C-3 (revised) (1969).

U.S. Navy Hydrographic Office: World atlas of sea surface temperatures. H. O. **225,** Washington: U.S. Government Printing Office, 49 pp. 1944, 1960.

U.S. Navy Oceanographic Office: Glossary of oceanographic terms. Special Publ. 35 U.S. Govt. Printing Office 1966.

U.S. Program in Biology, IIOE: Final cruise report Anton Bruun cruises 4A and 4B. Woods Hole: Oceanogr. Inst. 1965.

VANNUCCI, M.: On Brazilian Hydromedusae and their distribution in relation to different water masses. Bol. Inst. Oceanogr., São Paulo **8,** 23–109 (1957).

VANNUCCI, M.: On the ecology of Brazilian Medusae at 25° lat. S. Bol. Inst. Oceanogr., São Paulo **13,** 143–184 (1963).

VANNUCCI, M., NAVAS, D.: Distribution of Hydromedusae in the Indian Ocean. In: The biology of the Indian Ocean, 273–281 (ZEITZSCHEL, B. Ed.). Berlin–Heidelberg–New York: Springer 1973.

VANNUCCI, M., SANTHAKUMARI, V.: New records of Hydromedusae from the shelf areas off the Kerala Coast. J. Mar. Biol. Assoc. India (1971) (in press).

VAN ZIJL, R. P.: A preliminary study of the salps and doliolids off the west and south coast of South Africa. Invest. Rep. Div. Fish. South Afr. **40,** 1–31 (1959).

VARADARAJAN, S., CHACKO, P. I.: The arrow worms of Krusadi. Proc. Natl. Inst. Sci. India. **9,** 245–248 (1943).

VERVOORT, W.: Biological results of the Snellius Expedition. The bathypelagic Copepoda, Calanoida of the Snellius Expedition. 1. *Temminekia* **8,** 1–181 (1946).

VINOGRADOV, A. P.: The elementary chemical composition of marine organisms. Mem. Sears Found. Mar. Res. **2,** 647 pp. 1953.

VINOGRADOV, M. E.: On the quantitative distribution of deep-water plankton in the northern part of the Indian Ocean. Okeanologiia **2,** 577–592 (1962).

VINOGRADOV, M. E.: Vertical distribution of the oceanic zooplankton. Acad. Nauk SSSR Inst. Oceanolog. 331 pp. Moscow (1968). English translation, 339 pp. Jerusalem: Ketter Press 1970.

VINOGRADOV, M. E., VORONINA, N. M.: On the influence of oxygen deficiency on the distribution of plankton in the Arabian Sea. Okeanologiia **1,** 670–678 (1961).

VINOGRADOV, M. E., VORONINA, N. M.: The distribution of different groups of plankton in accordance with their trophic level in the Indian Equatorial Current area. Rapp. P.-V. Réun. Cons. Inst. Explor. Mer **153,** 200–204 (1962).

VINOGRADOV, M. E., VORONINA, N. M., SUKHANOVA, I. N.: The horizontal distribution of the tropical plankton and its relation to some specific structural features of open ocean waters. Okeanologiia **1,** 283–293 (1961).

VINOGRADOVA, N. G.: Some problems of the study of deep-sea bottom fauna. J. Oceanogr. Soc. Jap. 20 Annivers., 724–741 (1962).

VISVANATHAN, R., GANGULY, A. K.: The distribution of phosphorus in the northern Indian Ocean 1962–1963. Bull. Natl. Inst. Sci. India **38,** 350–362 (1968).

VONDER HAAR, T. H., SUOMI, V. E.: Satellite observations of the earth's radiation budget. Science **163,** 667–669 (1969).

VORONINA, N. M.: On the surface plankton of the Indian Ocean. Tr. Inst. Okeanol. Akad. Nauk SSSR **58,** 67–79 (1962).

VORONINA, N. M.: The distribution of surface plankton in the Pacific Equatorial Current area. Tr. Inst. Okeanol. Akad. Nauk SSSR **65,** 95–106 (1964).

VOYTOV, V. I., DEMENTYEVA, M. G.: The relative transparency of the Indian Ocean water. Okeanologiia **10,** 48–50 (1970).

WARASHINA, I., HISADA, K.: Spawning activity and discoloration of meat and loss of weight in the southern bluefin tuna. Bull. Far Seas Fish. Res. Lab. **3,** 147–165 (1970).

WARK, D. Q., HILLEARY, D. J.: Atmospheric temperature: successful test of remote probing. Science, **165,** 1256–1258 (1969).

WARNECKE, G., MCMILLIN, L. M., ALLISON, L. J.: Ocean current and sea surface temperature observations from meteorological satellites. NASA Techn. Note, NASATND–5142 (1969).

WARREN, B., STOMMEL, H., SWALLOW, J. C.: Water masses and patterns of flow in the Somali Basin during the southwest monsoon of 1964. Deep-Sea Res. **13,** 825–860 (1966).

WATANABE, H.: Studies on the depth of hooking tunas by longline gear. Kanagawa-ken Suisan Shikenjo Shiryo **4,** 1–11 (1961).

WATERS, A.: Bryozoa from Madeira. J. Microsc. Soc. 6–16 (1899).

WATERS, A.: Report on the marine biology of Sudanese Red Sea. 12. The Bryozoa. I. *Cheilostomata.* J. Linn. Soc. Lond. (Zool.) **31**, 123–181 (1909).

WEIGMANN, R.: Zur Ökologie und Ernährungsbiologie der Euphausiaceen (Crustacea) im Arabischen Meer. "Meteor"-Forschungsergeb. **D** (5) 11–52 (1970).

WEIGMANN, R.: Eine isolierte Population von *Pseudeuphausia latifrons* (Crustacea: Euphausiacea) im Persischen Golf. Mar. Biol. **8**, 351–355 (1971).

WIBORG, K. F.: Zooplankton in relation to hydrography in the Norwegian Sea. Rep. Norw. Fish. Mar. Invest. **11**, 1–66 (1955).

WICKSTEAD, J. H.: A quantitative and qualitative study of some Indo-West-Pacific plankton. Fish. Publ. Colon. Off. **16**, 1–200 (1961a).

WICKSTEAD, J. H.: Plankton on the North Kenya Banks. Nature **192**, 890–891 (1961b).

WICKSTEAD, J. H.: Plankton from the East African area of the Indian Ocean. Nature **196**, 1224–1225 (1962).

WICKSTEAD, J. H.: The Cladocera of the Zanzibar area of the Indian Ocean with a note on the comparative catches of two plankton nets. East Afr. Agric. J. **39**, 164–172 (1963).

WOOD, E. J. F.: Checklist of dinoflagellates recorded from the Indian Ocean. Rep. Div. Fish. Oceanogr. CSIRO, Aust. **28**, 3–63 (1963).

WOOD, E. J. F.: Studies in the microbial ecology of the Australasian region. III. Ecological relations of some oceanic dinoflagellates. Nova Hedwigia **7**, 35–54 (1964).

WOOSTER, W. S., SCHAEFER, M. K., ROBINSON, M. K.: Atlas of the Arabian Sea for fishery oceanography. Univ. Calif. IMR Ref. 67–12, 35 pp., 140 pls. (1967).

WÜST, G.: Proposed International Indian Ocean Expedition. Deep-Sea Res. **6**, 245–249 (1959).

WYRTKI, K.: The Antarctic circumpolar current and the Antarctic polar front. Dtsch. Hydrogr. Z. **13**, 153–174 (1960).

WYRTKI, K.: Physical oceanography of the southeast Asian waters. Naga Rep. **2**, 1–195 (1961).

WYRTKI, K.: The upwelling in the region between Java and Australia during the south-east monsoon. Aust. J. Mar. Freshwat. Res. **13**, 217–225 (1962).

WYRTKI, K.: Oceanographic Atlas of the International Indian Ocean Expedition. National Science Foundation. U.S. Government Printing Office. Wash. D.C. 531 pp. 1971.

WYRTKI, K.: Physical oceanography of the Indian Ocean. In: The biology of the Indian Ocean, 18–36 (ZEITZSCHEL, B. Ed.). Berlin–Heidelberg–New York: Springer 1973.

YABE, H., YABUTA, Y., UEYANAGI, S.: Comparative distribution of eggs, larvae and adults in relation to biotic and abiotic environmental factors. FAO Fish. Rep. **6**, 979–1009 (1963).

YENTSCH, C. S.: Distribution of chlorophyll and phaeophytin in the open ocean. Deep-Sea. Res. **12**, 653–666 (1965).

YONGE, C. M.: The biology of coral reefs. Adv. Mar. Biol. **1**, 209–260 (1963).

YOSHIDA, H. O., OTSU, T.: Synopsis of biological data on albacore *Thunnus germo* (Lacépède). 1800 (Pacific and Indian Oceans). FAO Fish. Synop. **9**, 49 pp. 1962.

ZEITZSCHEL, B.: The quantity, composition and distribution of suspended particulate matter in the Gulf od California. Mar. Biol. **7**, 305–318 (1970).

ZENKEVITCH, L.: Immediate problems in the development of marine biology. In: Perspectives in Marine Biology. 27–31 (BUZZATI-TRAVERSO, A. A. Ed.) Berkeley, Los Angeles: Univ. Calif. Press 1960.

ZERNOVA, V. V.: Quantitative distribution of the phytoplankton in the northern Indian Ocean. Tr. Inst. Okeanol. Akad. Nauk SSSR **58**, 45–53 (1962).

ZERNOVA, V. V.: On the bioluminescence plankton of the Indian Ocean from the data collected during the 35th cruise of the "Vityaz". Council on Biophysics Siberian branch. Nauka, SSSR, 46–52 (1967).

ZERNOVA, V. V., IVANOV, J. A.: On the distribution of phytoplankton as depending from hydrological conditions in the northern part of the Indian Ocean. Tr. Inst. Okeanol. Akad. Nauk. SSSR **64**, 257–264 (1964).

ZOUTENDYK, P.: Zooplankton density in the south western Indian Ocean. Symp. Oceanogr. S. Afr., C.S.I.R. 1–13 (1970).

Subject Index

Page numbers in **bold** type indicate major sections, *italicezed* numbers refer to table and figure citations, and standard roman type numbers refer to text discussion.

Ecological Studies

Analysis and Synthesis

Edited by J. Jacobs, München
O. L. Lange, Würzburg
J. S. Olson, Oak Ridge
W. Wieser, Innsbruck

Distribution rights for this series
for the U.K., the Commonwealth,
and the traditional British market
(excluding Canada):
Chapman & Hall, Ltd., London

Prices are subject
to change without notice

Vol. 1
Analysis of Temperate Forest Ecosystems

Edited by D. E. Reichle, Oak Ridge

With 91 figures. XII, 304 pages. 1970
Cloth DM 52,—; US $18.40

This book is an attempt to unify and synthesize massive landscape research at the meaningful level of ecological structure—the ecosystem. The approach follows a coordination of primary and secondary productivity studies, emphasizing for all trophic levels the need for compatible methodology and integrated research programs. Specific topics of interest include production data for forest ecosystems and the transfers of energy and nutrient cycling on both local and world-wide scales. It is recognized that other environmental studies, e.g., climate, soils, and management practices, are essential for interpreting ecological processes.

The book is suitable for general audiences, e.g., outside reading or primary text in ecology courses. However, in content the book goes much beyond generalities. It is a thorough and detailed analysis of an ecosystem.

Vol. 2
Integrated Experimental Ecology

Methods and Results of Ecosystem Research in the German Solling Project

Edited by H. Ellenberg, Göttingen

With 53 figures. XX, 214 pages. 1971
Cloth DM 58,—; US $20.50

Ecosystems, that is, communities of plants and animals interacting with climate, soil and other environmental factors, are today becoming a major concern of biologists and others engaged in environmental research. They are complex systems, and it is only through the cooperation of workers in many disciplines that they can be studied and better understood.

The International Biological Program (IBP) expects that such integrated studies in experimental ecology will yield new information on the productivity, internal dynamics, and energy budget of ecosystems. The IBP will be continued and strengthened in this endeavor by Unesco's program, Man and the Biosphere, due to start in 1972.

The West German IBP Working Group for the Study of Terrestrial Biological Communities was one of the first groups to initiate field work in accordance with the guidelines internationally agreed under the 1964 outline plan. This volume presents preliminary results in the form of a joint report which may well serve as a textbook on methods for the study of temperate-zone forest and grassland ecosystems.

Contributions to this report are made by botanists and zoologists specialized in various fields, microbiologists, forestry and agricultural experts, climatologists and soil scientists. The area studied, the High Solling, lies approximately in the center of the Federal Republic of Germany. The reports are written in English in order to make them accessible to an international readership.

Springer-Verlag
Berlin · Heidelberg · New York
München · London · Paris · Tokyo · Sydney · Wien

Ecological Studies

Prices are subject
to change without notice